SOIL
MECHANICS

BY THE SAME AUTHOR

The Frost Penetration Problem in Highway Engineering
Thermal Soil Mechanics
Experimental Studies on Moisture Transfer in a Silty Soil upon Freezing
 as a Function of Porosity
Thermal Geotechnics
Glossary of Terms in Thermal Soil Mechanics

Soil Mechanics
Mechanics of Soils: Fundamentals for Advanced Study
Introduction to Soil Mechanics
Theoretical Soil Mechanics

Red Brunswick Shale and Its Engineering Aspects (*with Andris A. Jumikis*)
Rock Mechanics

Active and Passive Earth Pressure Coefficient Tables
Stability Analyses of Soil-Foundation Systems (*based on logarithmically*
 spiraled rupture curves)*: A Design Manual*
Stress Distribution Tables for Soil under Concentrated Loads
Vertical Stress Tables for Uniformly Distributed Loads on Soil
Settlement Tables for Centrically Loaded, Rigid Circular Footings on
 Multilayered Soil Systems

Foundation Engineering

SOIL
MECHANICS

ALFREDS R. JUMIKIS

Dr. Eng. Sc., Dr. techn., Dr.—Ing.
Professor Emeritus of Rutgers University,
The State University of New Jersey

Robert E. Krieger Publishing Company, Inc.
Malabar, Florida
1984

Original Edition 1984

Printed and Published by
ROBERT E. KRIEGER PUBLISHING COMPANY, INC.
KRIEGER DRIVE
MALABAR, FL 32950

Printed in the United States of America

Library of Congress Cataloging in Publication Data

Jumikis, Alfreds R.
  Soil mechanics.

New Edition of the 1967 ed. published by Van Nostrand,
New York, under title: Introduction to soil mechanics.
  Includes bibliographies and index.
  1. Soil mechanics. I. Title.
TA710.J785 1983   624'.1513   79-12978
ISBN 0-88275-969-8

To Zelma
- my affectionate consort in my life and work,
and
to our son Andris

PREFACE TO INTRODUCTION TO SOIL MECHANICS

The purpose of this book is to provide a clear-cut and stimulating one-semester text for students of civil engineering, architecture, architectural engineering, agricultural engineering, soil and water management, and engineering geology, and for junior college and technical institute students who are beginning the study of soil mechanics.

There are several reasons why civil engineering, architecture and technician students should study soil mechanics and why this subject is a requirement of the civil engineering curriculum.

1) to learn to understand and evaluate the properties of soil materials;
2) to apply the knowledge of soils in a practical way to the safe and economical design and construction of earthworks and the foundations of structures;
3) through research and experience to develop and advance the knowledge of soil mechanics, thus adding to the store of man's knowledge, and
4) to extend the knowledge to other branches of learning still to be developed.

The civil engineer, in pursuing his field of endeavor, has a two-fold responsibility: (1) the designing and building of stable structures, and (2) the safeguarding of the lives of the people using or passing by these structures. For these reasons, and also because soil is considered to be not only a foundation material (which supports structures), but a construction material as well (earth dams, highway and other fills, ingredients in mortars), engineers should have solid knowledge of the properties and behavior of soils.

From this short review one may see that there are fundamental soil engineering problems in earthworks and in highway and foundation engineering requiring solutions for safe and economical design of structures. It can also be inferred that the application of the knowledge of soil mechanics to earthworks, highways and foundation engineering is of great importance, particularly where large amounts of soil masses are to be moved, or highway fills and cuts are to be made. To illustrate the importance of soil mechanics to a civil engineer, the following parallel example can be drawn:

As in structural design the statics of a structure depend upon the knowledge of strength of materials, so does the design of foundations and earthworks depend upon the discipline of soil mechanics. Hence, it may be concluded that soil mechanics is a basic subject in the scientific education of civil engineers which forms the foundation of a civil engineering curriculum. The value and necessity of soil mechanics for training students is now generally recognized as fundamental and, therefore, has been introduced into the curricula of most institutions of higher technical learning.

Soil is made by nature. As a natural construction material, it possesses a variety of physical properties, most of which are not constant. This tendency of soils to fluctuate in their physical properties is in contradistinction to the behavior of artificially manufactured materials, iron and steel, for example, the properties of which are relatively constant.

The physical properties of soil, depending upon the type of soil, can be more or less adversely affected by several factors, including the presence of moisture in it, the proximity of ground water, atmospheric water and flood waters (natural or artificial), and freezing and thawing. One of the difficulties with soil as a material is that its physical properties in the field may vary within a distance of a couple of feet, or sometimes even less. The influence of water on the performance of soil under load, or the effect of freezing temperatures on silty soil in a highway body, play paramount roles in the behavior of soil. In soil mechanics, moisture in soil is considered to be one of the principal governing factors affecting soil properties.

Water influences the bearing capacity of soil. It may transform a cohesive soil into a plastic state. A soil may swell; it may also shrink. Water is controlled in compacting highway fills; it affects the shear strength of a soil. Upon expulsion of water from the voids of a soil under a structural load, the structure may settle uniformly or differentially. Therefore, as in the manufacturing of portland cement concrete, for example, one of the most frequent operations in the program of soil testing is water control in soil, better known as the determination of the soil moisture content. Thus one can understand the popular saying that no foundation and the structure supported by it is better than the soil upon which the foundation rests. The diverse nature of soil is the most difficult problem with which a civil engineer is confronted.

No engineer, architect, builder, or owner planning to build the foundation of a structure, a highway, railway, waterway, or airport runway can afford to ignore the problem of investigating the physical properties of soils encountered at the site and the possibility of changes in soil physical properties due to moisture during construction. Thorough investigation of soil properties is the best way to avoid failure of the "soil-structure" system and the exploitation, maintenance, legal, and financial troubles which may ensue. If the properties of soil are properly studied and the site explored, and the results of soil exploration correctly understood and intelligently applied to the design and construction of earthworks and structural foundations, failures usually can be avoided.

It is hoped that this volume on soil mechanics will not only give the student the necessary knowledge, but also that it will become a source of satisfaction and enjoyment, as well as develop in him an attitude which will enable him to attain confidence and competence in the solution of practical problems in soil mechanics.

ACKNOWLEDGMENTS TO INTRODUCTION TO SOIL MECHANICS

The author expresses his cordial thanks to all of those who contributed intellectually and materially, in words and in deeds, to the preparation of this manuscript for publication.

For his encouragement and heartening support and furtherance of this work the author expresses his appreciation to Dr. E. C. Easton, Dean, College of Engineering, Rutgers—The State University, New Brunswick, New Jersey.

It is also a pleasure to acknowledge the furtherance of the manuscript by Dr. M. L. Granstrom, Chairman of the Department of Civil Engineering, Rutgers—The State University, and to thank Dr. R. L. Handy, Professor of Civil Engineering, of the Engineering Experiment Station of the Iowa State University of Science and Technology, who reviewed thoroughly and in a very fair manner the entire manuscript, pointed out unclear passages, and made many valuable suggestions.

To the authors credited in the documentation of this book the writer owes a great deal, because some of their ideas and work helped in building up this work. It was possible to contribute to this book the chapter on frost action in soil, through the author's work in heading for several years the Joint Highway Research Project, a cooperative effort between Rutgers University and the New Jersey State Highway Department, and in studying soil moisture migration upon freezing for the past seven years (1955-1962) under two sizable grants given to the author by the National Science Foundation.

In particular, the author is glad to acknowledge the permissions granted by Dr. A. Casagrande, John Wiley and Sons, Inc., McGraw-Hill Book Company, Inc., Rutgers University Press, U.S. Corps of Engineers Army Engineer Waterways Experiment Station; in Germany, the Julius Springer Verlag and the Wilhelm Ernst und Sohn Verlag, and in Vienna, Austria, the Franz Deuticke Verlag and the Springer Verlag.

Some of the author's early studies on deformation in soil were made under Dr. O. K. Fröhlich in Vienna. These studies are now sponsored by the Bureau of Engineering Research, Rutgers—The State University.

The author is also most appreciative of the excellent library service at Rutgers University under the general direction of Dr. D. F. Cameron, University Librarian, and of the good offices of Mr. H. G. Kelley, Head of the Reference Department, and Miss Rose E. Sieber, Reference Librarian. Their efforts in procuring the many reference sources and books now out of print were valuable in preparing the historical part on soil mechanics in this book, as well as in permitting personal examination, checking and verification of facts in bona fide references of an original nature.

A separate word of thanks is directed also to my wife and son Andris for help with the organization and systematization of the manuscript, illustrations and photographs, and for assisting the author on his field trips and for taking some of the photographs, respectively.

The author also expresses his thanks to Mrs. Ruth Ahrens for her whole-hearted technical aid in reading the manuscript, and in examining the proofs.

The publisher has lived up to its best tradition, and the author's cordial thanks go to all concerned in the production of this book.

May this volume be found useful in providing the reader with necessary knowledge in the basic principles of soil mechanics.

ALFREDS R. JUMIKIS

PREFACE

Because the author's well received popular book entitled *Introduction to Soil Mechanics* is now out of print, a new edition seems to be advisable. Also, this new volume was prompted in order to conform to several changes and some advancements made in this geotechnical discipline during the past decade as to ideas, concepts and analyses.

The many changes and revisions made, and the amount of new material incorporated in this new, updated book justify that the book be titled as Soil Mechanics. All of the changes made bear directly on scope, presentation, and methodology of teaching in engineering education.

The purpose of this book on Soil Mechanics is to provide for a relevant, clear, and stimulating discussion about the various aspects of some important fundamentals in soil mechanics in a simple, and easily readable and usable form.

The book is suitable as a one-semester text for undergraduate students in civil engineering, agricultural engineering, architectural engineering, soil and water management, engineering geology, and for junior college and technical institute students who are beginning their studies in soil mechanics. This book may also serve well for one's self-tuition on soil mechanics; for a review of, and as a quick refresher about the fundamentals of soil mechanics. It may also serve as a ready reference source in practice.

The importance of soil mechanics in geotechnical engineering for laying foundations of structures and for designing of earthworks may be characterized by the following parallel: like the design of elements of a superstructure where its stability and safety depend on the engineering disciplines such as statics, dynamics, and strength of materials, so does the stability and safety of a soil-foundation system depend on the geotechnical discipline of soil mechanics. In other words, soil mechanics is the discipline of strength of materials in soil- and substructure engineering. One recalls the popular saying that no structure, no structural foundation supported by soil is any better than the soil upon which the foundation is laid. Thus, soil mechanics is a basic subject in the scientific-technical education of civil engineers. It forms the basis of a civil engineering curriculum.

The value and necessity of soil mechanics in educating civil engineering students for the design and construction of safe and economical structures is now generally recognized. Therefore, today soil mechanics is introduced into civil engineering curriculum of most institutions of higher technical learning.

For the student, this book contains, within the limits of a general text, a discussion on the basic principles involved in dealing with soil as an engineering construction material by means of which (earthworks), upon which (foundations), and within which (underground facilities) civil engineers build structures. The knowledge of soil mechanics is a cardinal prerequisite for civil engineers necessary for the design and construction of safe structural foundations, and for the right choice of a foundation to use. The book also points out the adverse effect of water on the strength and performance of soil (water—"public enemy No. 1").

The contents of this book includes discussions of topics such as a short historical review on soil mechanics; physical properties of soil; groundwater and moisture in soil; frost action in soils; hydraulics of wells; seepage in soil and through earth dams; "quick" condition in soil; consolidation and settlement theory of soils; vertical sand drains; elastic settlement of soil brought about by a rigid circular surface loading; stress distribution in soil from various surface loadings; lateral earth pressure on rigid and flexible retaining walls; bearing capacity of soil; stability analyses of groundbreak, and of earth slopes; and soil exploration.

The concept of groundbreak is vividly illustrated by means of photographs from author's own research showing the nature of the form of rupture surfaces (logarithmic spirals) in sand brought about by various surface loading condition.

The application of computer techniques pertaining to some phases of soil mechanics is reflected in this book by the author's stress distribution influence value charts for any point in the elastic medium (viz., soil) brought about by square, rectangular, strip, and circular loading at the ground surface.

The book is well illustrated. The illustrations are all interesting, sufficient in number, are well integrated within the text, and each complements the other. Many of the line drawings as well as the photographs are derived by the author from his own consulting engineerng practice; travel; research (such as those on frost action in soil; the form of rupture surface in soil formed upon groundbreak; glacial soils; soil exploration; engineering soil survey, and the stress influence value studies in elastic medium from various kinds of surface loadings, for example). Also, attention has been given to graphical methods in solving lateral earth pressure problems.

There are also many interesting numerically worked-out examples included in this book. They probe into the theories presented. The examples and the problems should appeal to students and to professors alike.

The book is well documented with pertinent bona-fide reference sources in respect to information accredited to them. All references in the book have been directly and personally examined by the author. The value of such bona-fide references is that

a) they establish the authority a book as important as this one deserves;

b) these references establish in the reader confidence as to the soundness of the material the book presents, and

c) the references permit penetrating deeper into the pertinent literature with little loss of time.

In conformity with the present trend in civil engineering, the SI units of measurement are introduced in this book. However, in order not to tear away in this respect from present-day engineering practice completely, in this book some problems are still dealt with by way of the commonly used units of measurement. This is done so because there are many educators and many engineering consulting and construction firms who still prefer to work with the foot-pound units. However, to facilitate familiarization with the SI units, appropriate conversion factors are included in the Appendix of this book.

All the above mentioned features make the book very interesting, attractive, useful and desirable to students and other readers. These features contribute to the effective teaching and studies of the important engineering science discipline soil mechanics.

May this volume be effective and profitable in the aquisition of basic knowledge in the useful and interesting civil engineering discipline of soil mechanics.

Alfreds R. Jumikis, Dr. Eng. Sc.,

Piscataway, New Jersey   et Dr. techn., et Dr.-Ing.

ACKNOWLEDGMENTS

The author expresses his cordial thanks to all of those who contributed intellectually and materially, in words and deeds, to the preparation of this book.

To the authors credited in the documentation of this book the author owes a great deal, because some of their ideas and work helped in building up this work.

It was possible to contribute to this book the chapter on frost action in soil through the author's work in heading for several years the Joint Highway Research Project, a cooperative effort between Rutgers University and the New Jersey State Highway Department, and sponsored by the U.S. Department of Commerce. The project pertained to the Engineering Soil Survey of New Jersey, and the preparation of Engineering Soil Maps for the entire State of New Jersey.

The authors experimental research on thermo-osmotic soil moisture migration in freezing soil systems as described in this book and elsewhere has been sponsored financially by three sizable research grants awarded to the author by the National Science Foundation. Later these frost action researches, as well as those about the form of rupture surfaces in sand were tangibly supported by the Department of Civil Engineering and the Bureau of Engineering Research of Rutgers University. Some of the author's early studies on deformation in soil were done at the University of Latvia in Riga, and also made under Dr. O.K. Fröhlich in the Technical University in Vienna, Austria.

Particularly, the author is glad to acknowledge the permissions granted for him to use and publish some of their material by various colleagues and organizations:

Dr. A. Casagrande, Harvard University
Dr. B. Fellenius, Stockholm, Sweden
Dr. V. A. Greenhut, Rutgers University
Dr. G. G. Meyerhof, Nova Scotia Technological College, Canada
Dr. E. Schultze, Technical University Aachen, Germany
Mr. E.J. Triglia, Engelhard Minerals and Chemical Corporation, Menlo Park, Edison, New Jersey
Dr. P. Wolfe, Rutgers University
Aero Service Corporation, Philadelphia, Pa.
Boston Society of Civil Engineers
The Trustees of Boston Public Library
Engelhard Minerals and Chemical Corporation, Menlo Park, Edison, New Jersey

U.S. Army Engineer, Waterways Experiment Station, Vicksburg, Miss.
U.S. Corps of Army Engineers, Philadelphia District, Philadelphia, Pa.
The Foundation Company, New York, N.Y.
Koninklijke Academie vor Wetenschappen, Letteren en Schone
    Kunsten Van Belgie, Brussels
Moretrench Corporation, Rockaway, N.J.
Norwegian Geotechnical Institute, Oslo, Norway
Sprague and Henwood, Inc., Scranton, Pa.
Swedisch State Railways' Geotechnical Commission, Stockholm, Sweden

Franz Deuticke Verlag, Vienna, Austria
Wilhelm Ernst und Sohn Verlag, Berlin, Germany
Alfred Kröner Verlag, Stuttgart, Germany
McGraw-Hill Book Company, Inc., New York, N.Y.
Rutgers University Press, New Brunswick, N.J.
Julius Springer Verlag in Berlin; in New York, and in Vienna
John Wiley and Sons, Inc., New York, N.Y.

For furtherance of this work, the author expresses his appreciation to Dr. E.H. Dill, Dean of the College of Engineering; to Dr. J. Wiesenfeld, Chairman, Department of Civil and Environmental Engineering, and to Dr. R.C. Ahlert, Executive Director of the Bureau of Engineering Research, all at Rutgers University, The State University of New Jersey. My colleague Dr. Yong S. Chae, Associate Dean and Professor of Civil Engineering in Geotechnics offered his professional comments about this book, for which comments this author is grateful.

The author is also most appreciative of the efficient library services of the Library of Science and Medicine of Rutgers University, and of the good offices of its Circulation, Government Documents, Book Loan and Procurement, Reference, and Periodical Departments, and the Office of the Engineering Bibliographer. Their efforts in procuring new books and many reference sources were valuable in permitting personal examination, checking, and verification of facts.

Sincere thanks are also expressed herewith to Mrs. Toshiye Aogaichi and to Mrs. Doris Clark who typed some parts of the manuscript.

A separate word of thanks is conveyed also to my wife Zelma A. Jumikis, mag. oec., and to my son Andris A. Jumikis, B.S. in Civil Engineering, P.E., for her help in organizing and systematizing of the extensive files of the material for the manuscript; and for his assisting the author in the laboratory; on the field trips, and for taking some of the photographs, respectively.

The author is also appreciative to the Publisher for his following of certain wishes of the author relative to the book. The publisher has lived up to its best tradition, and the author's cordial thanks go to all concerned in the production of this book.

ALFREDS R. JUMIKIS.

CONTENTS

PART I THE SUBJECT

PART II PHYSICAL PROPERTIES OF SOIL

PART III   WATER IN SOIL

CHAPTER 10

CHAPTER 11

PART IV   CONSOLIDATION OF SOIL AND
SETTLEMENT OF STRUCTURES

PART V   STRENGTH PROPERTIES OF SOIL

PART VI   SOIL EXPLORATION

LIST OF TABLES

LIST OF FIGURES

PART I

The Subject

Chapter 1

INTRODUCTION

1-1. Soil as a Construction Material. Soils can be considered as the oldest and the most complex of the construction materials used by engineers.

Unless it is built on hard rock, every structure, whether it is a building of any kind, a bridge, a fortification, a dam, a railroad, a type of pavement, an airport, or a hydraulic structure (harbors, quays, wharves, docks, bulkheads, piers, power stations, irrigation facilities) must be founded on soil. Therefore, the choice of an adequate foundation soil is one of the first problems to be considered in any construction project. Because most structures are supported by soil, the importance of soil as a foundation-supporting material as well as a construction material is of utmost significance. Hence it can be understood that the stability and function of a structure will largely depend upon the behavior of the soil upon which and/or of which it is built.

Because of the undeveloped state of soil mechanics as an engineering discipline several decades ago, or wrong assumptions which involved the use of soil, or even because of ignorance of the principles of soil mechanics, engineers have been faced, in the past, in various parts of the world with an increasing number of failures due to:

    1) unanticipated action of water,

    2) frost action in soils,

    3) unexpected settlements of soils,

    4) lateral displacement of soil (creeps and slides), or

    5) other unexpected performance of the soil.

Hundreds of miles of highway and airfield runway pavements have disintegrated because of the unpredicted performance of the soil due to excessive loads, or to change in soil moisture content, or to variable climatologic factors such as frost.

Many earth dams have collapsed because engineers were unable to ascertain with any accuracy the performance of remolded and compacted soil or the effect of the action of the existing water regime on the performance of soil. The collapse of tunnels, bridge piers and abutments, and the failure of many earth retaining structures and various waterfront and other hydraulic structures have been much too frequent because engineers were unable to evaluate satisfactorily how much pressure this soil would exert on these structures under various conditions, and what was the pressure distribution in soil underneath the contact areas of the bases of footings.

3

Differential settlements of the foundations under large engineering structures were directly responsible for serious structural damage in some cases and, in others, have added materially to maintenance expenses. Earth slides and ruptures of slopes of cuts and fills, as well as supported banks, continually endanger the safety of buildings, bridges, highways, railroads, and canals in many regions of the world. It can be said that almost no year has passed without some great failure in foundation and earthwork engineering.

FIG. 1-1. Failure of the Transcona Grain Elevator, Winnipeg, Manitoba, Canada. Courtesy of the Foundation Company, New York, N.Y.

Figures 1-1 to 1-2 illustrate the nature of failures of some engineering structures.

Figure 1-1 illustrates the failure of a 1,000,000 bushel grain elevator, weighing 20,000 tons, at North Transcona, Manitoba, Canada, in 1914, when it broke into the soil, which was of a "loose nature." The elevator consisted of 65 great circular silos, each 24.4 m high. The silos were mounted as a single unit on a reinforced mat foundation. When the silos were first filled, they began to settle and tilt on one side, burying the low side of the structure to a depth of about 12.2 m in the ground and leaning over at an angle of about 30° from the vertical. The silos were rolled back and successfully restored to an upright position. Altogether 70 piers, 1.8 m in diameter, were sunk to bedrock to force the structure upright.[1,2,3,4]

When soil mechanics had provided the basis for computing the ultimate bearing capacity of soil, it was realized that the Transcona grain elevator failure afforded one of the best of the few opportunities for a full-scale check as well as a test of the validity of such computations.

Extensive ruptures of slopes in the Panama Canal cuts are also often cited as examples of extensive soil failure,[5] and the settlement of structures in Mexico City is attracting the close attention of civil engineers.[6]

Fig. 1-2 shows a rupture of slope of the Delaware-Chesapeake Canal bank at the north pier of the Summit Bridge, Delaware. The bridge approach, made of soil, has been excavated and replaced by a light timber trestle. The pier was underpinned by H-piles. The embankment was dewatered by a permanent groundwater lowering system.

FIG. 1-2. Rupture of slope of the Delaware-Chesapeake Canal bank at the north pier of the Summit Bridge, Delaware. Courtesy of U.S. Corps of Army Engineers, Philadelphia District.

In the course of time engineers have learned that problems dealing with soils and foundations are very difficult and complex in comparison with those dealing with superstructures, which are capable of being treated mathematically. The physical and mechanical properties of the most frequently used materials of construction, such as wood, stone, brick, concrete, reinforced concrete, and steel are well known by the engineer. The allowable stresses have been determined. By means of proved theories, methods of computing the resistance of these materials have been developed. This, in turn, gives safer, more economical designs. Unexpected performance of one of these materials is quite rare.

On the contrary, soils used for supporting foundations and soils used as construction material for dams, roads, canals, etc., possess many and different properties. It is known that vibrations can transform a loose sand into a dense one; because of increasing loads, soils may settle, move laterally, or slide.

Soils may seem dense or loose, saturated or stiff, depending on the moisture content. Soils are permeable to air and water; they also absorb water. Some soils swell when wet, whereas other soil types give frost heaves, which are undesirable, especially in highway, railway, and canal engineering. It is more than a coincidence that most of the failures with structures as described above are caused by the unanticipated action of water, the regime of which changes as a result of the interference of the structural activity of the engineer. Water is the most important independent variable governing the subject of soil mechanics and foundation engineering.

One sees that the mechanical properties of soils are far more complex and difficult to determine than those of steel, concrete, or wood. No material has greater variation of properties than soil, probably because it is not a manufactured standard product like steel. This is because the soil with which the engineer must work was placed by nature in a great variety of kinds and conditions. Thus it can be understood that soils present the most serious problem of design because they are not homogeneous.

However, as mentioned before, the foundations of every building, bridge, dam, power station, road, railroad, or other structure must be laid on soil. This indicates the importance of soil as a foundation and construction material. The solution of foundation problems, therefore, requires a proper understanding of the properties and behavior of the soil. Moreover, soil investigation must be done before the project is laid out, or before any field work is attempted.

Soil investigations and a knowledge of the physical and mechanical properties of soils can help to protect the owner of a building and the engineer in charge from otherwise unforeseeable conditions and the troubles which usually accompany them. These are the first steps to a proper understanding of problems in conjunction with the laying of a foundation.

1-2. Necessity for Studying Soils. Many engineers have had the experience, at least once, that the "opponent soil" has buried the results of their work; and that the "opponent water", seeping or flowing out of every pore of the soil and every hole in the soil, has flooded or washed away the results of all their efforts. It is therefore the duty of every engineer who erects structures supported on soil or uses soil as a structural material to understand clearly that water and soil are his natural opponents. Moreover, because the civil engineer in charge is the man who is responsible for the final success or failure of a structural project, it is also his duty to acquire a proper and thorough knowledge and understanding of the principles of soil mechanics. In modern times the civil engineer should rely less upon rule of thumb; rather, he should draw increasingly from the proper sciences, among which soil mechanics is of outstanding service.

From the sequence of the matter as reviewed in the previous section, it can be understood that soil mechanics has developed from practical necessity. Since its development in the middle 1920's, it has been proved that soil mechanics has saved this nation millions of dollars. If we think only of the inadequately built and frost-damaged roads and other structures which have failed, the reconstruction of which requires much money and effort, it is obvious that soil mechanics is of national importance.

REFERENCES

1. Anon., "Righting a Twenty-Thousand-Ton Grain Elevator," *Scientific American*, December 26, 1914, vol. 111, no. 26.
2. A. Allaire, "The Failure and Righting of a Million Bushel Grain Elevator," *ASCE Transactions*, 1916, vol. 80.
3. R. B. Peck and F. G. Bryant, "The Bearing Capacity Failure of the Transcona Elevator," *Géotechnique*, 1952-1953, vol. 3.
4. L. S. White, "Transcona Elevator Failure: Eye-Witness Account," *Géotechnique*, 1952-1953, vol. 3.
5. Report of the Committee of the National Academy of Sciences on Panama Canal Slides. *Memoirs of the National Academy of Sciences*, Washington, D.C., 1924, vol. 17.
6. N. Carillo, "Influence of Artesian Wells in the Sinking of Mexico City," *Proceedings*, 2d Conf. on Soil Mechanics and Foundation Engineering, Rotterdam, 1948, vol. VII, pp. 156-159.
7. L. Zeevaert, *Foundation Engineering for Difficult Subsoil Conditions*, New York, N.Y., Van Nostrand Reinhold, 1973.

SUGGESTIONS FOR FURTHER READING

1. B. Broms and H. Stille, "Failure of Anchored Sheet Pile Walls," *Proc. ASCE, Journal of the Geotechnical Engineering Division*, Vol. 102, No. GT 3, March 1976, pp. 235-251.
2. F.H. Chen, *Foundations on Expansive Soils*, Amsterdam, Elsevier Scientific Publishing Company, 1975, pp. 195-259.
3. R.N. Nordlund and D.U. Deere, "Collapse of Fargo Grain Elevator," *Proc. ASCE, Journal of Soil Mechanics and Foundations Division*, Vol. 96, No. SM2, 1970, pp. 585-607.

Chapter 2

HISTORICAL REVIEW

2-1. Soil Problems in Prehistoric Times. Although in the old days the subject of soil mechanics was not known to our predecessors in the same sense as we know it now, it can be said that since prehistoric times soils occupied people's minds.

In the more primitive civilizations, soil was used as a construction material for foundations of structures and for the structures themselves. The value of soil as a construction material was appreciated in building huge earth mounds for burial sites; for places of refuge during flood periods; for religious purposes; in making caves to live in, such as the ancient loess village of Su Chia Chiao, near Kalgan, and loess dwellings (caves dug into the side of a ravine) at Yang Shao Tsun; and in constructing canals, ditches and fortifications.[1,2,3,4] It can be said that man's prehistoric progress in learning, understanding, and managing soils was very slow.

2-2. Soil Problems in Ancient Times. Soil problems in ancient times were associated with ancient roads, waterways and canals, and bridges.[5] For example, the *Chou-Li*, i.e., a book on the customs of the Chinese *Chou* dynasty, written about 3000 years ago, contains provisions and instructions for roads and bridges.[6]

The use of both timber and stone caissons for soft-ground shaft construction was known in Egypt in 2000 B.C. The shaft led to the underground burial chamber in the pyramids of Se'n Woster I, who reigned in Egypt about that time. The cutting edge was made of a round limestone block with a vertical hole pierced through its middle. The brick caisson was sunk down through conglomerate and sand layers until it hit the limestone bedrock.[7] The outside surface of the caisson was made smooth in order to reduce sinking resistance caused by friction.

Soil as a construction material was also used for impounding of water and in building dikes and levees.

Quicksand conditions of soil seem to have been a really serious and troublesome topographical problem to all great warriors in moving troops and supplies through river valleys and in performing tactical maneuvers. Alexander the Great, for example, was very conscious of these conditions, and in military operations he was known to be skillful in avoiding terrain where quicksand conditions in soil were apt to develop.

From the professional point of view it is interesting to note that the engineer held a position of power and influence in all ancient communities.

2-3. Soil and Foundation Problems in Roman Times. In the course of time structures became larger and heavier. By the time the Roman Empire attained its peak of glory, engineers built very heavy structures, requiring solutions of earthwork and foundation designs. It is known that the Romans built notable engineering structures, for example: harbors, moles, breakwaters, aqueducts, bridges, large public buildings, sewage lines (the arch-covered Cloaca Maxima), and a vast network of durable and excellent roads.[8] Some sections of Roman roads are intact even today. The basic principles in Roman road design and construction, founded on the understanding of the performance of soil under the action of load and water, are (a) a solid foundation and (b) good drainage. These principles we still honor in our modern road design.

Probably the oldest written information and the only such evidence we have, although meager, about soil investigation for earthworks and foundation engineering purposes in Roman times is reflected by the correspondence exchanged between the Roman Emperor Trajan and Plinius.[9]

The technical literature of the time supplies ample evidence that the Romans paid much attention to some properties of soils and to the stability of foundations.

The Roman engineer Vitruvius (first century B.C., during the reign of Emperor Augustus) in his *Ten Books on Architecture*, described in Book II[10] that:

"Neither the same kind of soil nor the same rocks are found in all places and regions, but some are earthly, others of gravel, others pebbly, in other places sandy material; and generally there are found in the earth qualities of unlike and unequal kind with the various regions."

In Book VIII, discussing foundation problems related to water supply, Vitruvius wrote that:

"The methods of nature must be considered closely in the light of intelligence and experience because the soil contains many various elements."

On the foundations of walls, towns, and temples Vitruvius advises:

"Let the foundations of those works be dug from a solid site and to a solid base if it can be found. But if a solid foundation is not found, and the site is loose earth right down, or marshy, then it is to be excavated and cleared and re-made with piles of alder or of olive or charred oak, and the piles are to be driven close together by machinery, and the intervals between are to be filled with charcoal."

To this J. Gwilt[11] translated one more sentence: "The heaviest foundations may be laid on such a base."

From these letters and books by Vitruvius, the latter of which are to be considered as a real treasure chest of empirical building knowledge, it can clearly be seen that soil problems were of great concern to the Roman builders, and that they were aware, according to their state of knowledge, of the problem of the safe bearing capacity of soil and the stability of a foundation, and that they knew how to increase and to improve the bearing capacity of a soil. Also, they knew how to estimate by experience the safe load on pile groups. But

the procedure of testing soils cannot be found in the technical sources by Vitruvius. However, the Roman road builders deserve credit for pioneering the
scientific art of road building.

2-4. Earthwork and Foundation Engineering in The Middle Ages. After the
collapse of the Roman Empire, European society and activities in soil engineering
and foundation engineering associated with it were very disorganized. As a
consequence, road construction and maintenance in the medieval period (about
A.D. 400 to 1400) declined to its lowest point. One gets the impression that in
those days neither bridges nor roads were necessary or desirable. Warfare and
religion were the universal activities in the Middle Ages. The old Roman
engineering works, such as roads, bridges, dikes, and drainage facilities, were
ravaged by war and neglect. Rain and frost, in their turn, broke up pavements
and disintegrated the foundations.

Aside from roads and canals, the only other medieval structures associated
with soil and foundation problems were

1) the heavy city walls, the bastions or flanking towers in the medieval
   fortifications which were of great extent and of dimensions commensurate
   with their importance,
2) the castles built and enclosed by heavy earthworks,
3) the great cathedrals, and
4) campaniles (bell towers) which usually were built separately from the
   churches.[12]

FIG. 2-1. "Holstentor" Gate in Lübeck, Germany. Photo by the author.

The main soil problem associated with the building of massive cathedrals is what today we would call the settlement problem and compression of soil brought about by their relatively large structural loads—relatively large loading areas of cathedrals or relatively small loading areas of the campaniles—as well as the long time elapsed since the start of construction of these monumental structures. During the past centuries the compressible soils upon which some of the cathedrals were built had enough time to consolidate under the structural loads of the cathedrals, causing, in many instances, large settlements of the structures or, in other instances, causing the mutual leaning toward each other of double gate towers (for example, the "Holstentor" gate of the old Hanseatic city of Lübeck, Germany, see Fig. 2-1). So, for example, cathedrals known originally to have been built with many entrance steps up, now have many entrance steps down into them as a result of the 2-meter-large settlement process in the past 400 years (as in the case of the Archbishop's cathedral in Riga).

The heavy Dom of Königsberg in East Prussia (about A.D. 1330), for example, was founded on a layer of peat. Underneath this peat there is, according to Tiedemann,[13] about an 18.3 m-thick layer of soil consisting of clayey-limey material. Because of the consolidation of the clayey soil material the structure has never come to rest. In the course of time it has been necessary to put in new floors over the old ones five times. The settlement of the Dom of Königsberg amounts to more than 1.5 m. The once graceful interior spaciousness of the Dom, of course, has suffered greatly.

The campaniles of Bologna and Venice, the tower of the 14th century San Stefano Church, the campanile of San George in Zaragoza, and the tower of Pisa, to name but a few, are well known as tourist attractions for their being out of the true vertical. For example, the construction of the tower of Pisa (popularly known as the leaning tower of Pisa) was started in A.D. 1174. After the first three galleries of the eight-galleried structure were built, the tower started to tilt. After some interruption in work and

FIG. 2-2. The Leaning Tower of Pisa. Photo by the author.

slight changes in plans, the construction was continued. The tall campanile, about 15 stories, 54.6 m in height was completed in 1350. In 1910 the tower had a visible slant, and its top was 7.9 m out of plumb. The leaning tower of Pisa is shown in Fig. 2-2.

Investigation of what caused the campanile of Pisa to lean revealed that it was due to settlement of the tower brought about by the consolidation of the clayey soil material underneath a layer of sand on which the tower was founded.[14] Hence, to a soil mechanics engineer, the leaning tower of Pisa and other leaning campaniles present classic examples of the settlement problems of the medieval period.

2-5. The Period from the 15th to the 17th Centuries. In the field of laying foundations for bridge piers, the builders of the Middle Ages followed in the footsteps of the Romans, i.e., they simply piled up pieces of loose rock or drove piles, upon the heads of which a timber grillage was constructed to receive the pier. The poor quality and ineffectiveness of foundations remained the most difficult and acute foundation engineering problem until the advent of modern knowledge in the 18th century.

The Rialto single arch bridge in Venice, Italy, completed in 1591, is, like other buildings in that city, noted for its difficult foundation operations because of the soft and marshy ground and adjacent large buildings—circumstances which make pile driving operations a real and responsible problem.

Another fragment of foundation engineering of the 17th century associated with soil problems is the famed mausoleum Taj-Mahal outside the city of Agra, India (see Fig. 2-3). It was built by the great Indian Mogul Emperor of Delhi,

FIG. 2-3.   The Taj-Mahal, India. Courtesy of Dr. Peter Wolfe, Professor of Geology, Rutgers—The State University, New Brunswick, New Jersey.

Shah-Jahan, to commemorate his favorite wife, Mumtaz-i-Mahal. The construction of the mausoleum began in 1632 and was completed in 1650. This tomb is of extreme delicacy and reflects a *chef-d'œuvre* of elegance in Indian art.[15]

The proximity of the river required special attention in the building of the

foundations of the Taj-Mahal. It was the practice of the Mogul builders to support the structures on masonry cylindrical foundations sunk into the soil at close intervals. Apparently the terrace and the mausoleum building, as well as the minarets, rest on one firm, compact bed of masonry. The method adopted was a sound one, for after three centures " . . . its lines and angles are still as accurate as when first produced".[16] Twenty thousand people were employed on the Taj-Mahal for seventeen years, and at that time the structure is estimated to have cost about $45,000,000.

In the 16th century, it is interesting to note, such famous artists as Michelangelo and Bramante were also known to be active in the field of building fortifications, and in executing drainage canal and water-supply problems. Leonardo da Vinci, as a civil engineer, was called in 1516 by Francis I to France to help in the latter's canal-building program.[17] Da Vinci also constructed with ease fortresses, canals, bridges, irrigation works, harbors, and locks.

The early builders were guided in their work by the knowledge and experience passed down from generation to generation, rather than by physical laws and scientific considerations.

2-6. Older Concepts on Lateral Earth Pressure. In the latter part of the 17th century French military engineers contributed some empirical and analytical data pertaining to earth pressure on retaining walls for the design of revetments of fortifications. In 1661, France undertook an extensive public works program which included the improvement of highways and the building of canals. The construction of the great fortification system along the border of France was begun in 1667 under Marquis Sebastian le Prestre de Vauban (1633-1707), who was commissary general of fortifications and Louis the XIV's chief engineer, and who later became marshal of France. Vauban is regarded as one of the greatest military engineers of all times.

Canals which were dug in those days, and later during the times of French mercantilism, presented soil problems in connection with the terrain through which the canals were dug; but retaining walls of the fortifications presented earth pressure problems in connection with their stability. It is known that at that time Vauban gave some rules for gauging the thickness of retaining walls. However, it is not known for sure whether these were based on theoretical considerations, or whether they were merely the results of Vauban's experience. In this respect thoughts were later expressed in France that the empirical rules by Vauban appeared to be so complete that it almost seemed as if those rules were based upon an earth-pressure theory now unknown to us.

Early in the 18th century the French government recognized that, through neglect in past centuries, many bridges and roads were in a poor condition and therefore had to be rebuilt. This gave France the impetus for the establishment in 1715 of a Department of Roads and Bridges. In 1716 Colbert created a corps of military engineers to train experts in fortifications and artillery, and in 1747 the famous *École des Ponts et Chaussées* was established under the famous engineer Jean Rudolphe Perronet, where engineers were educated in sound principles of physics, mechanics, and mathematics for the construction of canals, highways, and bridges. This engineering school had a great influence upon the scientific development of civil engineering in France and abroad.

2-7. The Period of the Classical Earth-Pressure Theories. Up to about 1773 almost all theoretical considerations in calculating the lateral earth pressure of an ideal soil upon a retaining wall were based on the presupposition of a definite, arbitrarily assumed, sliding or failure plane.

Charles Augustin Coulomb (1736-1806), a famous French scientist and also a military engineer of that time, was not satisfied with such an arbitrary presupposition. On the contrary, Coulomb considered it as his principal task to determine the real or true position of the sliding surface mathematically and thus give the theory a scientific basis. Coulomb contributed much to the science of mechanics of elastic bodies, and is regarded as the founder of the so-called "Classical Earth-Pressure Theory." The period beginning with Coulomb and extending to the second half of the 19th century is usually known in the technical literature as "the period of the Classical Earth-Pressure Theories," and the theories themselves sometimes are termed "the Classical Theories of Soil Mechanics." In his widely cited essay on the application of the rules of maximum and minimum,[18] Coulomb presented an analysis of the so-called "sliding wedge theory," to bring about the calculations of the earth pressure against a retaining wall, as well as the critical height of retaining walls. In this analysis Coulomb applies the laws of friction and cohesion for solid bodies, an analysis which he assumed also valid for granular bodies such as soil; and he determines the earth pressure upon a retaining wall from the "wedge of maximum pressure."

Coulomb's ideas about the shapes of the rupture surfaces in soil are reflected in his Fig. 7, Plate I (see Fig. 2-4). Coulomb also treated the problem of surcharge on the ground surface. (For more historical notes on Coulomb's earth pressure theory see Ref. 19.)

The significance of Coulomb's theoretical work may be recognized best by the fact that his ideas on earth pressure still prevail in their principal points, with a few exceptions, and are used and recognized as valid even today, particularly in calculations of stability of retaining walls.

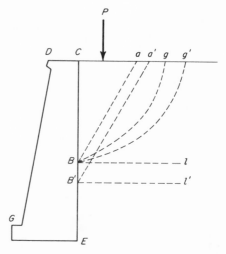

FIG. 2-4. Coulomb's ideas about the shapes of rupture surfaces in soil.

Poncelet (1788-1867),[20] a famous geometer and founder of our modern subject, projective geometry, extended Coulomb's theory giving an elegant, graphical method of finding the magnitude of the earth pressure on the wall, vertical as well as inclined wall surfaces on the backfill side, and for arbitrarily broken polygonal ground surfaces. Also, Poncelet is to be credited as being the first to apply the direction of the earth pressure inclined to the normal of the wall under an angle of friction between the soil and wall material. Later, in 1866, Karl Culmann (1821-1881)[21] gave the Coulomb-Poncelet theory a geometrical formulation, thus supplying the method with a broad scientific basis. Culmann's theory is the most general one permitting the graphical solution of the most complicated cases of earth pressure upon a retaining wall.

Alexandre Collin[22] dealt with ruptures of slopes of canals and dams. Collin writes that he measured the slides and, upon analyzing the observed curved rupture or sliding surfaces, they were revealed to be cycloidally curved.

Darcy's law of permeability of soil has been known since 1856.[23] Also, Stokes' law of the velocity of solid particles through liquids dates back to 1856.[24]

William J. Macqorn Rankine (1820-1872), professor of Civil Engineering in the University of Glasgow, published in 1857 a notable theory on earth pressure and equilibrium of earth masses, thus offering an analytical method of dimensioning retaining walls.[25] The theory is based on an infinitesimal wedge within the mass of a uniform soil of laterally unlimited extent having a plane ground surface and subjected to its own weight only. The soil is assumed to be homogeneous, granular, cohesionless, and incompressible. The particles of the soil are held in position by friction only, the magnitude of which is proportional to the normal pressure on the rupture surface. In other words, Rankine's theory is based on the principle of the internal stress condition in soil.

O. Mohr[26] (1835-1918) contributed in 1871 the so-called "rupture theory" to the subject of strength of materials, and gave a graphical representation of stress at a point, popularly known as "Mohr's stress circles." Mohr also noticed and called attention to the fact that in the older theories, in case of equilibrium, the forces acting on a sliding wedge do not intersect in one common point.[26] In soil mechanics, Mohr's stress circles are extensively used in the analysis of the shear strength of soils.

Coulomb-Poncelet earth pressure theories were elaborated by graphical analyses also by Rebhann,[27] Weyrauch,[28] and others.

The history of strength of materials[29] indicates that from the point of view of practical value one of the most important contributions to the engineering sciences was offered by Joseph Valentin Boussinesq (1842-1929).[30] This is his theory of stress distribution and deformation under loaded bearing areas in a semi-infinite, homogeneous, and isotropic medium induced by externally applied forces at the boundary plane. This theory is being applied in soil mechanics to calculate stress distribution in homogeneous soil caused by structural loads. The soil, in applying this theory, is tacitly assumed to be an ideal, noncohesive, homogeneous, and isotropic material.

The impetus for the development of early soil mechanics, it must be recognized, was given by the increased activities in bridge design and construction for highways and railways with which the following two popular names are associated: Perronet[31] and Rankine. Besides his academic activities Rankine was also known as a famous Scottish railroad engineer.

It should also be mentioned that besides Müller-Breslau, contributions to the earth pressure theory were later likewise made by O. Franzius,[32] H. Krey,[33] J. Feld,[34] K. Terzaghi,[35] the *DEGEBO* (German Society for Soil Mechanics at the *Technische Hochschule Berlin-Charlottenburg*[36]), G. P. Tschebotarioff,[37] and others with their experimental research with earth-retaining structure models on a large scale.

2-8. The Beginning of the Modern Soil Mechanics Era. The period from the beginning of the twentieth century until now may be divided into two epochs, namely, the years that preceded 1925 and the years that followed it.

The first 25 years of the 20th century should be considered the pioneer years of the modern science of soil mechanics. Scientists and engineers gradually realized the increasing need for studying the physical properties of soils. The following description covers some highlights in the development of modern soil mechanics during the first 25-year period.

The pioneering in practical soil mechanics must be credited to the Swedish Geotechnical (Soil Mechanical) Commission of the State Railways of Sweden. On December 29, 1913, after a number of serious railway, canal, and waterfront failures involving quays, docks, retaining walls, and ruptures of slopes in railroad cuts and fills, the Royal Board of State Railways appointed a committee, headed by Professor Wolmar Fellenius. It was commissioned in part to investigate the government railway lines from a geological point of view, and to state whether there might be any fear of displacements of the roadbeds in consequence of a land-slip or any similar occurrence; and in part, if such should be the case, to enter proposals for the steps which should be taken in order to secure the railway against such displacements.

This investigation resulted in 1922 in an extensive final report containing some data on modern soil sampling and testing methods applied to more than 300 places with 2400 soil profiles.[38] Also, a method (the so-called "Swedish circle method") for the calculation of stability of slopes made of cohesive soils under the assumption of a circular, cylindrical sliding surface, is published in that report.[38,39]

The proponents of the circular sliding surface theory are two Swedish engineers, K. Petterson,[40] and S. Hultin.[41]. The circular sliding theory with the so-called "friction circle" was used by Petterson and Hultin in 1916 in stability calculations in connection with the failure of the Stegberg quay in the Swedish port of Göteborg.[40,41,42]

The slide shown in Fig. 2-5 at Vita Sikudden, a railway section Nyköping-Norrköping, Sweden, occurred on October 1, 1918, at 7 p.m. Just after the slide took place, a passenger train plunged into the slide; 41 people lost their lives and many were injured. The upper part of the slope toward the Bråviken shore consists of sand and silt, whereas the lower part consists of loose clay.

The cause of the slide appears to have been an exceptional water infiltration in the embankment fill during the unusually heavy rains before the slide took place. In Fig. 2-5, which is an aerial photograph of the slide, note the earth

Fɪɢ. 2-5.   Aerial view of a railway embankment slide at Vita Sikudden, Sweden. Courtesy of the Swedish State Railways Geotechnical Commission.

wedge of the slide in the Bråviken Bay, the interrupted railway line, the highway buried by the sliding earth masses, the overturned locomotive and cars in the slide, and some cars still on the tracks.

The progressive highway construction program in the United States during the years 1920 to 1925, as well as the industrial development during those years, induced intensive research on soils for engineering purposes. This research was in the hands of the U.S. Bureau of Public Roads and various other establishments such as universities and technical and professional societies (for example the American Society of Civil Engineers).

Thus, the first 25 years (since 1925) of modern soil mechanics can be briefly characterized as follows: research in soil mechanics expanded and was gaining impetus for its development on a scientific basis.

The period from 1925 to date may be characterized as the most fruitful in soil mechanics history. It is now fairly well agreed upon that the modern discipline of Soil Mechanics began in 1925 with the publication of the book *Erdbaumechanik* by K. Terzaghi.[43]

In this book Terzaghi gave a new philosophical view relative to soil as a material and showed how to treat the physical properties of soil, as well as how the soil material performs under various loading and moisture conditions.

Another important step in the new discipline was the co-authored publication by Terzaghi and Fröhlich of the settlement theory of clays.[44]

Terzaghi's publications, and the work in soil mechanics done by other authorities in this field, gave a great impetus to soil mechanics studies and produced a considerable amount of knowledge on engineering properties of soils in the United States and abroad.

In the course of time laboratory tests of soils became very much appreciated by the profession, and soil testing methods are continuously being refined and improved. Most of the progressive engineering colleges and universities have by now already established soil mechanics and foundation engineering laboratories and geotechnical institutes for studying soils for engineering purposes. Also, the accreditation committee for college instruction curricula of the Engineers Council for Professional Development shows a great interest in the inclusion of a soil mechanics course in the civil engineering program.

The proceedings of the many national and international conferences on soil mechanics and foundation engineering here and abroad also attest to the need, progress and importance of soil mechanics.

To summarize the progress of soil mechanics since 1925, it can be said that the pioneering in the new soil mechanics discipline is completed and that today this discipline has research as its standard-bearer.

Today, the civil engineer has a much better knowledge of soils to enable him to encounter the two opponents—soil and water—in foundation engineering than had his colleagues only 50 years ago.

2-9. Most Recent Developments. As to the most recent developments in soil mechanics, it can be observed that notable achievements have been made in soil stabilization, dynamic compaction of soil,[45] in frost action research in soil, in the field of moisture movement through soil by means of electro-osmosis, and in the techniques of airphoto interpretation for the purpose of engineering surveys and for the preparation of engineering soil maps.[46] It is interesting to note that soil mechanics has introduced a new subject, namely, snow mechanics,[47] and most recently there has occurred the development of nondestructive tests to determine in place some soil properties, such as density and moisture content, by means of radioactive isotopes.

In general, modern practice continuously improves upon the methods of yesterday. Techniques of today may become inadequate tomorrow unless supplemented, completed, and changed to meet new requirements.

To sum up the review, the combined efforts of engineers and research workers from all over the world in this discipline contributed to what we may call modern soil mechanics.

REFERENCES

1. T. Beckwith, *The Indian or Mound Builder*, Cape Girardeau, Mo., Naeta Brothers Publishers, 1911.
2. A. R. Verrill, *Old Civilizations of the New World*, New York, The New York Home Library, 1942.
3. C. Thomas, *The Circular, Square and Octagonal Earthworks of Ohio*, Washington, D.C., Smithsonian Institution, 1889.
4. J. G. Anderson, *Children of the Yellow Earth*, New York, The Macmillan Co., 1934.

5. Anon., *Public Roads of the Past*, (3500 B.C. to 1800 A.D.), Washington, D.C., AASHO, 1952.
6. A. Speck, *Der Kunststrassenbau*, Berlin, Wilhelm Ernst und Sohn, 1950.
7. Anon., *Eng. News-Record*, December 7, 1933, p. 675.
8. S. B. Platner, *The Topography and Monuments of Ancient Rome*, Boston, Allyn and Bacon, 1904.
9. *Letters of Gaius Plinius Caecelius Secundus*, trans. by W. Melmoth, from the Harvard Classics, New York, P. F. Collier and Son Company, 1909.
10. Vitruvius, *Ten Books on Architecture*, trans. by Frank Granger, New York, G. P. Putnam's Sons, 1934.
11. *The Ten Books of Vitruvius*, trans. by Joseph Gwilt, London, Lockwood and Company, 1874, Book III, Chapt. III, p. 72.
12. S. Painter, *A History of the Middle Ages 284-1500 A.D.*, New York, Alfred A. Knopf, 1953.
13. B. Tiedemann, *Die Bedeutung des Bodens im Bauwesen, Handbuch der Bodenlehre* by E. Blanck, Berlin, Julius Springer, 1932, vol. 10.
14. K. Terzaghi, "Die Ursachen der Schiefstellung des Turmes von Pisa," no. 1/2, *Der Bauingenieur*, 1934.
15. J. Ferguson, *History of Indian and Eastern Architecture*, John Murray, 1876.
16. Sir Wolsley Haig, *The Cambridge History of India*, vol. 4, *The Mogul Period*, At the University Press, Cambridge, 1937.
17. R. J. Forbes, *Man the Maker, A History of Technology and Engineering*, New York, Henry Schuman, 1950.
18. C. A. Coulomb, "Essai sur une application des règles de maximis et minimis à quelques problèmes de statique relatifs à l'architecture." *Mémoires de la mathématique et de physique*, présentés à l'Académie Royale des Sciences, par divers savans, et lûs dans sés Assemblées, vol 7, Année 1773. Paris, De L'Imprimerie Royale, 1776 (pp. 343-382, plus two plates of drawings).
19. A. R. Jumikis, *Active and Passive Earth Pressure Coefficient Tables*, New Brunswick, N.J., Rutgers—The State University, College of Engineering, Engineering Research Publication no. 43, 1962.
20. J. V. Poncelet, *Mémoire sur la stabilité des revêtements et de leurs fondations*. Note additionnelle sur les relations analytiques qui lient entre elles la poussée et la butée de la terre. *Mémorial de l'officier du génie*, vol. 13, Paris, 1840, pp. 261-270.
21. K. Culmann, "Die Graphische Statik," Section 8, *Theorie der Stütz- und Futtermauern*, Zürich, Meyer und Zeller, 1866, pp. 545-633, plus Plates 28-34.
22. A. Collin, *Recherches expérimentales sur les glissements spontanés des terrains argileux accompagnées de considérations sur quelques principes de la mécanique terrestre*, Paris, Carilian-Goeury, 1846. Collin's work is now translated by W. R. Schriever and published by the University of Toronto Press in 1956, Toronto, Canada, bearing the title *Landslides in Clays*.
23. H. Darcy, *Les fontaines publiques de la ville de Dijon*, Paris; Dijon, Victor Dalmont, Éditeur, 1856.
24. G. G. Stokes, "On the Effect of the Internal Friction of Fluids on the Motion of Pendulum," *Trans.* Cambridge Philosophical Society, 1856, vol. 9, part 2.
25. W. J. M. Rankine, "On the Stability of Loose Earth," *Philosophical Transactions*, Royal Society, London, 1857, vol. 147.
26. O. Mohr, *Technische Mechanik*, Berlin, Wilhelm Ernst und Sohn, 1906.
27. G. Rebhann, *Theorie des Erddruckes und der Futtermauern mit besonderer Rücksicht auf das Bauwesen*, Wien, Carl Gerold's Sohn, 1871.
28. J. Weyrauch, "Zur Theorie des Erddrucks," *Zeitschrift für Baukunde*, 1878, vol. 2, no. 2, p. 193.
29. S. Timoshenko, *History of Strength of Materials*, New York, McGraw-Hill Book Company, Inc., 1953.

30. J. V. Boussinesq, *Application des potentiels à l'étude de l'équilibre et du mouvement des solides élastiques*, Paris, Gauthier-Villars, 1885.
31. J. R. Perronet, *Description des Projets et de la Construction des Ponts de Neuilly, de Mantes, d'Orleans, de Louis XVI, etc.*, Paris, Francois-Ambroise Didot, 1788.
32. O. Franzius, "Erddruckversuche im natürlichen Maßstabe," *Der Bauingenieur*, 1928, vol. 9, pp. 787-792; 813-815.
33. H. Krey and J. Ehrenberg, *Erddruck, Erdwiderstand und Tragfähigkeit des Baugrundes*, Berlin, Wilhelm Ernst und Sohn, 1936.
34. J. Feld, "Lateral Earth Pressure," *Trans. ASCE*, 1923, Paper no. 1529, vol. 86.
35. K. Terzaghi, "Large Retaining Wall Tests," *Eng. News-Record*, Sept. 29, 1932; Feb. 1, 22, March 8, 29, and April 19, 1934.
36. A. Hertwig, "Bemerkungen über neuere Erddruckuntersuchungen," *Veröffentlichungen* des Instituts der Deutschen Gesellschaft für Bodenmechanik, Berlin, Julius Springer, 1939, pp. 1-9.
37. G. P. Tschebotarioff, "Large-scale Model Earth Pressure Tests on Flexible Bulkheads," *Proc. ASCE*, 1948.
38. *Slutbetänkande*, Statens Järnvägars Geotekniska Kommission 1914-1922, Statens Järnvägar, Stockholm, 1922.
39. W. Fellenius, "Kaj- och Jordraset i Göteborg," *Teknisk Tidskrift*, no. 2, 1918.
40. K. E. Petterson, "Kajraset i Göteborg, den 5 Mars, 1916," *Teknisk Tidskrift*, 1916, nos. 30, 31.
41. S. Hultin, "Grusfullningar för Kajbiggnader," *Teknisk Tidskrift*, No. 31, 1916.
42. K. E. Petterson, "The Early History of Circular Sliding Surfaces," *Géotechnique*, vol. 5, London, 1955.
43. K. Terzaghi, *Erdbaumechanik auf bodenphysikalischer Grundlage*, Leipzig und Wien, Franz Deuticke, 1925.
44. K. Terzaghi and O. K. Fröhlich, *Theorie der Setzung von Tonschichten*, Leipzig und Wien, Franz Deuticke, 1936.
45. R. K. Bernhard, *Dynamic Compaction of Soil*, Engineering Research Bulletin No. 37, New Brunswick, N.J., Rutgers University, 1952.
46. *Engineering Soil Survey of New Jersey*, 22 bulletins accompanied by engineering soil maps for all 21 counties of New Jersey, Rutgers University, Bureau of Engineering Research, 1950-1957.
47. R. Haefeli, *Schneemechanik, mit Hinweisen auf die Erdbaumechanik*, Der Schnee und seine Metamorphose, in Beiträge zur Geologie der Schweiz, Geotechnische Serie, Hydrologie, Bern, 1939. Trans. Jan C. Van Tienhoven for the Snow, Ice and Permafrost Research Establishment, Corps of Engineers, U.S. Army; *Snow and its Metamorphism* by H. Bader, R. Haefeli, E. Bucher, J. Heher, O. Eckel and Chr. Thams, Translation 14, January 1954, Wilmette, Illinois.

SUGGESTIONS FOR FURTHER READING

1. N. Fitzsimons, "Civil Engineering History: An Appraisal." Paper No. 9875, *Proc., ASCE,* Journal of Professional Activities. Vol. 99, No. PP3, July, 1973, pp. 327-329.
2. J. Heyman, *Coulomb's Memoir on Statics,* Cambridge at the University Press, 1972.
3. A.R. Jumikis, *The Frost Penetration Problem in Highway Engineering,* New Brunswick, N.J.: Rutgers University Press, 1955.
4. A.R. Jumikis *Thermal Soil Mechanics,* New Brunswick, N.J.: Rutgers University Press, 1966.
5. A.R. Jumikis, *Thermal Geotechnics,* New Brunswick, N.J.: Rutgers University Press, 1977.
6. W. Ratigan, *The Long Crossing,* Grand Rapids, Mich.: 1959, W. B. Eerdmans, 1959, (about Mackinac-Straits bridge).
7. L. Reti, ed., *The Unknown Leonardo,* New York, N.Y.: McGraw-Hill Book Company, 1974.
8. V. Smartt, "Great Moments in Construction History—The Brooklyn Bridge," Contractor, July, 1973, pp. 23-35.
9. L. Sprague de Camp, *The Ancient Engineers,* Garden City, New York: Doubleday and Company, Inc., 1963.
10. *Transactions, ASCE,* New York, N.J.: Centennial Transactions, Vol. CT, 1953.
11. *Proceedings ASCE,* Journal of the Construction Division, vol. 101,
    No. CO1, March 1975
    No. CO2, June 2, 1975
    No. CO3, September, 1975
    No. CO4, December, 1975.
    Golden Jubilee Issues Nos. I, II, III and IV. Contain papers for everybody on construction, and current material of lasting interest, as well as historical and predictive topics in connection with the 50th Anniversary of the ASCE Construction Division.
12. L. Bjerrum, A. Casagrande, R.B. Peck and A.W. Skempton, *"From Theory to Practice in Soil Mechanics"* (Selections from the writings of Karl Terzaghi), 1960, John Wiley and Sons, 1960, New York, N.Y.

Chapter 3

SOIL MECHANICS

3-1. Definition. Soil mechanics, sometimes also called géotechnique or geotechnics, is one of the youngest disciplines of civil engineering. From the logical contents of the subject matter as discussed in the foregoing sections, one can deduce that soil mechanics is not the discipline known by the term "soil science". The latter is an agricultural and forestry science which studies soil from the angle of plant nutrition.

Soil mechanics can be defined as that discipline of engineering sciences which studies theoretically and practically soils, by means of which and upon which engineers build their structures. The essence of this definition is that the soil mechanics discipline treats soil as a construction material in any way associated with engineering. The effect of forces on the equilibrium and/or behavior of soil under static and dynamic conditions, as well as under the influence of water and temperature, is studied theoretically and experimentally. A knowledge of physics, mechanics, hydraulics, and heat transfer in soil studies is applied either to verify old or to establish new theories about the behavior of soil subjected to stress, water, and heat or cold. In other words, soil mechanics studies the mutual interaction of structure and soil.

The term "soil" as used in this book refers to the unconsolidated sediments and deposits of solid particles derived from the disintegration of rock.

Terzaghi[1] defines soil mechanics as follows:

"Soil Mechanics is the application of the laws of mechanics and hydraulics to engineering problems dealing with sediments and other unconsolidated accumulations of solid particles produced by the mechanical and chemical disintegration of rocks regardless of whether or not they contain an admixture of organic constituents."

It is probable that the English term "soil mechanics" is derived from the title of Terzaghi's book *Erdlaumechanik auf bodenphysikalischer Grundlage*[2], published in 1925.

The term "soil mechanics" is now accepted quite generally to designate that discipline of engineering science which deals with the properties, behavior, and performance of soil as a structural material.

The practice of engineering which applies the principles of soil mechanics to the design of engineering structures is called soil engineering.

Purpose. The purpose of soil mechanics is to replace by scientific methods the empirical methods of design applied in foundation engineering in the past.

3-2. Objectives of Soil Mechanics. The objectives of soil mechanics are

1) to perform engineering soil surveys;
2) to develop rational soil sampling devices and soil sampling methods;
3) to develop suitable soil testing devices and soil testing methods;
4) to collect and classify information on soils and their physical properties in the light of fundamental knowledge of soil mechanics, earthworks, and foundation engineering;
5) to investigate the physical properties of soils and to determine coefficients to characterize these soil properties;
6) to evaluate and interpret soil test results and their application to the use of soil in place or as a construction material;
7) to endeavor to gain more light in understanding the physical processes which actually take place in soils subjected to various factors such as static and dynamic loads, water, and temperature;
8) to apply the knowledge of soil mechanics for the solution of practical engineering problems, and
9) to replace by scientific methods the empirical ones of design used in foundation and earthwork engineering in the past, thus contributing to the advancement of this discipline.

3-3. Soil Mechanics Problems. Some of the problems listed below indicate the important kind of relationship which exists between foundations and soil:

How deep should borings for soil exploration be made?
What is the bearing capacity of a soil on its surface and at various depths to carry various loads?
What is the load to be applied on a particular soil?
What is the intensity and what is the stress distribution in a soil induced by various kinds of loading?[3]
How thick should a layer of a good soil over a poor one be in order to prevent the foundation from punching through it into the layer of poor soil?
Does a soil possess properties (friction and cohesion) which will assure satisfactory stability for foundations or slopes?
How much counterweight should be placed as a remedial measure against lateral motion of soil masses in order to maintain the stability of a structure?

The engineer is also interested in settlement considerations caused by applied loads: structures on soil, ground-water lowering, vibrations, tunneling, or mining, for example. Also the rate and amount of settlement are of great importance, especially in a case where structures are built as statically indeterminate systems.

When does settlement cease?[4]
What is the mutual interaction between soil and foundation, and what kinds and magnitudes of stresses are induced in the foundation and soil of a rigid highway or runway pavement due to various loading schemes under consideration?

The following problems apply, in addition to the bearing capacities and settlement, particularly to highways and airfields:

What is the frost penetration depth?[5]
What will be the effect on pavements of frost heave and thaw?
What remedial measures can be taken to prevent frost damage?
How suitable is a particular soil as a base for highways, for railway earthfills and cuts, and for the construction of dams?
Does the soil in question swell, or shrink, and how much?
What treatment should be given to such soils?
To what degree can a waterlogged soil be drained?[6]

From these questions one can see that "soil mechanics vs. foundation" problems are attached to the soil, and that they should be studied as problems of stability and deformation.

REFERENCES

1. K. Terzaghi, *Theoretical Soil Mechanics*, New York, John Wiley and Sons, Inc., 1948.
2. K. Terzaghi, *Bodenmechanik auf bodenphysikalischer Grundlage*, Wien, Franz Deuticke, 1925.
3. O.K. Fröhlich, *Druckverteilung im Baugrunde*, Wien: Springer, 1934.
4. K. Terzaghi and O.K. Fröhlich, *Theorie der Setzung von Tonschichten*, Leipzig und Wien: Franz Deuticke, 1936.
5. A.R. Jumikis, *Thermal Geotechnics*, New Brunswick, N.J.: Rutgers University Press, 1977.
6. H.R. Cedergren, *Seepage, Drainage and Flow Nets*, New York, N.Y.: John Wiley and Sons, 1967.
7. L. Bjerrum, A. Casagrande, R.B. Peck, A.W. Skempton, *From Theory to Practice in Soil Mechanics* (Selections from the writings of Karl Terzaghi), New York, N.Y.: John Wiley and Sons, 1960.

PART II

Physical Properties of Soil

Chapter 4

SOIL

4-1. Definition. The noun "soil" originates from the Latin "solum" which commonly had the same meaning as our modern word. The term soil has various shades of meaning and connotation, however, depending upon the general professional field in which it is being considered.

Geologists Ries and Watson[1] say: "The soil may be considered as the superficial unconsolidated mantle of disintegrated and decomposed rock material, which, when acted upon by organic agencies, and mixed with varying amounts of organic matter, may furnish conditions necessary for the growth of plants. In this broadest sense, the term soil has been used by geologists to include all the mantle or rock decay."

According to pedologist Joffe,[2] the term soil is defined as follows:

"The soil is a natural body, differentiated into horizons of mineral and organic constituents, usually unconsolidated, of variable depths, which differs from the parent material below in morphology, physical properties and composition, and biological characteristics."

Thus one sees that to the agronomist and pedologist the soil is limited to the surface or near-surface materials of the regolith.

From the viewpoint of soil technology, the term "soil" comprehends the entire thickness of the earth's crust which is accessible and feasible for practical utilization and exploitation in solving engineering problems.[3] This concept comes particularly vividly to light in considering subsurface mining operations where shafts and borings are put down to considerable depths as long as such methods prove to be economical.

In foundation and earthworks engineering a great many foundations are laid in unconsolidated rock, particularly when bedrock is deep below the ground surface. This necessitates the investigation and evaluation of the physical properties and the behavior of soil subjected to structural and, where necessary, to earthquake stresses. Hence, in civil engineering, the term soil includes not only the pedologist's soil but also any unconsolidated material, including water in soil, which can be found between the ground surface and consolidated rock. In other words, the engineer's definition of the term soil includes all regolith material, or the entire soil profile down to, and sometimes even into, the underlying consolidated rock, referred to also as bedrock (borings, wells, tunneling for subsurface exploration, shelters, storage tanks).

In soil engineering, a sharp demarcation between rock and soil is no longer made. In this sense the term soil is adopted and used also in soil mechanics, and in this book only the engineer's definition of the term soil is to be understood. From an engineer's viewpoint, soil is a material by means of which and upon which he builds his structures.

4-2. Formation of Soil. As already indicated, soil, which is a complex mixture of inorganic matter that may or may not contain decomposed organic residues and other substances and which blankets the earth's crust, is formed by the process of weathering, that is, disintegration and decomposition of rocks and minerals at or near the earth's surface through the action of many natural physical or mechanical and chemical agents into smaller and smaller particles. The two latter kinds of weathering processes are concomitant, and occur simultaneously.

The factors of weathering in the process of soil formation may be atmospheric, such as the work of oscillations of temperature (heat, frost); wind and water (for example rain, and also ice); erosion and transportation by wind; water (rain, river, sea) and glaciers; plant and animal life; chemical action, for example the complex phenomena of solutions, crystal growth, oxidation, hydration, hydrolysis, carbonation, and leaching that are brought about by water, especially when it contains carbonic acid; man's activities, and time.[3]

4-3. Soil Types. One distinguishes between glacial soils, residual soils, alluvial soils, and wind-borne soils.[4,5]

Glacial soils are those which have been transported and deposited by glaciers. The principal glacial deposits are of the Pleistocene Age. The glacial ice sheet filled up river valleys with the so-called *glacial drift*. Glacial drift is the glacial deposit from all types of the superficial material of rock debris of any sort, handled in any way, by the continental glacier—for example by erosion, transportation, deposition from ice, or running meltwaters emanating from the ice. The glacial deposits may be sorted, assorted, or stratified. These deposits consist of boulders, rock fragments, gravel, sand, silt, and clay in various proportions.

The position of the southern boundary of the continental glacier is distinctively recognized by the geologic feature called the terminal moraine.[6] The landform of the terminal moraine, consisting of glacial debris material, is characterized by irregular, hummocky hills. Their width varies from one to two miles, and their height can be about 30 m.

One of the engineering aspects of terminal moraine soil materials containing lenses of silty clay and clay is the disposal of domestic wastes by means of domestic septic tanks. Septic tanks built in clayey soils, soils which by nature are of low permeability, may function improperly, thus creating unpleasant odors and becoming a nuisance to the community. Another engineering aspect of glacial soils relative to foundation engineering is the thickness of the glacial drift. On ridges of bedrock the glacial drift may be thin, whereas in preglacial valleys the glacial drift may be thick. In New Jersey, the extreme known thickness of glacial drift is about 140 m. Generally, the thickness of the glacial drift varies from zero to about 76 m. An average thickness of the glacial drift may be said to be from about 6 to 12 m. The practical engineering aspect of knowing the thickness of the glacial drift may be brought to the fore by a case from the construction years ago of the earth dam for the Boonton, New Jersey, water reservoir. The dam site originally selected had to be abandoned because of a loose drift material; it could not properly support the weight of the dam, nor could it meet satisfactory permeability requirements. Hence, a new dam site had to be chosen where the bedrock was encountered at a shallow depth covered with but a thin stratum of glacial drift. The thickness or depth of the glacial drift in a valley has its economic aspect, since this factor governs the cost of a dam— regardless of whether it is of earth or concrete—or a highway, or railway. It also governs the cost of foundations of bridges, locks, and other engineering and hydraulic structures.

Excavation operations in glacial till (unsorted, unstratified, unconsolidated, heterogeneous material) in a dense state require a power shovel or explosives. Ordinarily, however, excavations in glacial till present no problem.

Unstratified drift consisting of saturated, gray rock flour, which is found in the Morristown area along the toes of the gneissic ridges, is termed by local contractors "the bull's liver." This rock flour presents to contractors great difficulties in excavation work because the rock flour has a tendency to slump, and to collapse unsupported walls of foundation pits if the groundwater table is not lowered. Also, contractors fear losing construction machinery operating on the rock flour.[7]

Some of the physiographic features of glacial drift are 1) eskers, 2) kames, 3) stratified drift, and 4) glacial clays.

1) *Esker.* An esker is a bed deposited by a subglacial stream confined by ice. An esker appears as a conspicuously long, narrow, low, sinusoidal ridge of crudely stratified gravel and sand. Eskers approximately parallel the direction of movement of the glacier.

2) *Kames.* Kames appear as low mounds and hills. They consist of poorly stratified gravel and sand.

3) *Stratified Drifts.* Stratified drifts are glacial deposits along the major drainage courses north of the terminal moraine. Stratified drift consists of comparatively homogeneous sand admixed with gravel and silt in various proportions. It usually provides the best road construction material and railroad ballast.

4) *Glacial Clay* (varved clay). During the course of geologic times the now extinct lakes were filled with stratified silt and clay, the so-called varved clay, Fig. 4-1. The Swedish term *varve* (turn, course, layer) means a distinctly marked annual deposit of sediment. Excavations in glacial clay reveal neat annual layers or varves. The varves indicate that the clay had once been the sediment at the bottom of a lake. The varves consist of a sequence of a thicker varve, light in color, which is the summer sediment (silt), and a thinner and darker varve which is the winter sediment (clay), when the finer sediment settled out at low velocities of flow beneath the frozen surface of the lake. Roughly, each pair of such summer-winter varves represents one year.

This brief review on glacial soils may be summarized like this: glacial soils are important sources of soil as a construction material for earthworks, as a foundation material, and as an aggregate for concrete.

Residual Soils. Residual soils are those which have been left in place as a result of decay of the underlying parent rock, concealing the parent rock below the ground surface. Residual soils are usually encountered south of the terminal moraine. In glaciated areas residual soils are buried by glacial drift because there may be more than one terminal moraine. The parent materials for residual soils are igneous rocks such as granite or basalt, and sedimentary rocks such as limestone, sandstone, and shale.

Fig. 4-1.   Varved clay. Photo by the author.

Alluvial Soils. Alluvial soils occur in former and present flood plains and deltas, often forming very thick deposits.

Wind-borne Soils. Under this group two kinds of soil material may be comprehended, namely: the loess and dune sand. Wind-borne soils are ones which have been transported and laid down by atmospheric currents such as winds. Loess is wind-blown silt or silty clay, light in color, porous and coherent. Loess as construction material is relatively unknown to engineers. Loess often may turn out to be a very dangerous material for dams, highways, and as a support of foundations, particularly when wet. Dunes develop when and where loose sand is exposed to wind (sandy shores of lakes, rivers, seas).

4-4. Some Soil Designations. Because there are no definitions giving accurate characterizations of a soil, in practice there still are some descriptive terms of soils used for this purpose based on the soil profile, the appearance, and on some of the properties one can "touch off" from the soil. Therefore, it was found to be appropriate to give here a short description of the meanings of some soil types which are generally used in practice.

Bedrock is any layer of rock either at the surface or beneath superficial deposits of soil. Bedrock may be soft or hard.

Boulders are detached rock fragments larger than about 300 mm in diameter.

Boulder Clay is a mixture of an unstratified sedimental deposit of glacial clay, containing unsorted rock fragments of all sizes ranging from boulders, cobbles, and gravel to finely pulverized clay material.

Calcareous soil denotes a soil containing calcium carbonate. Such a soil effervesces when tested with weak hydrochloric acid.

Caliche is a soil conglomerate of gravel, sand, and clay, the particles of which are cemented by calcium carbonate.

Cobbles are rock fragments ranging in size from about 75 to 300 mm in diameter.

Diatomaceous earth is a fine, light gray, soft sedimentary deposit of the siliceous remains or skeletons of diatoms. Diatoms are minute unicellular marine organisms. Such a soil is very porous, and of fine structure.

Gumbo is a very fine-particled clay deposit, devoid of sand. This clay is dark, plastic, and very sticky. When moist it is sticky and spongy. It is one of the most difficult soils to handle either in excavation or as a road material.

Hardpan is a relatively hard, densely-cemented (by limonite) soil layer, like rock. It will not soften when wet. The material may be clays or silts, and cohesion-less materials. Hardpans offer great resistance to the penetration of soil-drilling tools. Hardpans are difficult to excavate.

Humus is the term used to denote a dark brown organic amorphous earth of the topsoil. It consists of partly decomposed vegetal matter. As a foundation or road material, humus is undesirable because it continues to decay, shrinks, and also holds water.

Lime soils contain calcium carbonate as the predominant ingredient, the proportions of which may be over 75%, although usually it is under 50%.

Loam (an agronomic term) is a mixture of sand, silt, and clay, sometimes containing some organic matter, such as humus. The terms sand, silt, and clay here refer to the particle size.

Loess denotes a uniform, cohesive, wind-blown, porous, but coherent deposit of very fine material. The sizes of its particles are very uniform, and usually range between about 0.01 mm to 0.05 mm, which size corresponds to silt or a silty clay fraction. The color of loess is yellowish light brown. Loess is encountered in dry continental regions. Slopes of cuts made in it are able to stand nearly vertically.

Marl is a very loose term denoting deposits which consist of mixtures of calcareous sands, or clays, or loam. The proportion of carbonate lime, however, may not fall below about 15%, nor does the quantity of clay rise above 75%.

Muck denotes a mixture of finely particled, inorganic soil and black, decomposed organic matter. This material is usually found accumulated under conditions of imperfect drainage—for example, in swamps—or is deposited by over-flowing rivers.

Mud designates a mixture of silt or clay with water. The consistency of mud is an almost fluid mass.

Peat is an organic soil formed of vegetal matter under conditions of excessive moisture, as found in swamps. Peat is very compressible, and therefore unsuitable for supporting even the lightest foundations.

Pebbles are a constituent part of gravels with diameters about 50 mm to 75 mm.

Quicksand is not a special type of soil, but a condition. Any granular material through which an upward flow of water takes place may become "quick" under proper hydraulic conditions.

Till is generally understood to be that part of glacial drift which is directly deposited by ice, without transportation or sorting by water. Till consists of an unstratified, unconsolidated to moderately consolidated, heterogeneous mixture of clay, sand, gravel, and boulders. Till is also known by the term boulder-clay.

These definitions reveal fully the inadequacy of the information on the properties of soils presented by the descriptive method. Soil as an engineering material is extremely complex. Each of the constituent parts of a soil has different physical properties, and the presence of them in varying proportions affects the different properties of the whole composite considerably.

More accurate information for the characterization of the physical and mechanical properties of soils can be obtained only from laboratory tests.

4-5. Soil Profile. To the engineer, the soil profile is a vertical cross section of the actual soil strata at a given site showing a natural sequence and thickness of soil layers below the ground surface. A good graphical representation of a soil profile, showing also the position of the groundwater table as well as engineering soil classification is very instructive and helpful in various geotechnical designs such as structural foundations, highways, and other kinds of earthworks. Soil profile drawings are prepared based on soil exploration data[8] (see also Chapter 25 of this book).

4-6. Cohesive and Noncohesive Soils. One of the distinctive properties of the various kinds of soils is bond or cohesion between the individual soil particles. Because of their cohesive properties, soils may be classified into two main groups, a) noncohesive soils and b) cohesive soils.

Noncohesive soils are those formed of uncemented, finely weathered rock particles, for example, gravel and sand.

Cohesive soils are those possessing cohesion. Cohesion is attributed partly to the intermolecular attraction of the soil particles for each other throughout the soil mass—called *true cohesion*—and partly to binding of the soil mass together by the action of the surface tension forces of the soil moisture—called the *apparent cohesion*. When submerged, the apparent cohesion of the soil mass (viz., air-water interface) is destroyed.

It is, of course, obvious that it is extremely difficult to make a strict delineation between a lean or light clayey sand and a fat sandy clay; hence the transition in gradation of cohesion of such soils. Silts, for example, possess a comparatively slight cohesion. With increasing amounts of the finer-sized particles, such as clay and colloids, the cohesion of the soil increases.

REFERENCES

1. H. Ries and T.L. Watson, 1947, *Engineering Geology*, New York, N.Y.: John Wiley and Sons, Inc.
2. J.S. Joffe, 1936, *Pedology*. New Brunswick, New Jersey: Rutgers University Press.
3. R.N. Yong and B.P. Warkentin, *Soil Properties and Behaviour*, Amsterdam: Elsevier Scientific Publishing Company, 1975, p.2.
4. M.G. Spangler and R.L. Handy, *Soil Engineering*, 3rd ed., New York, N.Y.: Intext Educational Publishers, 1973, pp. 34-52.
5. Earth Manual, 2nd edition, Washington D.C.: U.S. Department of the Interior, 1974, p. 87-100.
6. R.D. Salisbury, *The Glacial Geology of New Jersey*, Trenton, N.J.: 1902.
7. A.R. Jumikis, *Engineering Aspects of Glacial Soils of the Newark Metropolitan Area of New Jersey*, New Brunswick, N.J.: College of Engineering, Rutgers, The State University of New Jersey. Engineering Research Bulletin No. 42, 1959.
8. H.F. Winterkorn and H.-Y. Fang (editors), *Foundation Engineering Handbook*, New York, Van Nostrand Reinhold Company, 1975, pp. 59-66.

SUGGESTIONS FOR FURTHER READING

1. D.U. Deere and R.P. Miller, Engineering Classification and Index Properties for Intact Rock, Technical Report No. AFWL-TR-65-116, Air Force Weapons Laboratory, Research and Technical Division, Kirtland AFB, New Mexico, December, 1966, pp. 136-139.
2. C. Jaeger, *Rock Mechanics,* Cambridge at the University Press, 1972.
3. A.R. Jumikis and A.A. Jumikis, *Red Brunswick Shale and its Engineering Aspects.* Engineering Research Bulletin 55, College of Engineering; Rutgers, The State University of New Jersey, New Brunswick, New Jersey, 1975.
4. *Rock Excavation Seminar* (Lecture Notes), October 1976. Foundations and Soil Mechanics Group, Metropolitan Section, ASCE, Committee on Continuing Education.

QUESTIONS

4-1. What is soil mechanics?
4-2. Define soil.
4-3. Describe some glacial landforms.
4-4. Why is it helpful for an engineer to recognize in nature glacial landforms?
4-5. What is varved clay?
4-6. What is soil profile?

Chapter 5

SOME PHYSICAL PROPERTIES OF SOIL

5-1. Mechanical Composition of Soil. By nature soil is a very complex physical system. Soils are aggregates composed of an assemblage of the most diverse granular mineral particles, humus or organic matter, and various inorganic chemical compounds. The physical make-up of a mineral soil is termed its mechanical composition.

5-2. Soil Phases. The word "phase" is derived from the Greek/φασις, meaning "appearance." By a phase of soil is understood any homogeneous part of a soil system different from other parts of the system and separated from them by abrupt transition—such as the solid soil particles and liquid water. A system consisting of more than one phase is called heterogeneous. Each physically or chemically different, homogeneous, and mechanically separable part of a system constitutes a distinct phase. Thus ice floating in water is a two-phase *system of water* (solid and liquid phases).

Because soil is a porous medium, a given volume of a *soil system* ordinarily may be regarded as a system consisting of three fundamental phases, namely:

1) the solid phase or skeleton which may be mineral, organic, or both;
2) the liquid phase or the soil water (and/or oil) filling part or all of the voids between the soil particles, and
3) the gaseous or vapor phase (e.g., soil air and/or entrapped gas) which occupies that part of the voids which is not occupied by liquid, viz., water.

In the studies of freezing or frozen soil, four phases are distinguished: 1) the solid phase, 2) the gaseous phase, 3) the liquid phase (undercooled, unfrozen water), and 4) the ice phase. The phase concept is also of great aid in designing asphalt mixes for the surfaces of road and street pavements.

The volumetric proportions of the solids and voids of a soil mass can most readily be studied by means of the soil phase diagram, Fig. 5-1b. Thus, such a phase diagram represents the relative volumetric proportions and also, as it will be shown further, the gravimetric proportions of the various soil phases. It is to be understood that there is no real means of separating the soil phases as shown in Fig. 5-1b. The separation of solids from voids can only be imagined here. However, such a theoretical phase separation is very convenient for the visualization of the phase relationships and for the solution of such phase problems as the volumes and weights (dry densities) of solids, amounts of soil moisture, gas volumes, porosities of a soil mass, and other related problems. Therefore, the concept of the theoretical phase separation should be firmly kept in one's mind.

Depending upon the degree of filling of the voids with water (or degree of

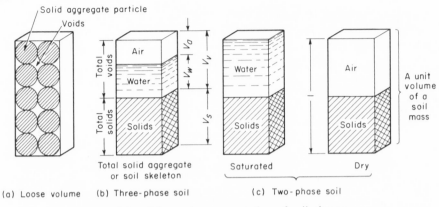

FIG. 5-1. Schematic representation of soil phases.

saturation) one distinguishes between a three-phase soil and a two-phase soil (Fig. 5-1). When the voids of the soil are only partially filled with water, and air occupies only that space not filled with water, such soil represents a three-phase soil. A three-phase soil is the one most often encountered in nature. When all of the voids are filled with water (saturated soil), such a soil is called a two-phase soil. It is a special case of a three-phase soil: the gaseous phase is lacking.

5-3. Soil Structure. Individual soil particles and combinations of them of which the soil is made up, depending upon their configuration (shape and size), commonly arrange or group themselves in the aggregate during the process of sedimentation in a suspension in various patterns of structural framework called soil structures. For classification purposes of soil texture such a definition is entirely adequate.

Terzaghi[1] grouped the most common patterns of soil structures into the following three principal groups:

1) granular or single-grained structures,
2) honeycomb or cellular structures, and
3) flocculent structures.

These structures are illustrated in Fig. 5-2.

In the United States, the term *soil texture* is used to indicate the size, characteristics and distribution of the individual soil particles and the proportion of soil material of each size (fraction) present in any given case as seen on the freshly exposed surface (shape of particles whether flaky,

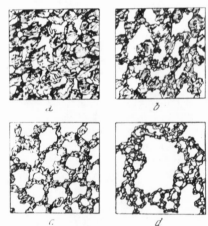

FIG. 5-2. Soil structures: a, b, Granular structure; c, Cellular structure; d, Flocculent structure. After K. Terzaghi, Ref. 1.

angular or rounded; their size and amount). Size and shape of soil particles are the most important soil parameters controlling ice segregation in a freezing system called here the soil-water-temperature system.

Soil texture is determined by sieving and sedimentation (hydrometer) analysis. It is a laboratory process of separating the soil into groups—fractions—of certain particle size.

5-4. Specific Gravity. The term specific gravity applies to the solid phase of the soil only, i.e., to the soil particle material (soil solids), and not to the composite soil as such. The latter contains, besides solids, the liquid phase or soil moisture (if present) and the gaseous phase (e.g., air).

TABLE 5-1. SPECIFIC GRAVITIES OF SOME SOILS

Nos.	Soil Types	Specific Gravity G
1	2	3
1	Bentonite clay	2.34
2	Chalk	2.63-2.73-2.81
3	Clay	2.44-2.53-2.92
4	Humus	1.37
5	Kaolin	2.47-2.50-2.58
6	Loess	2.65-2.75
7	Lime	2.70
8	Peat	1.26-1.50-1.80
9	Peat, sphagnum, 25% decomposed	0.50-0.70-0.80
10	Quartz sand	2.64-2.65
11	Quartzite	2.65
12	Silt	2.68-2.72
13	Silt with organic admixtures	2.40-2.50

The specific gravity G of dry solids of a soil is defined as the ratio of the density γ_s of a given volume of the soil solids to the greatest density γ_w (at $+4°$ C) of an equal volume of pure water. The density of the substance of the soil particles is their mass per unit volume of the particles. The density of water at $+4°$ C is 1.000. Therefore, specific gravity is calculated as follows:

$$G = \frac{\text{weight of soil particles in grams}}{(\text{volume of soil particles})(1.000)} = \frac{W_s}{V_s\gamma_w} = \frac{\gamma_s}{\gamma_w}, \qquad (5\text{-}1)$$

where γ_s = unit weight of soil solids (absolute volume),

γ_w = unit weight of water, and

$W_s = V_s\gamma_s$.

The quantity G is dimensionless, and it shows how many times heavier is the substance of the solid particles of soil than an equivalent amount of water. The "(volume of soil particles) times $(1.000) = V_s\gamma_w$" actually means the weight of water displaced by the soil particles.

Use of specific gravity. Specific gravity, as an auxiliary factor, is used in computing other soil properties, for example, the porosity and void ratio of a soil, its unit weight, the velocity of fall of a particle through a viscous fluid, soil particle size determination by means of the hydrometer method. It is also used in consolidation studies of clays, in calculating the degree of saturation of soil, in studies of the critical hydraulic gradient in soil when a quick condition of sand is estimated, in zero-air-void calculations in the compaction theory of soils, and in other calculations.

The specific gravity of a mixture of the various minerals a soil may contain varies, on the average, from 2.50 to 2.70. The heavier the minerals composing the soil, the greater is the specific gravity of the soil. A normal, average value of specific gravity of the mineral particles made up of quartz is usually about $G = 2.65$. Average specific gravities of some soils are listed in Table 5-1.

5-5. Porosity. Depending upon the degree of soil density or packing, soil particles are surrounded by a certain amount of voids, which are termed pores. The total volume of all voids within a unit volume of soil, regardless of whether fully or partially filled with liquid, is termed the *soil porosity*. Porosity, n, is expressed by the ratio of volume of all voids V_v to the total volume of soil (solids plus voids), see Fig. 5-3, and is usually expressed quantitatively in percent:

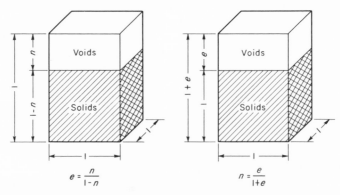

(a) Volumetric relationship by
total volume of soil

(b) Volumetric relationship by
total volume of solids

FIG. 5-3.   Relationship between coefficient of porosity n and void ratio e.

$$n = \frac{\text{volume of all voids in soil}}{\text{total volume of soil}} 100\%, \tag{5-2}$$

or

$$n = \frac{V_v}{V} 100 = \frac{V_v}{V_s + V_v} 100\%, \tag{5-3}$$

where V_s = volume of solids, and

$$V = V_s + V_v = \text{total volume}. \tag{5-4}$$

Also, n can be expressed as

$$n = \frac{V - V_s}{V} = 1 - \frac{V_s}{V} = 1 - \frac{W_s}{G\gamma_w V}, \tag{5-5}$$

where W_s = weight of solids of soil, and

$$V_s = \frac{W_s}{G\gamma_w},$$ (5-6)

where G = specific gravity of the soil, and
γ_w = unit weight of water.

The volume of voids in natural sands depends to some extent on their mechanical composition, degree of packing, and the natural processes of their deposition. Sands which have been deposited by rapidly receding floodwaters have a porosity of about $n = 50\%$. Sands which were deposited slowly have on the average a porosity of about $n = 25\%$.

5-6. Void Ratio. The change in volume of soil voids, which can take place under the action of loads, brings in its turn a change in the total volume of soil. Therefore, the total volume of soil is to be regarded as a variable quantity which causes inconveniences in calculating porosity by Eq. (5-3). For this reason, in soil mechanics practice it is customary to express porosity by a ratio of volume of total pores or voids to the total volume of solids, the latter of which can be considered a constant quantity and is taken as a unit of volume. The quantity expressing the ratio of the volume of voids to the volume of solids is termed the relative porosity or void ratio e, Fig. 5-3.

$$e = \frac{\text{volume of voids in soil}}{\text{volume of solids in soil}},$$ (5-7)

or

$$e = \frac{V_v}{V_s} = \frac{V - V_s}{V_s} = \frac{V}{V_s} - 1 = \frac{VG\gamma_w}{W_s} - 1,$$ (5-8)

where all symbols have the same meaning as before.

The quantity e is more convenient and preferred in mathematical calculations of practical problems over porosity n. One sees that void ratio e is a figure which shows how many times more voids than solids there are in a soil.

The volume of voids includes all voids, both those visible and those invisible to the naked eye. Void ratio e is extensively used in calculating unit weight, critical hydraulic gradients, water tranmissibility, soil consolidation tests and settlement analyses of soil, as well as in determining the relative density of soil. From the variation in pore volume or void ratio it is possible to evaluate the density of soil and thus the degree of compaction of the soil. Also, it can be said that void ratio characterizes the natural state of density of a soil.

5-7. Relationship Between Porosity and Void Ratio. The physical meaning of the soil properties porosity and void ratio can be explained by means of the soil phase diagram, Fig. 5-3. Assume that a unit volume of soil, the total height of which is one unit of length ($= 1$), contains a volume of pores the amount of which is $V_v = nV$. Then, obviously, the volume of solids can be expressed as $V_s = (1 - n)V$.

The void ratio e can now be expressed as follows:

$$e = \frac{V_v}{V_s} = \frac{n}{1-n}.$$ (5-9)

From this relationship, the porosity n is

$$n = \frac{e}{1+e}.$$ (5-10)

This expression can also be obtained directly from Figure 5-3b.

The total volume of a soil sample V is made up of the sum of the volume of solids and the volume of voids in that sample:

$$V_v + V_s = V.$$ (5-11)

By Eq. (5-8), if the void ratio of a soil is known, the volume of voids can be calculated:

$$V_v = eV_s = \frac{n}{1-n} V_s.$$ (5-12)

Substituting this V_v-value into Eq. (5-11), obtain the volume of solids:

$$V_s = \frac{1}{1+e} V = (1-n)V.$$ (5-13)

By a similar method of calculation the volume of voids is obtained:

$$V_v = \frac{e}{1+e} V = nV.$$ (5-14)

Dividing Eq. (5-14) by Eq. (5-13), obtain

$$\frac{V_v}{V_s} = e = \frac{n}{1-n}.$$ (5-9)

The sum of these two volumes, V_s and V_v, must be equal to the total volume V of the soil:

$$V_s + V_v = \frac{1+e}{1+e} V = V.$$ (5-15)

If also the volume of air-voids V_a is to be considered, then the total volume V is written as

$$V = V_s + V_v = V_s + V_w + V_a,$$ (5-16)

where V_w = volume occupied by soil moisture.

5-8. Soil Moisture Content. Soil moisture content is defined as that amount of water which is contained in the voids of the soil. The amount of water contained in the voids of a soil in its natural state is termed the natural moisture content of the soil. The natural moisture content characterizes in general the consistency and strength properties of that soil, as well as its performance under the action of load and temperature.

The knowledge of moisture content in soil is necessary in soil compaction control, in determining consistency limits of soil, and for the calculation of the stability of all kinds of earthworks and foundations.

The soil moisture content is determined by the so-called *gravimetric method* by drying the soil sample in a drying oven at $105°C$ until a constant weight of the soil sample is attained. The moisture content w is expressed as a percentage of the dry weight of the soil, and is called the absolute moisture content of the soil:

$$w = \frac{\text{weight of water}}{\text{weight of solids}} \, 100\% = \frac{W_w}{W_d} \, 100\%, \qquad (5\text{-}17)$$

where W_w = weight of water in the voids of the soil, and
W_d = weight of solids (weight of oven dry soil).
For example, let $W_w = 11.0$ g and $W_d = 67.0$ g. Then the moisture content, based on dry weight, is calculated as

$$w = \frac{11.0}{67.0} \, 100\% = 16.4\%.$$

If the soil moisture content and the wet weight W of the soil are known, then the dry weight of the soil is calculated as

$$W_d = \frac{W_w + W_d}{1 + (w/100)} = \frac{W}{1 + (w/100)}. \qquad (5\text{-}18)$$

Using the same figures as above,

$$W_d = \frac{78.0}{1 + 0.164} = 67.0 \text{ g.}$$

The wet weight, dry weight, and moisture content relationship, Eq. (5-18), is applied in soil compaction operations for highway and runway fills and for the construction of earth dams.

5-9. Degree of Saturation. The condition when voids are partially filled with water is expressed by the degree of saturation S, or relative moisture content. It is the ratio of the actual volume of water in voids V_w to the total volume of voids V_v, expressed in fractions of the total volume of voids:

$$S = \frac{\text{actual volume of voids filled with water}}{\text{total volume of voids}}, \qquad (5\text{-}19a)$$

or

$$S = \frac{V_w}{V_v} = \frac{W_w}{W_v} = \frac{w}{w_{sat}}, \qquad (5\text{-}19)$$

where W_w = weight of water in voids present,

W_v = weight of water that can occupy the total volume of voids in soil,

w = percent of moisture by dry weight in soil, and

w_{sat} = percent of moisture by dry weight when all voids are totally filled with water.

Degree of saturation in terms of porosity:

$$S = \frac{n_w}{n}. \tag{5-20}$$

1) When $S < 1$, the voids in the soil are merely partially filled with water.
2) When $S = 1$, all voids are totally filled with water ($n_w = n$).
   a) When $S = 0$, the soil under consideration would represent a two-phase system, soil and air.
   b) When $S = 1$, the soil is a two-phase system.
   c) When $1 > S > 0$, the soil is a three-phase system.

Table 5-2 illustrates the various degrees of saturation of soil for classification purposes.

TABLE 5-2. DEGREE OF SATURATION

Description	Degree of Saturation (S)
1	2
Dry soil	0
Damp soil	> 0 -0.25
Moist soil	0.26-0.50
Very moist soil	0.51-0.75
Wet soil	0.76-0.99
Saturated soil	1.00

Examples

5-1. Determine the void ratio of a soil whose porosity is 32%.
By Eq. (5-9), the void ratio e is

$$e = \frac{n}{1-n} = \frac{0.32}{1-0.32} = 0.471.$$

The result indicates that there are in the soil 0.471 times more voids than solids.

5-2. a) The porosity of a soil fully saturated with water is 57%. Calculate the corresponding void ratio.
By Eq. (5-9),

$$e = \frac{0.57}{1-0.57} = 1.318.$$

There are 1.318 times more voids in the soil than solids.

b) When $n = 50\%$, then $e = 1.000$.

5-3. A laboratory test reveals that the void ratio of a certain soil is $e = 1.234$. What is the porosity of this soil?
By Eq. (5-10),

$$n = \frac{e}{1+e} = \frac{1.234}{1+1.234} = 0.553,$$

or $n = 55.3\%$.

From these examples one sees that voids furnish a means of identifying the character of the particular soil. The less the total volume of voids the denser the soil.

5-10. Soil Texture. Engineers recognize a soil property commonly known as *texture*. The term soil texture is used to express the percentage of the three main fractions (sand, silt, and clay) present in the soil sample passing the No. 10 mesh (2 mm) sieve. Thus, soil texture refers to the relative proportions of the various size groups of individual soil particles in a soil mass.

Table 5-3 shows the terms of the various soil fractions and their limiting sizes adopted as a standard by the U.S. Department of Agriculture, Bureau of Soils; the American Society for Testing Materials, and by the International Society of Soil Science. Note that in the International Scale the successive fractional limits are at equal decimal logarithmic intervals.

TABLE 5-3. SOIL PARTICLE FRACTIONS

	Diameter of Soil Particle (mm)		
Designation of Soil Fractions	U.S. Department of Agriculture, Bureau of Soils 1951	American Society for Testing Materials 1964	International Society of Soil Science
1	2	3	4
Fine gravel	2 to 1	> 4.760	
Coarse sand	1 to 0.5	4.760 to 2.000	2.0 to 0.2
Medium sand	0.5 to 0.25	2.000 to 0.420	
Fine sand	0.25 to 0.10	0.420 to 0.074	0.2 to 0.02
Very fine sand	0.10 to 0.05		
Silt	0.05 to 0.002	0.074 to 0.005	0.02 to 0.002
Clay	< 0.002	< 0.005	< 0.002
Colloids	—	< 0.001	—

5-11. Soil Particle Size Analysis. The soil physical make-up, or textural composition, sometimes termed granulometry, is determined by means of its particle size analysis—also known by the term "mechanical" analysis of soil. It is a screening process in which coarser fractions of soil are separated by means of a series of sieves of graded mesh. The mechanical analysis is one of the oldest test methods for soil materials, and it has been practiced for centuries.

The proportions by dry weight of each of these fractions relative to the total dry weight of the dry composite soil sample used for the analysis are established by weighing.

Soils, the particle sizes of which are larger than 0.074 mm (U.S. Standard No. 200 mesh sieve), are usually analyzed by means of sieving. Soil materials finer than 0.074 mm (− 200 material) are analyzed by the method of sedimentation of soil particles by gravity.

Descriptions of details for performing particle size analyses of soils are given by various agencies in their manuals or specifications of standard test methods of soils.[2,3,4] The material retained on sieves Nos. 4, 10, 20, 40, 60, 100, 140, and 200 are designated as "plus 4" material ($+4$), $+10$, $+20$, $+40$, $+60$, $+100$,

+140, and +200 material, respectively. This means soil particles which are larger than the openings in a corresponding mesh screen.

Conversely, "minus 4" material (-4), -10, -20, -40, -60, -100, -140, and -200 soil material are those passing the corresponding mesh screen.

5-12. Calculations and Representations. The percent fraction, $p\%$, retained on a certain sieve in the soil particle size analysis is calculated as

$$p = \frac{g}{G} \cdot 100\%,\qquad(5\text{-}21)$$

where g = dry weight (dried till constant weight at 105°C) in grams of a given fraction of soil retained on a certain sieve, and

G = dry weight at 105°C in grams of the total soil sample used in the particle size analysis.

The concept of soil particle size analysis by means of sieving is illustrated in Fig. 5-4. This figure shows a nest of sieves with the larger opening on top of the

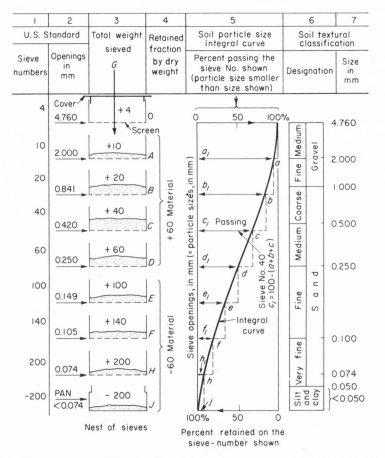

FIG. 5-4. Sieving process. (The classification is in accordance with ASTM (1964), Reapproved 1972, pp. 69-79.)

column, and with the finer sieves at the bottom. Fractions by dry weight retained on the sieves are designated by A, B, C, D, E, F, H, and J. The sum of these fractional weights is the total weight G of a soil sample sieved. The fractional weights A, B, . . . , J, expressed in percent retained on each sieve, thus are calculated as

$$a = \frac{A}{G} \cdot 100\%,$$

$$b = \frac{B}{G} \cdot 100\%,$$

$$c = \frac{C}{G} \cdot 100\%, \qquad (5\text{-}22)$$

$$\cdots\cdots\cdots$$

$$j = \frac{J}{G} \cdot 100\%.$$

Percent fractions passing the size of sieve shown are calculated, for example, as

$$a_{,} = 100 - a,$$

$$b_{,} = 100 - (a + b),$$

$$c_{,} = 100 - (a + b + c),$$

$$\cdots\cdots\cdots\cdots\cdots \qquad (5\text{-}23)$$

$$h_{,} = 100 - (a + b + c + \cdots + h),$$

$$j_{,} = 100 - \underbrace{(a + b + c + \cdots + h + j)}_{100} = 0,$$

where $(a + b + c)$ is the cumulative percent of soil fractions retained on sieves Nos. 4, 10, 20, and 40. Retention on sieve No. 4 in this example is shown as zero percent. The integral curve, or summation curve, separates the cumulative percents of particle sizes smaller than the size shown from the cumulative amount in percent of all soil particles which are retained on that sieve and above it. For example, the cumulative amount of particles retained on sieve No. 40 is $(a + b + c)$ percent; the cumulative amount of particles passing No. 40 sieve (-40 material) is $c_{,} = 100 - (a + b + c)$ percent. The Bureau of Soils classification of the USDA is also shown on Fig. 5-4 (see Column 6, "Designation").

A sample calculation of fractionating a 200 g dry soil sample is shown in Fig. 5-5.

For gravelly and sandy soils sieving is a fundamental part of the particle size analysis to sort out the coarser grades. For clayey soils sieving is just a constituent part of, or preparatory operation in, the particle size analysis. The fine-particled fractions are usually separated by the method of sedimentation in

U.S. Standard sieve Nos	Total dry weight of soil sample sieved 200.0 g	Retained on sieve		Cumulative retained		Cumulative passing	
		g	%	g	%	g	%
1	2	3	4	5	6	7	8
4		0.00	0.00	0.00	0.00	200.00	100.00
10		2.84	1.42	2.84	1.42	197.16	98.58
20		5.66	2.83	8.50	4.25	191.50	95.75
40		46.04	23.02	54.54	27.27	145.46	72.72
60		44.00	22.00	98.54	49.27	101.46	50.73
100		23.64	11.82	122.18	61.09	77.82	38.91
140		11.26	5.63	133.44	66.72	66.56	33.28
200		63.16	31.58	196.60	98.30	3.40	1.70
-200 (Pan)		3.40	1.70	200.00	100.00		
		200.00g	100.00%				

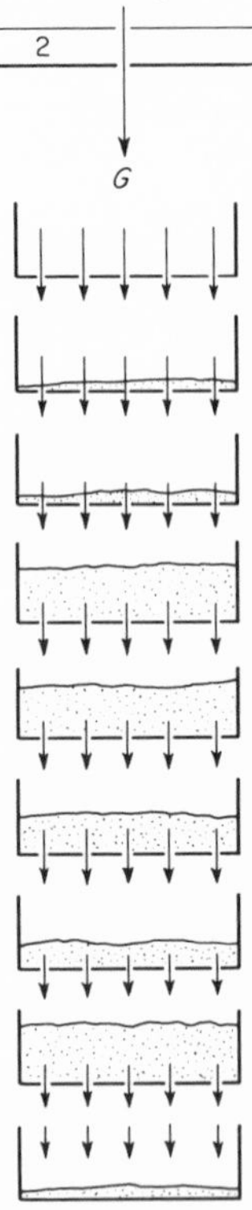

FIG. 5-5.   Fractioning of a soil sample.

water. The sedimentation method is based on the fact that the velocity of sedimentation is a function of soil particle size.

5-13. Specific Surface of a Soil Mass. As already indicated, many of the physico-chemical phenomena and processes in fine-particled soils, such as condensation of gases, the manifold effects of surface tension of liquids, and the majority of electrokinetic phenomena occur on the surfaces of the soil particles exposed, and their intensity increases in certain proportion with the absolute and specific surfaces of the soil particles. Likewise, many soil properties so important in soil mechanics and soil engineering depend very much upon the extent of the surfaces exposed. Because water can be held between the flat clay and colloidal particle surfaces, these surfaces are called *internal* surfaces of a soil mass. *Absolute* surface is the amount of surfaces of the various soil phases which are in contact with each other. *Specific* surface of a soil mass is the total amount of all surfaces of all particles contained (entire disperse phase) in a unit weight (or sometimes in a unit volume) of the soil mass. Of course, the chemical composition of the fine particles also influences the performance of a clayey soil.

The enormous increase of surface area with decrease in size of a geometrical particle is readily illustrated by imagining a cubic centimeter of a mineral material subdivided successively and decimally into smaller and smaller cubes (see Table 5-4). One notices that the total surface area upon successive sub-

TABLE 5-4. SUCCESSIVE SUBDIVISION OF A CUBE

Length of one edge of various sizes of cubes	Number of cubes	Total surface	Specific surface
1	2	3	4
1 cm $= 10$ mm	1	6 cm^2	6×10^0
1 mm $= 1 \times 10^{-1}$ cm	10^3	60 cm^2	6×10^1
0.1 mm $= 1 \times 10^{-2}$ cm	10^6	600 cm^2	6×10^2
0.01 mm $= 1 \times 10^{-3}$ cm	10^9	6000 cm^2	6×10^3
1.0 μ $= 1 \times 10^{-4}$ cm	10^{12}	6 m^2	6×10^4
0.1 μ $= 1 \times 10^{-5}$ cm	10^{15}	60 m^2	6×10^5
0.01 μ $= 1 \times 10^{-6}$ cm	10^{18}	600 m^2	6×10^6
1.0 $\mu\mu$ $= 1 \times 10^{-7}$ cm	10^{21}	6000 m^2	6×10^7
0.1 $\mu\mu$ $= 1 \times 10^{-8}$ cm	10^{24}	6 ha	6×10^8
0.01 $\mu\mu$ $= 1 \times 10^{-9}$ cm	10^{27}	60 ha	6×10^9
0.001 $\mu\mu$ $= 1 \times 10^{-10}$ cm	10^{30}	6 km^2	6×10^{10}

division of a cube of one cubic centimeter can increase from 6 cm^2 to 60,000,000 cm^2 (6000 m^2 = 0.6 hectares = 2.471 × 0.6 = 1.428 acres).

Baver[5] shows that in about 0.52 cm^3 of coarse silt containing spherical particles the size of which is 0.05 mm (50 μ) there is a very large surface area of 628.32 cm^2, and that in the same volume with spherical particles of 0.0002 mm (20 $\mu\mu$) in diameter (colloidal clay size) there is a surface area of 157,080 cm^2.

The great difference in specific surface area is probably one of the important factors causing dissimilarities in the physical properties of clayey and sandy soils.

For spherical particles, the specific surface area per unit volume of the solids is

$$A = \frac{\pi d^2}{\pi d^3/6} = \frac{6}{d} \quad (cm^2/cm^3). \quad (5\text{-}24)$$

TABLE 5-5. SPECIFIC SURFACE AREA OF SOME NEW JERSEY SOILS

Agronomic name of soil	TRB Soil Classification	Specific surface area, m^2/g	Predominant minerals
1	2	3	4
Merrimac	A-1-b	2.1	Quartz, feldspar
Dunellen	A-2-4	5.7	Quartz, feldspar, muscovite
Montalto	A-2-4	22.6	Quartz, feldspar muscovite
Penn	A-2-4	22.4	Quartz, feldspar, muscovite
Lansdale	A-7-6	17.5	Quartz,feldspar

The specific surface area was determined by the SOR-BET method

5-14. Colloids. The term "colloid" is a translation from the Greek words *kolla* and *oidos*, meaning glue and alike, respectively. Colloid is any substance in a certain state of fine subdivision—the so-called colloidal state. According to Hauser,[6,7] the colloidal range of dimensions of particles of a colloid matter lies within a size interval from 1 $\mu\mu$ to 500 $\mu\mu$ or even up to 1 μ. The colloid particles are too small to be seen with a conventional microscope, but they can be observed by means of the electron microscope. In some of the soil classification systems colloids are classified as a separate soil fraction which, thus, is only a finer subdivision of clay. Under proper conditions almost every mineral can be transformed into the colloidal state by simply grinding it fine enough. Therefore, a colloid state is just a state of matter. Soil colloids, hence, are formed in the ordinary, natural weathering process, and they may be organic as well as inorganic. In this treatment only the inorganic colloids will be considered.

5-15. Clay Minerals. Clay minerals are groups of crystalline substances of which clays are made up. Among the minerals that occur in clay particles most scientists now recognize three main groups of clay minerals, namely: kaolinite, montmorillonite, and illite. A definite identification of clay minerals, which is required in major engineering works, involves complicated and sophisticated analytical mehtods in mineralogy.

Kaolin, also kaoline, is a fine-particled, usually white, or slightly stained clay, a product of the decomposition of a highly feldspatic rock. Kaolin is composed essentially of clay minerals of the kaolinite group, most commonly kaolinite.

Kaolin is one of the earth's most abundant clay. The term kaolin derives its name from the Chinese Kao-ling, which is a hill in China where the white China (porcelain) clay is·mined. In the United States of America, kaolin clay deposits are found mainly in the eastern part of the Georgia Piedmont Plateau, and is also widely exploited in the northern states.

The kaolin mineral is derived from aluminum silicates in soils in warm, humid climates from the alteration of feldspars and micas in earlier rocks such as granite and pegmatite, for example. The kaolin clay occurs in compact masses of clay beds.

The substance of the kaolin clay itself is essentially a hydrated silicate of alumina, and to this material the name kaolinite is frequently given.

Kaolinite is a common clay mineral. It occurs in soils of humid-temperate and humid-tropical regions which soils have undergone considerable weathering.

The kaolinite group, a hydrous alumino-silicate, has the general chemical composition of

$$Al_2(Si_2O_5)(OH)_4$$

The kaolinite crystal system consists of repeating layers, each layer consisting of a silica sheet and an aluminum sheet sharing a layer of oxygen between them -a system's combination that repeats itself indefinitely. The hydrated silicate of alumina is the base of the kaolin clays that gives them plasticity.

When kaolinite is mingled with varying amounts of comminuted quartz, and yields a pure, white clay, the resulting mixture is kaolin. Thus, kaolinite is the principal mineral in kaolin clay.

The kaolin clay consists of fine, platy- or scaly-like particles. The scanning electron micrographs reveal interesting pictures of the kaolin plates. For example, the scanning electron microscope has revealed that the Georgia kaolin clay, as it is mined, consists of "books" or "stacks of cards" of tiny, thin platelets (see scanning electron micrographs in Figures 5-6a and 5-6b). These micrographs indicate that the kaolin stacks separate into sheets or plates of flat particles.

Montmorillonites occur in sediments of semiarid regions of low rainfall, for example in deserts and prairies. Montmorillonites are the dominant clay minerals in bentonite rock. It forms from the weathering of volcanic ash in marine waters or under condition of restricted drainage. They are also found during weathering in soil.

The composition of the siliceous montmorillonite clay mineral is

$$Al_2[Mg] \cdot (Si_4O_{10})(OH)_2 \cdot x \cdot H_2 \cdot O$$

Electron micrographs show that the structure of the montmorillonite clay ranges from an amorphous type of material to clearly defined thin plates. Figure 5-7 shows a scanning electron micrograph of a montmorillonite.

Montmorillonites are more colloidal than kaolinites, and on wetting, montmorillonites swell considerably.[8]

The swelling is explained by water entering easily the space between the plate-like montmorillonite particles and forcing the platy particles apart. Thus the individual flaky montmorillonite particles become enclosed by a water film. It is this intersticial soil water that is responsible for the swelling or expansion of the clay. More than one molecular layer of water can be accomodated between the platy- or scaly-like particles. Hence, wet montmorillonites are very plastic, and therefore, they have a low coefficient of internal friction. When a saturated montmorillonite dries out, it shrinks and cracks considerably.

Because of the markedly expressed colloidal properties, montmorillonites present in themselves a very active fraction of the soil mass.

The thickness of montmorillonite (bentonite) particles is $1 \times 10^{-3}\mu$. Their length varies from $1 \times 10^{-1}\mu$ to $3 \times 10^{-1}\mu$. The particle sizes of montmorillonite clay merely reflect the degree of dispersion, and the ultimate dispersion breaks the mineral down in unit crystals or plates (scales).

The expansive, viz., plastic, properties of the montmorillonite clays are a matter of geotechnical engineering concern: highway pavements and building slabs cast directly on the subgrade soil (viz., ground surface) made up of montmorillonite clay may be lifted and brought to failure because of the swelling force of the clay; heavy structures founded on such clays may suffer a distress; and natural as well as artifically made earth slopes of, or cut in, a montmorillonite clay may rupture accompanied by sliding, and flowing down when such a clay becomes saturated by precipitation or other possible causes.

Illite is the general term for the mica-like clay minerals. Illites are also known by the term hydrous micas. They are so termed because of their structural similarity to micas.

Illite occurs widely in sedimentary rocks in temperate and in arid regions. Illite is the principal constituent of many shales.

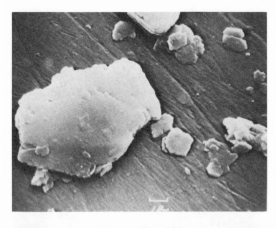

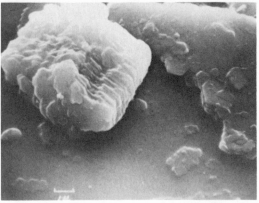

FIG. 5-6.   Scanning electron micrographs of Georgia Kaolin clay. a) Clay platelets b) Clay "books;" 14,000 × magnification. Photo courtesy of Engelhard Minerals and Chemicals Corporation, Menlo Park, Edison, New Jersey.

FIG. 5-7. Scanning electron micrograph of a montmorillonite; 10,000 × magnification. Photo courtesy of Dr. Victor A. Greenhut, Department of Ceramics, Rutgers University.

Illite is a group of clay minerals (clayey mica) intermediate between the kaolinite and montmorillonite groups. The structural unit of an illite is similar to that of montmorillonite with some changes in chemical composition. According to Hauser,[7] the composition of the complex illite group (colloidal siliceous matter) is

$$K_y \cdot Al_2 \cdot [Fe_2 Mg_2 Mg_3] \cdot (Si_{4-y} Al_y) \cdot O_{10}$$

The symbols in the brackets indicate that they may substitute for the symbol written to the left of the bracket. The subscript y varies between 1 and 1.5.

Whereas the montmorillonites consist of exceedingly fine particles, the flakes of illites frequently form aggregates. The aggregate-like structure of illite exposes less surface for attracting water than the montmorillonite. Hence, the expansive, viz., plastic properties of illites are also less than those of montmorillonite. Consequently, the coefficient of friction of illites is higher than that of montmorillonites. A scanning electron micrograph of an illite is shown in Figure 5-8.

FIG. 5-8. Scanning electron micrograph of illite; 10,000 × magnification. Photo courtesy of Dr. Victor A. Greenhut, Department of Ceramics, Rutgers University.

5-16. Bentonite. Bentonite, a geologic rock formation, is one of the well-known ultra-fine clays, composed mainly of the montmorillonite group of clay minerals, and is noted for its expansive properties. Bentonite is formed from the alteration of volcanic ashes. The color of bentonite clays varies from white to light green or light blue. When a dried bentonite is immersed in water, the former increases in volume or swells more than any other dried clay. For example, 1 g of bentonite would take 7 cm^3 of water to prepare it in a thixotropic paste. Sodium bentonite can absorb from 600% to 700% of water. Calcium bentonite absorbs about 200% to 300% of water. When moist bentonites are dried, they shrink. When in contact with water, sodium (natrium) bentonite exhibits larger volume changes than calcium bentonite. Highly colloidal bentonites swell in water just like glue or gelatin. With an ultramicroscope the dimensions of a bentonite particle can be estimated as being in ratio of (1) : (0.1) : (0.01) micron. When properly conditioned, clays are used in the construction of dams, reservoirs, ponds or lagoons for preventing seepage of water through them. The swelling property of the clays is utilized here to advantage, namely, to line canals, to seal off the voids, thus reducing seepage flow by decreasing permeability. Upon swelling, the colloidal matter seals off the voids, thus preventing losses of water by percolation. Also, bentonite injections are used to seal cracks in concrete dams and to fortify walls of excavations for building cutoff walls (cores) for dams and foundations in weak soils.

  5-17. Thixotropy. The word "thixotropy" consists of two parts: thixis = the touch, the shaking, and tropo = to turn, to change. Thus, thixotropy means "to change by touch." In the mechanical agitation of a colloidal suspension it is the structure of the suspension that changes "by touch." Thus thixotropy is defined as a reversible gel-sol-gel transformation in certain materials brought about by a mechanical disturbance followed by a period of rest.

  There exist many colloidal systems which have the properties of thixotropic flow, and there is a wide range in consistency. The thixotropic phenomenon is especially pronounced with sodium (natrium) bentonite suspension, and particularly in systems where large volumes of water are adsorbed upon and held between the colloidal particles. Hvorslev[9] writes that the presence of colloids in soil has a considerable effect on the properties of that soil. For example, in his doctoral thesis Hvorslev explains that some of the structural strength of a clayey material that is lost by remolding is in time slowly recovered. This strength recovery is termed by Hvorslev the *thixotropic recovery*. The necessary time for the recovery of the strength depends on the moisture content, and particularly on the salts in solution in the soil water. By definition, thixotropy is the property of a material to undergo an isothermal gel-to-sol-to-gel transformation upon agitation and subsequent rest. Thus, upon mechanical agitation gels liquefy, and resolidify when agitation is stopped.[7,10] This gel-sol transformation process can be repeated indefinitely without any fatigue. The gelation time under similar external conditions is the same.

  Instead of mechanical agitation, a gel can also be transformed into a sol by warming the gel. Upon cooling, the sol again reverts to the gel. Gel-sol-gel transformation upon the application of mechanical energy can take place without the application of heat externally. If the change by warming is reversed by cooling, the gel is said to be thermally reversible.

  Essentially, the sol-gel change is the change in consistency of colloidal suspensions: upon agitation gels lose their consistency and viscosity; after allowing the shaken suspension to rest, gels regain their original consistency. The loss of consistency is caused by a temporary breakdown in the structure of the thixotropic matter. Hence, the thixotropic phenomenon is the reversible, isothermal gel-sol change in state which takes place with some colloidal matter in suspension when shaken, i.e., when subjected to shear stress.

At present, the thixotropic phenomenon is not yet very well understood, and no completely satisfactory theory on thixotropy has yet been suggested. The only thing that can be said is that the thixotropic phenomenon is a function of such a structure of the colloidal matter that, when broken down by applied energy, it can reestablish itself.

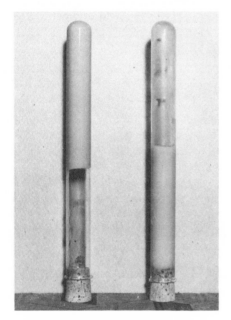

An old, simple test for thixotropy consists of shaking vigorously a colloidal suspension in a test tube and observing the time necessary for it to gelate to such a consistency that it can no longer flow out from the test tube when inverted (Fig. 5-9). In the left tube is a bentonite suspension in the form of a gel; in the tube on the right-hand side in that figure the suspension is in a sol state.

Shaking or tapping the test tube containing a thixotropic gel would prevent the orientation of the colloidal particles and the water molecules, and the gel would be transformed into a sol.

FIG. 5-9. Simple test for thixotropy.

In thixotropic soil, due to the energy transferred to the soil, pile driving operations are greatly facilitated: under the exerted blows the pile penetrates more and more easily in the softened soil. However, when the pile driving is interrupted for a certain period of time, during which the pile is given a rest and then the driving is resumed, it is noted that the resistance to penetration has considerably increased, approximately 4 to 8 times.

5-18. Thixotropic Fluids in Engineering Operations. As mentioned earlier, thixotropic suspensions are used as a means of sealing against leakage or loss of water where cement injections fail. The thixo-fluids are used in foundation operations for building an impounding as well as a sealing apron on lowering the groundwater table. The thixo-suspensions during their transport through pipes and in the voids of the soil remain liquid as long as they are in motion. As soon as they are allowed to rest, they gelate. Another application of thixo-fluids in engineering is as a lubricant to facilitate the sinking of wells and caissons, as well as in driving piles, in order to reduce the resistance to penetration of a resistive soil. The bentonite slurry is injected at a concentration of 100 to 120 grams per liter of water. In winter it is advisable to warm the slurry up to about 30°C.

Thixotropic fluids are also extensively used in the drilling of oil wells, as well as in drilling bore holes for soil exploration purposes. In these fields of endeavor such fluids are known as drilling fluids or drilling muds.

The usual drilling fluid consists of a water base, 98 to 65 percent by volume, and admixed with 2 to 30 percent by volume of clay.[11] Other ingredients may also be admitted. The proportions of those depend upon the requirements of permeability, density, and flow properties. In order that the drilling fluid be stable, the clay ingredients should be so fine in size that they will not settle out of the fluid, or at least will settle out slowly. The clay used in preparing drilling fluids is a commercial bentonite or a clay material from the bore hole.

The basic function of drilling fluid is:

1) to transport bit cuttings up to the ground surface;
2) to buoy the drill shaft;
3) to exert a hydrostatic pressure on the geologic material forming the wall of the bore hole to prevent the entry of soil water, or oil, and gas into the borehole which might bring about the collapse of the wall of the hole if it is of unconsolidated material;
4) to aid the hydrostatic pressure through the rotary action, to form a few millimeters thick anti-filter layer on the wall of the bore hole made in pervious soil, thus stabilizing the hole. Due to centrifugal force the base-water of the fluid permeates into the soil, leaving on the wall a thin coating of the clay;
5) to suspend the cuttings in the hole when circulation of fluid is stopped for a while. During such a stopping time the thixotropic drilling fluid gelates, gains strength in shear and thus is able to support the bit cuttings by its mass.

These properties of a drilling fluid must be retained under various temperature conditions in the bore hole.

To form the coating on the inside wall of the bore hole, and to prevent ground-water flowing from soil into the hole, particularly when the drilling is temporarily stopped, the pressure of the drilling fluid must be greater than the combination of the earth pressure and the groundwater pressure.

5-19. Representation of Particle Size Analyses Data. The results of soil particle size analyses can be represented in various ways, for example, in tabular form or by means of various graphical methods.

Among the graphical methods, the most popular are by means of triangular coordinates and by integral (summation = cumulative) curves, known also as granulometric, or grading, curves.

5-20. Triangular Coordinates. When a soil is represented by only three fractions—sand, silt, and clay, for example—then for the representation of these three fractions graphically, triangular coordinates sometimes are used in the form of an equilateral triangle, a triangle which in concrete technology is also

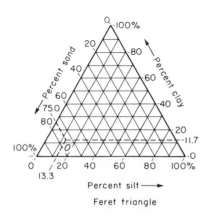

FIG. 5-10. Triangular coordinates.

known by the term *Feret triangle*[12] (Fig. 5-10). For example, assume that the three major fractions of the Dunellen soil are:

$$+ \begin{cases} \text{sand} & -75.0\% \\ \text{silt} & -13.3\% \\ \text{clay} & -11.7\% \end{cases}$$

Total 100.0%.

Then point O in Fig. 5-10 represents the granulometric contents of this tri-fractional soil. The soil is a silty-clayey sand.

The advantage of the triangular coordinate system is that for a tri-fraction soil its graphical representation is very simple. Besides, from the position of the "soil" point in the Feret triangle one immediately can give the soil designation according to the tri-fractional classification, for example: silty clay, clayey sand, or other designation. The disadvantage of the triangular graph is the incomplete characteristic of the total granulometric contents of the soil, because it indicates only three fractions when there may be 5, 6, 7, or 8.

5-21. Integral, or Cumulative, or Granulometric Curves.

General Notes. When the dry weights of each soil fraction, expressed in percent of total dry weight, are added up and these results are plotted, there results a smooth, integral, or cumulative fraction, viz., particle size accumulation curve (Fig. 5-11). It is called an integral or accumulation curve because its ordinates represent not separate fractions, but the sum of fractional particles less than a given fraction, or diameter.

Cumulative soil particle size accumulation curves are plotted either to a decimal (arithmetical) scale or to a decimal logarithmic scale.

Logarithmic Scale. Because of the wide range in diameter between the coarsest and finest soil particles, and in order that the contents of the fine sizes may become more visual, the diameters of the soil particles are plotted to a decimal logarithmic scale, thus obtaining a more compact curve. The use of the logarithmic scale simplifies the graphic presentation of the results of soil particle size analysis considerably. Without stretching the curve along the abscissa axis very much, the decimal logarithmic scale permits plotting the contents of the fine fractions of soil with a satisfactory degree of accuracy. Note that the range of the fine sizes is more recognizable in the logarithmic scale than in the linear scale. The ordinates of the granulometric curve drawn to arithmetic decimal scale then represent percent by dry weight of particles equal to or smaller than the size (equivalent diameter) shown by the abscissa.

Because the abscissas are plotted to a logarithmic scale, but the ordinates to a linear, decimal scale, the plot of the granulometric curve is said to be plotted as a semilogarithmic graph.

Experience indicates that the decimal logarithmic scale for plotting soil particle diameters is, for engineering purposes, one of the best graphical representations of particle size accumulation.

The shape of the cumulative particle size distribution curve is an indication of the uniformity of the soil.

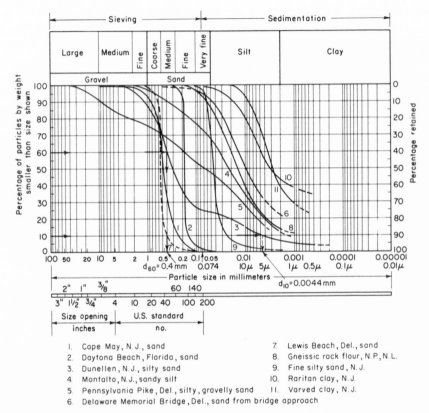

1. Cape May, N.J., sand
2. Daytona Beach, Florida, sand
3. Dunellen, N.J., silty sand
4. Montalto, N.J., sandy silt
5. Pennsylvania Pike, Del., silty, gravelly sand
6. Delaware Memorial Bridge, Del., sand from bridge approach
7. Lewis Beach, Del., sand
8. Gneissic rock flour, N.P., N.L.
9. Fine silty sand, N.J.
10. Raritan clay, N.J.
11. Varved clay, N.J.

FIG. 5-11.   Various soil particle size accumulation curves.

From the uniformity curves the *coefficient of nonuniformity* U of a soil is obtained. This coefficient, which expresses the variation in the proportions of large and small particles, and thus is a *numerical measure* of soil uniformity, and which in the technical literature is also termed the *coefficient of uniformity* of a soil, is defined as the ratio of the diameter of the particle which has 60 percent of the sample finer than the size shown to the size which has 10 percent by weight material finer than this size d_{10}:

$$U = \frac{d_{60}}{d_{10}}, \tag{5-25}$$

where U = coefficient of uniformity,

d_{60} = 60% diameter of soil particle, and

d_{10} = effective size of the particle, or the effective diameter, i.e., the 10% diameter, Fig. 5-11.

The diameters d_{60} and d_{10} are scaled off directly from the uniformity graph (granulometric curve) of that soil.

The effective diameter of a soil particle is the diameter of a hypothetical sphere that is assumed to act in the same way as the particle of an irregular shape, and that data obtained from hydrometer analysis using Stokes' law lead to effective diameters, d_e of the soil particles.

Allen Hazen[13] tried to establish what diameter in actual spheres would cause the same effect as a given soil, and he decided that the diameter for which 10% was finer would give this result. This diameter is called the *effective diameter*, $d_e = d_{10}$. Thus, the effective diameters d_e, obtained by hydrometer analysis, are the d_{10}-diameters.

When $U < 5$, the granulometry of the soil is very uniform.

With $U = 5$ to 15, the soil is said to be of medium uniformity, and when

$U > 15$, the soil is very nonuniform.

Thus, the greater is U, the less uniform is the granulometric content of the soil. For the Dunellen soil, Fig. 5-11, the uniformity coefficient is

$$U = \frac{d_{60}}{d_{10}} = \frac{0.40}{0.0044} = 90.9 > 15,$$

which indicates a very nonuniform soil.

A comparison of granulometric curves of sands, silts, and clays reveals that clays are less uniform than sands. Silty soils take a medium place.

On the average, for sands $U = 10$ to 20,

for clays $U = 10$ to 100, and

for loess (silts) $U = 2$ to 4.

Thus, the uniformity coefficient, expressing the shape of the cumulative particle size distribution curve, gives one a general impression of the range of the size distribution and the magnitude of natural soils. Strictly speaking, the concept of uniformity pertains to granular material only.

Description of Soil Particle Size Accumulation Curves. As discussed already, a steep particle size accumulation curve indicates a uniform soil (curve *a*, see Fig. 5-12). Humps in the curve indicate a soil composed of a mixture of two or more uniform soils (curve *b*). A steep curve in the sand sizes that gradually flattens out into a long, flat curve in the fine sizes would characterize a soil that was formed by weathering (curve *c*) (compare also with curve 3, a glacial out-wash soil, Fig. 5-11).

A flat curve indicates a wide range in particle sizes. Such a soil is called well-graded (*d*). A flat section in a wavy curve indicates that the particle distribution in that soil is not normal and that there is a deficiency of particle sizes at the flat interval ($d_1 - d_2$, Fig. 5-12) of curve *e*. This means that the soil is either made up of a mixture of two types of soil material of approximately normal

PHYSICAL PROPERTIES OF SOIL

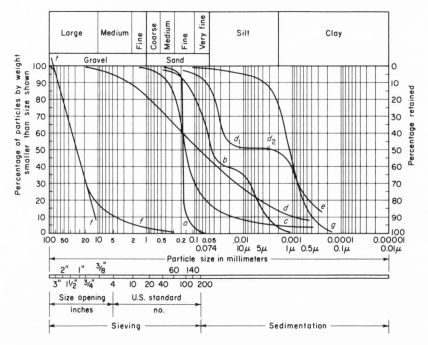

FIG. 5-12. Various shapes of soil particle size accumulation curves.

particle distribution, one fine and one coarse, or in some way all particles of the intermediate sizes have been removed.

Soils in the early stages of their development, for example in the Alpine regions, are mainly the result of physical weathering. They are generally characterized by the presence of large amounts of coarse material. Their cumulative particle size curves often show an approximation to a linear form in their upper range (Fig. 5-12, curve f). Soil g in Fig. 5-12 varies widely in its coarser range. However, the finer fractions are more uniform.

5-22. Differences Between Sand and Clay. Based on discussions and experience of the various physical properties of soils it is possible to summarize in Table 5-6 the physical differences between sand and clay. Note that the main difference between sand and clay is the size and shape of their particles, and that the relationship of particles of various sizes in a composite soil is one of the principal factors which determine the physical properties of soils and their behavior under load, water, and temperature.[14]

5-23. Unit Weight of Soil. As the term implies, the unit weight of soil is the weight of soil per unit of its volume. This weight comprises the whole soil mass, i.e., the solid particles plus all voids; the latter may or may not contain soil moisture. The weight of air is considered negligible and therefore ignored.

The soil unit weight γ is expressed as the ratio of the weight W of a volume

TABLE 5-6. PHYSICAL DIFFERENCES BETWEEN SAND AND CLAY

	Properties	Sand	Clay
1	Particle size	Large: 1.00 to 0.05 mm, mostly distinguishable by eye	Minute, less than 0.005 mm, not visible to the naked eye
2	Appearance of particles	Bulky and rigid	Flexible
3	Particle shape	Angular and rounded	Scaly-like
4	Texture	Coarse	Fine
5	Uniformity	Uniform	Less uniform
6	Internal friction	High	Small, or negligible
7	Size of pores	Large	Very minute
8	Volume of voids	Relatively small, about 50% at a maximum	Very high, as high as approx. 98% of the total volume
9	Void ratio	Low	High
10	Specific surface	Small	Large
11	Plasticity	Non-plastic	Plastic
12	Cohesion	Negligible	Marked
13	Surface tension	Low	Immense surface tension forces
14	Capillarity	Not appreciable	Very high
15	Capillary pressure	Low	Great
16	Shrinkage upon drying	Negligible	Very high
17	Swelling	None	Considerable
18	Expansion	Practically none	Most expansive
19	Compressibility	Slight	Very compressible
20	Compression when load applied to surface	Immediate	Slow
21	Elasticity	Low	High
22	Permeability	High degree, drains readily	Low degree, drains slowly
23	Frost Proneness	Little	High degree, especially silts

V of a soil mass to that volume V:

$$\gamma = W/V.$$

The unit weight can be expressed in g_f/cm^3, or kg_f/m^3, or t_f/m^3, or lb/ft^3. Unit weight of water γ_w is its weight W_w per unit of its volume V_w:

$$\gamma_w = W_w/V_w.$$

For calculation purposes, the unit weight of water in the British system of units is taken as 62.4 lb/ft^3. In the metric system, $\gamma_w = 1 g_f$ $cm^3 = 1 kg_f/1000$ $cm^3 = 0.001$ $kg_f/cm^3 = 1000$ $kg_f/m^3 = 1 t_f/m^3 = 62.4$ $lb/ft^3 = 9.81$ kN/m^3.

In approximative calculations, the unit weight of salt water can be taken as 64.0 lb/ft^3, or 1.025$g_f/cm^3 = 1.025$ $kg_f/liter = 1025$ $kg_f/m^3 = 1.025$ $t_f/m^3 = 10.05$ kN/m^3.

TABLE 5-7. SUMMARY OF UNIT WEIGHT FORMULAS

Soil Condition	Degree of Saturation	Unit Weight Symbol	Unit Weight formulas	
			$\gamma = f(n)$	$\gamma = f(e)$
1	2	3	4	5
General equation (bulk unit weight)	S	γ	$(1-n)G\gamma_w + nS\gamma_w$	$\dfrac{eS+G}{1+e}\gamma_w$
Dry soil	$S=0$	γ_d	$(1-n)G\gamma_w$	$\dfrac{G}{1+e}\gamma_w$
Moist soil	$1>S>0$	γ	$(1-n)G\gamma_w + nS\gamma_w$	$\dfrac{(1+w)G\gamma_w}{1+e}$ $\dfrac{eS+G}{1+e}\gamma_w$
Saturated soil	$S=1$	γ_{sat}	$(1-n)G\gamma_w + n\gamma_w$	$\dfrac{G+e}{1+e}\gamma_w$
Buoyant (submerged)	—	γ_{sub}	$(1-n)(G-1)\gamma_w$	$\dfrac{G-1}{1+e}\gamma_w$

$G\gamma_w$ = unit weight of solid matter
$wG\gamma_w$ = weight of water
$eS = wG$

TABLE 5-8. APPROXIMATE UNIT WEIGHTS OF SOME SOILS,
1 t_f/m^3 = 62.4 lb/ft^3 = (9.80665)(10^3) N/m^3

Nos.	Soil Type	Unit Weight		
		lb/ft^3	t_f/m^3	kN/m^3
1	2	3	4	5
1	Gravel, wet	125	2.0	19.61
2	dry	106	1.7	16.67
3	Sand, gravelly, dense	125	2.0	19.61
4	dry	100	1.6	15.69
5	wet	100	1.6	15.69
6	10% moisture	120	1.9	18.63
7	loose	81	1.3	12.75
8	Silt	112	1.8	17.65
9	Loess	100	1.6	15.69
10	Loam	100	1.6	15.69
11	Clay	131	2.1	20.59
12	fresh, 30% moisture	125	2.0	19.61
13	dry, hard	137	2.2	21.57
14	plastic	100	1.6	15.69
15	organic	88	1.4	13.73
16	Peat	68	1.1	10.79
17	Building wreckage and debris	87	1.4	13.73

For conversion purposes the relationship of pressure, 1 ton/ft$^2 \approx 1$ kg$_f$/cm$^2 \approx 9.80665$ N/cm^2 can be used.

Besides the unit weight of soil containing moisture, other unit weights are distinguished: for example, dry unit weight γ_d; unit weight of solids by absolute volume $\gamma_s = G\gamma_w$; saturated unit weight of soil γ_{sat}, and submerged or buoyant unit weight of soil γ_{sub}.

The difference in meanings between the terms saturated and submerged unit weights should be carefully noticed. The saturated unit weight of soil is a combined or soil-and-water unit weight, whereas the submerged unit weight is the effective or buoyant unit weight of a soil.

A summary of unit weight formulas of soil is given in Table 5-7. Some approximate values of unit weights of some soils are compiled in Table 5-8. These values reveal that the range of the unit weights of soils may vary between wide limits, and that their influence upon the static effects in stability problems in soil engineering, in some instances, may be relatively large. Therefore, it is advisable in each particular engineering problem to determine the unit weight of soil by actual test.

Dry unit weight of soil (degree of saturation: $S = 0$) after lowering the ground-water table:

$$\gamma_d = (1 - n)G\gamma_w, \tag{5-26}$$

where γ_d = dry unit weight of soil,
  n = porosity,
  G = specific gravity of soil particles, and
  γ_w = unit weight of water.

Submerged unit weight of soil before lowering the groundwater table:

$$\gamma_{sub} = (1 - n)(G - 1)\gamma_w \tag{5-27}$$

Ratio:

$$\lambda = \frac{\gamma_d}{\gamma_{sub}} = \frac{(1 - n)G\gamma_w}{(1 - n)(G - 1)\gamma_w} = \frac{G}{G - 1} > 1, \tag{5-28}$$

or, assuming for quartz sand $G = 2.65$, the ratio is

$$(\gamma_d/\gamma_{sub}) = 1.606,$$

which means that the dry unit weight of the sand soil is approximately 1.6 times greater than the submerged unit weight.

For a saturated soil, shortly after draw-down of the groundwater table, and with an average porosity of $n = 30\%$,

$$\frac{\gamma_{sat}}{\gamma_{sub}} = \frac{(1 - n)G\gamma_w + n\gamma_w}{(1 - n)(G - 1)\gamma_w} = 1.865. \tag{5-29}$$

This means that in this case the saturated soil is 1.865 times heavier than the submerged weight.

SEDIMENTATION

Soil particle sizes smaller than 0.074 mm (passing the 200-mesh sieve) are usually determined by the so-called *hydrometer method*. A hydrometer (or areometer) is an instrument used to determine the density of liquids and sedimenting suspensions, for example, soil.

The hydrometer method is ba⸀ed on the process of sedimentation of soil particles in water by gravity.

5-24. Sedimentation by Gravity. The principle of sedimentation of soil particles by gravity is the separation of particles of various sizes by their velocity of fall in a calm, viscous fluid, like water. The velocity of the settling soil particle depends upon its specific gravity, weight, and configuration. The settling velocity of the soil in water is slower with decreasing particle size. Coarse soil suspensions settle out more rapidly than the finer ones of the same specific gravity. To utilize the principle of separation of soil particles according to their velocity of fall in a viscous medium, the soil suspension is usually placed in a cylindrical vessel, such as a tall, graduated cylinder.

5-25. Stokes' Law. The study of sedimentation by gravity is usually based on Stokes' law:

$$v = \frac{2}{9} g r^2 \cdot \frac{\gamma_s - \gamma_w}{\eta}, \qquad (5\text{-}30)$$

where v = settling velocity of particle, in cm/sec,
  g = 981 cm/s^2 = constant of acceleration due to gravity,
  r = radius of soil particle, in cm,
  γ_s = unit weight of soil particles, in g/cm^3,
  γ_w = unit weight of a homogeneous liquid, for example water, and
  η = dynamic, or absolute viscosity of water($=$ internal friction of liquid),
    in g/(cm · s),
Note that by Eq. 5-1, the unit weight of soil solids γ_s is expressed as

$$\gamma_s = \gamma_w \cdot G \qquad (g/cm^3), \qquad (5\text{-}31)$$

where G = specific gravity of solid particles.

If, as in the metric system, the density of water is $\gamma_w = 1$ g/cm^3, and because G is dimensionless, the magnitude of the unit weight γ_s is the numerical value of the magnitude of G with units in g/cm^3:

$$\gamma_s = (1) \cdot G = G \qquad (g/cm^3). \qquad (5\text{-}32)$$

Thus, Stokes' law expresses the rate of settling in free movement of suspended soil particles of spherical shape under the influence of gravity for an ideal system where the liquid is at rest and of constant and equal density and viscosity.

Equation (5-30) applies only to the steady state of motion. It also says that in a given dispersion medium and at constant temperature, the rate of settling, or the *terminal velocity* of a spherical particle, is proportional to the square of its effective radius:

$$v = Kr^2, \qquad (5\text{-}33)$$

where

$$K = \frac{2}{9} g \frac{\gamma_s - \gamma_w}{\eta} \qquad (5\text{-}34)$$

is a constant, which depends upon the properties of the liquid and the sphere.

The *process of sedimentation* of a soil particle in a liquid medium can be described as follows: when the spherical particle is released from rest (at $v = 0$), it begins to sink, or to settle out. The viscous forces at $v = 0$ are also zero. Then, as the particles begin to sink under the influence of gravity, their velocity increases until the force of gravity is just balanced by the frictional resistance which increases as the velocity increases. At this instant the sinking particle ceases to accelerate, but it moves through the liquid with a uniform, constant velocity, which is the terminal velocity. It is this constant velocity which is considered in Stokes' equation. This terminal velocity v can be measured from the time of transit between two fixed marks on the wall of a tall glass cylinder. Thus, such a method permits the calculation of the size of the sinking sphere as a function of v and a constant $C = 1/\sqrt{K}$, where

$$C = 1/\sqrt{K} = \sqrt{\frac{9}{2} \frac{\eta}{(\gamma_s - \gamma_w)g}} ; \qquad (5\text{-}35)$$

hence,

$$r = f(v, K). \qquad (5\text{-}36)$$

Also, when v, r, and $(\gamma_s - \gamma_w)$ are known, viscosity η can be found.

5-26. Derivation of Stokes' Law. A spherical soil particle, falling with a terminal velocity through a homogeneous liquid that is at rest and of infinitely large volume as compared with the soil particle, is subjected to the following forces:

1) its weight W;
2) buoyant force of the liquid B; resulting in
3) $W - B$ = effective weight of soil particle, and
4) viscous retarding or frictional force on the sphere, called also the drag force D, see Fig. 5-13.

The terminal velocity v is then calculated from the relationship that the drag force D plus the buoyant force B is equal to the weight W of the spherical particle:

$$D + B = W, \qquad (5\text{-}37)$$

see Fig. 5-13a.

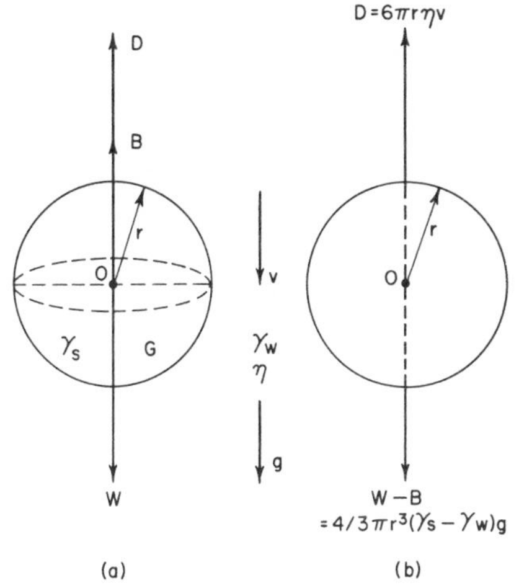

FIG. 5-13.   Sedimentation of a spherical particle.

The weight W of a spherical particle, whose specific gravity is G and whose unit weight is γ_s, is calculated as

$$W = mg = \tfrac{4}{3}\pi r^3 \gamma_s g, \tag{5-38}$$

where m = mass. Other symbols are as previously noted.

The buoyant force $\mathbf{B}$ of a submerged sphere is

$$B = \tfrac{4}{3}\pi r^3 \gamma_w g. \tag{5-39}$$

The drag force D exerted on the sinking spherical particle by the liquid around it can be calculated, by Reference 15, as

$$D = C_D \cdot \gamma_w \frac{v^2}{2} A, \tag{5-40}$$

where $C_D = 24/N_R$ is the drag coefficient of a sphere at low velocities,

$N_R = v d \gamma_w / \eta$ = the Reynolds number,

$A = (\pi d^2)/4$ = the projected area of the sphere normal to the direction of v, and

$d = 2r$ = diameter of spherical particle.

Thus, the magnitude of the viscous retarding, or drag, force exerted on the downward moving sphere with a very small, constant velocity v through a liquid the viscosity of which is η, is

$$D = C_D \gamma_w A \frac{v^2}{2} = \frac{24}{N_R} \gamma_w A \frac{v^2}{2} = 3\pi d \eta v, \tag{5-41}$$

or, expressed in terms of radius,

$$D = 6\pi r \eta v. \tag{5-42}$$

If the spherical soil particles, settling through the liquid, which is at rest, attain a constant velocity of fall (= terminal velocity), the drag force plus the buoyant force must algebraically just equal the gravity force of the spherical particle:

$$W = D + B, \tag{5-43}$$

or

$$\tfrac{4}{3}\pi r^3 \gamma_s g = 6\pi r \eta v + \tfrac{4}{3}\pi r^3 \gamma_w g. \tag{5-44}$$

Regrouping terms in Eq. (5-37), one obtains

$$W - B = D, \tag{5-45}$$

or

$$\tfrac{4}{3}\pi r^3 g(\gamma_s - \gamma_w) = 6\pi r \eta v, \tag{5-46}$$

where $W - B = \tfrac{4}{3}\pi r^3 g(\gamma_s - \gamma_w)$ = the effective gravity force of the suspended spherical soil particle. This condition is illustrated in Fig. 5-13b.

Solving Eq. (5-46) for v, the terminal velocity as a function of r is

$$v = \frac{2}{9} g r^2 \frac{\gamma_s - \gamma_w}{\eta}, \tag{5-47}$$

or as a function of diameter d,

$$v = \frac{g}{18} \frac{\gamma_s - \gamma_w}{\eta} d^2, \qquad (5\text{-}48)$$

where $v = h/t$ = velocity, and
  h = the distance of fall or sedimentation height of a particle during a time period t, or the sedimentation time.

Equations (5-47) and (5-48) are known as Stokes' law. This relationship holds if the velocity is not so great that turbulence sets in (valid for low Reynolds numbers N_R!). When turbulence occurs, the drag is much greater than that given in Stokes' law.

Because v varies directly with r^2, the rate of sedimentation drops off rapidly with decreasing particle size.

By Eq. (5-47), the radius of a particle is

$$r = \sqrt{\frac{9}{2} \frac{\eta}{(\gamma_s - \gamma_w)g}} \cdot \sqrt{v} \qquad \text{(cm)}. \qquad (5\text{-}49)$$

If $\eta_{20°C} = 0.0101$ g/(cm·sec),

$\gamma_s = 2.70$ g/cm^3,

$\gamma_w = 1.00$ g/cm^3, and

$g = 981$ cm/s^2,

then $r = (5.222)(10^{-3})\sqrt{v}$ cm.

5-27. The Hydrometer Method in Soil Particle Size Analysis. At the beginning of the hydrometer analysis (time $t = 0$) the soil suspension is thoroughly mixed and uniform. It can therefore be assumed that at each horizontal section of the soil suspension in the graduated cylinder throughout its entire height there are soil particles of all sizes present in the composite soil sample taken for this analysis, Fig. 5-14a. With time, the coarser particles gradually settle out. Thus, during sedimentation the density, or unit weight of the suspension, decreases with time as the particles settle, and the hydrometer floats deeper in the suspension, Figs. 5-14b, c, d, e. The density at any given depth below the surface of the suspension is determined by the amount of soil particles which remain in suspension at that depth. A hydrometer immersed in a soil suspension of a certain density would float to a certain depth and would read as if it were immersed in a suspension of uniform density which corresponds to the actual density at the center of the hydrometer bulb. Here it has to be noted that the hydrometer, because of the length of its bulb, does not measure the density of the soil suspension at one point, but rather reads the average density of a fairly large section of the sedimentary column (Fig. 5-14b). Nevertheless, it is assumed that a hydrometer actually indicates the density of the suspension at the center of buoyancy, which, however, can be assumed to coincide approximately with the center of the bulb. The position of this center-point determines the depth of fall h of the soil particles from the surface of the suspension. Assuming that the process of sedimentation takes place according to Stokes' law, it is possible to calculate the maximum diameter of the soil particles which, after a certain time t,

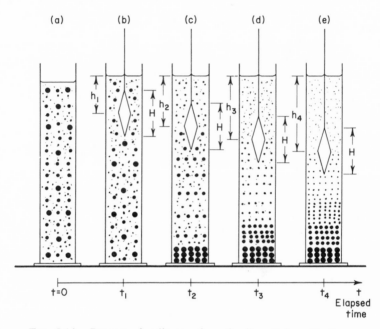

Fig. 5-14.   Process of sedimentation of soil particles with time.

elapsed from the beginning of sedimentation, have arrived through their fall at a horizontal section of the cylinder located at a distance h from the surface of the suspension. At depth h there are no particles coarser than d because all of them have fallen below h in time t. In a small cylindrical element of volume of the suspension at depth h, the amount of the soil particles smaller than d remains unaltered. The change in weight of the element at h is due only to the loss of particles larger than d. The velocity of fall of these particles can be expressed as

$$v = h/t. \tag{5-50}$$

Rearranging Eq. (5-48), expressing time t in minutes, and substituting velocity v from Eq. (5-50), the effective diameter of the particle size in question in milli- meters at depth h cm after time lapse t is

$$d = \sqrt{\frac{30\eta}{g(\gamma_s - \gamma_w)} \cdot \frac{h}{t}} \quad \text{(mm)}, \tag{5-51}$$

or

$$d = k_1 \sqrt{\eta \cdot \frac{h}{t}}, \tag{5-52}$$

where

$$k_1 = \sqrt{\frac{30}{g(\gamma_s - \gamma_w)}} = \text{const} \qquad (5\text{-}53)$$

for a given suspension. Note that the measured densities of the soil suspension in the hydrometer test are based on "equivalent" particle sizes with "effective" diameters.

The effective diameters d_e can then be calculated by applying Stokes' law if the depth of fall h and the time elapsed t are known or determined from tables or nomograms.[16]

Because the fine particles in a composite soil determine its physical behavior, all hydrometer analyses should be performed down to the 0.002 mm particle size.

REFERENCES

1. K. Terzaghi, *Erdbaumechanik auf bodenphysikalischer Grundlage,* Wien, Franz Deuticke, 1925.
2. "Standard Specifications for Sieves for Testing Purposes," ASTM Designation E11-61, 1976 *Book of ASTM Standards,* ASTM, Philadephia, 1976, Part 19.
3. *ASTM* "Standard Method for Particle-size Analysis of Soils," ASTM Designation D422-63, *Procedures for Testing Soils,* ASTM, Philadephia, 1976, Part 19, pp. 69-79.
4. American Association of State Highway and Transportation Officials, "Standard Method of Mechanical Analysis of Soils," AASHTO Designation T88-72, published in *Standard Specifications for Highway Materials and Methods of Sampling and Testing,* Part 1, Washington, D.C., 1970.
5. L. D. Baver, W. H. Gardner, and W. R. Gardner, *Soil Physics,* 4th ed., New York, John Wiley and Sons, 1972.
6. E. A. Hauser, "The Importance of Colloid Science for Highway Construction and Research," a paper presented at the 35th annual meeting of the Highway Research Board, January 17-20, 1956, Washington, D.C., p.5.
7. E. A. Hauser, *Silicic Science,* Princeton, N.J., D. Van Nostrand Company, Inc., 1955, p. 8.
8. *Dana's Manual of Mineralogy,* 17th ed., revised by C. S. Hurlbut, Jr., New York, John Wiley and Sons, Inc., 1959.
9. M. J. Hvorslev, *Über die Festigkeitseigenschaften gestörter bindinger Böden,* Copenhagen, Danmarks Naturvidenskabelige Samfund, 1937.
10. E. A. Hauser and C. E. Reed, "Studies in Thixotropy. The Thixotropic Behavior and Structure of Bentonite," *The Journal of Physical Chemistry,* vol. 4, 1937.
11. D. A. Larsen, "Colloid Features of Drilling Fluids," *Colloid Chemistry,* edited by J. Alexander, New York, Reinhold Publishing Corporation, 1946, vol. 6, pp. 509-534.
12. René Feret, "Sur la compacité des mortiers hydrauliques," *Annales des Ponts et Chaussées,* Paris, 1892, vol. 4, pp. 5-164.
13. A. Hazen, *Some Physical Properties of Sands and Gravels, with Special Reference to their Use in Filtration,* 24th Annual Report of the State Board of Health of Massachusetts, 1892, Public Document no. 34, Boston, Wright and Potter Printing Co., 1893, p. 553.
14. K. Terzaghi, "Principles of Soil Mechanics," *Engineering News-Rec.,* 1925, 1 to 9, vol. 95, pp. 742, 796, 832, 874, 912, 987, 1026 and 1064.
15. J. K. Vennard, *Elementary Fluid Mechanics,* 2nd ed., John Wiley and Sons, Inc., New York, 1950.
16. A. Casagrande, *Die Aräometermethode zur Bestimmung der Kornverteilung von Böden und anderen Mineralien.* Berlin, Springer, 1934.

SUGGESTIONS FOR ADDITIONAL READING

1. *1976 Annual Book of ASTM Standards, Part 19.* Philadelphia, Pa.: ASTM, 1976.
Designation: D 2488-69 (Reapproved 1975). Standard Practice for Description of
soils, pp. 314-320. (Visual-Manual Procedure).
Designation: D 422-63 (Reapproved 1972): Standard Method for Particle-Size
Analysis of Soils, pp. 69-79.
Designation D 854-58 (Reapproved 1974): Standard Method of Test for Specific
Gravity of Soils, pp. 154-156.
Designation D 698-70 (Editorial change made in 1973): Standard Method of Test
for Moisture-Density Relations of Soils Using 5.5-lb (2.5 kg) Rammer and 12-in.
(304.8 mm) Drop, pp. 145-150.
Designation D 2049-69: Standard Method of Test for Relative Density of
Cohesionless Soils, pp. 251-259.
Designation D 2922-71: Standard Methods of Test for Density of Soil and Soil-
Aggregate in Place by Nuclear Methods (Shallow Depth), pp. 357-364.
2. L.D. Baver, W.H. Gardner and W.R. Gardner, *Soil Physics* (4th ed.), New York,
N.Y.: John Wiley and Sons, 1972. Bureau of Reclamation, Earth Manual (2nd ed.)
Washington, D.C.: U.S. Department of the Interior, 1974.
3. J.E. Gieseking (editor), *Soil Components,* New York, N.Y.: Springer; vol. 2,
Inorganic Components, 1975.
4. D. Kirkham and W.L. Powers, *Advanced Soil Physics,* New York, N.Y.: John Wiley
and Sons, 1972.
5. W.N. Townsend, *An Introduction to Scientific Study of the Soil,* (5th ed.) New York,
N.Y.: St. Martin's Press, 1973.

QUESTIONS

5- 1. Define and describe soil.
5- 2. What is varved clay and how was it formed?
5- 3. What is a soil profile a) in the pedological sense? b) in the sense of engineering?
5- 4. What is soil texture?
5- 5. What is soil structure?
5- 6. Describe soil as an engineering material.
5- 7. What is
   a) unit weight of soil?
   b) specific gravity of soil particles?
   c) wet density of soil?
   d) dry density of soil?
   e) porosity and
   f) void ratio of soil?
5- 8. What are the commonly noted differences between sand and clay?
5- 9. What is a soil particle size accumulation curve?
   What is a grading curve of a soil?
5-10. What is the effective size (effective diameter) of soil particles? What is the
   coefficient of uniformity of soil particles?
5-11. Calculate the coefficients of uniformity of soils, the particle size accumulation
   curves of which are shown in Figs. 5-11 and 5-12.
5-12. The effective diameter of a soil is 0.1 mm, and the coefficient of uniformity of this
   soil is $U = 10$. Sketch the soil particle size accumulation curve and report the
   uniformity classification of this soil.
5-13. What soil characteristics are revealed by the slope of the soil particle size
   accumulation curve?
5-14. Distinguish between the concept of uniform soil material and uniform (even)
   gradation.
5-15. Why is semilogarithmic plotting of soil particle size accumulation curves
   preferable to the arithmetical scale?
5-16. What are the principal soil textural groups?
5-17. Explain Feret triangle.

Chapter 6

VOLUMETRY AND GRAVIMETRY

6-1. Functional Relationships Between Various Soil Properties. The dependence of some of the various soil constants upon γ, w, G and γ_w are summarized in the Soil Physical Constants Table 6-1. Again, it is to be remembered that in precise laboratory and research work, the actual temperature of water in specific gravity determinations of soil and water should be taken into account.

6-2. Volumetric and Gravimetric Relationships. The calculation of the various functional relationships as illustrated in Table 6-1 can best be performed, and the relative volumetric and gravimetric proportions of soil solids, moisture, and air phases can readily and visually be illustrated, by means of the soil phase diagram, Fig. 6-1.

The phase diagram helps considerably in understanding and solving various basic problems involving certain soil physical properties. For example, if the unit weight of water γ_w, the specific gravity of solids G, the moist unit weight of soil W, its volume V, and the dry weight W_s, of the solids are known, then the weight of water W_w, the volume of solids V_s, volume of water V_w, volume of air V_a, dry unit weight γ_d, and the relative values such as porosity n, void ratio e, moisture content w, and the degree of saturation S, can be calculated. For this purpose the soil phase diagram (Fig. 6-1) should be drawn, and the proper spaces in the volume and weight columns of the soil phase diagram should be filled in with the known or given quantities such as γ_w, G (Col. 10), W_s (Col. 11), W (Col. 12), and V (Col. 7). Then calculate

a) the weight of water (Col. 11):

$$W_w = W - W_s,$$

b) the absolute volume of solids (Col. 9):

$$V_s = W_s/G\gamma_w,$$

c) the absolute volume of voids (Col. 8):

$$V_v = V - V_s = V - W_s/G\gamma_w,$$

and

d) the absolute volume of moisture (Col. 9):

$$V_w = W_w/\gamma_w.$$

71

TABLE 6-1. SOME SOIL PHYSICAL CONSTANTS

Properties to be Determined by Test	Quantities to be Calculated for a Soil in its Undisturbed State	
	Description	Equation
1	2	3
1. γ = unit weight of soil	1. Unit weight of soil skeleton or dry unit weight	(a) $\gamma_d = \dfrac{\gamma}{1+w}$ (b) $\gamma_d = \dfrac{G}{1+e}\gamma_w$
2. w = moisture content by dry weight	2. Porosity	$n = 1 - \dfrac{\gamma_d}{G\gamma_w}$
	3. Void ratio	$e = \dfrac{n}{1-n} = \dfrac{G\gamma_w - \gamma_d}{\gamma_d}$
3. G = specific gravity of soil particles	4. Relative volume of voids	$n = \dfrac{e}{1+e}$
	5. Relative volume of solids	$n_s = \dfrac{1}{1+e}$
4. γ_w = unit weight of water	6. Relative volume of water in soil	$n_m = nS$
	7. Soil moisture content by dry weight	$W_w = w\gamma_d$
	8. Soil moisture content by volume	$V_w = \dfrac{W_w}{\gamma_w}$
	9. Moisture content upon full saturation	$w_{sat} = \left(\dfrac{1}{\gamma_d} - \dfrac{1}{G\gamma_w}\right)\gamma_w$
	10. Degree of saturation	$S = \dfrac{w}{w_{sat}} = \dfrac{w\gamma}{n(1+w)\gamma_w}$
	11. Void ratio upon full saturation	$e = wG$
	12. Volume of air in a unit volume of soil	$n_a = (1-S)n$
	13. Saturated unit weight of soil	$\gamma_{sat} = \dfrac{G+e}{1+e}\gamma_w$
	14. Submerged (buoyant) unit weight	$\gamma_{sub} = \dfrac{G-1}{1+e}\gamma_w$ $= (G-1)(1-n)\gamma_w$

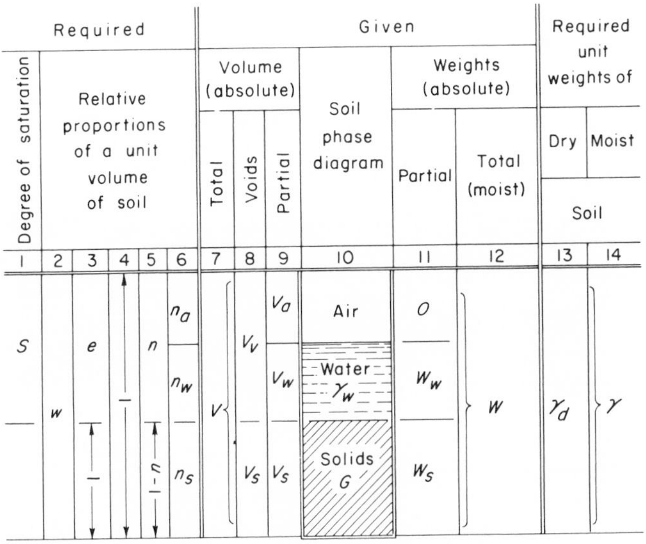

Degree of saturation	Required Relative proportions of a unit volume of soil					Volume (absolute) Total	Voids	Partial	Given Soil phase diagram	Weights (absolute) Partial	Total (moist)	Required unit weights of Dry	Moist
												Soil	
1	2	3	4	5	6	7	8	9	10	11	12	13	14
S	w	e		n	n_a n_w n_s	V	V_v	V_a V_w V_s	Air $\overline{\text{Water}}$ γ_w Solids G	W_w W_s	0 W	γ_d	γ

FIG. 6-1. Phase diagram illustrating absolute and relative volumetric and gravimetric proportions of solids, water, and air in a unit of mass of soil.

e) The absolute volume of air voids (Col. 9):

$$V_a = V_v - V_w.$$

The calculations now permit one to compute the quantities required at the outset of this problem.

1) Moisture content (Col. 2):

$$w = W_w/W_s. \tag{6-1}$$

2) Relative proportion of void spaces, or porosity (Col. 5):

$$n = \frac{V_w + V_a}{V} = \frac{V_v}{V} = \frac{V - V_s}{V} = \frac{V - W_s/G\gamma_w}{V} = .1 - \frac{W_s}{VG\gamma_w} = 1 - \frac{\gamma_d}{G\gamma_w} =$$

$$= 1 - \frac{\gamma}{G\gamma_w(1 + w)}. \tag{6-2}$$

3) Relative proportion of volume of air voids (Col. 6):

$$n_a = V_a/V. \tag{6-3}$$

4) Relative proportion of volume of water (Col. 6):

$$n_w = V_w/V. \tag{6-4}$$

5) Relative proportion of volume of solids (Col. 6):

$$n_s = V_s/V. \tag{6-5}$$

The total relative volume is $n_a + n_w + n_s = 1$.

6) Void ratio (Col. 3):

$$e = \frac{V_v}{V_s} = \frac{n}{1-n}.$$ (6-6)

7) Degree of saturation (Col. 1):

$$S = \frac{V_w}{V_v} = \frac{n_w}{n} = \frac{wG}{e} = \frac{wG(1-n)}{n}.$$ (6-7)

The weight of the water can now also be calculated (Col. 11):

$$W_w = \frac{Se}{1+e}\gamma_w,$$ (6-8)

the quantity of which should check with W_w as calculated under point a).

8) Dry unit weight of soil (Col. 13):

$$\gamma_d = \frac{W_s}{V} = \frac{V_s G \gamma_w}{V} = \frac{G}{1+e}\gamma_w.$$ (6-9)

9) Moist unit weight of soil (Col. 14):

$$\gamma = \frac{W}{V} = \frac{V_s G \gamma_w}{V} + V_w \gamma_w = \frac{G}{1+e}\gamma_w + W_w = \frac{G}{1+e}\gamma_w + \frac{eS}{1+e}\gamma_w =$$

$$= \frac{G}{1+e}\gamma_w + \frac{wG}{1+e}\gamma_w = \frac{G(1+w)}{1+e}\gamma_w.$$ (6-10)

PROBLEMS

6- 1. The wet density of a glacial outwash soil is $120 \, lb/ft^3 = 18.83 \, kN/m^3$, the specific gravity of the solid particles of the soil is $G = 2.67$, and the moisture content of the soil is $w = 12\%$ by dry weight. Calculate:
  a) dry density
  b) porosity
  c) void ratio
  d) degree of saturation
  e) percent of air voids.
  Draw a phase diagram of this soil showing the absolute and relative volumetric and gravimetric relationships.

6- 2. From a borrow pit in which the void ratio is $e = 1.20$, 250,000 cu yd of soil have to be excavated for building a fill with a void ratio of $e = 0.70$. How many cubic yards of fill can be constructed?

6- 3. The moisture content of a saturated clay sample is 345%. The unit weight of the solids is 2.38 g per cc. Determine the unit weight of the saturated clay (in pounds per cubic foot). Draw a phase diagram.

6- 4. The unit weight of the solids of a given sand is 2.60 g per cc. Its void ratio is 0.572. Calculate:
  a) the unit weight of dry sand
  b) the unit weight of the sand when saturated
  c) the submerged unit weight of the sand.
  Draw phase diagrams for each of the cases mentioned.

6- 5. Plot a curve expressing $e = f(n)$. Read the curve and report.

6- 6. Plot the moisture content, w in percent, of a soil (by dry weight) on the abscissa axis and the moisture content based on total weight of the soil, w_t, in percent, on the ordinate axis. Complete the curve expressing the total weight of the soil as a function of its dry weight: $w_t = f(w)$. First, derive $w_t = f(w)$, then plot the soil moisture content relationship by dry and total weights.

6- 7. Derive the following equation: $e = (w/100)G$, which expresses the relationship between the void ratio e, the true specific gravity G, and the moisture content w for full saturation of voids.

6- 8. Derive a formula for soil moisture content w, as a function of void ratio e, degree of saturation S, and specific gravity of soil particles G.

6- 9. The porosity n of a medium sand is 33%. Determine its void ratio. Sketch e and n by means of a phase diagram.

6-10. Prove that $\gamma_{dry} = G\gamma_w/(1 + e) = G\gamma_w(1 - n)$.

6-11. One cubic foot of wet soil weighs 124 lb or 1 m³ weighs 19.48 kN. Its dry weight is 112 lb or 17.59 kN. The specific gravity of the solid particles of soil is $G = 2.67$. Determine the moisture content, porosity, void ratio, and degree of saturation S. Draw a phase diagram, and show relative and absolute volumetric and gravimetric relationships.

6-12. A sheet of water the thickness of which is one unit of length is to be used to saturate the voids of a noncohesive soil. The void ratio of the soil in question is e (given). How thick a soil layer is required to accommodate this amount of water?

6-13. A clay sample, containing its natural moisture content, weighs 34.62 g. The specific gravity of the solids of this soil is 2.70. After oven-drying, the soil sample weighs 20.36 g. To determine the volume of the moist clay, the sample is immersed in mercury prior to oven-drying. The displaced volume of the clay sample is found to be 24.26 cm³. Calculate:
  a) moisture content,
  b) void ratio, and
  c) degree of saturation of the soil.

6-14. A clay sample, originally 1.000 in. thick and at initial void ratio of 1.120, was subjected to a compressive load. After the clay sample was completely consolidated, the thickness of it was measured to be 0.955 in. Compute the final void ratio.

6-15. A soil has a unit weight of 100 lb/ft^3 = 15.69 kN/m^3, and a moisture content of $w = 8\%$ by dry weight. Assuming that the void ratio of the soil remains the same, calculate how much water in gallons (and in cubic feet) should be added to a cubic yard of soil to increase the soil moisture content to 10%. Explain each step of computation performed.

6-16. The soil natural moisture content is $w = 54.0\%$, its void ratio $e = 2.075$, and specific gravity $G = 2.65$. Calculate the degree of saturation S of this soil and indicate whether this soil is moist or saturated. $S = (w)(G)/e = (0.54)(2.65)/2.075 = 0.689$. The soil is characterized as very moist, see Table 5-2.

6-17. An airport runway fill needs 600,000 cu yd = 45876m^3 of soil compacted to a void ratio of 0.75. The engineering soil map shows that there are two available borrow pits designated by the geologic formations of the soil as Bridgeton and Cape May. The void ratio of the soil in each of the aforementioned pits, and the estimated transportation cost of the soil from the pits to the airport are compiled in the following tabulation.

Borrow Pit	Void Ratio	Transportation Cost
Bridgeton	0.80	80 cents/cu yd = 105 cents/m^3
Cape May	1.70	58 cents/cu yd = 76 cents/m^3

Determine the minimum expense of soil transportation, indicating which borrow pit is the most economical for the contemplated job.

6-18. For an airport runway, a base course 125 ft wide, 2 miles long and 6 in. in compacted thickness of crushed rock with a 30% achieved porosity is to be constructed. The moisture content of the crushed rock material in the stockpile is 8.2%. The specific gravity of this aggregate is 2.67. In its loosest state, the porosity of the crushed rock is 46%. The crushed-rock material is to be weighed loose in trucks as it is taken from the stockpile. Determine for both dense and loose states where this applies:

   a) the dry weight in lb/ft^3 for the loosest state of the crushed rock, and for the compacted state;

   b) the thickness of the crushed rock in its loosest state necessary to compact it down to the required 6 in. thickness with $n = 30\%$;

   c) the ratio of the loose and compacted volume;

   d) the amount of water in pounds and cubic feet contained in one cubic foot of moist crushed rock;

   e) degree of saturation of the crushed rock;

   f) the number of cubic feet of solids and water transported from the stockpile to the airport to build one mile of runway base course;

   g) with the moisture content given, the number of tons of crushed rock required per one mile of the runway base course;

   h) the number of 5-cu-yd truck loads of crushed rock required for the construction of one mile of runway base course.

Draw phase diagrams and other pertinent sketches. Assume other engineering properties and values where necessary.

6-19. Prepare a diagram which would illustrate for classification purposes the degree of saturation of soil as a function of moisture content. Given: $w=54\%$ at $G=2.65$ and $e=2.075$. Classify degree of saturation of this soil.

Hint. Designate the corresponding moisture content with w_s at any degree of saturation S. By Eq. (6-7), the degree of saturation is

$$S = w_s G/e, \qquad\qquad (6\text{-}7)$$

or

$$S = \frac{(0.54)(2.65)}{2.075} = 0.69.$$

The general expression of the soil moisture content at any degree of saturation is, by Eq. (6-7)

$$w_s = eS/G. \qquad\qquad (6\text{-}7a)$$

Let us designate the moisture contents corresponding to 0%, 25%, 50%, 75%, and 100% saturation as w_0, $w_{0.25}$, $w_{0.50}$, $w_{0.75}$ and $w_{1.00}$, respectively. Then

$$w_{0.25} = (S_{0.25}e/G)100\%,$$

and upon saturation, with $S = 1.00$, or $S = 100\%$,

$$w_{1.00} = (e/G)$$

By Eq. (6-7a) find and plot to scale the moisture contents w_s on the abscissa axis, using for S the classification boundary values of $S = 0, 0.25, 0.50, 0.75$, and 1.00. The points with coordinates w_s/S can now be connected with a line, giving the required graph. Thus, the soil classification by degree of saturation can now be represented graphically by a diagram. At $w = 54\%$ or at $w = 0.54$, $S = 0.69$ (very moist soil).

Chapter 7

MOISTURE-DENSITY RELATIONS OF SOILS

SOIL COMPACTION

7-1. Definition. In general the term "compaction" is understood to mean the increase in the dry density* of soil by a dynamic load. This concept should not be confused with that of consolidation. "Consolidation" is the gradual decrease in volume of voids, and thus the increase in density of a cohesive soil brought about under the action of continuously acting *static* load over a period of time (for example, fill under its own weight, or soil under the pressure of a structure). In cohesive, saturated soils the process of consolidation is accompanied by the gradual expulsion of some of the saturation water and air/or gas out of the voids of the soil with a consequent decrease in volume of the soil. To learn the soil moisture-density relationship, and to evaluate a soil as to its suitability for making highway, runway, and other fills, the soil is subjected to a compaction test.

In 1933 Proctor[1,2] showed that

1) there exists a definite relationship between the soil moisture content and the degree of dry density to which a soil may be compacted, and

2) that for a specific amount of compaction energy applied on the soil there is one moisture content termed the "optimum moisture content" at which a particular soil attains its maximum dry density.

Such a maximum dry density-optimum moisture content relationship gives a practical and satisfactory method of construction control of earthworks.

The standard Proctor soil compaction test is performed as follows.[3] A 6 lb = 26.69 N soil sample of the soil material passing the No. 4 sieve is air-dried, thoroughly mixed, and compacted in a standard compaction cylinder or mold, 4.6 in. high, 4 in. in diameter, and 1/30 cu ft. in volume (11.68 cm high, 10.16 cm in diameter, and 9.4387×10^{-4} m^3 in volume). The soil compaction in the mold is performed in three layers by means of a metal rammer, 2 in. = 5.08 cm in diameter, weighing 5.5 lb = 24.47 N.

Each of the three layers of soil should receive 25 blows from the rammer falling freely from a height of 12 in. = 30.48 cm above the elevation of each finally compacted layer. The net dry weight of the compacted soil is then determined, as well as the compacted moisture content. These two quantities, moisture content

---

*In soil mechanics, traditionally and tacitly the term "soil density" is used in lieu of the term "unit weight of soil," meaning weight per unit volume of soil.

and dry density, form a pair of coordinates, or a point "1" on a dry density graph, Fig. 7-1. Compaction is repeated at various moisture contents the moisture content of the soil sample being increased each time to produce data for plotting a complete moisture content-dry density graph.

The calculation of the dry density, viz., dry unit weight of the compacted soil in terms of its wet density and moisture content is calculated for each test made as follows:

$$w = \frac{A - B}{B - C} \, 100 \, \%, \qquad (7\text{-}1)$$

$$W_d = \frac{W_w}{1 + (w/100)}, \qquad (7\text{-}2)$$

where w = percent of moisture by oven-dry weight in the specimen of the soil,
A = weight of dish and wet soil,
B = weight of dish and oven-dried soil,
C = weight of dish,
W_d = dry weight per cubic foot or m^3 of compacted soil,
W_w = wet weight per cubic foot or m^3 of compacted soil.

The soil moisture contents are plotted on the graph, Fig. 7-1, as abscissas, and the dry unit weights as ordinates. When the plotted points are connected with a smooth line, a curve is obtained the shape of which is, generally, of a hyperbolic form. In order to determine better the course of the curve, it is advisable to obtain the test points before, at, and past the peak of the curve.

The moisture content corresponding to the peak, or maximum ordinate of the curve, is termed the "optimum moisture content" of the compacted soil sample at a specified amount of energy applied on that soil.

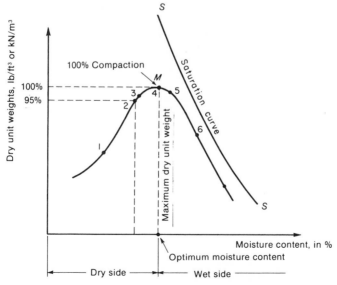

FIG. 7-1.   Moisture content - dry unit weight graph.

The oven-dried soil weight in pounds per cubic foot or in kN/m^3 of the soil tested at "optimum moisture content" is termed the "maximum dry density" or "maximum dry unit weight" for the compaction as specified by the test procedures under discussion. The maximum dry unit weight point M, obtained at the optimum moisture content, is commonly adopted as the 100% compaction when determinations of relative compactions are made.

Just above the compaction curve (points 1-2-3-4-5-6, Fig. 7-1), there is a complete saturation curve s-s (also called zero-air-voids curve) showing for various moisture contents the densities if the voids are entirely occupied with water.

7-2. Moisture-Dry Unit Weight Relationships of Some Soils. Depending upon the type of soil and the specified compaction method, the numerical values of the optimum moisture contents range from about 9% to about 35%. Dry weights per cubic foot of soil as determined by the standard compaction test vary from 75 to 130 lb.

The dry unit weight of soil in terms of percent air voids, viz., degree of saturation, is

$$W_d = \frac{G\gamma_w[1 - (n_a/100)]}{1 + \frac{Gw}{100} - \frac{n_a}{100}}. \tag{7-3}$$

This equation permits one to plot the dry unit weight curve, viz., lines of percent of constant air-voids curve (or at various constant degrees of saturation), as a function of soil moisture content. The specific gravity G of the soil particles must be known.

When all of the air voids of the soil are fully saturated, then $V_a = V_w = V_v$, $n_v = 0$, and $S = 1$ (100% saturation). In such a case Equation (7-3) transforms into Equation (7-4):

$$W_{d0} = \frac{G\gamma_w}{1 + (Gw/100)} = \frac{G\gamma_w}{1 + e}, \tag{7-4}$$

an equation which is known as the zero air void equation, or the saturation line (100% saturation, when $S = 1$). Here $e =$ void ratio.

The dry unit weight equation, Eq. (7-3), for a constant percent of air voids n_a, can also be expressed in terms of degree of saturation S as follows:

$$W_d = \frac{G\gamma_w}{1 + (Gw/100S)}. \tag{7-5}$$

For full (100%) saturation $S = 1$, and Eq. (7-5) transforms into "zero-air-voids curve"

$$W_{d0} = \frac{G\gamma_w}{1 + (Gw/100)} = \frac{G\gamma_w}{1 + e}, \tag{7-6}$$

where $e =$ void ratio.

Example 1. Derive the dry unit weight equation, Eq. (7-5), for any constant degree of saturation as a function of moisture content, specific gravity of the soil, and unit weight of the water.

Solution.

1) Degree of saturation S in decimal fractions:

$$S = \frac{V_w}{V_v} = \frac{V_v - V_a}{V_v} = 1 - n_a. \tag{7-7}$$

2) Volume V_w of water in soil:

$$V_w = \frac{wW_d}{\gamma_w}. \tag{7-8}$$

3) Total volume V_v of voids occupied by air and water in each unit of volume of soil:

$$V_v = 1 - V_s = 1 - \frac{W_d}{G\gamma_w}. \tag{7-9}$$

4) Substitute Eqs. (7-8) and (7-9) into Equation (7-7):

$$S = \frac{wW_d}{\gamma_w[1 - (W_d/G\gamma_w)]}. \tag{7-10}$$

5) Rearrangement of Eq. (7-10) yields:

$$S_w\gamma_w - SW_d/G - wW_d = 0, \tag{7-11}$$

6) The dry unit weight of soil W_d, at any moisture content w and any constant degree of saturation S, is:

$$W_d = \frac{G\gamma_w}{1 + (Gw/S)}, \qquad \text{Q.E.D.} \tag{7-12}$$

The moisture content percentage w is here expressed in decimal fractions. For example, if the moisture content were 9%, then w here is $w = 0.09$.

Example 2. In Table 7-1 are given standard compaction test results on Dunellen soil.

1) Plot the wet unit weight, and the dry unit weight curves of this soil.
2) Determine the maximum dry unit weight and the optimum moisture content of this soil. Also, calculate the relative compaction if the field unit weight of the same soil has been attained at 118.6 lb/ft³.
3) Plot the zero air void (100% saturation) curve.
4) Draw the percent air void curves for 4%, 8%, 12%, and 16% air voids.

Solution.

1) The required wet and dry unit weight curves are plotted in Fig. 7-2.
2) The maximum dry unit weight of the soil is 125.4 lb/ft³ or 19.70 kN/m³ at an optimum moisture content of w = 10.4% for that method of compaction.
   If the field unit weight is 118.6 lb/ft³ or 18.63 kN/m³ then the relative compaction is

$$\frac{18.63}{19.70}100\% = \frac{118.6}{125.4} \ 100\% = 94.5\%.$$

3) The zero air void curve (100% saturation, $S = 1$), s-s, is calculated by Eq. (7-5), viz., Eq. (7-6), for each even percent of moisture, from $w = 7\%$ to $w = 14\%$:

$$W_d = \frac{G\gamma_w}{1 + \dfrac{G_w}{100S}} = \frac{(2.66)(62.4)}{1 + \dfrac{(2.55)(w)}{(100)(1)}} = \frac{165.98}{1 + (0.0266)(w)} \ \left[\text{lb}/\text{ft}^3\right],$$

or

$$W_d = \frac{(2.66)(9.80665)}{1 + (0.0266)(w)} = \frac{26.09}{1 + (0.0266)(w)} \left[\text{kN}/\text{m}^3\right].$$

The W_d-values as a function of moisture content, w, are compiled in Table 7-2 (slide rule calculation):

TABLE 7-1. COMPACTION TEST RESULTS

Point Nos. on Curve	Moisture Content $w\%$	Wet Unit Weight		Dry Unit Weight		Remarks
		lb/ft^3	kN/m^3	lb/ft^3	kN/m^3	
1	2	3	4	5	6	7
1	6.8	129.2	20.30	121.0	19.01	Specific
2	8.5	133.5	20.97	123.2	19.35	Gravity
3	9.4	136.5	21.44	124.8	19.60	of soil
4	10.2	138.1	21.69	125.3	19.68	particles
5	11.3	139.1	21.85	125.0	19.64	$G = 2.66$
6	12.5	138.0	21.68	122.7	19.27	
7	13.6	136.9	21.51	120.5	18.93	

The zero air void curve is plotted on Fig. 7-2.

4) The percent of air voids n_a can be expressed in terms of degree of saturation S. By Eq. (7-7),

$$S = 1 - n_a. \tag{7-7}$$

(see Table 7-3).

The constant degree saturation curves are calculated by Eq. (7-5):

$$W_d = \frac{G\gamma_w}{1 + \frac{Gw}{100S}} = \frac{165.98}{1 + \frac{(0.0266)(w)}{S}}$$

If the standard method of compaction is modified by, say, increasing the amount of compaction, by increasing the weight of the rammer, increasing the height of the fall of the rammer, or increasing the number of blows on the soil specimen to be compacted, singly or combined, then the moisture-dry density curve appears above the standard compaction curve and somewhat shifted to the left relative to the standard curve. Such a modified compaction curve, differing from the standard one, is shown by a dotted curve on Fig. 7-2. Thus, the dotted curve represents a high compactive effort as compared with the standard compaction curve, which represents a low compactive effort. The modified standard compaction test specification prescribes the use of a 10 lb = 44.96 N rammer falling from a height of 18 in. = 45.72 cm.

The modified compaction test was not invented out of curiosity, but because the U.S. Corps of Army Engineers needed a specification test for use with soils

TABLE 7-2. ZERO AIR VOIDS UNIT WEIGHT

Moisture Content w·%	Dry Unit Weight lb/ft³	kN/m³
1	2	3
7	140.5	22.07
8	136.8	21.49
9	134.0	21.05
10	131.0	20.58
11	128.4	20.17
12	125.9	19.78
13	123.5	19.40
14	121.0	19.01

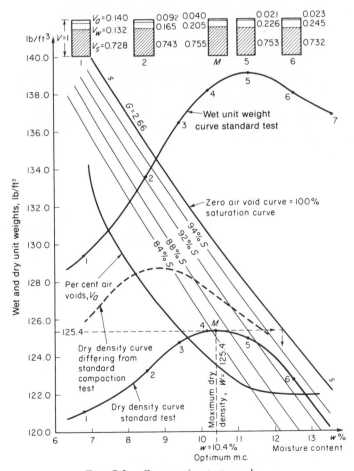

FIG. 7-2. Compaction test graphs.

under heavy-duty aircraft pavements. It should be noted that there is a great difference in foot-pounds or N·m between the standard and modified compaction test methods for the relatively small gain in density. In other words, density costs money. For the modified density test see Ref. 4.

The soil phase diagrams show an interesting picture of the changing relationships in unit weight, volume of air and moisture with varying moisture content in soil. The phase diagram is here calculated for point "1" on the dry-unit-weight curve. For other points the calculations are not shown. Only the final calculations in Table 7-4, and the phase diagrams, Fig. 7-2, are shown.

Phase Calculations. Point No. 1.
Volume of solids:

$$V_s = \frac{W_d}{G\gamma_w} = \frac{121.0}{(2.66)(62.4)} = \frac{121.0}{165.98} = 0.728(\text{ft}^3).$$

Volume of water:

$$V_w = \frac{W_w - W_d}{\gamma_w} = \frac{129.2 - 121.0}{62.4} = \frac{8.2}{62.4} = 0.132(\text{ft}^3).$$

Volume of air:

$$V_a = 1 - V_s - V_w = 1 - 0.728 - 0.132 = 0.14(\text{ft}^3).$$

The soil phase diagrams are shown on Fig. 7-2.
Soil moisture films affect the densities to which soils may be compacted. The density of soil moisture varies with temperature, and so does the viscosity and the surface tension of water. With decrease in temperature these properties of

TABLE 7-3. DRY UNIT WEIGHT AS A FUNCTION OF AIR VOIDS n_a
AND DEGREE OF SATURATION

Moisture Content, w%	$n_a \rightarrow$	0		4		8		12		16	
	$S \rightarrow$	1.00		0.96		0.92		0.88		0.84	
	—	lb/ft³	kN/m³	lb/ft³	kN/m³	lb/ft³	kN/m³	lb/ft³	kN/m³	lb/ft³	kN/m³
1	2	3	4	5	6	7	8	9	10	11	12
7	—	140.5	22.07	139.0	21.84	138.1	21.69	137.1	21.54	136.0	21.36
8	—	136.8	21.49	136.0	21.36	134.8	21.18	133.5	20.97	132.5	20.81
9	—	134.0	21.05	133.2	20.92	132.0	20.74	130.5	20.50	129.5	20.34
10	—	131.0	20.58	130.1	20.44	129.0	20.26	127.5	20.03	126.3	19.84
11	—	128.4	20.17	127.2	19.98	126.0	19.79	124.5	19.56	123.2	19.35
12	—	125.9	19.78	124.5	19.56	123.5	19.40	122.0	19.16	120.5	18.93
13	—	123.5	19.40	121.8	19.13	120.5	18.93	119.0	18.69	117.6	18.47
14	—	121.0	19.01	119.7	18.80	118.0	18.54	116.5	18.30	115.0	18.04

water increase; hence a greater amount of compaction energy must be applied to the soil at lower temperatures (compaction operations in fall and winter, for example) than at higher temperatures. Thus changes in soil moisture film characteristics furnish a reasonable explanation of the observed phenomenon that compacting soil in cold weather is more difficult than in warm weather.

TABLE 7-4. CHANGE IN VOLUMETRIC RELATIONSHIPS WITH
VARYING MOISTURE CONTENT

Point Nos. on Curve	Moisture Cont. $w\%$	Relative Volume of Solids V_s	Relative Volume of Water V_w	Relative Volume of Air V_a	Total Volume of Voids V_v
1	2	3	4	5	6
1	6.8	0.728	0.132	0.140	0.272
2	8.5	0.743	0.165	0.092	0.257
3	9.4	0.752	0.187	0.061	0.248
4	10.2	0.755	0.205	0.040	0.245
M	10.4	0.755	0.205	0.040	0.245
5	11.3	0.753	0.226	0.021	0.247
6	12.5	0.732	0.245	0.023	0.268

QUESTIONS

7-1.   Which is the most economical and feasible method of improving the bearing capacity of subgrade soils and fills?
(Densification by compaction and vibration).

7-2.   Upon what depends the stability of a subgrade soil or embankment?
(Upon the shear resistance of the soils of which they are composed).

7-3.   Of what properties does the shear resistance of soils consist?
(The combined properties of internal friction and cohesion of soil).

7-4.   By what factors are internal friction and cohesion affected?
(By the amount of voids in the soil and the amount of water within these voids).

7-5.   What will happen to a soil containing a high percentage of voids when exposed to high moisture content?
(It will become very unstable. Conversely, a soil with low porosity will resist the entrance of water into the voids and thus be much more stable than a soil having a high porosity).

7-6.   What is densification?
(Any process which reduces the amount of voids in a soil mass is termed densification).

7-7.   Upon what depends the density to which any soil can be compacted?
(Upon its moisture content and the amount of compactive energy applied on the soil).

PROBLEM

Given soil compaction test results as follows:

TABLE PROBLEM 7-1

Trial Nos.	Moisture Content $w\%$ by Dry Weight	Wet Weight of Compacted Soil	
		lb/ft^3	kN/m^3
1	8.3	126.2	19.82
2	9.6	131.9	20.72
3	10.5	135.3	21.25
4	11.3	137.4	21.58
5	12.2	136.6	21.49
6	13.4	135.8	21.33
7	13.8	134.7	21.16

The specific gravity of this silty soil is $G = 2.65$. The test is a standard test.

Required:
1) Plot the moisture-dry unit weight curve.
2) Plot the saturation (zero air voids) curve.
3) Plot the percent air-voids curve.
4) Determine the optimum moisture content and the achieved maximum dry unit weight of this soil.
5) Discuss the three curves.

RELATIVE DENSITY

7-3. The Concept. The concept of "relative density" is a criterion for the density of a sand deposit. This criterion is of an arbitrary character; it is not based on any plausible physical concept of density of any one physical body. Relative density applies only to sand, not silt and/or clay.

The coefficient of relative density is given as

$$D = \frac{e_{max} - e}{e_{max} - e_{min}} = \frac{(n_{max} - n)(1 - n_{min})}{(n_{max} - n_{min})(1 - n)} = \frac{1/\gamma_{min} - 1/\gamma}{1/\gamma_{min} - 1/\gamma_{max}},\qquad(7\text{-}13)$$

where e = void ratio of sand at its natural density under investigation, viz., density in its natural state in the field or laboratory;

e_{max} = void ratio of the same sand in its loosest state (to be established in the laboratory);

e_{min} = void ratio of the same sand under investigation in its densest or most compact state (to be established in the laboratory); ·

n_{max} = maximum possible porosity of the given sand soil (loosest state);

n_{min} = minimum possible porosity of the given sand soil (densest state); and

n = natural porosity of the given sand soil (natural state in the field, or prepared in the laboratory).

The most effective means of densifying sand fills is by the soil vibration method.

Analyzing the D-equation one notes the following. If the sand in its natural condition already is in its loosest state ($e = e_{max}$), then, according to the D-equation, the coefficient of the relative density of the sand is $D = 0$.

If the sand in its natural condition is in its densest state ($e = e_{min}$), then its coefficient of relative density is $D = 1$. For intermediate values of e the D-values are between 0 and 1.

7-4. Definition. Physically, relative density expresses the ratio of actual decrease in volume of voids in a soil to the maximum possible decrease in volume of voids. In other words, relative density indicates how far a sand under investigation is capable of further densification beyond its natural state of density under externally applied loads or energy.

7-5. Degree of Relative Density. Attempts have been made to characterize the various degrees or states of densities by means of numerical coefficients. The analysis of the D-equation indicates the possibility of doing so. According to Terzaghi,[5] the conventional coefficients are:

For loose sand $0 < D < \frac{1}{3}$
Medium-dense sand $\frac{1}{3} < D < \frac{2}{3}$
Dense or well-compacted sand $\frac{2}{3} < D < 1$

Loose sand can best be densified by vibration.[6,7,8] In evaluating sandy soils, their natural and relative densities are of paramount importance for the evaluation of their properties as a material upon which to found structures.

Depending upon the properties of the particles of the sand and the texture of the latter, two kinds of sands of the same volume of voids (porosity) may possess totally different abilities of densification (compaction). Hence, the coefficient of relative density of a given sand usually gives us a clearer idea of the density than the value of the void ratio itself. For determination of relative density of sand the reader is referred to Reference 9.

Example. Calculate the relative density of a sand soil whose void ratios are as follows:

$$e_{max} = 0.55; \quad e = 0.30, \text{ and } \quad e_{min} = 0.20.$$

Also, evaluate whether the sand deposit is in a loose state, medium dense or dense state.

$$D = \frac{e_{max} - e}{e_{max} - e_{min}} = \frac{0.55 - 0.30}{0.55 - 0.20} = 0.71.$$

Because $1.00 > 0.71 > 0.67$, the result, $D = 0.71$, indicates that the sand is in a dense state of compaction.

7-6. Applications. The relative density theory finds its application in compaction of granular material; in various soil vibration problems associated with engineering operations in earthworks, foundations of structures (pile driving), foundations of machinery, vibrations transmitted to sandy soil from trains and automobiles, and a number of other applications. In such instances the relative density values of sand give us an indication whether or not unpleasant consequences can be expected from engineering operations which might affect structures or foundations due to *vibration settlement*.

REFERENCES

1. R.R. Proctor, "Fundamental Principles of Soil Compaction," *Engineering News-Record*, vol. 111, nos. 8, 10, 12, and 13, 1933.
2. C.A. Hogentogler, Jr., "Essentials of Soil Compaction," *Proceedings*, 16th Annual Highway Research Board Meeting, Washington, D.C. 1936.
3. AASHTO "*Standard Method of Test for The Moisture-Density Relations of Soils Using A 5.5 lb (2.5 kg) Rammer and a 12-in. (305 mm) Drop.*" AASHTO Designation: T99-74, Part II, pp. 301-308.
4. AASHTO "Standard Method of Test for Moisture-Density Relations Using a 10-lb (4.54 kg) Rammer and an 18-in. (457 mm) Drop." AASHTO Designation: T 180-74, pp. 601-608 (Part II).
5. K. Terzaghi, *Erdbaumechanik auf bodenphysikalischer Grundlage*, Leipzig und Wien, Franz Deuticke, 1925.
6. R.K. Bernhard and J. Finelli, *Compaction and Dynamic Properties of Soils* (mimeographed), New Brunswick, N.J., Rutgers—The State University, 1952.
7. R.K. Bernhard and J. Finelli, *Pilot Studies on Soil Dynamics*, Special Technical Bulletin no. 156, ASTM, 1953,.
8. R.K. Bernhard, *Dynamic Compaction of Soil*, Engineering Research Bulletin no. 37, New Brunswick, N.J., Rutgers—The State University, 1952.
9. A.R. Jumikis, *Soil Mechanics*, Princeton, N.J., 1962, D. van Nostrand Company, Inc., pp. 120-123.

OTHER PERTINENT REFERENCES

1. ASTM, *1976 Annual Book of ASTM Standards, Part 19*, Philadelphia, Pa., 1976.
2. Bureau of Reclamation, Earth Manual (2nd ed.), Washington, D.C.: U.S. Department of the Interior, 1974.
3. Bureau of Reclamation, *Dams and Control Work* (3rd ed.), Washington, D.C.: U.S. Department of the Interior, 1954.

Chapter 8

SOIL CONSISTENCY

8-1. Definition. Consistency, in general, is that property of material which is manifested by its resistance to flow. The term "soil consistency" conveys the idea of the degree of cohesion (adhesion) between the soil particles. Also, consistency can be regarded as the outward result of the forces of cohesion and adhesion acting at various degrees of moisture contents. In this sense, "consistency" refers to the resistance of soil offered against forces that tend to deform or rupture the soil aggregate.

Consistency pertains to cohesive soils only. Consistency is commonly described by such terms as cemented, solid, hard, brittle, stiff, sticky, plastic, mellow, or soft. These gradations of soil consistency, as mentioned already several times before, are greatly influenced by the soil moisture content.

8-2. Plasticity. In the arts and industries plasticity is an important property of materials. The most generally accepted definitions of plasticity in the arts and industry are:

"That property which enables a material to be deformed continuously and permanently without rupture," or

"Plasticity is the ability of a body to undergo dislocation of its smallest structural particles, a consequence of the application of external forces, at ordinary temperature, without disturbance by their coherence."

In soil mechanics: The problem of plasticity does not concern the "plasticity" in itself, but it is considered merely from the standpoint of the *degree of plasticity*. This simply means the capacity of a soil to undergo certain important changes of shape which may involve a complete rearrangement of particles, without a noticeable change in volume. Plasticity is probably the most conspicuous property of clay.

Also, a soil is said to be in a *plastic state* when the water content is such that it can change its shape *without* producing surface cracks.

Depending upon the water content soils can change their state from a solid to a liquid.

Cohesive soils may also have a consistency between both states mentioned above, i.e., *cohesive soils may also be in a plastic state.* Therefore, for purposes of classification, degrees or *limits of plasticity* have been set up.

8-3. States of Consistency and Their Limits. Suppose that a soil-water mixture is now subjected to drying. Drying of soil means a decrease in its moisture content. At the beginning of the drying process the soil mass represents a more or less uniform dense liquid. It is said to be in the *liquid state*. During the drying process the thickness of the moisture films between the soil particles decreases. Upon further drying, the cohesive soil mass becomes dryer and somewhat stiffer, and at a certain moisture content, the so-called *liquid limit*, $w_{L.L.}$, the soil transforms from the liquid into the *plastic state*, thereby losing its ability to flow as a liquid. In this plastic state the soil can be readily molded, holding its shape, or can change shape without the appearance of cracks in it. Any material which allows a change of form without rupture and which will retain this form when the pressure is removed, is said to be plastic. Upon a further decrease in moisture, the plastic properties of the cohesive soil are lost, and at a certain moisture content, termed the *plastic limit*, $w_{P.L.}$, the clayey soil transforms from the plastic state into the *semisolid state*. At the plastic limit the change in consistency, viz., the change in shape of a cohesive soil, is accompanied by visible cracks; when worked upon, the soil crumbles.

The next stage of the drying-out process below the $w_{P.L.}$-point gradually approaches from the semisolid to the *solid state*. The moisture content of the soil at which the soil transforms from the semi-solid state to the solid state is termed the *shrinkage limit, $w_{s.l.}$*. The shrinkage limit is attained at that moisture content at which the cohesive soil, regardless of drying, remains volume-constant. Also, the change in color, upon drying, from dark to light approximately indicates the shrinkage limit. The moisture contents characterizing consistency limits are based on dry weight of the soil.

The previously discussed consistency limits of soils may be conveniently represented graphically as illustrated in Fig. 8-1. Consistency limits of soil,

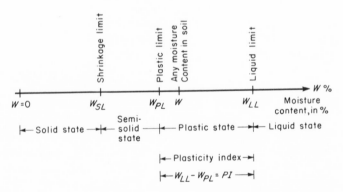

FIG. 8-1.   States of consistency, consistency limits, and plasticity index.

$w_{L.L.}$ and $w_{P.L.}$, give one an idea about the plastic properties and volume-constancy or stability and also about the internal friction of soil.

The consistency limits, liquid limit, plastic limit, and shrinkage limit, at which the transition from one state of soil consistency to another one takes place, were suggested by the Swedish soil scientist Atterberg.[1]

The consistency concepts are extensively used in soil engineering for identification, classification, and characterization purposes of soil as construction material.

8-4. Plasticity Index. With reference to the Atterberg consistency limits cohesive soils, through their change in moisture content, can assume the following state of consistency: 1) liquid, 2) plastic, 3) semisolid, and 4) solid.

The difference in moisture content or interval between liquid and plastic limits is termed the *plasticity index*, $P.I. = w_{P.I.}$:

$$P.I. = w_{L.L.} - w_{P.L.} \quad (\%). \tag{8-1}$$

The plasticity index, *P.I.*, indicates the moisture range through which a cohesive soil has the properties of a plastic material.

According to Atterberg[2,3] when *P.I.* < 7, the soil is said to be of low plasticity. When $7 \leq P.I. \leq 17$, the soil is of medium plasticity. When *P.I.* > 17, the soil is of high plasticity. These relationships are shown in Table 8-1.

TABLE 8-1. PLASTICITY INDEXES

Plasticity Index	Soil Characteristics By Plasticity	Soil Type	Cohesiveness
1	2	3	4
0	Non-plastic	Sand	Non cohesive
<7	Low-plastic	Silt	Partly cohesive
7-17	Medium plastic	Silty clay (Clayey silt)	Cohesive
>17	High plastic	Clay	Cohesive

All of the cohesive soils can be at three different consistencies, depending upon the moisture content present. When the moisture content of a soil is greater than the liquid limit, i.e., when $w > w_{L.L.}$, the soil is in a liquid state. When $w = w_{L.L.}$, the moisture content is at the liquid limit of the soil. When $w_{P.L.} < w < w_{L.L.}$, the soil is in a plastic state of consistency. When $w_{S.L.} < w < w_{P.L.}$, the soil is in a semisolid state of consistency. When $w < w_{S.L.}$, the soil is in the solid state of consistency. (Refer to Fig. 8-1.)

Many construction companies in highway engineering use the plasticity index not to exceed 6 as a criterion for specifying soil material used close under the pavement, whereas others specify a $P.I. \leq 3$. Table 8-2 illustrates soil classification by its plasticity index.

There is a very pronounced difference in the plasticity of some soil materials which are composed of very fine particles. Rock flour, for example, will exhibit practically no plasticity, whereas a clay composed of equally fine material will exhibit a marked plasticity. A similar comparison may be made between bentonite and kaolinite clays.

Some sands and rock flour free of cohesive material cannot be subjected to the consistency test. They will continue to decrease moisture content. Such

TABLE 8-2. EXAMPLE OF SOIL CLASSIFICATION BY ITS PLASTICITY INDEX

Type of Soil	Degree of Plasticity	Consistency Limits			
		Liquid Limit $w_{L.L.}$	Plastic Limit $w_{P.L.}$	Plasticity Index P.I.	Limits of Plasticity Indexes
1	2	3	4	5	6
Sand	Non-plastic	20	20	0	0
Silt	Low-plastic	25	20	5	<7
Silty Clay ⎫ Clayey silt ⎬	Medium-plastic	40	25	15	$\left\{ \begin{array}{l} >7 \\ <17 \end{array} \right.$
Clay	High-plastic	70	40	30	>17

soils are indicated as nonliquid (N.L.) and nonplastic (N.P.). Such soils may follow the same general process in volumetric change caused by drying out as the cohesive soils. The difference, however, is that upon drying the sandy soils do not pass through the $w_{P.L.}$-point from the liquid state into the solid state of solid, coherent, hard structure as do clays. Contrary to clays, sands change states from the liquid to the semisolid abruptly, resulting in noncoherent material. Noncohesive soils do not possess plasticity, the limit of which, therefore, cannot be determined by test. Such soils are indicated as nonplastic (N.P.). In short, cohesionless soils have no plastic state, and the liquid and plastic limits can be imagined to coincide. Thus, their plasticity index, theoretically, is zero.

Example. Determine the plasticity index P.I. for a cohesive soil the properties of which are given as follows:

$$\text{specific gravity } G = 2.65$$
$$\text{porosity } n = 38\%$$
$$\text{natural moisture content } w = 13\%$$
$$\text{liquid limit } w_{L.L.} = 22\%$$
$$\text{plastic limit } w_{P.L.} = 9\%.$$

Solution. The plasticity index, P.I., is calculated as $P.I. = w_{L.L.} - w_{P.L.} = 22\% - 9\% = 13\%$.

Saturation Moisture Content

$$w_{sat} = \frac{n}{G(1-n)} = \frac{0.38}{2.65(1-0.38)} = 0.232, \text{ or } 23.2\%.$$

Degree of Saturation

$$S = \frac{w}{w_{sat}} = \frac{13.0}{23.2} = 0.56 < 1.00. \tag{8-2}$$

State of Consistency
   a) Because $9 < w < 22$, where $w = 13\%$, the soil in its natural condition is in the plastic state
   b) Because $w_{sat} > 22$, where $w_{sat} = 23.2$, the soil, when saturated, would be in the liquid state.

8-5. Shrinkage Limit. When a moist, cohesive soil is subjected to drying out, it loses moisture and shrinks. During the drying process the compressive forces produced by surface tension forces of the pore water compress the particles of the skeleton of the cohesive soil together into a compact, coherent mass and thus densify it (Fig. 8-2). Hence, the void ratio of the soil decreases. The moisture loss continues down to a certain moisture content. When this moisture content is attained, any further decrease in moisture content ceases, and no further decrease in volume, viz., shrinkage, takes place. This is the time when the induced reactive stresses in the soil skeleton attain the magnitude of the capillary pressure; at this instant the menisci of the capillary moisture are

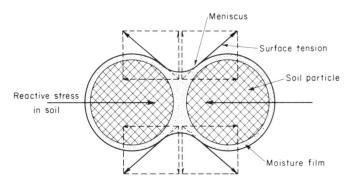

FIG. 8-2. Illustrating the concept of compressive forces produced by surface tension forces and induced reactive stress in soil.

tearing off and the pore moisture retires into the interior of the soil mass. At this point it can be noted that the soil changes its color from dark to light, and the soil ceases to shrink. The moisture content at this condition is termed the *shrinkage limit*. At the shrinkage limit the soil passes from the semisolid to the solid state. The relative position of the shrinkage limit ($w_{S.L.}$) on the consistency scale is shown in Figs. 8-1. On the average, soil shrinkage limits vary from about 10 to 15 percent by dry weight of soil.

The shrinkage limit is expressed as follows:

$$w_i W_d - w_{S.L.} W_d = (V_i - V_f)\gamma_w, \qquad (8\text{-}3)$$

where $w_i W_d$ = initial amount of soil moisture, in grams, before drying out;

w_i = initial moisture content, in percent;

W_d = dry weight of a soil sample, in grams;

$w_{S.L.} W_d$ = amount of moisture, in grams, at shrinkage limit;

$\gamma_w = 1$ = unit weight of water = 1 g/cm^3;

V_i = initial volume of a soil sample before drying;

V_f = final volume of a soil sample after drying. The final volume V_f is the dry volume V_s.

Equation (8-3), thus, represents an expression of loss in moisture in a shrinking process. From this equation the shrinkage limit, $w_{S.L.}$, is expressed, which is nothing else than a particular moisture content:

$$w_{S.L.} = w_i - \Delta w = w_i - \frac{(V_i - V_s)\gamma_w}{W_d}, \tag{8-4}$$

where Δw = moisture loss in percent by dry weight upon drying out the soil sample from its initial moisture content w_i to the moisture content $w_{S.L.}$ which corresponds to the shrinkage limit of the soil.

The concept shrinkage limit of cohesive soil is useful in evaluating the behavior of slopes of dams and cuts, particularly relative to the possibility of development of cracks in earthworks. In rainy seasons shrinkage cracks may be filled with water and saturate the soil, thus increasing the weight of the earth mass, which in its turn may slide down. The effects of shrinkage are more pronounced in cohesive, colloidal soils, which have high liquid limit values.

DETERMINATION OF CONSISTENCY LIMITS OF SOILS

8-6. General Notes. The routine procedures and devices used for testing consistency limits (or Atterberg limits) of soils are standardized and provided in standard specifications for testing soils by the various materials testing agencies, as for example, the American Association of State Highway and Transportation Officials (A.A.S.H.T.O.), by the American Society for Testing Materials (ASTM), or other agencies. From the descriptions of the particular consistency limit tests note that the soil consistency tests, as well as many other soil tests, are conventional tests. These tests are sometimes called *the physical tests*.

8-7. Liquid Limit Test. The liquid limit test of soils can be performed, for example, according to ASTM Standard Specification D423-66.[4]

FIG. 8-3. A. Casagrande's device for determining liquid limits of soils.

A. Casagrande's Method. To eliminate the variable factors or the so-called personal effects, A. Casagrande[5] devised the mechanical device illustrated in Fig. 8-3. This device for the determination of the liquid limit of soil in accordance with Atterberg's definition consists essentially of

1) a specified size cup made of brass and weighing 200 g $\pm$ 10 g,
2) a cam and crank mounted on a hard rubber block, and
3) a grooving tool.

The cranking of the cam lifts the brass cup up to a specified height of 1 cm from which height the cup drops upon the block exerting a blow on the latter. The cranking is to be performed at a specified rate of two rotations per second. In this mechanical method, the number of blows required to close the groove in the soil at its bottom along a distance of about one half of an inch is recorded, and the corresponding moisture content of the soil taken from around the closed groove determined. This operation is to be repeated three more times at different consistencies or moisture contents. The soil samples should be prepared at such consistencies that the number of blows or shocks required to close the groove will be below and above 25 blows. The relationships between the number of blows and their corresponding moisture contents thus attained are plotted on a one cycle, semilogarithmic graph paper. The best fit to the plots results in the so-called flow graph of the soil tested. The moisture content, $w_{L.L.}$, corresponding to the intersection of the flow graph with the 25-blow ordinate is taken as the liquid limit of the soil (Fig. 8-4).

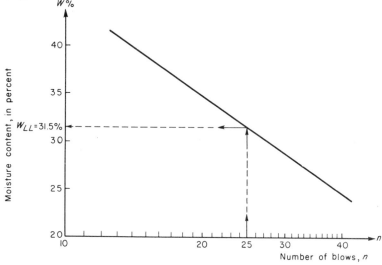

FIG. 8-4.   Flow graph.

According to Atterberg and A. Casagrande, liquid limit tests performed at temperatures of 7°C and 24°C, and between 35°C and 40°C, respectively, showed no difference from the values obtained at 20°C.

Example. Given the following liquid limit test data.

Trial Nos.	Number of Blows	Moisture Content (%)
1	14	40.0
2	21	34.4
3	31	28.0
4	39	25.0

Determine the liquid limit of this soil.

The liquid limit test data are plotted in Fig. 8-4. The liquid limit of the soil tested is scaled off from the flow graph at 25 blows as $w_{L.L.} = 31.5\%$.

In describing his research on Atterberg limits of soils, A. Casagrande explains the nature of the liquid limit test and the physical significance of the flow curve as follows:

"The force resisting the deformation of the sides of the groove made in the soil pat is the shearing resistance of the soil. Therefore, the number of blows or shocks required to close the groove of a soil paste represents a relative measure of the shearing resistance of this soil at this moisture content".

The slopes of the flow curves distinguish between the various degrees of cohesiveness and shear strength of the various soils. Consider, for explanatory purposes, two flow curves, one with a steep slope (curve 1) and one with a flat slope (curve 2) (Fig. 8-5). Curve 1 and curve 2 represent here, for the purpose of

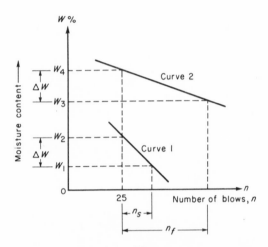

FIG. 8-5. Flow curves.

elucidating the point, two different soils but with the same $P.I.$-values. In this method of presentation it can be seen that in order to decrease the moisture content Δw in both soils by the same amount, the soil with a flat flow curve (2) takes a greater number of blows; here $n_f > n_s$. The comparison of the slopes of the flow curves thus gives us an indication that the soil with a flow curve (1) possessed a lesser shear strength than the soil with a flow curve (2).

8-8. Plastic Limit Test. The plastic limit of a soil can be determined, for example, according to the ASTM Standard D424-59[4]. It is performed by trial and error. According to this standard, the plastic limit is defined as follows:

"The plastic limit of a soil is the lowest moisture content, expressed as percentage of the weight of the oven-dried soil, at the boundary between the plastic and semisolid states. The water content at this boundary is arbitrarily defined as the lowest water content at which the soil can be rolled into threads $\frac{1}{8}$ in. in diameter without the threads breaking into pieces":

$$w_{P.L.} = \frac{\text{weight of water lost}}{\text{weight of oven-dried soil}} \, 100\%. \qquad (8-5)$$

The moisture content at which the soil thread crumbles is defined by convention as the plastic limit. According to this definition the plastic limit merely means the moisture content at which a soil ceases to be plastic, where the word "plastic" means the capacity of a soil to be rolled out into threads of a definite diameter. This means that, in cohesive soils, during the process of rolling in the test, considerable pressure is exerted on the thread of soil by the hands—water is forced out of the pores of the soil mass. Thus, the plastic limit test, like the liquid limit test, is a conventional test. Besides, in both of these tests the natural structure of soil is disturbed or destroyed; the tests are performed on remolded soil samples.

Example. When the plastic limit test is made, the moisture lost by drying the collected crumbled soil threads is 3.48 g. The dry weight of the soil threads is 15.38 g. The plastic limit is calculated as

$$w_{P.L.} = \frac{3.48}{15.38} = 0.2262, \text{ or } 22.62\%.$$

Plasticity Index. The plasticity index is the difference between the liquid and plastic limits:

$$w_{P.I.} = w_{L.L.} - w_{P.L.} = 36.8\% - 22.6\% = 14.2\% = P.I.$$

In this example, the liquid limit of the soil is given as $w_{L.L.} = 36.8\%$. Because $7 < w_{P.I.} < 17$, the soil tested has a degree of medium plasticity. The soil is classed as silty clay or clayey silt.

8-9. Shrinkage Limit Test. According to the ASTM standard method of test for shrinkage factors of soils, D427-61 of 1974,[4] the shrinkage limit of a soil is defined as that maximum water content, expressed as a percentage of the weight of the oven-dried soil, at which a reduction in water content will not cause a decrease in the volume of the soil mass. Some shrinkage cakes of soil are

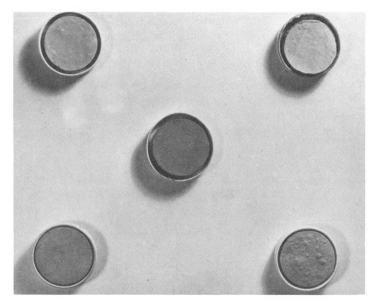

FIG. 8-6.   Illustrating shrinkage of soil.

shown in Fig. 8-6. Shrinkage limit tests can be performed on undisturbed as well as on remolded (disturbed) soils. For more discussion on consistency limits, among them shrinkage limit, of soils the reader is referred to the author's book *Soil Mechanics* (Reference 6).

Example. Given: $w_i = 51.78\%$; $V_i = 15.10$ cm^3; $V_s = 9.95$ cm^3;
$\gamma_w = 1$ g/cm^3; $W_d = 16.84$ g; $G = 2.66$.
Determine the shrinkage limit.
By Eq. (8-4):

$$w_{S.L.} = w_i - \frac{(V_i - V_s)\gamma_w}{W_d} \cdot 100\% =$$

$$= 51.78 - \frac{(15.10 - 9.95)(1)}{16.84} \, 100\% = 21.2\%.$$

There are also some other soil consistency concepts used in geotechnical engineering, for example:

Consistency index, $\quad I_c = \dfrac{LL - w}{LL - PL}$ (8-6)

Flow index, $\quad I_f = $ slope of flow curve[7]

Liquidity index $\quad I_L = \dfrac{w - PL}{LL - PL}$ (8-7)

Activity of clay $\quad A = \dfrac{LL - PL}{\% \text{ by dry weight finer}}$ (8-8)
$\qquad\qquad\qquad\qquad\qquad\qquad$ than 0.002 mm

Herein all symbols are same as before.

If the consistency index is $I_c = 0$, the soil is at its liquid limit. If $I_c = 100$, the soil is at its plastic limit.

The slope of the flow curve I_f is obtained from a plot of number of blows on a semi-decimal-log scale as a function of moisture content in the LL test.

The liquidity index I_L is also known by the term water-plasticity ratio.

If the liquidity index is $I_L = 1.0$, the soil is at its liquid limit (suggests a low strength). If the liquidity index is $I_L = 0$, the soil is at its plastic limit (suggests a stiff soil).

The concept "activity of clay," characterizes the plasticity of the fraction of "fines", viz., clay minerals.[8,9] The "activity" thus reflects the moisture-holding capacity of the clay particles. Also, the term "activity" indicates whether it is a low-activity clay, $A < 1$ (kaolinite, for example); or an intermediate-activity clay, between $A = 1$ to $A = 2$ (illite, for example); or a high-activity clay, $A > 4$ (montmorillonite, for example).

REFERENCES

1. A. Atterberg, "Die Konsistenz und die Bindigkeit der Böden," *Internationale Mitteilungen für Bodenkunde,* vol. II, Heft 2/3, 1912. Verlag für Fachliteratur G.M.B.H., Berlin, pp. 149-189.

2. A. Atterberg, "Die Plastizität der Tone," *Internationale Mitteilungun für Bodenkunde,* vol. I, no. 1, 1911, Verlag für Fachliteratur G.M.B.H., Berlin, p. 10.

3. A. Atterberg, *Die Plastizität and Bindigkeit liefernden Bestandteile der Tone,* vol. 3, no. 4, 1913, Verlag für Fachliteratur G.M.B.H., Berlin, pp. 291-330.

4. ASTM, *1976 Annual Book of ASTM Standards, Part 19.* Philadelphia, Pa.: ASTM, 1976:

   a) Designation: D 423-66 (Reapproved 1972): Standard Method of Test for Liquid Limit of Soils, pp. 80-83.

   b) Designation: D 424-59 (Reapproved 1971): Standard Method of Test for Plastic Limit and Plasticity Index of Soils, pp. 84-85.

   c) Designation: D 427-61 (Reapproved 1974): Standard Method of Test for Shrinkage Factors of Soils, pp. 88-91.

5. A. Casagrande, "Research on the Atterberg Limits of Soils," *Public Roads,* October 1932, vol. 13, no. 8, pp. 121-130.

6. A.R. Jumikis, *Soil Mechanics,* Princeton, N.J., D. Van Nostrand Company, Inc., 1962, pp. 125-148.

7. A.R. Jumikis, *Engineering Aspects of Glacial Soils of the Newark Metropolitan Area of New Jersey.* Engineering Bulletin No. 42. New Brunswick, New Jersey. Rutgers, The State University, College of Engineering, 1959, pp. 60-66.

8. A.W. Skempton, "The Colloidal Activity of Clays." *Proceedings of the 3rd International Conference on Soil Mechanics and Foundation Engineering,* Held at Zürich, 1953, vol. 1, p. 57.

9. D.T. Davidson and R.L. Handy, "Studies of the Clay Fraction of Southwestern Iowa Loess." *Proceedings of the Second National Clay Conference,* 1953, pp. 190-208.

SUGGESTIONS FOR FURTHER READING

1. E. D'Appolonia (1970) "Dynamic Loadings." *Proc. ASCE,* Journal of the Soil Mechanics and Foundation Division, Vol. 96, No. SM1, January, 1970, p. 49.

2. W.L. Dunn and F.H. McDougall, (1970) "Minimizing Errors in Gamma-Ray Surface-Type Density Gages: Existing Gages and New Design Concepts" *HRB Record, No. 301,* HRB, Wash., D.C.

3. "Control of Earth Construction," in *Earth Manual,* 2nd ed., U.S. Department of the Interior, Bureau of Reclamation U.S. Government Printing Office, Washington, D.C., 1974. pp. 165-260.

4. J.W. Hilf, "Compacted Fill," in *Foundation Engineering Handbook,* New York, N.Y.: Van Nostrand Reinhold Company, 1975, pp. 244-311.

5. L.D. Baver, W.H. Gardner and W.R. Gardner, *Soil Physics* (4th ed.), New York, N.Y.: John Wiley and Sons, Inc., 1972.

6. T.W. Lambe and R.V. Whitman, *Soil Mechanics,* New York, N.Y.: John Wiley and Sons, Inc., 1969.

7. G.A. Leonards, "Engineering Properties of Soils." In *Foundation Engineering,* Chapter 2, New York, N.Y.: McGraw-Hill Book Company, 1962, pp. 66-240.

8. *AASHTO, Standard Specifications for Highway, Materials and Methods of Sampling and Testing, Part I,* 1970.

9. J. Bowles, *Engineering Properties of Soils and their Measurement.* New York, N.Y.: McGraw-Hill Book Company, 1970.

10. *ASTM Annual Book of ASTM Standards, Part 19,* 1976.

11. *Earth Manual* (2nd ed.), U.S. Department of the Interior, Bureau of Reclamation, U.S. Government Printing Office, Washington, D.C. 1974, pp. 25-28.

QUESTIONS

8- 1. What is consistency of soil?

8- 2. Is the liquid limit of soil a natural or conventional soil index?

8- 3. Is the liquid limit a constant or variable factor of one sort of soil? Why?

8- 4. Is the liquid limit a constant or variable factor of different sorts of soils? Why?

8- 5. What is the distinction between natural soil moisture content and liquid limit?

8- 6. Could the content of natural soil moisture be equal to liquid limit?

8- 7. Why is the index "liquid limit" valuable in connection with highway subgrading?

8- 8. What is plasticity of soil?

8- 9. Is plastic limit a natural or conventional soil constant?

8-10. Has sand plasticity?

8-11. To what property of the soil particles is the plasticity of clays due?

8-12. In what state (disturbed or undisturbed) should soil samples be sampled for testing the liquid limit? Plastic limit? For determining the plasticity index?

8-13. Of which consistency are soils, if

a) $w > w_{L.L.}$?

b) $w_{L.L.} > w > w_{P.L.}$?

c) $w_{P.L.} > w$?

Here w means the natural moisture content of a soil.

8-14. Does a dry soil change its bearing capacity at the plastic limit?

8-15. What is the numerical value of the plasticity index if the soil is not plastic?

8-16. What happens to a soil whose $P.I. = 0$, if it is submerged in water?

8-17. Are soils in the solid and plastic states suitable for laying of foundations?

8-18. What is the purpose of classifying soils according to their plasticity index?

8-19. What is the technical meaning of the expression "soft clay"? Of what value is such a term?

8-20. What is the nature of shrinkage of soil?

8-21. Is shrinkage limit a natural or conventional soil constant?

8-22. Does the shrinkage phenomenon occur in sand? In clayey soils? Why?

8-23. When and why may one expect a greater capillary pressure and greater shrinkage in clays than in sands?

8-24. Upon what does the height of capillary rise in tubes depend?

8-25. Why do soils shrink?

8-26. When is the maximum value of surface tension reached?

8-27. Does the shrinkage limit depend also upon the shape of the soil particles? The uniformity of the soil? How?

8-28. In what kind of soils do you expect greater capillary height and pressure—in uniform or less uniform soil?

8-29. What conclusions can be drawn in connection with highway and railway construction on uniform and non-uniform soils as to their performance under load and water?

8-30. What could happen during heavy rains with slopes made in or with clay soil if the slope surfaces are shrunk?

8-31. Are shrinkage limits different for undisturbed and disturbed soil samples?

8-32. Of what value are shrinkage limits of soils anyway?

8-33. What are the physical differences between sand and clay?

8-34. Given the following data obtained from a liquid limit test of a soil:

Number of Shocks	Moisture Content (%)
38	16.2
34	18.0
20	19.9
12	19.4

Determine the value of the liquid limit for this soil.

8-35. A soil the liquid limit of which is 60% and the plastic limit of which is 27% is excavated from a borrow pit for use in an earthwork. The natural moisture content of the excavated soil is 32%. Determine:

a) the plasticity index of the soil.

b) What would be the effect of a light rain on the consistency of the soil?

8-36. The plastic limit test on a soil sample rendered the following moisture contents:

Trial Nos.	$w_{P.L.}$
1	12.9
2	11.2
3	12.5
4	14.6

Determine the plastic limit of this soil, calculate the plasticity index, and characterize this soil if the liquid limit of this soil is $w_{L.L.} = 16.0\%$.

8-37. The plasticity index of the soil in Problem 6-38 is equal to 8%, and the liquid limit is 20%. Characterize this soil. Refer to Chapter 6.

Chapter 9

CLASSIFICATION OF SOILS

9-1. Classification. In soil mechanics, a soil classification system may be defined as a specially coordinated body consisting of a fundamental division of the various types of soil into groups according to certain principles, for example: certain common physical properties; soil component parts or texture; or field performance under load, water, and upon freezing.

There exist several different soil classification systems. Each of them is accepted by various branches of the engineering profession as represented by their respective organizations as being the system best suited for their expressed need and use. For instance, the Public Roads Administration and the American Association of State Highway and Transportation Officials (AASHTO) soil classification systems are honored by the Bureau of Public Roads and by many state, county, municipal and township highway departments. The so-called "Unified Soil Classification System" is accepted by the U.S. Army Corps of Engineers and is most commonly used, with a few minor modifications, by the Bureau of Reclamation and several other organizations. The Civil Aeronautics Administration's soil classification system is used in airfield work. In fact, there is no such thing as a soil classification system accepted by all soil engineers and pavement technologists. Therefore it can be concluded that an "accepted" soil classification system would simply be nothing else than a system which satisfies best the engineering profession in its particular endeavor.

One of the reasons for the existence of the many soil classification systems is, perhaps, the fact that the geologist, the agronomist, and the engineer have slightly different concepts about the matter of soil. In engineering, soil is defined as the material by means of which (earthworks) and upon which engineers build their structures (foundations on soil). As to their performance under load, water, and temperature, soils are anything but simple. The properties of the materials the soil engineers have to work with are very complex indeed.

9-2. Textural Soil Classification Systems. Although the textural soil classification is not too satisfactory for the prediction of the performance of soil for many engineering purposes, it is felt that its review here would be necessary to form the basis for the understanding of the more extended highway and airfield subgrade soil classification systems.

In soil mechanics, soil texture is understood to be the combination of the size or granulometry of individual soil particles and the proportions by dry weight of the material of certain groups of particle sizes present.

The size of a soil particle is one of the most apparent physical properties of a soil. It is, therefore, no wonder that most of the older soil classification systems used in soil technology are based on soil particle size or diameter. Accordingly, such systems are termed *textural soil classification systems*.

9-3. Soil Classification System of the Bureau of Soils. In the United States one of the earliest soil classification systems was put forward before 1896 by the Bureau of Soils, United States Department of Agriculture (USDA). The divisional soil fractions and particle sizes in mm in this system are shown in Table 9-1.

TABLE 9-1. USDA BUREAU OF SOILS CLASSIFICATION

Fractions	Particle Size (mm)	
Gravel	> 1	
Sand	1	-0.05
Silt	0.05	-0.005*
Clay	0.005*	-0.0005
Colloids	< 0.0005	

* In 1938 the USDA Bureau of Soils changed the 0.005 mm size limit to 0.002 mm. However, by tradition probably, engineers still favor and continue to use the original 0.005 millimeter limit.

The Bureau of Soils soil classification shows that, in this system, the basic components of a soil, or the limits of the principal soil fractions, are broadly and arbitrarily separated on a particle-size basis, viz., their predominance in the composite soil. This textural soil classification system is still used by many soil technologists.

It should be noted that in different countries in the world, as well as in the United States of America, the limits of divisions between the sand and silt fractions and those between the silt and clay fractions were fixed arbitrarily.

9-4. Other Textural Soil Classification Systems. The textural soil classification systems adopted for their use by other organizations have other particle sizes for the division points. A comparison between the Bureau of Soils soil classification system and some others is shown in Table 9-2. The systems shown are:

1) Bureau of Soils, USDA[1]
2) American Society for Testing Materials (ASTM)[2]
3) Massachusetts Institute of Technology (MIT)[3]
4) The International Soil Classification System, established by the International Society of Soil Science[4] upon suggestion by A. Atterberg in 1908.
5) The Unified Soil Classification System.[5]

TABLE 9-2. SOME TEXTURAL SOIL CLASSIFICATION SYSTEMS

1. Bureau of Soils USDA

2.0 mm		1.0	0.5	0.25	0.1	0.05		0.002 mm
Gravel		Coarse	Medium	Fine	Very Fine		Silt	Clay
			Sand					

2. ASTM

2.0 mm	0.420	0.074	0.005	0.001 mm = 1 Micron
Medium sand	Fine sand	Silt	Clay	Colloidal clay

3. MIT nomenclature

2.0 mm	0.6	0.2	0.06	0.02	0.006	0.002	0.0006	0.0002 mm
Coarse	Medium	Fine	Coarse	Medium	Fine	Coarse	Medium	Fine (colloidal)
	Sand			Silt			Clay	

4. International nomenclature

2.0 mm	1.0	0.5	0.2	0.1	0.05	0.02	0.006	0.002	0.0006	0.0002 mm
Very Coarse	Coarse	Medium	Fine	Coarse	Fine	Coarse	Fine	Coarse	Fine	Ultra fine
	Sand				Mo*		Silt		Clay	

* Mo is a Swedish term used for glacial silts or rock flour having little plasticity.

5. Unified soil classific

2.0 mm	0.42mm	0.074mm
Medium fine	Fine	
Sand	Silt and Clay	

Besides these soil textural classification systems, there are also other systems which are based on particle size fractions, for instance: the British classification system (in agreement with the MIT soil classification system), the German Industrial Norms (DIN), and others.

All these textural soil classification systems have in common the decimal logarithmic scale for plotting of the soil particle size accumulation curve.

The soil classification system of the American Association of the State Highway and Transportation Officials (AASHTO) by soil particle size is shown in Table 9-3.[6]

TABLE 9-3. AASHTO SOIL CLASSIFICATION SYSTEM

Fractions	Particle Size (mm)
Gravel	75 - 2.00
Sand, coarse	2.00 - 0.42
Sand, fine	0.42 - 0.074
Silt and clay	<0.074

Because of its simplicity, the textural soil classification system does not require great skill to use and is still one of the most popularly accepted systems used in American engineering practice. The various textural soil classification systems, which are based on soil particle size only, are suitable for classifying noncohesive, coarse-particled soils for many purposes and, among other things, are also used in highway engineering. A certain size soil fraction, or a mixture of fractions or soils from several borrow pits is used to give a road a stable base and subbase course. Unfortunately, classification by particle size alone does not characterize the other properties of soil, such as the fine sizes, shapes, specific surfaces (more moisture films adsorbed in a unit of weight of soil upon the surfaces of particles, hence more frost-susceptible), plasticity, compressibility, nor the mineralogic properties of the soil particles, which influence considerably the performance of a soil.

For example, a fine rock flour, a nonplastic silt material derived from the gneisses by a grinding action (glacier), and locally (in Morristown, New Jersey) known by the unscientific term "bull's liver,"[7] may have a particle-size summation curve similar to a clayey silt or silty clay, containing some clay minerals and thus having some plastic properties. The performance, though, of these two materials under load, water, and freezing temperatures may be entirely different. Even with coarser materials the behavior may be different. For instance, two sands consisting of uniform size particles may have similar particle size accumulation curves, but would have different frictional properties, depending upon whether their particles are smooth, rounded, or sharp and angular, providing for better interlock between particles. For these reasons engineers tried to devise new and more satisfactory soil classification systems than those based on texture.

9-5. Highway Subgrade Soil Classification.

At the 25th Annual Meeting of the Highway Research Board a committee, appointed in 1943 to review the status of the subgrade soil classification, presented in 1945 a report on three different systems in order to establish a useful classification of subgrade materials that may be made by simple, routine tests performed by practically all highway departments.[8] The three systems are:

1) that prepared by a group representing highway organizations,

2) that in use by the Corps of Engineers, U.S. Army, and

3) the Civil Aeronautics Administration (CAA) soil classification system.

a) *The AASHTO Soil Classification System.* The soil classification system presented by the highway representatives is a modification of the PRA soil classification system. This modified system is summarized in Tables 9-4 and 9-5†[9] from which it can be noted that all soils are classed in *seven* groups, from *A*-1 to *A*-7. This system classifies soils based on their texture, physical properties (such as liquid limit and plasticity index), and on their expected field performance as subgrade materials for supporting pavements. The highway representatives' system has been adopted as one of the AASHTO standards for subgrade soil classification. The AASHTO system appears now in the 1974 and 1976 Specifications for Highway Materials as AASHTO Designation M145-73.[10] The AASHTO system divides the *A*-1, *A*-2 and *A*-7 groups into subgroups (Table 9-5). Also, the AASHTO system permits making a relative evaluation of the effect of both coarse and fine soil particles within a given group.

A-2 groups are borderline materials between soil groups *A*-1 and *A*-3, and silt-clay materials of Groups *A*-4, *A*-5, *A*-6, and *A*-7. It includes all materials containing 35% or less passing the 0.075 mm sieve which cannot be classified as *A*-1 or *A*-3, due to fines content or plasticity or both, in excess of the limitations for these groups.

The two subgroups *A*-2-4 and *A*-2-5 include various granular materials containing 35% or less passing the 0.075 mm sieve and with a minus 0.425 mm (No. 40) portion having the characteristics of the *A*-4 and *A*-5 groups. These groups include such materials as gravel and coarse sand with silt contents or plasticity indexes in excess of the limitations of Group *A*-1, and fine sand with nonplastic silt content in excess of the limitation of Group *A*-3.

Subgroups *A*-2-6 and *A*-2-7 include materials similar to those described under subgroups *A*-2-4 and *A*-2-5 except that the fine portion contains plastic clay having the characteristics of the *A*-6 and *A*-7 group.

The subgroup *A*-7-5 indicates elastic soil with moderate plasticity indexes, which is subject to considerable volume change. The *A*-7-6 subgroup comprehends soils with high plasticity indexes and subject to large volume changes.

b) *Group Index.* A new factor in the AASHTO soil classification system is the so-called group index.

The group index is calculated from the following formula:

---

† Tables 9-4 and 9-5 can also be found in AASHTO *Specifications,* 1974, on p. 223 in Ref. (5).

Group index=(F−35)[0.2+0.005 (LL−40)]+0.01(F−15)(PI−10),

The group index is calculated from the following formula: Group index = (F−35)[0.2 + 0.005 (LL−40)] + 0.01 (F−15)(PI−10), in which

F = percentage passing 0.074 (No. 200) sieve, expressed as a positive whole number. This percentage is based only on the material passing the 75 mm (3 in.) sieve;

LL = liquid limit;

PI = plasticity index.

The group index should be reported to the nearest whole number.

According to these specifications, when the calculated group index is negative, the group index shall be reported as zero (0).

When calculating the group index of A-2-6 and A-2-7 subgroups, only the PI portion of the formula shall be used.

Under average field and construction conditions, drainage and compaction, for instance, the good qualities of a subgrade material are rated as being in inverse ratio to its group index. For example, a group index the value of which in zero generally indicates a good subgrade material. A group index the value of which is 20 indicates a poor subgrade material.

The group index, based on actual soil performance, permits a closer determination of the probable performance of the soil in question than by the soil classification alone. The group index is used for determining empirically the combined thickness of flexible bituminous or Portland cement concrete pavement, base and subbase courses to be placed on a given subgrade. An empirical group index design diagram is shown in Fig. 9-1.[11] The original of this group index thickness diagram was published by D. J. Steele in 1946 (see Ref. 9).

The following are examples of calculation of the group index.

1) Assume that an A-6 material has 55% passing the 0.075 mm sieve, liquid limit of 40, and plasticity index of 25. Then

$$\text{Group index} = (55−35)[0.2 + 0.005 (40−40)]$$
$$+ 0.01 (55−15)(25−10) = 4.0 + 6.0 = 10.$$

2) Assume that an A-7 material has 80% passing the 0.075 mm sieve, liquid limit of 90, and plasticity index of 50. Then

$$\text{Group index} = (80 − 35)[0.2 + 0.005 (90 − 40)]$$
$$+ 0.01 (80 − 15)(50 − 10) = 20.3 + 26.0 = 46.3$$

(should be recorded to the nearest whole number, which is 46).

3) Assume that an A-4 material has 60% passing the 0.075 mm sieve, liquid limit of 25, and plasticity index of 1. Then

$$\text{Group index} = (60 − 35)[0.2 + 0.005 (25 − 40)]$$
$$+ 0.01 (60 − 15)(1 − 10) = 3.1 − 4.1 = -1.0$$

Report as 0.

TABLE 9-4. CLASSIFICATION OF SOILS AND SOIL-AGGREGATE MIXTURES

General Classification	Granular Materials (35% or less passing No. 200)			Silt-Clay Materials (More than 35% passing No. 200)			
Group Classification	A-1	A-3*	A-2	A-4	A-5	A-6	A-7
Sieve analysis: Percent passing:							
No. 10	50 max	—	—	—	—	—	—
No. 40	25 max	51 min	—	—	—	—	—
No. 200	10 max	10 max	35 max	36 min	36 min	36 min	36 min
Characteristics of fraction passing No. 40:							
Liquid limit				40 max	41 min	40 max	41 min
Plasticity index	6 max	NP	—	10 max	10 max	11 min	11 min
Group index	0	0	4 max	8 max	12 max	16 max	20 max
General rating as subgrade	Excellent to good			Fair to poor			

*The placing of A-3 before A-2 is necessary in the "left to right elimination process" and does not indicate superiority of A-3 over A-2.

From "Standard Specifications for Highway Materials and Methods of Sampling and Testing." Courtesy American Association of State Highway and Transportation Officials.

TABLE 9-5. CLASSIFICATION OF SOILS AND SOIL-AGGREGATE MIXTURES (WITH SUGGESTED SUBGROUPS)

General Classification	Granular Materials (35% or less passing No. 200)							Silt-Clay Materials (More than 35% passing No. 200)			
	A-1		A-3	A-2				A-4	A-5	A-6	A-7
Group Classification	A-1-a	A-1-b		A-2-4	A-2-5	A-2-6	A-2-7				A-7-5: A-7-6
Sieve analysis: Percent passing:											
No. 10	50 max										
No. 40	30 max	50 max	51 min								
No. 200	15 max	25 max	10 max	35 max	35 max	35 max	35 max	36 min	36 min	36 min	36 min
Characteristics of fraction passing No. 40:											
Liquid limit				40 max	41 min	40 max	41 min	40 max	41 min	40 max	41 min
Plasticity index	6 max		NP	10 max	10 max	11 min	11 min	10 max	10 max	11 min	11 min*
Group index	0	0	0	0	0	4 max		8 max	12 max	16 max	20 max
Usual types of significant constituent materials	Stone fragments gravel and sand		Fine sand	Silty or clayey gravel and sand				Silty soils		Clayey soils	
General rating as subgrade	Excellent to good							Fair to poor			

*Plasticity index of A-7-5 subgroup is equal to or less than LL minus 30. Plasticity index of A-7-6 subgroup is greater than LL minus 30.
From "Standard Specifications for Highway Materials and Methods of Sampling and Testing." Courtesy American Association of State Highway and Transportation Officials.

If, for example, the daily volume of truck and bus traffic is heavy—about 625 —and the group index of the subgrade soil is 13, then the total thickness of a bituminous or Portland cement concrete pavement, according to Fig. 9-1, is

top (pavement + base):	$7''$	$= 17.5$ cm
subbase:	$14''$	$= \underline{35.0\text{ cm}}$
a total of	$\overline{21''}.$	$= 52.5$ cm

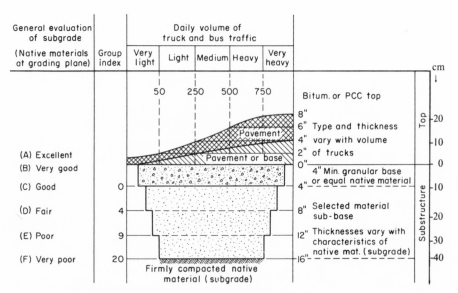

FIG. 9-1.   Group index design chart (after D. J. Steele). Courtesy of John Wiley and Sons, Inc., and the Highway Research Board.

The AASHTO soil classification system is now also the Bureau of Public Roads soil classification system.

9-6. Unified Soil Classification System. This soil classification system is in use by the Corps of Engineers and by many consultants and agencies.

The Unified Soil Classification System was developed jointly by the Bureau of Reclamation and the Corps of Engineers, Department of the Army, from the Airfield Classification System proposed by Professor A. Casagrande of Harvard University. It was adopted jointly in 1952.

The Unified Soil Classification System is a descriptive one, and takes into account the engineering properties of soils. Its greatest advantage is that a soil can be classed readily by visual and manual examination without the necessity for laboratory testing. The Unified Soil Classification System is based on the size of the soil particles, the amount of the various sizes (fractions), and the characteristics of the very fine particles.

Size distinction is not made between silt and clay in the Unified Soil Classification System; rather, the two fine-particled soil materials are differentiated by their behavior.

The textural part in the Unified Soil Classification System is (Table 9-2):

Gravel, coarse	3 "	(76.2 mm)	to	19.1 mm
fine	3/4 "	(19.1 mm)	to	4.0 mm
Sand, coarse		4.0 mm	to	2.0 mm
medium		2.0 mm	to	0.42 mm
fine		0.42 mm	to	0.074 mm
Fines, silt or clay		<0.074 mm		

Particle sizes larger than 3 inches = 76.2 mm are excluded from the Unified Soil Classification System.

In the Unified Soil Classification System soils are primarily classed into coarse-particled soils (50% or less −200 material), fine particled soils (50% or more −200 material), and highly organic soils. The first two groups are distinguished by the degree of their plasticity. The gravelly soils are designated by the symbol G, sandy soils by S. Well-graded gravel and sand is designated by the symbols GW and SW. Poorly-graded material is indicated by symbols GP and SP.

Fine-particled soils are subgrouped based on their liquid limit ($L.L.$):

if the $L.L. < 50$, the symbol is L;
if the $L.L. > 50$, the symbol is H.

The fine-particled soils are classed by their liquid limits and plasticity indexes by means of Casagrande's plasticity chart (see Fig. 9-2). Organic soils are symbolized by Pt. Other symbols and features of the Unified Soil Classification System can be seen and inferred, respectively, from Table 9-6.†

Columns 5, 6, and 7, Table 9-6, describe the suitability of the soil groups for use as subgrades, subbase courses, and base courses, respectively, when not subjected to frost action. The suitability of soil groups for the same purposes

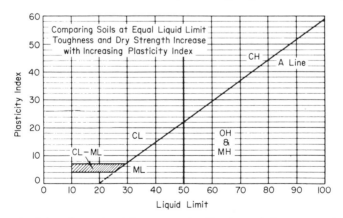

FIG. 9-2. Plasticity chart, for laboratory classification of fine-particled soils. By permission, U.S. Army Engineer, Waterways Experiment Station.

†This Table 9-6 is an abstract from the Vicksburg Experiment Station's Table B 1, in Ref. 5, 1957, omitting columns 4, 5, 11, 13, 14, 15, and 16.

TABLE 9-6. THE UNIFIED SOIL CLASSIFICATION SYSTEM;*
CHARACTERISTICS PERTINENT TO ROADS AND AIRFIELDS

Major Divisions		Symbol Letter		Name	Value as Subgrade when Not Subject to Frost Action	Value as Subbase when Not Subject to Frost Action	Value as Base when Not Subject to Frost Action	Potential Frost Action	Drainage Characteristics
(1)	(2)	(3)		(4)	(5)	(6)	(7)	(8)	(9)
Coarse-grained soils	Gravel and gravelly soils	GW		Well-graded gravels or gravel-sand mixtures, little or no fines	Excellent	Excellent	Good	None to very slight	Excellent
		GP		Poorly graded gravels or gravel-sand mixtures, little or no fines	Good to excellent	Good	Fair to good	None to very slight	Excellent
		GM	D	Silty gravels, gravel-sand-silt mixtures	Good to excellent	Good	Fair to good	Slight to medium	Fair to poor
			U		Good	Fair	Poor to not suitable	Slight to medium	Poor to practically impervious
		GC		Clayey gravels, gravel-sand-clay mixtures	Good	Fair	Poor to not suitable	Slight to medium	Poor to practically impervious
	Sand and sandy soils	SW		Well-graded sands or gravelly sands, little or no fines	Good	Fair to good	Poor	None to very slight	Excellent
		SP		Poorly graded sands or gravelly sands, little or no fines	Fair to good	Fair	Poor to not suitable	None to very slight	Excellent
		SM	D	Silty sands, sand-silt mixtures	Fair to good	Fair to good	Poor	Slight to high	Fair to poor
			U		Fair	Poor to fair	Not suitable	Slight to high	Poor to practically impervious
		SC		Clayey sands, sand-clay mixtures	Poor to …	Poor	Not suitable	Slight to …	Poor to practically impervious

Major Divisions (1)	(2)	Symbol Letter (3)	Name (4)	Value as Subgrade when Not Subject to Frost Action (5)	Value as Subbase when Not Subject to Frost Action (6)	Value as Base when Not Subject to Frost Action (7)	Potential Frost Action (8)	Drainage Characteristics (9)
Fine grained soils	Silts and clays LL is less than 50	ML	Inorganic silts and very fine sands, rock flour, silty or clayey fine sands or clayey silts with slight plasticity	Poor to fair	Not suitable	Not suitable	Medium to very high	Fair to poor
		CL	Inorganic clays of low to medium plasticity, gravelly clays, sandy clays, silty clays and lean clays	Poor to fair	Not suitable	Not suitable	Medium to high	Practically impervious
		OL	Organic silts and organic silt clays of low plasticity	Poor	Not suitable	Not suitable	Medium to high	Poor
	Silts and clays LL is greater than 50	MH	Inorganic silts, micaceous or diatomaceous fine sandy or silty soils, elastic silts	Poor	Not suitable	Not suitable	Medium to very high	Fair to poor
		CH	Inorganic clays of high plasticity, fat clays	Poor to fair	Not suitable	Not suitable	Medium	Practically impervious
		OH	Organic clays of medium to high plasticity, organic silts	Poor to very poor	Not suitable	Not suitable	Medium	Practically impervious
Highly organic soils		Pt	Peat and other highly organic soils	Not suitable	Not suitable	Not suitable	Slight	Fair to poor

* Abstracted, by permission, from "The Unified Soil Classification System," Appendix B, Characteristics of Soil Groups Pertaining to Roads and Airfields, U.S. Army Engineer, Waterways Experiment Station (Ref. 5).

PHYSICAL PROPERTIES OF SOIL

TABLE 9-7. COMPARISON OF THE UNIFIED AND PUBLIC ROADS ADMINISTRATION'S SOIL CLASSIFICATION SYSTEMS

Soil Symbols in the Unified System	Potential Frost Action	Soil Symbols in the PRA System
1	2	3
GW	None to very slight	A-3
GP	None to very slight	A-3
GM	Slight to medium	A-2
GC	Slight to medium	A-1
SW	None to very slight	A-3
SP	None to very slight	A-3
SM	Slight to high	A-2
SC	Slight to high	A-1
ML	Medium to very high	A-4
CL	Medium to high	A-4, A-6, A-7
OL	Medium to high	A-4, A-7
MH	Medium to very high	A-5
CH	Medium	A-6, A-7
OH	Medium	A-7, A-8
Pt	Slight	A-8

under freezing conditions is tabulated in column 8. Drainage characteristics of this soil classification system are indicated in column 9. The special reference to frost action is an important feature of the Unified Soil Classification System.

According to A. Casagrande,[12] "Under natural freezing conditions and with sufficient water supply (from groundwater) one should expect considerable ice segregation in non-uniform soils containing more than three percent of grains smaller than 0.02 mm, and in very uniform soils containing more than 10 percent smaller than 0.02 mm. No ice segregation was observed in soils containing less than one percent of grains smaller than 0.02 mm."

For a discussion of other frost criteria see Reference 13. For a discussion of the upward migration of soil moisture upon freezing, see References 14, 15, 16 and 17. On frost-susceptible glacial soils of the Newark, N.J., metropolitan area, see Ref. 7.

Table 9-7 is an approximate comparison, according to Casagrande's idea (see Ref. 18), of the symbols used in the Unified Soil Classification System and in the Public Roads Administration's soils classification system. The value of these soil materials when subjected to frost action is also indicated in Table 9-7.

The Unified Soil Classification System is a quick visual system for the evaluation of the probable soil performance for highway and airfield design and construction. One notes that the Unified system employs simple symbols easy to use, thus disclosing the type and nature of the soil. The tests required to group a given soil are not many, and they are simple to perform. The main basis for the classification of the soils is the soil texture for the coarse fractions and plasticity for the fine fractions. This system comprehends 15 soil groups instead of seven as in the AASHTO system. The USC system correlates soil performance under frost conditions, drainage conditions, compaction characteristics, and the California Bearing Ratio (CBR) of the soils.

9-7. The Civil Aeronautics Administration's (CAA) Soil Classification System.
The CAA soil classification system[19,20] lists 13 groups of subgrade soils, marked by symbols E-1 to E-13. This table could be applied directly to the problem of determining the thickness of flexible (F) and rigid (R) airfield pavements under various climatic conditions, including freezing, in the United States and Alaska. The subgrade soil classification is based on texture, soil plasticity and the California Bearing Ratio (CBR).

In the CAA system, soils E-1 through E-4 are granular materials (50% or more sand). Soils E-5 to E-10 are nongranular (containing less than 55% sand), which means nonplastic or moderately plastic A-4 silt. Soils designated E-7, E-8, and E-9 are clay soils, and E-10 (A-5) is very elastic soil.

The CAA system also classifies the granular soil into nonfrost-heaving (E-1, E-2) and frost-susceptible soils (E-3, E-4).

REFERENCES

1. M. Whitney, *Methods of the Mechanical Analysis of Soils*, U.S. Department of Agriculture, Division of Agricultural Soils. Bulletin no. 4, Washington, D.C., Government Printing Office, 1896.
2. ASTM, *1976 Annual Book of ASTM Standards, Part 19*. Philadelphia, Pa.: ASTM, 1976.
   Designation: D 448-54 (Reapproved 1973) : Standard Specifications for Standard Sizes of Coarse Aggregate for Highway Construction, pp. 92-94.
   Designation: D 3282-73: Standard Recommended Practice for Classification of Soils and Soil Aggregate Mixtures for Highway Construction Purposes, pp. 421-428.
3. D. W. Taylor, *Fundamentals of Soil Mechanics*, New York, John Wiley and Sons, Inc., 1948.
4. A. Atterberg, "Die mechanische Bodenanalyse und die Klassifikation der Mineralböden Schwedens," *Internationale Mitteilungen für Bodenkunde*, Verlag für Fachliteratur, G.m.b.H., Wien-Berlin-London, 1912, vol. 2, no. 4, pp. 312-342.
5. U.S. Army Waterways Experiment Station. "The Unified Soil Classification System." Technical Memorandum No. 3-357, Office of the Chief of Engineers, U.S. Army. Revised June 1957, reprinted May 1967.
6. AASHTO, "Recommended Practice for the classification of Soils and Soil Aggregate Mixtures for Highway Construction Purposes." AASHTO Designation: M 145-73.

Washington, D.C.: American Association of State Highway and Transportation Officials, September, 1974, pp. 218-224.

7. A. R. Jumikis, *Engineering Aspects of Glacial Soils of the Newark Metropolitan Area of New Jersey*, Engineering Research Bulletin no. 42, Bureau of Engineering Research, Rutgers—The State University, New Brunswick, N.J., 1959.

8. "Report of Committee on Classification of Materials for Subgrades and Granular Type Roads" (Chairman, H. Allen), *Proceedings*, 25th Annual Meeting of the Highway Research Board, Washington, D.C., 1946, pp. 375-392.

9. D. J. Steele, "Classification of Highway Subgrade Materials," *Proceedings*, 25th Annual Meeting of the Highway Research Board, Washington, D.C., January 1946, pp. 376-384.

10. "Standard Recommended Practice for the Classification of Soils and Soil-Aggregate Mixtures for Highway Construction Purposes," pub. in *Standard Specifications for Highway Materials and Methods of Sampling and Testing*, Part I, AASHTO, Washington, D.C., 1974, pp. 218-224; 1976.

11. D. J. Steele, "Application of the Classifications and Group Index in Estimating Desirable Subbase and Total Pavement Thickness," *Proceedings*, 25th Annual Highway Research Board Meeting, Washington, D.C., January 1946, pp. 388-392.

12. A. Casagrande, "Discussion on Frost Heaving," *Proceedings*, Highway Research Board, Washington, D.C., 1932, Part I, p. 169.

13. A. R. Jumikis, *The Frost Penetration Problem in Highway Engineering*, New Brunswick, N.J., Rutgers University Press, 1955, pp. 139-144.

14. A. R. Jumikis, "The Soil Freezing Experiment," published in *Factors Influencing Ground Freezing*, Highway Research Board, Washington, D.C., 1956, pp. 150-165.

15. A. R. Jumikis, "Some Concepts Pertaining to the Freezing Soil System," published in the Highway Research Board International Water Symposium, *Special Report no. 40*, HRB, Washington, D.C., 1958.

16. A. R. Jumikis, "Concerning a Mechanism for the Soil Moisture Translocation in the Film Phase Upon Freezing," *Proceedings of the Highway Research Board*, vol. 39, January 1960, Washington, D.C., pp. 619-639.

17. A.R. Jumikis, *Thermal Geotechnics*, New Brunswick, New Jersey, Rutgers University Press, 1977.

18. A. Casagrande, "Classification and Identification of Soils," *Transactions, ASCE*, New York, 1948. Paper no. 2351, vol. 113, pp. 901-930. Discussions start on p. 931.

19. A. H. Hadfield, "Soil Classification and Evaluation of Subgrade Supporting Power for Airfields," *Proceedings*, 25th Annual Highway Research Board Meeting, Washington, D.C., January 1946, pp. 386-388.

20. Federal Aviation Administration, Department of Transportation. *Airport Paving*. Washington, D.C., 1967.

SUGGESTIONS FOR FURTHER READING

1. American Association of State Highway Officials. *Standard Specifications for Highway Materials and Methods of Sampling and Testing*, Part I, AASHO Designation: M145-66, 10th ed., Washington, D.C., 1971.
2. *Earth Manual* (2nd ed.), U.S. Department of the Interior, Bureau of Reclamation, U.S. Government Printing Office, Washington, D.C. 1974.
3. R.D. Krebs and R.D. Walker, *Highway Materials*, New York, N.Y.: McGraw-Hill Book Company, 1971.

QUESTIONS

9-1. What are the various soil classification systems?

9-2. What are the fractional limits of gravel, sand, silt, and clay in the USDA Bureau of Soils soil classification system? In the AASHTO system? In the International system?

9-3. Explain the concept of "group index."

9-4. Upon which soil test properties is based the AASHTO soil classification system?

PROBLEMS

9-1. Laboratory soil tests gave the following results on soil No. S-86-2:
Liquid limit = 20%. Plastic limit = 12%.
Sieving analysis: percent of soil material passing sieve No.   10—100%
No.   40— 85%
No. 200— 38%

Determine the plasticity index and the group index of this soil. Classify the soil according to the Highway Research Board's soil classification system and according to the Unified soil classification system.

9-2. If the daily number of buses and trucks on a road on this soil is 700, determine by means of Steele's diagram the thickness of the flexible pavement to use, and report also the thickness of the base and subbase courses if the latter ones are necessary.

9-3. The following table contains the results of particle size analysis and liquid limits and plastic limits of seven soils. Which of these soils would be considered frost susceptible? Explain.

Sieve Nos. Size	Percent Passing						
	Soil Sample Numbers						
	1	2	3	4	5	6	7
No. 10	80.0	35.2	84.0	37.3	98.3	100.0	78.2
20	78.4	25.1	79.7	26.0	97.6	98.7	75.1
40	75.0	19.8	72.8	19.0	87.6	97.2	71.6
60	69.0	17.8	67.5	15.9	58.2	95.5	68.7
140	50.1	15.5	60.3	12.5	9.2	90.2	64.5
200	43.2	14.8	60.0	12.3	9.0	85.3	63.2
0.05 mm	33.0	11.5	53.0	10.5	5.0	70.0	59.5
0.01 mm	10.5	5.0	24.0	6.0	2.0	40.0	32.0
0.005 mm	6.3	3.0	17.0	4.0	1.0	10.0	21.0
L.L. in %	23.2	28.0	30.8	27.5	NL	41.6	48.0
P.L. in %	15.7	19.5	19.9	21.5	NP	36.4	30.8
P.I. in %							

9-4. The combined mechanical analysis of a soil yielded the following results:

Sieve Number	Soil Particle Size in mm	Percent Passing
1	2	3
10	2.00	100
20	0.841	96
40	0.420	85
60	0.250	69
140	0.105	41
200	0.074	38
	0.034	30
	0.025	27
	0.016	23
	0.009	22
	0.006	18
	0.005	15
	0.002	12
	0.0009	9

Plot the soil particle size accumulation curve. Is the soil frost-susceptible? Describe this soil by means of the Feret triangle.

PART III

Water in Soil

Chapter 10

THE LIQUID PHASE OF SOIL—WATER

10-1. The "Opponent" Water. The "opponent" water in many cases appears especially troublesome in connection with the construction of foundations and earthworks when it is necessary to carry their footings below the groundwater table. The water head, causing an upward flow into the open excavation, may loosen the soil. In such cases where the hydraulic gradient exceeds the critical one, the so-called "quicksand" phenomenon occurs. Here water really presents the most difficult of the foundation engineering problems to be solved. It then means the adoption of a more elaborate and expensive method of construction.

Therefore, no planning or foundation engineering operations of any importance that must be carried out below the ground surface level should be started before accurate information about the "opponent" at the site is obtained. In foundation and highway engineering the "opponent" water is justly termed "public enemy No. 1."

10-2. Modes of Occurrence of Water in Soil. Water in soil can occur in the form of aqueous vapor, in the form of films adsorbed to the surfaces of the soil particles, as free water (gravitational water), or water in bulk, and as water in the solid state of aggregation, such as ice.

Hygroscopic Soil Moisture. All mineral matter is covered with a very thin film of moisture. Soils which appear quite dry nevertheless contain an amount of water—the so-called hygroscopic moisture. In the technical literature hygroscopic moisture is also termed adsorbed moisture, contact moisture, or surface-bound moisture. This form of soil moisture is in a dense state and surrounds the surfaces of the individual soil particles as a very thin hull of film of water.

Hygroscopic moisture is not in union with the groundwater. Therefore, it does not take part in the fluctuation of the groundwater table nor does it transmit hydrostatic pressure. Whether the hygroscopic moisture film consists of a single molecular layer of water or of a polymolecular layer is not clearly known. However, the hygroscopic moisture film is known to be bound or attached rigidly to the soil particles with an immense physical force—up to about 10,000 atmospheres. Under the action of these forces, the hygroscopic soil moisture film is densified. The nearer the hygroscopic soil moisture is attracted to the surface of the solid soil particle, the more it is densified. The latest research explains these physical forces as being of an electrochemical nature.

Hygroscopic moisture can be removed by drying the soil particles at $+105°C$.

The difference between the weight of the air-dried soil sample and its weight after oven-drying at $+105°C$ determines the amount of hygroscopic moisture present in a soil.

Hygroscopic moisture has a very definite effect on the cohesion and plasticity of a clayey soil. The thickness of the hygroscopic moisture hull, according to figures given in the literature, varies greatly. So, for example, according to Zunker's[1] figures in Table 10-1, one can see that hygroscopic moisture is present

TABLE 10-1. HYGROSCOPIC SOIL MOISTURE FILMS†

Soil type	Particle size, in mm	Hygroscopically bound soil moisture in percent of dry weight of the soil	Thickness of hygroscopic soil moisture film, in $\mu\mu$	Number of the densified layers of the molecules of the hygroscopic moisture
1	2	3	4	5
Silt	0.006	1	23.1	110
Clay	0.002	3	22.4	107
Colloids	0.0004	8	13.2	63
Colloids	0.00005	16	3.3	16
$1 \mu\mu = 10^{-6}$ mm				

† After F. Zunker, Ref. 1

in considerable amount in fine-particled soils. This is because of the large internal surface area in such soils. The greater the internal surface, the greater the content of the hygroscopic moisture which can be adsorbed from the atmosphere by that soil.

Briggs[2] estimated the thickness of the water film on powdered quartz in an atmosphere of 99% humidity to be 4.5 $\mu\mu$. Odén[3] found that the thickness of water film in a saturated atmosphere was about 2×10^{-5} to 3×10^{-5} mm, whereas at a very low vapor pressure the thickness was of the order of 1×10^{-6} mm.

Moisture film. Film moisture forms in soil upon the condensation of aqueous vapor, or remains there after the removal of the bulk of the free water. The moisture film is attached to the surfaces of the soil particles as a hull or film upon the layer of the hygroscopic moisture film. The moisture film is held by molecular forces of considerable intensity but not as large as in the case of the hygroscopic moisture film.

Moisture film is connected to the groundwater table if one is present but is not affected by gravity. The moisture film is set in motion or migration by the application to the soil system of an external energy potential, called *primary potential*—a thermal or electrical potential, for example.[4-7] The moisture in soil then will migrate from places of higher temperatures (or higher electric potential, whichever the case is) to places of lower temperatures.

Film water freezes below $0^{\circ}C$, depending upon the thickness of the film, the degree of stressed condition, and the intensity and duration of freezing.

Considering the mode of water film, it can thus be concluded that the greater the specific surface area of soil, the more water film the soil particles can contain.

10-3. Gravitational Water. Gravitational water can further be classed as a) free water (or bulk water) and b) capillary water.

Free water, in its turn, is distinguished as follows: i) free surface water and ii) groundwater.

Gravitational water is the water which is in excess of the amount of moisture the soil can retain. It translocates as a liquid and it can be drained away by the forces of gravity. It transmits hydraulic pressure.

a) *Free water* (bulk water) possesses the usual properties of liquid water. It translocates at all times under the influence of gravity forces, or because of a difference in hydrostatic pressure head, or b) it can be in a suspended condition held by the surface tension forces of the liquid, when it is called *capillary water*.

i) *Free Surface Water.* Free surface water conditions (precipitation, runoff, melting snow, flood-water, water flowing from broken mains or from certain hydraulic operations) should be investigated when a structure comes in direct or indirect contact, or when it influences the groundwater in one way or another. For the construction work as well as for the exploitation of the structure it is of importance to determine the *amount* and the *fluctuation* of the free water.

Rainfall and *runoff* are erosive agents that are very destructive because they detach soil and transport it away. The tremendous force of the uncontrolled, downslope running water carves deep gullies and channels in unprotected soil. Hence, uncontrolled water can wash out road, railroad, and canal embankments; dams and levees; bridge piers; foundations of structures. It can destroy cofferdams for foundation work and equipment and construction material. Or, the eroded and transported material may be deposited in reservoirs, thus filling them up with silt and taking the volume needed to store water for irrigation, flood control, domestic water supply, power, and recreation.

The freezing point, the boiling point, the surface tension, and the viscosity of the free surface water correspond to those of ordinary water.[8.]

ii) *Groundwater.* Groundwater is that kind of gravity water which fills up the voids and other open spaces in the soil up to the groundwater table and translocates through them. It obeys the laws of hydraulics. Groundwater fills coherently and completely all the voids of the soil. In such a case it is said that the soil is saturated, and the water content by volume is equal to the volume of the voids.

The upper surface of the zone of the full saturation of the soil, at which the groundwater is subjected to atmospheric pressure, is called the *groundwater table.* On construction sites, or generally, in the field, the groundwater table is the locus of the water levels to which it rises and levels itself out in observation wells, bore holes, test pits, and open basins in free communication through the voids of the soil. If the soil is of poor permeability or is practically impermeable, establishment of the levels often takes a very long period of time, or sometimes it does not even take place at all.

Perched Groundwater. Runoff water, seeping into the soil, may also be trapped in depressions in pockets of moraine clay located below ground surface in permeable sand, thus forming a perched groundwater. The amount of groundwater accumulated depends upon the season, rate of evaporation from the depression in the direction of ground surface, and freezing (if this occurs). If there prevails a certain freezing temperature gradient between the ground surface and the perched groundwater table, and if the freezing period lasts long enough, and all other physical conditions are favorable, the perched water may migrate from the warmer, perched water zone towards the colder, downward-penetrating cold front, and the whole amount of the perched groundwater may be transferred upwards. Thus it can be understood that freezing, in a way, is a drying process.

Artesian Water. Artesian water is confined groundwater under hydrostatic or pressure head (a permeable water-bearing soil layer or aquifer sandwiched between impermeable zones above and below it).

10-4. Capillary Moisture. Capillary water is that soil moisture which is located within the interstices and voids of capillary size of the soil.

Capillarity, in general, is a phenomenon of the rise or depression of liquids in tubes having a bore so fine as to be comparable in diameter with a hair (capillus). The rise takes place and the liquid is held by means of a force called the surface tension force of the menisci at the top of the water column in a capillary tube, or by surface tension forces plus the effect of gravity.

Capillary movement in soil is the movement of the soil moisture through the minute pores between the soil particles. The minute pores serve as tortuous capillary tubes through which the soil moisture rises above the groundwater table. Movement results whenever the soil moisture "surface tension pull" is increased by loss of water through evaporation from the ground surface. Thus, capillary water is hydraulically and *continuously connected* to the groundwater table or to a perched groundwater table, and can be raised against the force of gravity.

For capillary rise in soil to exist, all of the voids should be completely and *uninterruptedly* filled with capillary water. The capillary-saturated zone between the groundwater table and the plane of the menisci is called the *closed capillary fringe.* This contains no air (Fig. 10-1). The thickness of this closed capillary fringe depends mainly on the fineness of the soil particles. The larger the pore size (diameter of the capillary), the less the height of rise, or the less the capillary fringe.

Above the closed capillary fringe there is the so-called *open capillary fringe,* i.e., the air-containing capillary zone which reaches to the height of the menisci in the finest pores of the soil. Here the larger pores are not filled with capillary moisture.

Capillary water cannot be drained by means of drainage systems installed

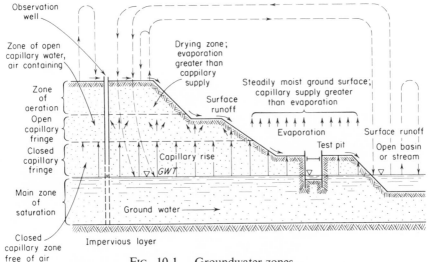

FIG. 10-1.   Groundwater zones.

within the capillary fringe, but it can be controlled by lowering the groundwater table. The drainage system must be installed in the groundwater to pull it down together with the capillary fringe, thus controlling the capillary height to which the capillary water can rise. Capillary water can also be removed by heating or by its evaporation at ordinary temperatures. It freezes at about $-1°C$.

Capillary moisture may translocate in soil in any direction, not just vertically upwards. The presence of capillary moisture in cohesive soil decreases considerably its cohesion and stability: the soil transforms into a sticky-plastic condition which makes it difficult to work with, to compact, or even to mix.

The freezing of a capillary-saturated soil results in an accumulation of a considerable amount of moisture at the cold isothermal boundary where the water freezes, causing heaves and other damage to roads.

Pore corner or *neck moisture*, known in German by the term *Porenwinkelwasser*, is the annular moisture wedge held by the concave menisci, or rather surface tension forces, in the angularities formed by the points of contact of the soil particles (Fig. 10-2).

Each of the principal kinds of soil moisture, viz., water, is represented diagrammatically in Fig. 10-3 after Zunker[9] so that fundamental differences can be distinguished easily and clearly.

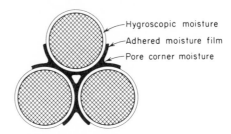

FIG. 10-2.   Pore corner moisture.

10-5. Effect of Temperature on Surface Tension. The surface tension of liquids at room temperatures are of the order of 0.03 g/cm. For water, the surface tension is more than double this figure and is equal to about 0.08 g/cm.

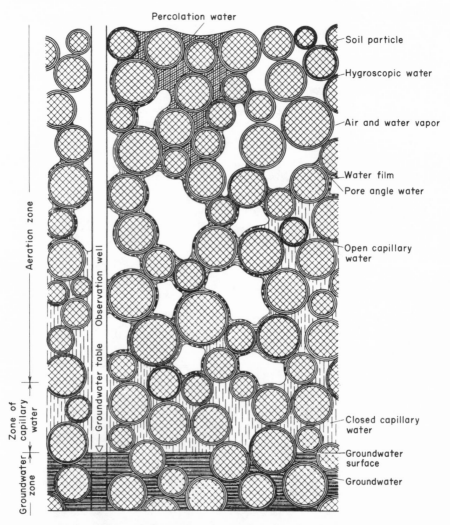

Percolation water
Soil particle
Hygroscopic water
Air and water vapor
Water film
Pore angle water
Open capillary water
Closed capillary water
Groundwater surface
Groundwater

Aeration zone
Observation well
Groundwater table
Zone of capillary water
Groundwater zone

FIG. 10-3. Modes of occurrence of water in soil. After F. Zunker, Ref. 9.

The values of the coefficients of surface tensions of water in dynes/cm at various temperatures are interpolated and compiled from the International Critical Tables,[10] calculated in g/cm, and tabulated in Table 10-2.

10-6. Capillary Rise. The capillary rise takes place by means of a force called the surface tension force of the menisci, acting at the top of the water column in a capillary tube between water and the wall surface of the tube, and distributed around the circular, wetted perimeter of the tube (Fig. 10-4). The force which brings about the capillarity is also called the capillary force. The curved, upper, crescent-shaped surface of the liquid column in the capillary tube is termed *meniscus*. This meniscus is concave relative to its top when the liquid wets the wall of the capillary, as in the case of water. It is convex relative to its top as in the case of mercury.

TABLE 10-2. SURFACE TENSION OF WATER TO AIR
AT ORDINARY TEMPERATURES

Temp. °C	Surface Tension			Capillary Constant $a^2 = \dfrac{2\sigma^*}{\gamma_w}$
	σ dynes/cm	σ^* g/cm	σ N/cm	(cm^2)
1	2	3	4	5
-8	76.96	78.48×10^{-3}	76.96×10^{-5}	0.1574
-5	76.42	77.91×10^{-3}	76.42×10^{-5}	0.1562
-4	76.26	77.76×10^{-3}	76.26×10^{-5}	0.1559
-3	76.11	77.61×10^{-3}	76.11×10^{-5}	0.1556
-2	75.95	77.45×10^{-3}	75.95×10^{-5}	0.1552
-1	75.80	77.29×10^{-3}	75.80×10^{-5}	0.1549
0		77.13×10^{-3}	75.64×10^{-5}	0.1545 (Average)
1	75.50	76.99×10^{-3}	75.50×10^{-5}	0.1543
2	75.30	76.83×10^{-3}	75.30×10^{-5}	0.1540
3	75.21	76.69×10^{-3}	75.21×10^{-5}	0.1536
4	75.06	76.54×10^{-3}	75.06×10^{-5}	0.1533
5	74.92	76.40×10^{-3}	74.92×10^{-5}	0.1529
6	74.78	76.25×10^{-3}	74.78×10^{-5}	0.1527
7	74.64	76.12×10^{-3}	74.64×10^{-5}	0.1525
8	74.50	75.97×10^{-3}	74.50×10^{-5}	0.1522
9	74.36	75.82×10^{-3}	74.36×10^{-5}	0.1519
10	74.22	75.67×10^{-3}	74.22×10^{-5}	0.1516
11	74.07	75.53×10^{-3}	74.07×10^{-5}	0.1513
12	73.93	75.39×10^{-3}	73.93×10^{-5}	0.1510
13	73.78	75.23×10^{-3}	73.78×10^{-5}	0.1508
14	73.64	75.06×10^{-3}	73.64×10^{-5}	0.1505
15	73.49	74.94×10^{-3}	73.49×10^{-5}	0.1502
16	73.34	74.78×10^{-3}	73.34×10^{-5}	0.1499
17	73.19	74.63×10^{-3}	73.19×10^{-5}	0.1496
18	73.05	74.49×10^{-3}	73.05×10^{-5}	0.1494
19	72.90	74.34×10^{-3}	72.90×10^{-5}	0.1491
20	72.75	74.18×10^{-3}	72.75×10^{-5}	0.1488
25	71.97	73.39×10^{-3}	71.95×10^{-5}	0.1474
30	71.18	72.58×10^{-3}	71.18×10^{-5}	0.1460
35	70.38	71.77×10^{-3}	70.38×10^{-5}	0.1446
40	69.56	70.93×10^{-3}	69.56×10^{-5}	0.1431
100	58.85	60.01×10^{-3}	58.85×10^{-5}	0.1253

In this table, the symbol σ^* means force grams per cm.
1 dyne = $(1.01971)(10^{-3})g_f = (1.00000)(10^{-5})$N.

When a capillary tube is placed in a liquid that wets the walls of its surface, the liquid will rise in the capillary above the free water surface of the liquid into which the capillary is dipped, provided that the liquid wets the tube.

The capillary ascent or rise of water inside the tube to a certain height h above the water level where the tube is immersed is termed the *height of the capillary rise*.

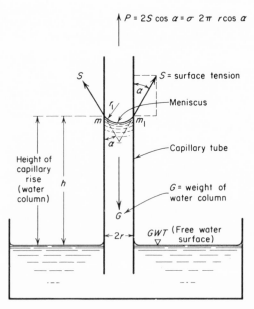

FIG. 10-4.   Capillary rise.   Equilibrium condition in a capillary system.

The height of the capillary rise in the tube depends upon the magnitude of the force of the surface tension pulling the liquid upward, as compared to the force of gravity pulling the liquid column downward. When the two forces are balanced, further rise is prevented and a condition of equilibrium results. This equilibrium condition is represented in Fig. 10-4. The capillary rise h is calculated, neglecting the density of saturated vapor above the meniscus, as

$$h = \frac{2\sigma^* \cos \alpha}{\gamma_w r} \quad \text{(cm)}, \tag{10-1}$$

where $\sigma^* =$ surface tension of liquid, in force-grams/cm, or in N/cm,

$\alpha =$ angle of contact, or angle of wetting,

$\gamma_w =$ unit weight of water, in g_f/cm^3 or in N/cm^3, and

$r =$ inside radius of capillary tube, in cm.

This means that in a capillary tube a liquid will rise to such a height that the gravitational force will just balance the force of surface tension.

The value $(2\sigma^*)/\gamma_w = a^2$ in Eq. (10-1) is called the *capillary constant* (see Table 10-2).

At $0°C$, the surface tension is $\sigma_0 = 77.13 \times 10^{-3}$ g/cm. At such a temperature, the capillary rise or height is

$$h_0 = \frac{2(0.07713)\cos \alpha}{\underbrace{(0.99986)r}_{\approx 1}} = \frac{(0.15426)\cos \alpha}{r} = \frac{0.30852}{d} \cos \alpha, \tag{10-2}$$

where $d = 2r =$ the diameter of the capillary tube.

It can be seen that the capillary height is proportional to the surface tension and the angle of contact, and inversely proportional to the unit weight of water and to the diameter of the capillary tube. Practically, the capillary height increases with the decrease in diameter of the tube.

Besides, the value of capillary height reaches a maximum when $\cos \alpha = 1$. This, in its turn, means that the contact angle α is zero. In such a case

$$h_{max} = \frac{2\sigma^*}{\gamma_w r},$$ (10-3)

or, with $\gamma_w = 1$ g/cm³,

$$h_{0max} = \frac{0.30852}{d}.$$ (10-3a)

When the density of saturated vapor above the meniscus is taken into account, the expression of the height of capillary rise is

$$h = \frac{2\sigma \cos \alpha}{r(\rho_L - \rho_v)g} \quad \text{(cm)},$$ (10-4)

where ρ_L = density of water, in g/cm³,
ρ_v = density of saturated vapor, in g/cm³.

The value of the contact angle α can be assumed to be zero for liquids which wet the tube, for example, water and alcohol.

When there is an air or gas plug in the capillary water column, the water will not rise. There should be an uninterrupted column of capillary water in the capillary tube above the free, plane water surface; then there will be a capillary rise of water in the tube as a function of its diameter.

When $\alpha = 0$, then the radius of curvature r_1 of the meniscus m-m equals the radius of the tube r.

When $\alpha = 90°$ and $\cos \alpha = 0$, the capillary height and capillary pressure are zero.

The height of the capillary rise does not depend upon the inclination of the capillary tube, nor does it depend upon the shape of the tube and the diameter of the tube below the meniscus of the liquid in the tube. The height depends, however, upon the diameter of the meniscus (Fig. 10-5). When the upper part of variously shaped capillary tubes is finished off by capillary orifices of one and the same diameter, the water in the capillaries reaches the same height above the

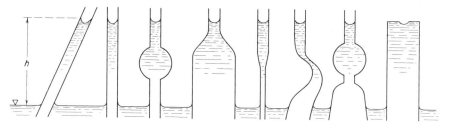

FIG. 10-5. The capillary height is the same with various shapes of capillary tubes if the diameter of their menisci is the same.

plane free water table no matter whether the tubes are broadened below it or not. The tubes must be filled and allowed to drain to the capillary height when there is an enlargement in the tube below the meniscus.

Note that in soils there are no perfect geometrical capillary tubes such as were discussed from the physical point of view. Rather, the voids, interstices, and passages in the soil are of irregular shape and various sizes, which might be filled partially or fully with water, air, or gas, or a combination of these substances. Besides, these passages are not necessarily vertical. However, the capillary concepts help us to understand certain phenomena occurring in soil. For example, soil particles are wetted by soil moisture in a manner similar to the wetting of the inside wall of a capillary tube. Also, the concepts of the capillary theory help us to understand the mode by which water is retained in the soil by surface tension forces.

10-7. Suspended Water in Soil. Suspended water in soil is observed in nature in the rapid draw-down of a water table, for example, on emptying a reservoir quickly or on lowering the groundwater table. If upon such a lowering the continuity of the capillary fringe is disrupted, or torn off, the former capillary fringe can be imagined as hanging, or suspended.

Also, suspended water in soil can be encountered under the following conditions (see Fig. 10-6). If the upper layer of silt or peat possesses capillary

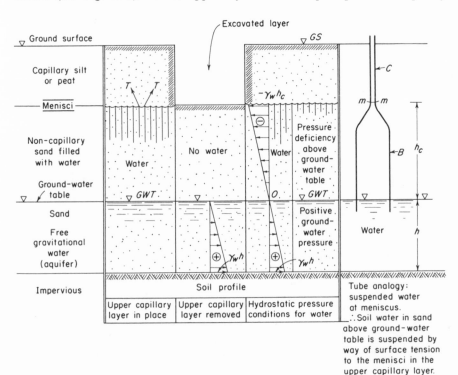

FIG. 10-6. Suspended water.

properties and its capillaries are saturated, then the soil water in the sand layer (assume the latter as having noncapillary properties) may be hanging from the menisci of the peat. This phenomenon is analogous to the one in which a glass bell B, with a capillary tube C at its top, is immersed into water and pulled out again as shown in Figs. 10-6 and 10-5. The water is imagined as suspended at the meniscus m-m. The suspension of water from the upper layer of soil possessing capillary properties can take place during lowering of the gravitational water after high tides or floods. In foundation work or highway construction, upon the removal of the upper capillary silt or peat layer (removal of upper menisci), water will drain out from the sand layer into the aquifer below the groundwater table. The hydrostatic pressure conditions for suspended and free water are also shown in Fig. 10-6.

The surface tension phenomenon and the ascent of soil moisture are most pronounced in soils composed mainly of fine sands, silts, or silty clays. The particle size of silt is enough smaller than that of sands to afford considerable height of moisture ascent above the groundwater table, and, at the same time, large enough to provide voids of such a size as to permit rapid translocation of soil moisture through them. This tendency of silt results in the rapid loss of the stability of such a soil under certain conditions.

The dependance of the capillary height on the particle size of the soil is shown in Table 10-3. The values given are for a closed capillary fringe, i.e., active capillary heights. The values shown are average values for average conditions.

TABLE 10-3. CAPILLARY HEIGHTS OF SOILS

Soil	Fractions, mm	Capillary Height, h_c cm	Stress p_c kg_f/cm^2	kN/m^2
1	2	3	4	5
Fine gravel	2 to 1	2 to 10	0.002 to 0.010	0.0196 to 0.0981
Coarse sand	1 to 0.5	10 to 15	0.010 to 0.015	0.0981 to 0.1470
Medium sand	0.5 to 0.25	15 to 30	0.015 to 0.030	0.1470 to 0.2940
Fine sand	0.25 to 0.05	30 to 100	0.030 to 0.10	0.2940 to 0.9807
Silt	0.05 to 0.005	100 to 1000	0.10 to 1.00	0.9807 to 9.8066
Clay	0.005 to 0.0005	1000 to 3000	1.00 to 3.00	9.8066 to 29.4188
Colloids	< 0.005	3000 and more	3.00 and more	29.4188 and more

1 kg_f/cm^2 = 9.8066 N/cm^2

10-8. Effect of Surface Tension on a Soil Mass.

Intergranular Pressure. At all points where moisture menisci touch soil particles, surface tension forces act, causing a grain-to-grain pressure within the soil similar to that of the capillary tube in compression under the surface tension forces. This grain-to-grain pressure is recognized as the *capillary pressure*, and is also called in soil mechanics the *intergranular*, or *contact*, or *effective pressure.* This intergranular pressure tends to force the solid particles together with a pressure equal and opposite to the tension through the water.

These compressive stresses on the soil skeleton contribute to the strength and stability of the soil mass. This surface tension-induced strength of soil under proper conditions of particle size, temperature, salinity, and other factors permits it to bear the weight of the heaviest auto races for speed and drag, as for example, the auto races held on the famous Daytona Beach in Florida.

The surface tension forces are relatively immense in magnitude. During the landing operations on the beaches of France by the Allied Forces, these surface tension forces proved to be capable of supporting heavy equipment such as tanks, guns, and construction machinery.

The surface tension-induced strength p_c of soil, however, is only temporary in character and may be destroyed entirely upon the full saturation of soil or inundation of the soil material by, for example, high tides or during flood conditions, because inundation eliminates interface menisci, and the contact pressure p_c reduces to zero.

Lowering of Capillary Fringe. The effect of surface tension forces on the performance of soils is thus very significant. This significance can be cited by another example. Capillary moisture, unlike free gravitational water, cannot be drained out of the soil, particularly from silt and clay, by any system of drainage (gravitational) installed within the capillary fringe. This is because capillary moisture is held within the soil by surface tension forces, and the capillary flow does not obey the law of gravity.

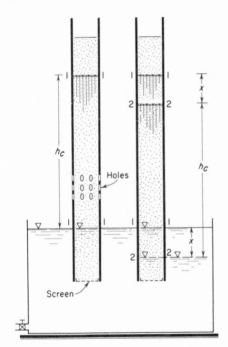

However, if the groundwater table is lowered (drainage facility installed in gravitational water, or pumping operations applied), the whole capillary fringe might be lowered. The clear establishment of the lowered capillary fringe takes place slowly with a great time lag, after the thermo-osmotic flow of capillary moisture has stabilized.

The fact that capillary moisture cannot be drained out of soils can be illustrated by the following experiment (Fig. 10-7).

FIG. 10-7. A capillary experiment.

Two transparent tubes with screened bottoms, one of which is provided with perforations in the cylindrical walls, are filled with capillary soil and immersed in water. After some time the active capillary height h_c can be observed in both cylinders. When the water table in the pan is lowered by an amount of x (from position 1 down to position 2), there is established after some time approximately the same capillary height h_c above the lowered water table. This indicates that in treating a practical case, such as a highway, which is built on soil with a high capillary rise and where the frost penetration reaches within the so-called capillary fringe, it is useless to install drains within the zone of capillary fringe in order to remove the capillary moisture. The groundwater table has to be lowered, or the fill raised, or layers of coarse soil or artificial, tight, impermeable membranes should be introduced to break capillary ascent.

10-9. Capillary Siphoning Phenomenon. One of the ways by which water may be lost from a storage reservoir is by capillary siphoning over the crest of the impervious core of an earth dam, as illustrated in Fig. 10-8. Siphoning takes place if the crest is not sufficiently high.

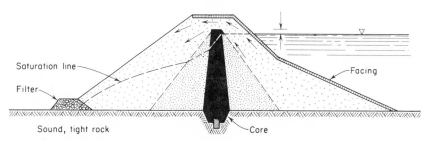

FIG. 10-8.   Capillary siphoning over the crest of an impervious core of an earth dam.

Capillarity in soils is also an important factor entering into underground reservoir calculations and exploitations, as in the petroleum industry.

10-10. Stress Conditions in Soil Caused by Surface Tension Forces.
The Closed Capillary Fringe. The effect of action of surface tension forces in a porous soil mass is analogous to that of a uniformly distributed load placed on the ground surface. The magnitude of this load is determined by the height of the closed and open capillary fringes which cause the additional pressure on the soil mass. The closed capillary fringe at a height of h_c above the ground-water table exerts a compressive stress on the soil mass whose magnitude is

$$p_c = \gamma_w h_c n,$$ (10-5)

where γ_w = unit weight of water and
n = porosity of soil.

Also, it can be said that the soil moisture increases the unit weight of a soil so that the pressure ordinates in the soil vertical pressure diagram are now increased by a constant amount p_c of capillary pressure (Fig. 10-9). For example, the vertical stress of a soil (self-weight) and the capillary moisture acting on a unit area can be expressed as

$$\sigma = \sigma_z + p_c = \gamma_s h + \gamma_w h_c n,$$ (10-6)

where γ_s = unit weight of the soil and
h = thickness of the soil layer.

If the capillary water in soil causes an additional load upon the solid particles, then the effect of this phenomenon on soil would be its tendency to decrease the swelling pressure of a soil.

The whole thickness h of the soil layer in question is affected by the additional height and weight of the closed capillary fringe by the additional load p_c, because it can be imagined that the capillary moisture might be attached and suspended to the surfaces of the menisci.

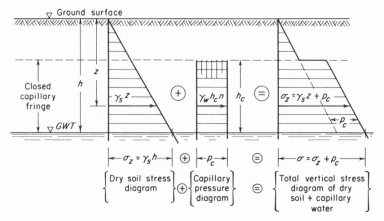

FIG. 10-9. Effect of capillary pressure p_c on soil vertical stress diagram.

Apparent Cohesion. The capillary or effective pressure, as can now be understood, endows the soil with an additional bond, which is called the apparent cohesion c. The solid phase of the system becomes more compressed and densified by this pressure, the effect of which is consolidation of the soil material. As mentioned earlier, this cohesion, upon the disappearance of the capillary pressure p_c, viz., the disappearance of the surface tension forces, also disappears.

Apparent cohesion permits the excavation of deep cuts in soil without shoring up the excavation walls. However, with an increase in moisture in the voids of the soil the surface tension forces may become destroyed, and after the amount of excess water in the soil has reached a certain magnitude, the walls of the excavation slump out and collapse.

ELECTROKINETICS OF SOIL-WATER SYSTEMS; STRUCTURE OF THE WATER MOLECULE

10-11. Polarity. According to Debye,[11-13] a molecule of water can be represented as a system of electrical charges arranged in a *polar structure.* One would expect that in the polar water molecules electrical poles would exist. Hence, water is designated as a polar substance. Figure 10-10a shows a simplified diagrammatic representation of the geometrical arrangement of the atoms in a polar water molecule. The "plus" and the "minus" poles form a dipole. Therefore, generally, polar molecules are called dipoles.

The property—polarity—of water is very important in that it gives water the ability to support ionization.

Ionization is a process which results in the formation of ions in a certain medium, in this case water. The polarity of water can thus be considered a link in the mechanism of the soil moisture transfer in the moisture film phase.

(a) Simplified representation of a polar
water molecule
The ⊕ and ⊖ poles form a dipole

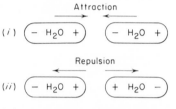

(b) Mutual orientation of polar water
molecules:
(i) Stability (attraction)
(ii) Instability (repulsion)

FIG. 10-10. Diagrammatic illustration of polar water molecules.

FIG. 10-11. Attraction and orientation of dipole water molecules by a positive ion.

10-12. Orientation of Water Molecules. Because of the presence of electrical charges, the polar water molecules have among themselves a mutual electrostatic interaction and orientation, namely, the positive pole of one molecule is attracted to the negative pole of another molecule, and vice versa. For example, in Fig. 10-10b(i) the two molecules attract each other and are said to be stable. Figure 10-10b(ii) indicates a mutual repulsion between two water molecules. They are said to be instable.

As a result of mutual interaction, polar molecules of one and the same substance combine among themselves and form complexes with the ions, leading to associations. Figure 10-11 illustrates the concept of attraction of dipole water molecules by a positive ion called a cation. In the case of a negative ion, the attraction and orientation of dipole water molecules is the converse of that shown in Fig. 10-11. Examples of associating liquids are water, acetone, liquid ammonia, and other ionizing solvents.

10-13. Electrical Charge on Surface of Colloidal Particles. Water molecules forming moisture films, or hulls, around the solid soil particles are not the only factors that are adsorbed on the surfaces of solid soil particles. One of the conspicuous characteristics of a soil particle in a medium of water is that under certain conditions it carries an electrical charge, which, in contrast to heat, tends to reside on its surface.

The charge on the particle is usually the result of adsorption of ions. The soil particles acquire their electric charges from naturally occurring solutions which act as electrolytes, the molecules of which upon solution separate into electrically charged units or ions. The more finely the soil is dispersed, the greater is its specific surface. Consequently, more ions can be accommodated on the surfaces of the soil particles. However, it must be understood that this simple explanation of the manner by which soil colloidal particles acquire their electric charges is far more complex in reality. The charge on the surface of a clay colloid particle in water is usually negative.[14]

10-14. The Electric Double Layer. If a soil particle immersed in water is considered individually, then from the previous description it can be deduced that the solid particle is surrounded by an *electric double layer*. One layer of this double layer is formed by the negative charge on the surface of the soil colloidal (clay) particle. The negatively charged soil particles tend to surround themselves with an ionic atmosphere, i.e., with ions of the opposite charge (cations), thus forming the second layer of the electrical double layer—the outer layer. This outer layer is formed by the excess of the oppositely charged ions in the solution (water). This means that polar molecules of water may be oriented at the interface between the solid soil particle and the dispersion medium—water.

10-15. Helmholtz's Electric Double Layer. Historically, Quincke[15] suggested that the solid particle in contact with the liquid becomes charged in some way with an electrical charge while in the immediate vicinity of the surface of the solid, but in the liquid there is a layer of electrical charges of the opposite kind, exactly equal in magnitude to the charge on the solid. This was the origin of the so-called *double layer theory* conceived by Quincke, usually called the *Helmholtz double layer* because of the fact that Helmholtz[16] formulated theoretically the concept of the existence of differently charged layers—the so-called electrical double layer—at the solid-liquid interface in a mathematical form expressing the relation between the various physical quantities involved (see Fig. 10-12).

It is also interesting to note that Helmholtz formulated the following: The layer of water molecules in contact with the wall of the solid particles is immobile. It is fixed to the wall regardless of the physical forces imposed on the liquid. That is, there is no slip. The rest of the molecules in the double layer are mobile and subject to the ordinary laws of friction of normal liquids.

10-16. Zeta (ζ) Potential. It was seen that, in general, when two phases—solid and liquid—come in contact, there is a separation of charges: one phase becomes negative in respect to the other. This separation of charges gives rise to an electric potential difference or a potential gradient at the interface between the two phases. According to Helmholtz, the gradient of this potential drop across the double layer is sharp and it varies linearly with distance (Fig. 10-12a).

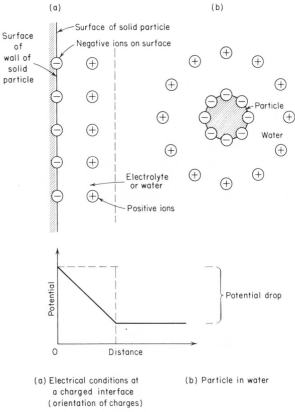

FIG. 10-12. The Quincke-Helmholtz electrical double layer.

The electric potential across the double layer is called the *electrokinetic* or *zeta potential*.

It is the potential difference created at the interface upon the mutual relative movement of two phases which is called the electrokinetic or zeta potential. This means that the electrokinetic potential can be measured only under conditions of phases in motion relative to each other, i.e., when electrokinetic processes are taking place. Up to now, the ζ-potential can be determined only indirectly.

The concept that the colloidal soil particles carry an electrical charge might give one the mistaken impression that the soil represents an aggregate of statically charged ideal spheres, and that an electroscope, therefore, when brought close to the soil (in situ, or a laboratory sample), would show a deflection. However, this is not so. It has to be remembered from the previous discussion that the electrical charges in the system are self-compensating. This principle finds its validity in the idea of the electrical double layer.

10-17. Gouy Double Layer. Gouy[17] thought that the charges of one sign in the liquid side of the Helmholtz double layer would attract charges of opposite sign. This attraction, in its turn, would cause a nonuniform distribution of the charges in the liquid near the solid-liquid interface that Helmholtz proposed.

Gouy's ideas about the electrical conditions at the solid-liquid interface are principally as follows: The rigid part of the electric double layer lies in the liquid adhering firmly to the surface of the solid particle; the second part lies in the mobile part of the liquid and extends into the homogeneous interior of the liquid.

Movement of the liquid takes place against the liquid adhering firmly to the surface of the solid, and thus the charge is imbedded in it, but not against the solid surface directly. At very low temperatures ions are rigidly adsorbed on the surface, thus forming a true Helmholtz layer. With increase in temperature —the room temperature, for example—a large amount of the adsorbed ions "dissipate" from the surface. However, these ions are unable to escape entirely from the influence of the charge on the wall.

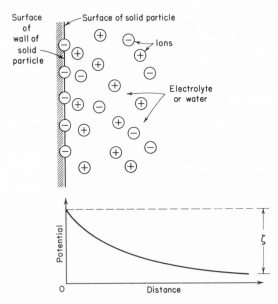

FIG. 10-13. Gouy-Chapman electric diffuse double layer.

Owing to these circumstances a *diffuse* double layer results, where the negative charges are adsorbed primarily near the surface or wall of the solid particle, but the positive ions farther away from the wall. The ionic atmosphere in the immediate vicinity of the surface is fairly dense, and at greater distances from the surface the ionic density decreases until the net charge density is zero.

While not all the ions in the diffuse double layer are of the opposite sign from those at the surface of the solid, the ions of opposite sign do predominate. Thus Gouy and Chapman[18] imagined the double layer as a diffuse distribution of electrification, an "ionic atmosphere." Also, Gouy supposed that the double layer frequently extends considerably farther out from the solid surface into the liquid phase than a distance of one molecule. The Gouy-Chapman diffuse double layer and the drop in zeta potential are illustrated diagrammatically in Fig. 10-13.

The thickness of the double layer, according to Rutgers,[19] is of the order of 10^{-6} or 10^{-7} cm.

Because the diffuse layer extends some distance into the water phase, it is necessary in soil moisture migration studies, particularly upon freezing, to take

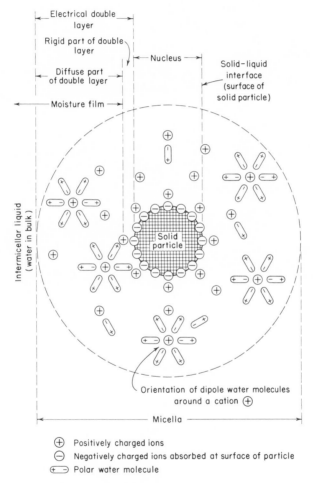

FIG. 10-14.   Schematic sketch of a colloidal micella.

into account the dielectric constant of water. This constant may probably be assigned the value it has in pure water.

When solid particles such as those of a colloidal clay are dispersed in liquids, as may occur with soil *in situ*, then there are many individual systems which consist of a charged nucleus surrounded by an adsorbed and more-or-less extended diffuse ionic atmosphere (Fig. 10-14).

ELECTRO-OSMOSIS

10-18. Fundamental Principle. The term *electro-osmosis* is used to describe the electrokinetic phenomenon of liquid (water) moving through a system of a porous medium relative to a fixed solid (i.e., the colloidal soil particles are prevented from moving) under the influence of a primary, externally applied electrical field. The derivation of this term is based on an analogy with osmotic phenomena which take place through organic and inorganic membranes, diaphragms, or porous plugs. Therefore such a movement of liquids through a porous plug under the influence of an electric potential is called "electric osmosis" or electro-osmosis. The porous system, such as soil, may be thought of as bundles of complicated, interconnecting passages of diverse ways.

From the foregoing discussion it can be understood that in electro-osmosis the mechanism for the translocation of soil moisture is possible due to the existence of the electric diffuse double layer in a moist soil system. The application of an electric potential to the soil system results in the displacement of the charged mobile moisture films relative to the immobile ones. Because the mobile part of the moisture film is free to move, whereas the soil particles are not, a flow of moisture takes place. The direction of moisture flow depends upon whether water is charged with positive or negative ions.

With the introduction of the dielectric constant in the Helmholtz double layer theory by Smoluchowski in 1893,[20] the Helmholtz theory by and large is still valid, particularly as a special case, or as a component part in other theories.

10-19. Application of Electro-osmosis in Engineering. The application of the electro-osmotic phenomenon to soil and foundation engineering has been studied by Leo Casagrande,[21,22] Schaad and Haefeli,[23] Winterkorn,[24] Vey,[25] Preece,[26] and others.

Electro-osmosis is utilized for dewatering silty and clayey soils difficult to drain by gravity. These soils cannot be drained easily by gravity because the relatively large surface tension forces of water in such soils tend to retain water in their voids.

Dewatering of soil is pursued to facilitate laying of foundations in a dry pit or excavation, for the stabilization of soil in natural or artificial slopes, and for other purposes.

The principle of dewatering fine-particled soils electrically is illustrated in Fig. 10-15. To keep the excavation dry, positive electrodes (anodes) in the form of rods are installed near the toes of the slopes of the excavation. The negative electrodes (cathodes) are installed in the soil mass away from the slopes of the cut and are made in the form of perforated pipes resembling a well-point. Their function is to collect the water flowing from the positive electrode when there exists in the soil an electric field between the electrodes, i.e., a D.C. circuit. The collected water in the negative electrode is pumped out and discharged.

One well-known example in engineering practice and technical literature of the successful application of electro-osmosis in soil mechanics is the dewatering of a silt with unfavorable physical properties by the Germans during the Second

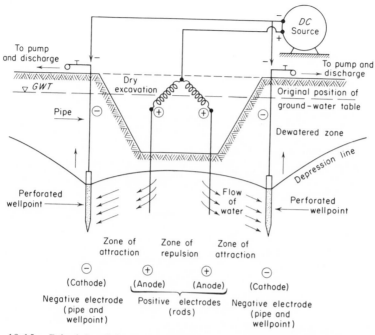

FIG. 10-15.   Principle of dewatering of a fine-particled soil by electro-osmosis.

World War at Trondheim, Norway, for the construction of their U-boat pens (see Ref. 22).

The volume V of water moved per unit of time by electro-osmosis is directly proportional to the applied electric current, the dielectric constant, and inversely proportional to the viscosity and electro-conductivity of water:

$$V = \frac{\zeta DI}{4\pi\eta\lambda} \quad (\text{cm}^3/\text{s}),$$ (10-7)

where ζ = zeta potential,
D = dielectric constant of water,
I = current,
η = dynamic viscosity of water,
λ = specific conductivity of water.

If the current is kept constant, the flow of water is independent of the length and area of the capillaries. Note that all these factors are functions of temperature.

10-20. Streaming Potential. In electro-osmosis, the application of a primary electrical potential causes in a moist porous system (which may be imagined as a fixed porous plug inside an imaginary cylinder) the motion of the liquid relative to the fixed solids.

Conversely, the motion of a liquid forced mechanically through a fixed porous plug, say a clay diaphragm, by means of a certain energy (heat energy, for example), induces an electrical potential difference or electromotive force,

E.M.F., between the two ends of the plug. A process of soil moisture translocation brought about by means of a primary thermal potential is termed *thermoosmosis*.

Because the film liquid is electrically charged, the translocation of the liquid through the porous soil system is accompanied by an induced electric current. The electric diffuse double layer is swept along by the flow of the mobile film water, so that opposite charges are built up at opposite ends of the system of the porous plug. This induced electric potential difference in a thermo-osmotic process is termed the *streaming potential*, which may be regarded as the converse phenomenon of electro-osmosis.

Hence it can be expected that an externally applied primary potential, for example, a thermal potential, will induce between the two ends of the porous system a secondary potential, namely an electric potential, upon displacing the mobile film. This principle was discovered by Quincke in 1859. The streaming liquid displaces the positive charges of the water molecules relative to the solid particles and thus induces an electrical potential along the height of the column of the moist, porous soil system. The induced E.M.F. is related to the zeta-potential.[27] Similarly, the amounts of moisture film transferred are thus connected with the zeta-potential. This phenomenon, converse to electro-osmosis, seems to be less known to the engineering profession than electro-osmosis. Yet the phenomenon of induced electric potentials gives an important basis on which to rest the theory of the mechanism for the translocation of soil moisture in the film phase (unsaturated flow), particularly upon freezing.

The induced streaming potential E_s by a thermal gradient is expressed as

$$E_s = \frac{\xi PD}{4\pi\eta\lambda} \quad \text{(volts)}, \tag{10-8}$$

where all symbols are the same as in electro-osmosis, and $P =$ net pressure necessary to stop the flow. This pressure is also called the *thermo-osmotic* or *driving pressure* of water.

REFERENCES

1. F. Zunker, *Bautechnik*, Berlin, Springer, 1935, p. 74.
2. L. G. Briggs, "Absorption of Water Vapor and Certain Salts in Aqueous Solution by Quartz," *Journal of Physical Chemistry*, 1905, vol. 9, pp. 617-64.
3. S. Odén, "Note on the Hygroscopicity of Clay and the Quantity of Water Adsorbed per Surface Unit," *Transactions of the Faraday Society*, London, 1921, vol. 17, pp. 18-21.
4. A.R. Jumikis, "Some Concepts Pertaining to the Soil Freezing Systems," *HRB Special Report No. 40* (International Water Symposium). National Academy of Sciences, Washington, D.C., 1958, pp. 178-190.
5. A.R. Jumikis, "Upward Migration of Soil Moisture by Various Mechanisms Upon Freezing," *Proceedings*, International Conference on Low Temperature Science, held at Institute of Low Temperature Science, Hokkaido University, Sapporo, Japan, August, 1966, *Part 2, Physics of Snow and Ice*, Hokkaido University, 1967, pp. 1387-1399.

6. A.R. Jumikis, *Thermal Soil Mechanics.* Rutgers University Press, New Brunswick, New Jersey, 1966, pp. 12-13.

7. A.R. Jumikis, *Thermal Geotechnics.* Rutgers University Press, New Brunswick, New Jersey, 1977.

8. N.E. Dorsey, *Properties of Ordinary Water-Substance*, Reinhold Publishing Corp., New York, 1940.

9. F. Zunker, "Das Verhalten des Bodens zum Wasser." Blanck's *Handbuch der Bodenlehre*, Die physikalische Beschaffenheit des Bodens, Berlin, Julius Springer, 1930, vol. 6, p. 70.

10. National Research Council: *International Critical Tables of Numerical Data, Physics, Chemistry, and Technology*, 1st ed., vol. 4, New York, McGraw-Hill Book Co., 1929.

11. P. J. W. Debye, *The Collected Papers of P. J. W. Debye*, New York, Interscience Publishers, Inc., 1954.

12. P. J. W. Debye, "The Structure of Matter," trans. by F. M. Denton, *The University of New Mexico Bulletin*, Albuquerque, N.M., 1934, vol. 1, no. 2, October 1, 1934.

13. P. J. W. Debye, *Polar Molecules*, New York, The Chemical Catalog Co., Inc., 1929.

14. F. F. Reuss, "Sur Un Nouvel Effet de l'Électricité Galvanique." Notice lue le 15 Avril 1808, *Mémoires* de la Societé Impériale Des Naturalistes de Moscou, 1809, à Moscou, de l'Imprimerie de l'Université Impériale, vol. 2, pp. 327-337.

15. G. Quincke, "Über die Fortführung materieller Teilchen durch strömende Elektrizität." Poggendorffs *Annalen der Physik und Chemie*, J. A. Barth, Leipzig, 1861, vol. 113, no. 8, pp. 513-598.

16. H. Helmholtz, "Studien über electrische Grenzschichten," G. Wiedemann's *Annalen der Physik und Chemie*. J. A. Barth, Leipzig, 1879. Neue Folge, vol. 7, pp. 337-382.

17. M. Gouy, "Sur la Constitution de la Charge Electrique à la Surface d'un Electrolyte," *Journal de Physique Théoretique et Appliquée*, Paris, 1910, vol. 9, pp. 457-468.

18. D. L. Chapman, "A Contribution to the Theory of Electrocapillarity, Sixth Series," *The London, Edinburgh, and Dublin Philosophical Magazine and Journal of Science*, April 1913, vol. 25, no. 148, pp. 475-481.

19. A. J. Rutgers, *Physical Chemistry*, New York, Interscience Publishers, Inc., 1954.

20. M. Smoluchowski, "Elektrische Endosmose und Strömungsströme," in Graetz's *Handbuch der Elektrizität und des Magnetismus*, J. A. Barth, Leipzig, 1914, vol. 2, p. 366.

21. L. Casagrande, *Die elektrische Entwässerung feinkörniger Böden*, Deutsche Wasserwirtschaft, 1941, vol. 36, pp. 556-559.

22. L. Casagrande, *The Application of Electro-osmosis to Practical Problems in Foundations and Earthworks.* Building Research Technical Paper no. 30, H.M. Stationery Office, London, 1947.

23. W. Schaad, and R. Haefeli, *Elektrokinetische Erscheinungen und ihre Anwendung in der Bodenmechanik*, no. 13, Mitteilungen aus der Versuchsanstalt für Wasserbau und Erdbau an der Eidgenössischen Technischen Hochschule in Zürich, Leeman und Co., 1947.

24. H. F. Winterkorn, "Fundamental Similarities between Electro-osmotic and Thermo-osmotic Phenomena," *Proceedings*, 27th Annual Meeting of the Highway Research Board, held at Washington, D.C., December 2-5, 1947, pp. 443-454.

25. E. Vey, "The Mechanics of Soil Consolidation by Electro-osmosis," *Proceedings*, 29th Annual Meeting of the Highway Research Board, held at Washington, D.C., December 13-16, 1949, pp. 579-589.

26. E. F. Preece, "Geotechnics and Geotechnical Research," *Proceedings*, 27th Annual Meeting of the Highway Research Board, held at Washington, D.C., December 2-5, 1947, pp. 384-416.

27. A. E. Alexander, and P. Johnson, *Colloid Science*, Oxford, The Clarendon Press, 1949, vol. 1, pp. 340-343.

SUGGESTIONS FOR FURTHER READING

1. L. Bjerrum, J. Moum and O. Eide, "Application of Electro-osmosis to a Foundation Problem in a Norvegian Quick Clay," Géotechnique, vol. 17, 1967, pp. 214-235.
2. L. Casagrande, "Review of Past and Current Work on Electro-osmotic Stabilization of Soils." Harvard Soil Mechanics Series No. 45, 1957.
3. L. Casagrande, "Practical Aspects of Electro-Osmosis in Foundation Engineering," Proceedings, First Pan American Conference of Soil Mechanics and Foundation Engineering, held September 9 to 12, 1959 at Mexico, D.F., vol. 1. Published by Sociedad Mexicana de Mecanica de Suelos, 1960, Mexico, D.F., Mexico, pp. 217-234.
4. L. Casagrande, R.W. Loughney and M.A. Matich, "Electro-osmotic Stabilization of a High Slope in Loose Saturated Silt." Proceedings Fifth International Conference on Soil Mechanics and Foundation, Paris, Dunod, vol. 2, 1961, pp. 555-561.
5. C.A. Fetzer, "Electro-osmotic Stabilization of West Branch Dam," Proceedings, ASCE, Journal of the Soil Mechanics and Foundations Division, vol. 93, No. SM4, 1967, pp. 85-106.
6. D.H. Gray and J.K. Mitchel, "Fundamental Aspects of Electro-osmosis in Soils," Proceedings ASCE, Journal of the Soil Mechanics and Foundations Division, vol. 93, No. SM 6, 1967, pp. 209-236.
7. A.R. Jumikis, "Thermo-Osmotic Soil Moisture Transfer Upon Freezing." Advanced Concepts and Techniques in the Study of Snow and Ice Resources. An Interdisciplinary Symposium held at Asilomar Conference Grounds, Monterey, California, December 2-6, 1973. — A United States Contribution to the International Hydrological Decade. National Academy of Sciences, Washington, D.C., July, 1974, pp. 119-134.
8. A.R. Jumikis and W.A. Slusarchuk, "Electrical Parameters of Some Frost-Prone Soils." Advanced Concepts and Techniques in the Study of Snow and Ice Resources. An Interdisciplinary Symposium held at Asilomar Conference Grounds, Monterey, California, December 2-6, 1973. — A United States Contribution to the International Hydrological Decade. National Academy of Sciences, Washington, D.C., July, 1974, pp. 765-781.
9. D. Kirkham and W.L. Powers, Advanced Soil Physics. New York, N.Y.: John Wiley and Sons, Inc., 1972.
10. T. Mise, "Electro-osmotic Dewatering of Soil and Distribution of the Pore Water Pressure," Proceedings of the Fifth International Conference on Soil Mechanics and Foundation Engineering, Paris, Dunod, vol. 1, 1961, pp. 255-257.
11. H.F. Winterkorn, "Water Movement Through Porous Hydrophilic Systems Under Capillary, Electric and Thermal Potentials," ASTM Special Technical Publication No. 163, 1955, Philadelphia, pp. 27-35.
12. R.N. Yong and B.P. Warkentin, Soil Properties and Behaviour, Amsterdam/Oxford/New York, N.Y.: Elsevier Scientific Publishing Company, 1975.

QUESTIONS AND PROBLEMS

10- 1. Distinguish between various kinds of soil moisture.

10- 2. Distinguish between groundwater and perched groundwater.

10- 3. Why does water rise in a capillary tube?

10- 4. How high will water rise in a capillary tube?

10- 5. In what direction does capillary moisture generally flow?

10- 6. Distinguish between water in bulk and film water.

10- 7. What happens to the capillary fringe if the soil becomes inundated?

10- 8. Why does groundwater flow?

10- 9. What is surface tension?

10-10. Explain the performance of Daytona Beach sand used for automobile races.

10-11. If the angle of wetting is zero, and the surface tension of water at $4°C$ is $\sigma = 75.06$ dynes per cm, and the capillary diameter is 0.10 mm, calculate, in centimeters, the height h of the capillary rise.

10-12. In what condition is the capillary system if the angle of wetting is zero?

10-13. What are the applications of the capillary tube theory to soil engineering?

Chapter 11

FROST ACTION IN SOILS

11-1. Frost Problems in Soil. In fine-particled soils, particularly in silts, the moisture of the upward capillary and/or film flow, if frost penetrates downward into the capillary fringe, forms ice lenses under certain freezing conditions. The growing ice lenses expand and cause frost heaves and frost boils which can be very detrimental to highway and airfield runway pavements, to sheeted excavations, and to the stability of slopes of cuts and fills (Fig. 11-1).

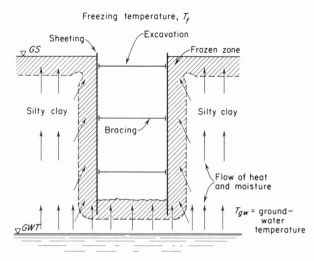

FIG. 11-1. Freezing of soil around a sheeted excavation.

Experience shows that shortly after the thawing of the soil beneath the pavement, the soil loses its bearing capacity for a certain period of time. This phenomenon is known as the "spring break-up" (Figs. 11-2 and 11-3).

Highway engineers have observed for quite some time the phenomenon of accumulation in large quantities of soil moisture underneath road pavements as a consequence of frost action. Naturally, the question arises: where does all this water come from?

Although the process of moisture migration through a porous medium such as fine-particled frost-prone soil is a relatively slow one, a considerable amount of

FIG. 11-2.   Spring "break-up" on earth roads.

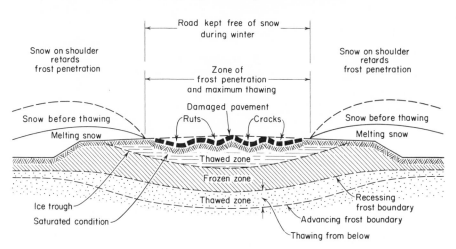

FIG. 11-3.   Sketch illustrating freezing and thawing damage to a road. Thawing
causes spring "break-up."

soil moisture may translocate from groundwater upward to the cold front
(= 0° C isothermal surface) during a relatively long period of time (winter
season, for example). However, it is the slow but long process of soil moisture
flow which often is overlooked and forgotten, and which is one of the main
factors in the moisture migration phenomenon in a freezing soil, where the
danger of damage by frost to roads, railroads and airport runways lies. Thus it
can be inferred that frost action imposes difficulties in design, construction,
exploitation, and maintenance of roads. It also impairs traffic safety. In addition,
repairs to roads damaged by frost usually cost huge sums. It becomes necessary,
therefore, in highway and airport engineering, to estimate, among other factors,

the frost penetration depth in soil to provide either for proper insulation or adequate drainage courses underneath the pavement to take care of the thawing waters, and to determine the necessary amount by which the groundwater table should be lowered.

The silty A-4 and clayey A-7-6 soils are most susceptible to frost action, resulting in large frost heaves and loss in soil bearing capacity upon thawing. The granular A-1-b and A-3 soils show the least amount of heaves and loss in bearing capacity upon thawing.

Because silt particles are small enough to provide a comparatively high capillary rise, and, at the same time, large enough to furnish voids of such a size as to allow a quick flow of moisture through the silt, silt absorbs moisture rapidly. This phenomenon causes, in turn, a rapid saturation of the voids of the soil, which subsequently results in rapid loss of bearing capacity of the silty soil.

11-2. Factors Contributing to Freezing Soils. Some of the factors which affect the frost action in soil are 1) the soil type itself; 2) proximity of groundwater (or perched groundwater); 3) the initial soil temperature; 4) the air temperature above the ground surface (microclimate); exposure, thermal and solar radiation, vegetative cover, type of pavement cover on the soil, dept of snow (insulating cover) on the soil, if any, and the density of the snow. When a soil is subjected to freezing temperatures, several phenomena take place, the intensity of which depends upon the intensity of freezing temperatures:

1) Moisture is translocated by upward flow from the groundwater to the growing ice lenses (change in soil moisture content).
2) Upon freezing, water is converted to ice (change in phase). On freezing, water increases by 9 % in volume.
3) Frost penetrates the soil.
4) Upon penetrating the soil, frost causes frost heaves (change in volume of soil) on the soil or ground surface and pavements.

11-3. Theoretical Considerations on the Freezing Soil System. The changes induced by surface temperature T_s are usually effectuated by a temperature potential as a driving force.[1-8] The freezing soil system is illustrated in Fig. 11-4.

If a vertical column of a soil system is subjected to freezing from its top downward, as occurs in highway soils in winter, several changes take place in the following manner. A curvilinear temperature gradient, $\partial T/\partial x$, sets in across the freezing soil system from the top down, Fig. 11-5. There takes place an upward heat transfer from a region of higher temperature T_g, in the soil system (groundwater) toward a region of colder temperature T_f (frozen layer of soil, for example). The thermal energy, in turn, initiates the upward migration of soil moisture in the porous soil system. A soil-water-temperature system is shown in Fig. 11-6.

Upon freezing of the soil moisture, latent heat is released. Similarly, the thermal properties of soil, water, and ice change, as do the density, viscosity, and dielectric constant of the water.

Some Modes of Soil Moisture Translocation Upon Freezing. Depending upon the state of packing of the soil, soil moisture can be translocated upward through the porous medium of soil upon freezing by one or another mechanism : 1) as a vapor, 2) as a liquid (in bulk or by film), or 3) in a simultaneous combination of vapor and liquid.

The manner in which the soil moisture migrates through a porous medium such as soil during a freezing process is termed "the mechanism" of moisture transfer.

Vapor Diffusion. If the voids of the soil are relatively large, and there is no continuous moisture in the liquid form in the voids connecting the groundwater with the downward freezing ice lenses, then the soil moisture from the groundwater is transported upward by way of the mechanism of vapor diffusion. Here the driving pressure is the vapor pressure difference between the vapor pressure at the warmer end of the freezing soil system (the free water surface = groundwater table) and the vapor pressure in the upper region of the soil system just below the ice, where it can be very small or even negligible compared with that of the free surface.[4-9] This is to say that moisture migration takes place in the

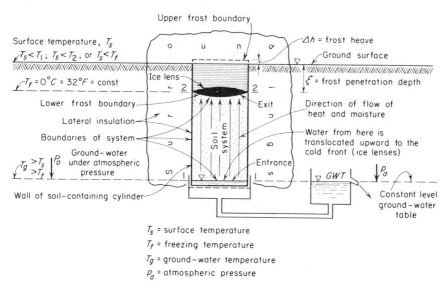

T_s = surface temperature
T_f = freezing temperature
T_g = ground-water temperature
P_a = atmospheric pressure

FIG. 11-4.   Freezing soil system.

direction along the drop of the thermal gradient. The vapor pressure decreases from the groundwater table up curvilinearly as the temperature decreases from the groundwater up to the freezing isothermal surface.

11-4. Water Film Transport. In a very dense, close packing of soil (for which there is a theoretical and practical limit), where the soil particles are packed so close to each other (small porosity) that the moisture around and between the soil particles forms uninterrupted liquid films through the entire soil system down to the groundwater supply, then, depending upon the texture of the soil (whether silt, silty clay, clayey silt, or clay) the water film transport mechanism becomes

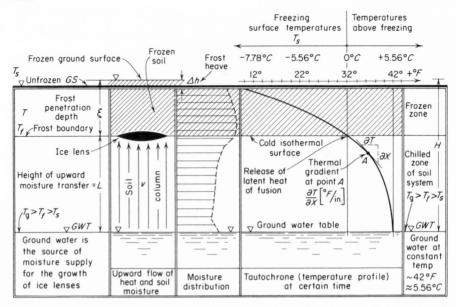

FIG. 11-5. Sketch illustrating the concept of unidirectional upward flow of soil moisture upon freezing. Open system.

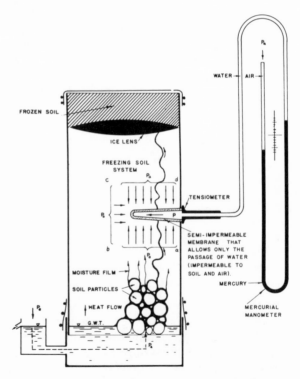

FIG. 11-6. Soil-water-temperature system.

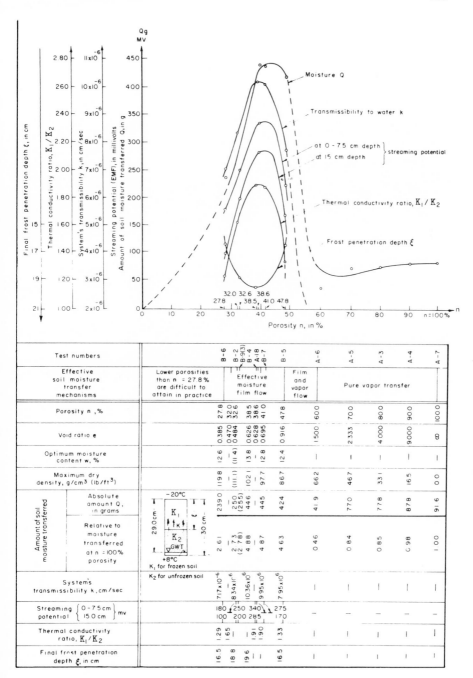

FIG. 11-7.   Soil moisture transfer upon freezing as a function of soil porosity. Author's
study.

more effective than that of the vapor mechanism (Fig. 11-7). The process of the upward moisture translocation via the moisture films in the freezing soil is slow. Note that in the film-transport mechanism, the ice lenses are connected via the moisture films with the groundwater (or perched groundwater) supply, Figs. 11-7 and 11-8.

If there is no groundwater present, the soil freezing is then a drying process until all of the soil moisture has been transferred to the freezing isothermal region.

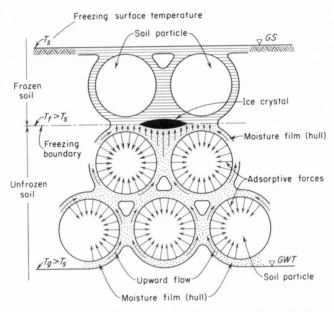

FIG. 11-8. Sketch illustrating the concept of the upward flow of soil moisture film toward an ice crystal.

11-5. Combination of Various Modes of Moisture Transport. Depending upon the texture and gradation of the soil, and the degree of packing, or the presence of a multilayered soil-system, a combination of the various soil moisture transport mechanisms may exist simultaneously upon freezing. For example, with large porosities, it is more likely that upward soil moisture transport in the vapor phase will be more effective than a film flow. In a densely packed clayey silt or silty clay the water film-transport mechanism may be more effective than vapor flow. Between the maximum possible and minimum possible densities, for different textures of soil, and in various combinations other than gravel and clay, there may set in several upward soil moisture transfer mechanisms in various proportions. There are no sharply defined boundaries between the various modes of moisture transport mechanisms and processes. It is quite reasonable to assume, rather, that a transition from one mode to another constitutes the combination of the simultaneously acting various modes of transport.

11-6. Ice Segregation. The amount of segregated ice in a frozen soil system (number, thickness, and distribution of visible ice layers or lenses) depends very much upon the intensity and rate of freezing. When the frost-prone soil system is frozen quickly, say 20 cm of frost penetration in three days at a temperature difference of 25° C between surface and groundwater, no ice layers are visible. The whole soil sample may be frozen solidly through. But upon splitting the soil sample longitudinally immediately after the test, examination of the frozen soil sample by eye or with the aid of a magnifying glass does not reveal any ice segregation in layers, although the moisture content in the soil after the freezing experiment is larger than before the experiment, and the moisture content is larger at the ends of the soil cylinder than at its mid-height. Slow freezing, on the contrary, brings about clearly visible ice layers of various thicknesses (see Fig. 11-9).

FIG. 11-9.   Segregated ice in a frozen soil system.
Author.

11-7. Frost Penetration Depth. J. Stefan (see Refs. 1, 4, 7) gives a simple formula for the formation of ice in calm water. This formula can be applied for computing approximately the frost penetration depth ξ in soil as a function of time t:

$$\xi = \sqrt{(2K_1/Q_L)\ (T_f\text{-}T_s)t} \quad (m), \tag{11-1}$$

where K_1 = thermal conductivity of frozen soil, in Cal/(m)(h)($^\circ$C);

$Q_L = L{\cdot}w{\cdot}\gamma_d$ = total amount of volumetric latent heat of fusion for ice per unit weight, in Cal/kg;

T_f = Freezing temperature = 0°C;

T_s = temperature at the road or ground surface, in $^\circ$C;

t = time, in hours; viz., duration of frost; and

w = total amount of water in % by dry weight of soil;

Stefan's formula is good when the conditions are such that the temperature gradient in the frozen zone (ice layer) is linear, the soil moisture present is motionless, and the surface temperature (air temperature) or the temperature of the microclimate T_s, is constant.

Example. Calculate the frost penetration depth ξ by means of Stefan's approximation using technical metric and SI units. Also, compute the rate of frost penetration.

Given: K_1 = 2.0 Cal/(m)(h)($^\circ$C) = (8.37358)(10^3)(N$\cdot$m)/(m)(h)($^\circ$C) =
  = thermal conductivity of frozen soil;

L = 80 Cal/kg = (33.49432)(10^4) J/9.80665N = (3.4154)(10^4)J/N

Q_L = (L)(w)(γ_d) = total amount of volumetric latent heat in
  Calories or Joules per one unit of volume
  (= 1 m^3) =
  (80)(4.18679)(10^3)(0.187)(1770);

w = 18.7% = total water content by dry weight of soil;

γ_d = 1770 kg/m^3 = 17357.68 N/m^3 = dry unit weight of soil;

T_f = 0°C = freezing temperature of water;

T_s = -10°C = surface temperature;

t = 6 days = 144 hours = duration of freezing.

Then, by Equation (11-1), using technical metric units, the frost penetration depth ξ is

$$\xi = \sqrt{\frac{2K_1}{Q_L} \cdot (T_f\text{-}T_s) \cdot t} = \sqrt{\frac{(2)(2.0)[0\text{-}(\text{-}10)]}{(80)(0.187)(1770)}} \cdot \sqrt{144} = \underline{0.47\ [m]}.$$

Using the SI units,

$$\xi = \sqrt{\frac{(2)(8.37358)(10^3)[0\text{-}(\text{-}10)](144)}{(80)(4.18679)(10^3)(0.187)(1770)}} = \underline{0.47\ [m]}.$$

The first derivative of ξ with respect to time t, gives the rate of the frost penetration:

$$\frac{d\xi}{dt} = \sqrt{\frac{K_1 \cdot (T_f\text{-}T_s)}{2 \cdot Q_L}} \cdot \frac{1}{\sqrt{t}}$$

$$= \sqrt{\frac{(2.0)[0\text{-}(\text{-}10)]}{(2)(80)(0.187)(1770)}} \cdot \frac{1}{\sqrt{144}} = \underline{0.0056\ [\frac{m}{h}]}$$

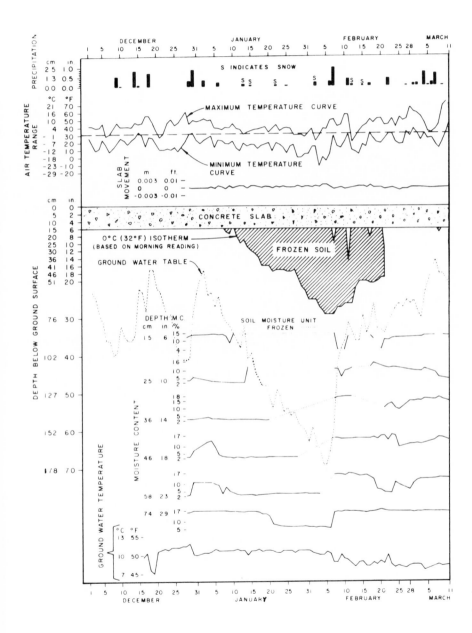

SLAB T.R.B. A-3

FIG. 11-10a. Changes in sandy soil (A-3) upon freezing

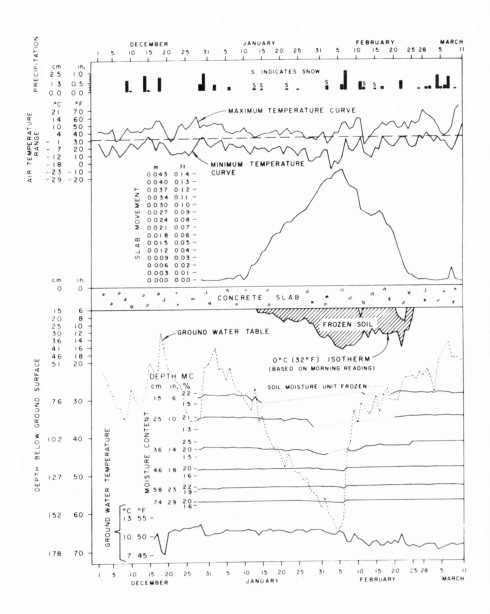

SLAB T.R.B. A-4

Fig. 11-10b. Changes in silty soil (A-4) upon freezing.

11-8. Outdoor-laboratory Soil Freezing Tests. Figures 11-10a, 11-10b and 11-10c show results obtained from outdoor-laboratory natural soil freezing tests on A-3, A-4 and A-5 soils. These figures show the relationship between time and precipitation, air temperature (microclimate) slab displacement (heave), frost penetration depth, variation in soil moisture content, position and fluctuation of groundwater table, and groundwater temperature. These soil materials were studied under the same natural environmental conditions in the outdoor-laboratory installation at Rutgers University. Under natural freezing conditions these base course materials would perform as a base course would when placed into the road structure. The winter during which these tests were performed is characterized as medium severe—158 deg. C-days.

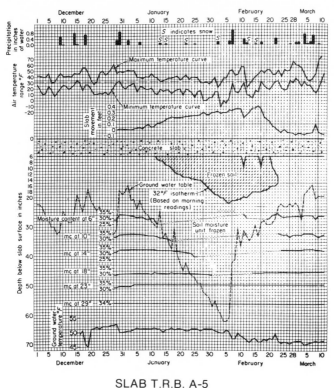

SLAB T.R.B. A-5

FIG. 11-10c. Changes in a sandy-silt-clay soil (A-5) upon freezing.

The experimental data in Figs. 11-10a, b and c, reveal that

1) the elevation of the groundwater table is a direct function of precipitation. During the period of these freezing tests, the groundwater temperature varied between 7.8°C and 11.7°C;

2) the greatest depth and rate of frost penetration occurs in the granular soil (A-3) because of its large coefficient of thermal conductivity as compared with that of the fine-particled soils (A-4 and A-5);

3) the frozen soil thaws from top and bottom. This is of particular importance

because the high rate of thawing beneath pavement slabs may bring about trough (thaw-bowls) of thawed soil at high entrapped meltwater content from which troughs the meltwater has no free passage to drain sideway because of the still unthawed, encompassing frozen soil. Traffic loads ultimately may finish pavements over saturated soils. This observation implies a longitudinal and lateral drainage problem concerning base and subbase courses;

4) the greatest frost penetration depth does not necessarily occur at the same time as the minimum microclimate temperature occurs;

5) the granular material (sand, A-3 soil) shows the least amount of frost heave and loss in bearing capacity upon thawing;

6) the silty A-4 soil is the most susceptible to frost action, resulting in large frost heaves and loss in bearing capacity;

7) the clayey soil (A-5) experienced a relatively moderate heave as compared with the silt soil (A-4);

8) maximum frost heaving does not necessarily occur simultaneously with the maximum depth of frost penetration;

9) the fine-particled soils normally retained higher moisture contents than the sandy soil;

10) the advantage of outdoor-laboratory soil freezing tests may be seen in that all processes are induced naturally by a natural thermal gradient. The freezing soil system works in its entirety comprehending all of the environmental factors including thermal radiation from the surface, cloudiness of the sky, geothermal heat, evaporation, various potentials and their effects - although some of the factors may be masked out - which all contribute to the total or net amount of the upward flow of soil moisture, freezing, ice segregation, and consequent frost heaving and soil thawing.

11-9. Criteria for Evaluating the Susceptibility of a Soil to Frost. Frost criteria serve to identify and evaluate in advance, by simple means, the frost susceptibility of soils used for engineering purposes.

Among other criteria, those by Taber[10] and A. Casagrande[11] are the better known. Taber showed that "the size of soil particles is one of the most important factors controlling segregation of ice during freezing." For the upper limit Taber gives the particle size of 0.07 mm which, under favorable conditions, is able to produce ice layers. Casagrande's frost criterion has already been given in Chapter 9, and therefore will not be repeated here.

Beskow,[12] after extensive laboratory experiments with Swedish soils, tried to separate frost-susceptible soils form non-frost-susceptible ones by means of soil particle size and height of capillary rise.

Although any one of these frost criteria makes possible a diagnosis of frost susceptibility of the particular soil under consideration, none of them indicates the degree of frost susceptibility and its intensity.

In construction work, however, it is very often desirable to know the depth to which frost may be expected to penetrate the soil in a given locality, and to predict the amount of heaving. Therefore, it is necessary to introduce the quantitative concept of a "degree of frost danger" η.

This characteristic can be found experimentally in the laboratory by determining the rate of heave, $\Delta h/t$ (cm/h), and the rate of frost penetration, ξ/t (cm/h). The quotient of the above two quantities multiplied by 100 % is then defined as the degree of frost danger (or relative frost heave):

$$\eta = (\Delta h/\xi)100\%. \tag{11-3}$$

The greater the degree of frost danger, the greater is the upward flow of soil moisture toward the ice lenses, which means that the heaving is greater.

Unfortunately, no plausible grouping limits for the classification of the degree of frost danger are available at present.

11-10. Some Remedial Measures Against Frost Damage to Roads. The practical objective of remedial measures against frost damage to roads is to try to keep the damage down to a minimum. As to such measures: relocation of a route, replacement of frost-susceptible soils, raising the grade, drainage, lowering groundwater table, insulation courses and membranes, chemical treatment of the soil, and other possible means are generally applied.

It appears that effective drainage is of importance to all soils upon which and of which roads are built.

REFERENCES

1. A. R. Jumikis, *The Frost Penetration Problem in Highway Engineering*, New Brunswick, N.J., Rutgers University Press, 1955.
2. A. R. Jumikis, "The Soil Freezing Experiment," Highway Research Board Bulletin no. 135, *Factors Influencing Ground Freezing*, National Academy of Sciences–National Research Council, Publication 425, Washington, D.C., 1956, pp. 150-165.
3. A. R. Jumikis, "Some Concepts Pertaining to the Freezing Soil Systems," Highway Research Board Special Report no. 40, *Water and its Conduction in Soils*, National Academy of Sciences–National Research Council, Publication 629, Washington, D.C., 1958, pp. 178-190.
4. A.R. Jumikis, *Thermal Soil Mechanics*, New Brunswick, N.J., Rutgers University Press, 1966, pp. 81-100.
5. A.R. Jumikis, *Experimental Studies on Moisture Transfer in a Silty Soil Upon Freezing as a Function of Porosity*, Engineering Research Bulletin No. 49. New Brunswick, N.J., College of Engineering, Rutgers University-The State University of New Jersey, 1969, pp. 34-49.
6. A.R. Jumikis, "Effect of Porosity on Amount of Soil Water Transferred in a Freezing Silt," *Permafrost*: The North American Contribution to the Second International Conference held July 1973 at Yakutsk. National Academy of Sciences, Washington, D.C., 1973, pp. 305-310.
7. A.R. Jumikis, *Thermal Geotechnics*, New Brunswick, N.J.: Rutgers University Press, 1977.
8. A.R. Jumikis, "The Cryogenic System Soil-Water-Temperature." Paper presented at the International Symposium on Frost Action in Soil," held February 16-18, 1977 at the University of Luleå, Sweden.
9. A. R. Jumikis, "Soil Moisture Transfer in the Vapor Phase Upon Freezing," Highway Research Board Bulletin no. 168, *Fundamental and Practical Concepts of Soil Freezing*, National Academy of Sciences–National Research Council, Publication 528, Washington, D.C., 1957, pp. 96-115.

10. S. Taber, "Freezing and Heaving of Road Pavements," *Public Roads*, 1930, p. 118.
11. A. Casagrande, "Discussion on Frost Heaving," *Proceedings*, Highway Research Board, Washington, D.C., 1932, Part I, p. 169.
12. G. Beskow, *Tjälbildningen och Tjällyftningen*, Stockholm, Meddelande 48, Statens Väginstitut, 1935, p. 132, p. 152.

OTHER PERTINENT REFERENCES

D.M. Anderson and A.R. Tice,"Predicting Unfrozen Water Contents in Frozen Soils from Surface Area Measurements." Highway Research Record No. 393, Washington, D.C., 1972, pp. 12-18.

T.C. Johnson, R.L. Berg, K.L. Clarey and C.W. Kaplar, *Roadway Design in Seasonal Frost Areas*. Cold Regions and Engineering Laboratory(CRREL) Technical Report 259. Hanover, New Hampshire, Corps of Army Engineers, U.S. Army (104 pages).

A.R. Tice, D.M. Anderson and A. Banin, *The Prediction of Unfrozen Water Content in Frozen Soils from Liquid Limit Determinations*. CRREL Report 76-8. Corps of Engineers, U.S. Army, Cold Regions Research and Engineering Laboratory (CRREL), Hanover, New Hampshire, 1976.

N.A. Tsytovich, *The Mechanics of Frozen Ground*, translated from the Russian. Edited by G.K. Swinzow. McGraw-Hill Book Company, New York, N.Y., 1975.

A.R. Jumikis, "The Cryogenic System Soil-Water-Temperature." Proceedings of the International Symposium on *Frost Action in Soils*, held February 16-18, 1977 at the University of Luleå, Sweden, vol. 1, pp. 112-120.

A.R. Jumikis, "Outdoor-Laboratory Soil Freezing Experiments," Proceedings of the International Symposium on *Frost Action in Soils*, held February 16-18, 1977, at the University of Luleå, Sweden, vol. 2, pp. 110-119.

A.R. Jumikis, *Glossary of Terms in Thermal Geotechnics*. Engineering Research Publication No. 57. Bureau of Engineering Research; Rutgers, The State University of New Jersey, New Brunswick, New Jersey, 1977, (a book, 159 pages).

A.R. Jumikis, "Cryogenic Texture and Strength Aspects of Artifically Frozen Soils." Proceedings of the *International Symposium on Ground Freezing*, held March 8-10, 1978 at the Ruhr-University-Bochum, Germany, pp. 75-85.

A.R. Jumikis, "Some Aspects of Artificial Thawing of Frozen Soils." Proceedings of the *International Symposium on Ground Freezing*, held March 8-10, 1978 at the Ruhr-University-Bochum, Germany, pp. 183-192.

A.R. Jumikis, "Graphs for Disturbance-Temperature Distribution in Permafrost under Heated Structures." *Proceedings of the 3rd International Conference on Permafrost*, held July 10-13, 1978 at Edmonton, Canada. Published by the National Research Council of Canada, Ottawa, vol. 1, pp. 589-595.

QUESTIONS AND PROBLEMS

11-1. What are the three basic factors necessary for bringing about frost heaves, viz., damage to roads?

11-2. What is the nature of frost damage to roads, to their pavements, and to railroads and canals?

11-3. Describe the various possible soil moisture transfer mechanisms upon freezing.

11-4. Under what conditions do visible ice lenses form in a freezing soil?

11-5. What is a freezing soil system?

11-6. In which soil does *capillary* moisture rise higher, a coarse-particled soil or a fine-particled one? Why?

11-7. What happens to a capillary fringe in a soil if the whole soil profile up to the ground surface becomes inundated?

11-8. Illustrate and describe what happens to an earth road when the frost penetration depth overlaps a part of the capillary fringe?

11-9. Which kind of placing of anti-frost-heave sand layer is correct, on left or right in Fig. Problem 11-9? Why?

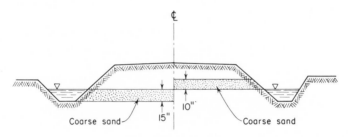

FIG. PROBLEM 11-9.

Chapter 12

GROUNDWATER

12-1. Permeability of Soil. Permeability is defined as the property of a porous material which permits the passage or seepage of fluids, such as water and/or oil, through its interconnecting voids.

The resistance to flow depends upon the type of soil, size and shape of the soil particles (rounded, angular, or flaky), the degree of packing (density of soil), and, thus, upon the size and geometry of the voids. Also, the resistance is a function of the temperature of water (viscosity and surface tension effects).

Soils, the textural sizes of which are smaller than fine gravel, are considered as preventing turbulence. Therefore, for practical purposes in studying groundwater flow through soils, only laminar flow is usually considered. Coarse-textured soils are more pervious than fine-textured soils.

Generally, the groundwater flow may be steady or unsteady, under pressure or under no pressure. An example of pressure flow is artesian water flowing under pressure head between two confining impermeable layers of soil or rock, causing an artesian condition. Seepage underneath a massive dam, or through an earth dam, at the beginning of flow will be of an unsteady nature. Only after some time lag does the flow attain a steady character.

A water flowing with a free, open surface would be under no pressure, or rather, under atmospheric pressure—for example, seepage through an earth dam after the flow has attained a steady character.

Although theoretically all soils are more or less porous, in practice the term "permeable" is applied to soils which are porous enough to permit the flow of water through such a soil. Conversely, soils which permeate with great difficulty are termed "impermeable."

At this point of study, it is good to familiarize oneself with the following concepts and pertinent definitions.

The state of water movement in soil is called *percolation.* The measure of percolation is called *permeability* to water of the soil. The factor relating permeability to unit conditions of control is called the *coefficient of permeability.* It is recognized that temperature and viscosity of water affect the magnitude of the coefficient of permeability k.

In soil mechanics the coefficient of permeability k expresses the degree of permeability of a soil. The coefficient of permeability k has a velocity dimension, in centimeters per second, for example.

12-2. Darcy's Law. The flow of seepage water is calculated by means of

164

Darcy's law of artificial filtration through a uniform, unstratified soil. The quantity v, expressing flow velocity in centimeters per second, is defined as

$$v = ki, \qquad (12\text{-}1)$$

and is termed Darcy's law.[1] It can be seen that the coefficient of permeability k is the filter velocity of laminar flow of water at a hydraulic gradient of $i = 1$. In other words, Darcy's law of permeability of saturated soil ($S = 1$) to water is directly proportional to the hydraulic gradient i. This velocity is the ratio of flow with respect to the unit gross cross-sectional area of the soil cylinder.

The proportionality in Darcy's law is valid for laminar flow up to a certain critical gradient, i_{cr}, at which the flow velocity is critical, v_{cr}, Fig. 12-1. Beyond

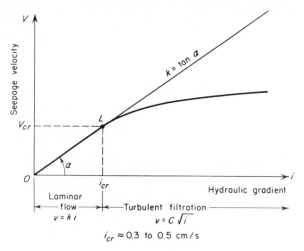

FIG. 12-1   Laminar region of Darcy's law from O to i_{cr}.

point L, where $i > i_{cr}$, the filtration is turbulent, with a seepage velocity, $v > v_{cr}$. In the turbulent region the seepage velocity can be approximately expressed as $v = C\sqrt{i}$, where C is a coefficient characterizing the seepage medium, the soil, and the turbulence of flow. The geometric representation of Darcy's law is shown in Fig. 12-2.

A water particle possesses energy in the following major forms:

potential energy owing to its position, height, or elevation;

pressure energy because of its weight or rather pressure, and also

kinetic energy due to its velocity of flow.

If the velocity of the groundwater flow were zero, then all of the water levels in the piezometric tubes would be at the same elevation, which coincides with the free, horizontal surface of the groundwater. With flowing groundwater, the water level in each of the consecutive piezometric tubes is at a lower elevation than in the preceding one. The difference in these pressure heads, $h = h_1 - h_2$, between both ends of a streamline represents the loss in potential energy along the length, L, used up in overcoming frictional resistance to flow in the voids and in the constrictions in soil.

In order that a flow of water through soil can take place, a driving pressure, p, is needed, viz., a difference in pressure, $p = p_1 - p_2$, between two points on the flow path. The quantity

$$\frac{p}{L} = \frac{p_1 - p_2}{L} = i_p \qquad (12\text{-}2)$$

is termed the pressure gradient.

Because the kinetic energy of the flow of groundwater associated with small seepage velocities is small, in practice it is not taken into consideration in seepage theory.

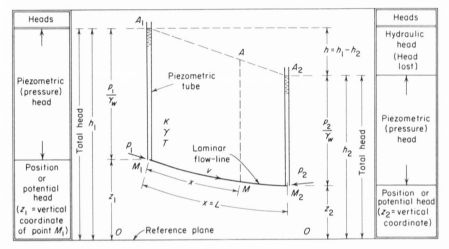

FIG. 12-2 Terminology and geometric representation of Darcy's law $v = kh/L = ki$.

The head lost, h, in overcoming the frictional resistance in soil to seeping water is then, calculated from Fig. 12-2 by means of Bernoulli's principle, that the total head of the energies of a liquid is the sum of potential head, pressure head and velocity head (here $= 0$), as

$$h = \left(z_1 + \frac{p_1}{\gamma_w}\right) - \left(z_2 + \frac{p_2}{\gamma_w}\right) = h_1 - h_2 \qquad (\text{cm}), \qquad (12\text{-}3)$$

where the quantities involved are shown in the figure. Here z_1 and z_2 are position heads, or geodetic heights; p_1/γ_w and p_2/γ_w are piezometric heads (head lost) and $h = h_1 - h_2$ is the hydraulic head.

As seen from Eq. (12-3), Bernoulli's equation for groundwater flow contains terms usually expressing potential energy of flow and loss in head by frictional resistance of soil.

The stress at point M_1 is $u_1 = \gamma_w p_1/\gamma_w = p_1$ in g/cm^2, or kg/cm^2, depending upon the units used. This stress, a hydrostatic water pressure, is termed the *neutral stress*. Similarly, the neutral stress at point M_2 is $u_2 = p_2$.

Average Flow Velocity. Recall that in hydraulics, the flow velocity v of water is expressed as

$$v = \frac{Q}{A} = \frac{\text{discharge in volume per unit time}}{\text{area of the soil through which flow takes place}} = ki \quad \text{(cm/s)},$$

$$(12\text{-}4)$$

where Q = volume of flowing water in cm³ per unit of time, which in hydraulics is called the discharge, and

A = gross cross-sectional area, in cm², for which the discharge is calculated.

Total Discharge. The total discharge Q of the permeating water through a soil, the gross cross-sectional area of which is A, and during time t in seconds, is

$$Q = vAt = kiAt \quad \text{(cm}^3\text{)}.$$

$$(12\text{-}4a)$$

For example, if the seepage velocity at a given hydraulic gradient is $v = 0.35$ cm/s, and the cross-sectional area through which seepage takes place is $A = 10 \text{ cm} \times 60 \text{ cm} = 600 \text{ cm}^2$, then during one day (=86,400 s) the discharge is

$$Q = (0.35)(600)(86,400) = 18,144,000 \text{ cm}^3 = 18,144 \text{ liters} =$$

$$= 18.144 \text{ m}^3 = 35.31 \text{ ft}^3 \times 18.144 =$$

$$= 640.66 \text{ ft}^3 = 7.481 \text{ gal} \times 640.66 =$$

$$= 4,792.78 \text{ gal}.$$

Example. Calculate the discharge per day of a uniform, parallel flow along an incline of $i = 0.003$ for a $b = 100$ m shore line (perpendicularly to the drawing plane). The thickness of the water sheet is 5 m. The coefficient of permeability is $k = (5)(10^{-3})$ (m/s).

Solution. By Eq. (12-4a) the discharge is

$$Q = kiAt = (5)(10^{-3})(0.003)(5 \times 100)(86,400) =$$

$$= 648.0 \quad \text{(m}^3\text{/day)}.$$

12-3. Artesian Groundwater Flow. If the groundwater flowing under pressure through a pervious layer of soil is fully *confined* from its top and bottom between impermeable geologic formations, such a groundwater is termed *artesian water* (Fig. 12-3). The pervious soil layer is termed the *aquifer*. If a well is drilled into the soil until groundwater in the aquifer is reached, then, depending upon the magnitude of the pressure p at the well point, artesian water will flow up through the well. The height of rise, $h_f = p/\gamma_w$, of artesian water may be higher than the ground surface. In such a case one speaks of a fountain of water. When the height of rise of artesian water is less than the elevation of the ground surface, one speaks of *semiartesian water*.

The need can be easily seen for establishing the position of the groundwater

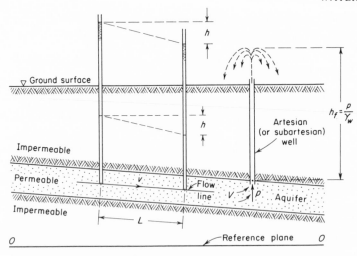

Fig. 12-3. Artesian (or subartesian) groundwater flow.

table before the commencement of foundation operations. If excavation in soil is carried down so deep that the bottom of the excavation pit is broken through by the pressure of the artesian water, then usually there is very little one can do to correct the conditions in the spoiled pit. Usually such sites are abandoned and a new site is sought if costly foundation methods are to be avoided.

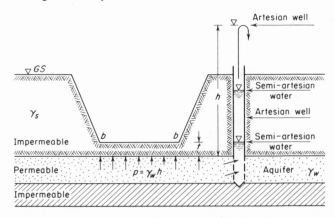

Fig. 12.4 Effect of artesian water on stability of bottom of pit.

The danger of the presence of artesian water at a construction site relative to excavation and stability of the bottom of the pit is illustrated in Fig. 12-4. To prevent the bottom of the pit from being broken through by water, the minimum thickness t of the bottom at pressures in equilibrium should be:

$$\uparrow\gamma_w h = \downarrow\gamma_s t, \tag{12-5a}$$

or

$$t = (\gamma_w/\gamma_s)h \quad \text{(cm)} \tag{12-5}$$

at an uplift coefficient of $\alpha = 1$. That is, the bottom of the pit, viz., clay, is then considered as absolutely impermeable, so that the bottom surface b-b receives the full, undiminished pressure. With an uplift coefficient of $\alpha < 1.0$, t then comes out less than $(\gamma_w/\gamma_s)h$.

If the porosity of the soil is $n = 30\%$, then the uplift coefficient α is theoretically calculated as[2]

$$\alpha = (1.21)n^{2/3}. \tag{12-6}$$

This calculation shows the thickness t to be less than before, namely:

$$\alpha = (1.21)(0.3)^{2/3} = 0.54,$$

and

$$t_\alpha = \alpha \frac{\gamma_w}{\gamma_s} h = (0.54)(t). \tag{12-7}$$

However, because of the uncertainties in the uniformity of porosity distributions, and to avoid an unpleasant experience with damaged pit-bottoms, it is safer to operate with an $\alpha = 1.00$ if the elevation of the structure permits one to do so.

Pile driving in soil containing artesian water is also troublesome. Cases are known where, upon the removal of the pile-driving rammer, the pile was pushed out of the soil by the pressure of artesian water.

The discharge through the aquifer in the direction of flow, again, is calculated as

$$Q = vA = kiA \qquad (\text{cm}^3/\text{s}),$$

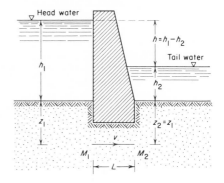

FIG. 12-5. Confined flow under a structure.

where $i = h/L$.

An example of a *partly confined* groundwater flow under pressure and with no free surface is illustrated in Fig. 12-5. The hydraulic gradient i is here calculated as

$$i = \frac{h_1 - h_2}{L}. \tag{12-8}$$

12-4. Permeability Through Stratified Layers of Soil

The Problem. In soil, foundation, and highway engineering compound-layer systems in several strata, rather than single, unstratified ones, are often encountered (Fig. 12-6). In such a case the permeability to water of each of the particular single component soil layers of the stratified soil system may be, and usually is, different because of the various types of soil. Besides, the permeability perpendicular to the stratified soil layers or bedding planes (usually approximately in the vertical direction) is different from that parallel (usually approximately in the

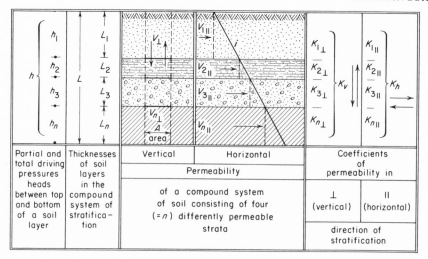

Partial and total driving pressures heads between top and bottom of a soil layer	Thicknesses of soil layers in the compound system of stratification	Vertical	Horizontal	Coefficients of permeability in	
		Permeability		$\perp$ (vertical)	$\parallel$ (horizontal)
		of a compound system of soil consisting of four ($=n$) differently permeable strata		direction of stratification	

FIG. 12-6. Compound system of soil layers.

horizontal direction) to the stratification. It therefore appears necessary to determine a weighted coefficient of permeability for the compound, stratified soil system.

Permeability Perpendicular to Stratification. If the groundwater flows through a compound soil layer consisting of several different types of soil, and if each layer is of different permeability perpendicular to stratification of the layered soil system, then an average system's coefficient of permeability can be calculated if the permeabilities $k_{1\perp}$, $k_{2\perp}$, $k_{3\perp}$, . . ., $k_{n\perp}$ are known.

With the symbols as shown in Fig. 12-6, the average coefficient of permeability k_v perpendicular to the bedding planes is calculated on the principle of continuity of flow as

$$k_v = \frac{L}{\dfrac{L_1}{k_{1\perp}} + \dfrac{L_2}{k_{2\perp}} + \dfrac{L_3}{k_{3\perp}} + \cdots + \dfrac{L_n}{k_{n\perp}}} \qquad (\text{cm}/\text{s}). \qquad (12\text{-}9)$$

For derivation of the equation of permeability k_v, and k_h, the reader is referred to the author's book *Soil Mechanics*, Ref. 3. The discharge through a unit area perpendicular to stratification is

$$q = v = k_v \frac{h}{L} = \frac{h}{\dfrac{L_1}{k_{1\perp}} + \dfrac{L_2}{k_{2\perp}} + \dfrac{L_3}{k_{3\perp}} + \cdots + \dfrac{L_n}{k_{n\perp}}} \qquad (\text{cm}^3/\text{s}). \qquad (12\text{-}10)$$

12-5. Permeability Parallel to Stratification. If the groundwater flows through a compound soil layer of different permeabilities parallel to the stratification or bedding planes, then all flow lines are also hydraulically parallel to the boundaries of the stratification. Besides, the hydraulic gradient i is the same at every point of each layer, because in this case i does not depend upon the permeability of the soil layer. Therefore, the average flow velocity v_h for an L-unit-thick compound layer of soil is calculated as

$$k_h = \frac{k_{1\parallel}L_1 + k_{2\parallel}L_2 + k_{3\parallel}L_3 + \cdots + k_{n\parallel}L_n}{L} \qquad \text{(cm/s)}, \qquad (12\text{-}11)$$

where k_h = average coefficient of permeability for the entire compound layer of soil parallel to stratification (usually horizontally);

$k_{1\parallel}, k_{2\parallel}, k_{3\parallel}, \ldots, k_{n\parallel}$ = coefficient of permeability of each of the respective component soil layers in the layered system;

L = total thickness of the compound soil layer, and

$L_1, L_2, L_3, \ldots, L_n$ = thicknesses of individual soil layers making up the compound layer of soil.

The discharge through the compound soil layer is

$$q = k_h i, \qquad (12\text{-}12)$$

where i = hydraulic gradient of the stream of groundwater, assumed constant and the same for all strata in the compound layer of soil.

The average coefficient of permeability of the entire thickness of the layered system k_{ave} is calculated as the geometric average of k_v and k_h:

$$k_{ave} = \sqrt{k_v k_h}. \qquad (12\text{-}13)$$

Example. Given a massive weir placed on a horizontal system of layered soil as shown in Fig. 12-7.

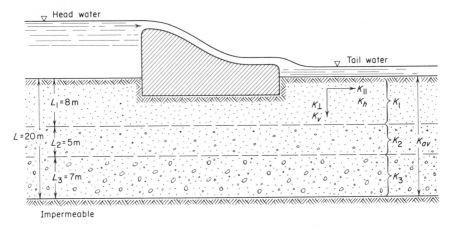

FIG. 12-7. Seepage through a layered system of soil.

The coefficients of permeability of soil representing each of the three layers are:

1) perpendicular to bedding planes:
$k_\perp : k_1 = 0.010$ m/s
$k_2 = 0.020$ m/s
$k_3 = 0.030$ m/s

2) parallel to bedding planes:
$k_\parallel : k_1 = 0.040$ m/s
$k_2 = 0.050$ m/s
$k_3 = 0.090$ m/s

Determine the average coefficient of permeability of the layered soil system.

Solution.

a) The system's coefficient of permeability k_v perpendicular to stratification is, by Eq. (12-9),

$$k_v = \frac{L}{\dfrac{L_1}{k_1} + \dfrac{L_2}{k_2} + \dfrac{L_3}{k_3}} = \frac{20.0}{\dfrac{8.0}{0.010} + \dfrac{5.0}{0.020} + \dfrac{7.0}{0.030}} = 0.0156 \ (\text{m/s}).$$

b) The system's coefficient of permeability k_h parallel to stratification is, by Eq. (12-11),

$$k_h = \frac{k_{1\parallel}L_1 + k_{2\parallel}L_2 + k_{3\parallel}L_3}{L} = \frac{(0.040)(8.0) + (0.050)(5.0) + (0.090)(7.0)}{20.0} =$$
$$= 0.060 \quad (\text{m/s}).$$

c) The system's geometric average coefficient of permeability k_{ave}, by Eq. (12-13), is

$$k_{ave} = \sqrt{k_v k_h} = \sqrt{(0.0156)(0.060)} = 0.0306 \quad (\text{m/s}).$$

12-6. Determination of k Experimentally in the Laboratory. Many methods of determining permeability of soil are described and discussed in Reference 4 on Permeability of Soils, the American Society for Testing and Materials, and in "Procedures for Testing Soils" by the same society.[5] See also References 6 and 7. Therefore, only the basic theoretical principles upon which such tests are based are discussed here.

a) *Constant-Head Vertical Permeameter.* A permeameter is an apparatus used for determining the coefficient of permeability of soil.

A constant-head permeameter consists of a vertical cylinder containing the soil sample for which the coefficient of permeability is to be determined, Fig. 12-8. The soil sample can be in a disturbed state or in an undisturbed state. Two or more piezometric tubes are attached to the permeameter cylinder spaced a distance L apart. The horizontal cross-sectional area of the cylinder, viz., soil sample, perpendicular to the direction of flow of water through the soil sample is A cm^2. The test cylinder is connected through its bottom by means of a pipe to a water or pressure reservoir, Fig. 12-8a. Note that h is constant. Thus, water pressure is applied, and water enters the permeameter from below the soil sample in an upward flow. The amount of water, V cm^3, flowing during a certain time, t is collected in a graduate cylinder; the temperature of the water is measured; the pressure difference $h = h_1 - h_2$ is determined, which is the loss in head spent for overcoming the resistance to flow over a length of flow L through the soil sample, and the following quantities calculated:

Discharge $\qquad\qquad Q = V/t \qquad (\text{cm}^3/\text{s}).$ $\qquad\qquad$ (12-14)

Seepage velocity $\qquad v = Q/A \qquad (\text{cm/s}).$ $\qquad\qquad$ (12-15)

Hydraulic gradient $\qquad i = h/L \qquad (\text{cm/cm}).$ $\qquad\qquad$ (12-16)

The coefficient of permeability is evaluated by means of Darcy's law per unit cross-sectional area, unit time, and unit gradient as

$$k = \frac{v}{i} = \frac{Q}{Ai} \qquad (\text{cm/s}). \qquad\qquad (12\text{-}17)$$

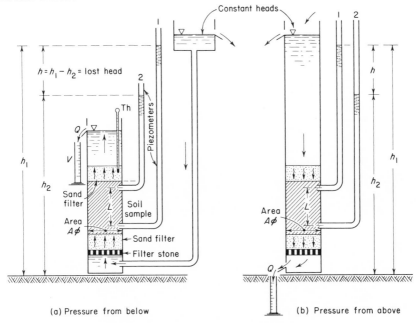

FIG. 12-8. Constant-head permeameters.

The coefficient of permeability is to be corrected for viscosity and reported at $20°C$: $k_{20} = (k)(\eta_T/\eta_{20})$. For viscosity correction factor tables see Appendix III.

A constant-head permeameter with water seeping through the soil sample from its top is illustrated in Fig. 12-8b. The flow is downward. The quantities to be observed and calculated to determine k are the same as with the constant-head permeameter with water seeping through the soil sample from below.

The constant-head permeability test is more suited for coarse soils such as gravelly sand and coarse and medium sand.

Permeability Correction for Temperature. In soil mechanics research and practice, for purpose of comparison, the coefficient of permeability k is conventionally reported at a standard temperature of $+20°C$. Therefore, coefficients of permeability obtained at other temperatures than standard are to be corrected for the viscosity of water at $+20°C$. The coefficient of permeability at $+20°C$, k_{20}, is calculated as

$$k_{20} = k \frac{\eta_T}{\eta_{20}}, \qquad (12\text{-}18)$$

where k = coefficient of permeability obtained at some temperature $T \neq 20°C$,

η_T = coefficient of dynamic viscosity, in $\text{g}/(\text{cm} \cdot \text{s})$ = poises at some temperature $T \neq 20°C$, and

η_{20} = coefficient of dynamic viscosity at $+20°C$.

Values of viscosity correction coefficients η_T/η_{20} at atmospheric pressure are given in Appendix III.

174 WATER IN SOIL

Example. A soil sample representing a sand has been tested in a constant-head permeameter. The inside diameter of the container holding the sand is $D = 10.2$ cm. The head loss h over a distance $L = 12.5$ cm between two piezometers is 86.0 cm. The amount of the permeating water collected during a time of 2 min is $V = 733$ cm³. The temperature of the permeating water was 15°C. Compute the discharge Q and the coefficient of permeability of this sand.

Solution.
1) Discharge

$$Q = \frac{V}{t} = \frac{733}{(2)(60)} = 6.1 \quad (\text{cm}^3/\text{s}).$$

2) Cross-sectional area of soil sample:

$$A = \frac{\pi D^2}{4} = (0.785)(10.2)^2 = 81.6 \quad (\text{cm}^2).$$

3) Hydraulic gradient

$$i = \frac{h}{L} = \frac{86.0}{12.5} = 6.88.$$

4) Coefficient of permeability

$$k_{15} = \frac{Q}{Ai} = \frac{(6.1)}{(81.6)(6.88)} = 0.01085 \quad (\text{cm}/\text{s}) =$$
$$= (1.085)(10^{-2}) \quad (\text{cm}/\text{s}).$$

5) Coefficient of permeability at standard temperature of 20°C, by Eq. (12-16), is

$$k_{20} = k_{15}(\eta_{15}/\eta_{20}) = (0.01085)(1.13432) = (1.23)(10^{-2}) \quad (\text{cm}/\text{s}).$$

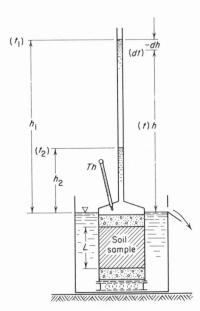

FIG. 12-9. Falling-head permeameter.

b) *Falling-Head Permeameter.* A falling-head or variable-head permeameter consists of a vertical test cylinder of cross-sectional area A (in cm²) containing the soil sample to be tested for permeability. To the test cylinder there is attached a vertical, transparent tube of constant diameter, viz., cross-sectional area a (in cm²), throughout (Fig. 12-9). The test cylinder is placed in an overflow container to maintain the tail water at constant level. The sample is allowed to saturate; the standpipe filled to a certain height with water h_1; the height of the water is marked, and time is clocked. If no more water is added, the height in the standpipe drops as the water seeps through the soil sample. During an elapsed-time interval between t_1 and t_2, the elevation of the water in the standpipe will drop from height h_1 to height h_2, measured from tail-water table.

The drop in head means a decrease in the volume of water in the standpipe. The coefficient of permeability k from a falling-head permeability test is calculated as

$$k = \frac{L}{(t_2 - t_1)} \frac{a}{A} \ln \frac{h_1}{h_2} \quad (cm/s), \tag{12-19}$$

or, expressed in terms of decimal logarithms,

$$k = \frac{(2.3026)L}{(t_2 - t_1)} \frac{a}{A} \log_{10}\left(\frac{h_1}{h_2}\right) \quad (cm/s). \tag{12-20}$$

If the coefficient of permeability k of a soil is tested at a temperature different from $+20°C$, then it has to be corrected for viscosity, viz., temperature, and reported as

$$k_{20} = k(\eta_T/\eta_{20}), \tag{12-21}$$

where η_T/η_{20} = viscosity correction coefficient.

The falling- or variable-head permeability test is more suited for fine sands, silts, and clays.

The presence of air in the voids of cohesive soils, particularly clays, when their permeability is being determined, is a very disturbing factor.

Example. An undisturbed clay sample of cylindrical shape has been tested for its permeability in a falling-head permeameter. The diameter of the soil sample was 5.0 cm, and its thickness, viz., height, was 2.5 cm. The inside diameter of the standpipe of the permeameter was 12.5 mm. At the start of the permeability test, the reading of the water column in the standpipe was 45.0 cm. Seven minutes and 25 seconds later the reading was 43.0 cm. The temperature of the permeating water was 20°C.

1) Sketch the test arrangement.

2) Calculate the coefficient of permeability of the clay sample.

Solution.

1) The principal sketch of the falling-head permeameter is like that shown in Fig. 12-9.

2) The coefficient of permeability k is calculated by Eq. (12-20) as

$$k = \frac{a}{A} \frac{L}{t} (2.3) \log_{10}\left(\frac{h_1}{h_2}\right).$$

a) The cross-sectional area of the soil sample:

$$A = \frac{\pi D^2}{4} = (0.785)(5.0)^2 = 19.6 \quad (cm^2).$$

b) The cross-sectional area of the standpipe:

$$a = \frac{\pi d^2}{4} = \frac{(3.14)(1.25)^2}{4} = 1.23 \quad (cm^2).$$

c) The thickness of the soil sample:

$$L = 2.5 \quad (cm).$$

d) The time t required for a drop in head from 45.0 cm to 43.0 cm:

$$t = t_2 - t_1; \quad t_1 = 0.$$
$$t_2 - t_1 = t = (7 \times 60) + 25 = 445 \quad \text{(s)}.$$

e) Falling head ratio:

$$\frac{h_1}{h_2} = \frac{45}{43} = 1.048.$$

f) $\ln (1.048) = (2.3) \log_{10} (1.048) = (2.3)(0.020361) = 0.0468.$

g) The coefficient of permeability of the clay sample tested at 20°C is:

$$k_{20} = \frac{(1.23)(2.5)}{(19.6)(445)} (0.0468) = (1.64)(10^{-4}) \quad \text{(cm/s)}.$$

Note. To judge whether this calculated permeability is high or low, it would be helpful for the engineer to know the density and porosity, or void ratio, of the soil.

c) *Horizontal Permeability Test.* A basic sketch of a horizontal permeameter is shown in Fig. 12-10. The discharge Q, head loss h, and temperature T are

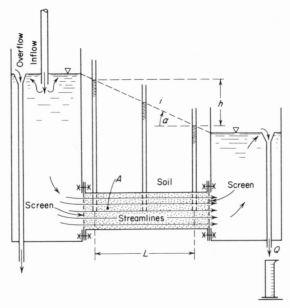

FIG. 12-10. Horizontal permeameter.

observed. The filtration length L between any two points along the flow path can be established as being constant, and the cross-sectional area perpendicular to the horizontal direction of flow can be ascertained. The coefficient of permeability k is then calculated as

$$k = \frac{V}{i} = \frac{Q}{Ai} = \frac{Q}{A(h/L)} \quad \text{(cm/s)}. \tag{12-22}$$

The horizontal permeability test is well suited for sand.

Example. In Fig. 12-10 the cross-sectional area of a soil sample, tested in a 30-cm-long horizontal permeameter, was $A = 100$ cm^2, and the discharged volume of water was $V = 750$ cm^3, at a head loss of $h = 60$ cm. The duration of this test was 10 min. The temperature of the water was measured as $T = 20°C$. Determine the coefficient of permeability of this soil.

Solution. By Eq. (12-22),

$$k_{20} = \frac{(750)(30)}{(10 \times 60)(100)(60)} = (6.25)(10^{-3}) \quad (cm/s).$$

A graphical presentation of values of coefficients of permeabilities of different types of soils, the application of k's to earth dams, and the method of determination of k's is shown after A. Casagrande and Fadum[8] in Fig. 12-11.

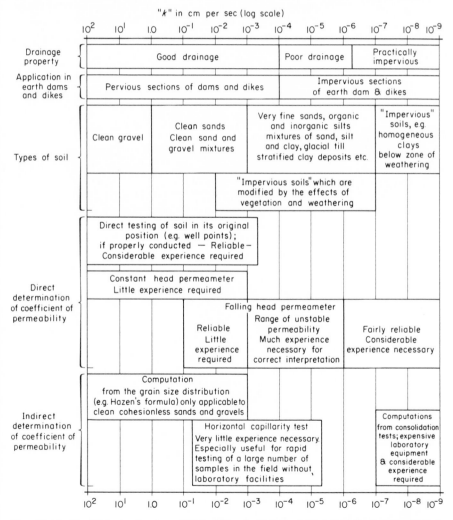

FIG. 12-11. Coefficient of permeability. After A. Casagrande and R.E. Fadum, Ref. 8.

REFERENCES

1. H.P.G. Darcy, *Les fontaines publiques de la ville de Dijon*, Paris, Victor Dalmont, Éditeur, 1856, pp. 570, 590, 594.
2. F. W. Hanna and R. C. Kennedy, *The Design of Dams*, New York, McGraw-Hill Book Co., 1931, p. 107.
3. A. R. Jumikis, *Soil Mechanics*, Princeton, N.J., 1962, D. Van Nostrand Company Inc., pp. 259-264.
4. ASTM. "Permeability and Capillarity of Soils," *Special Technical Publication No. 417*, by the American Society for Testing and Materials, Philadelphia, Pa., 1967.
5. ASTM Standard Method of Test for Permeability of Granular Soils. Designation D 2434-68, Reapproved 1974. Published in *1976 Annual Book of ASTM Standards*, Part 19, Philadelphia, Pa., 1976, pp. 298-304.
6. *Earth Manual* (2nd ed.), Washington, D.C., U.S. Department of the Interior, Bureau of Reclamation, 1974, pp. 55-61.
7. H.R. Cedergren, "Drainage and Dewatering," in *Foundation Engineering Handbook*, New York, N.Y., Van Nostrand Reinhold Company, 1975, pp. 221-243.
8. A. Casagrande and R.E. Fadum, *Notes on Soil Testing for Engineering Purposes*, Cambridge, Mass., Harvard University, Publication no. 268, 1939/40, Fig. 11. p. 23.

QUESTIONS AND PROBLEMS

12-1. Compute the value of conversion factors for permeability of soil k required to convert centimeters per second into a) meters per day, b) feet per second, c) feet per minute, and d) feet per day.

12-2. What are the assumptions for the validity of Darcy's law?

12-3. A canal, the surface elevation of which is $+ 85$ m, runs parallel to a river, the elevation of the water table of which is $+ 81$ m. All other conditions necessary for the solution of this problem are shown on the accompanying sketch, Fig. Problem 12-3. The coefficient of the horizontal permeability of the undercut sand layer is $k_h = 0.006$ m/min, and vertical permeability of this sand layer is $k_v = 0.0012$ m/min. Calculate the loss of water from canal to river per 100 m of shore per day. Indicate remedial measures to decrease the seepage loss of water from the canal.

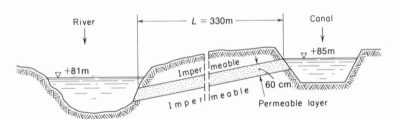

FIG. PROBLEM 12-3.

12-4. A sample of sand, 5.0 cm in diameter and 10.0 cm thick, was subjected to a permeability test. The test apparatus was of the constant-head type. The test lasted 10 sec under a hydrostatic head of 100 cm and at 20°C. The weight of the collected discharge water was 600 g. Determine the coefficient of permeability k in cm/s of the specimen of sand. Sketch the test apparatus.

12-5. Given: the falling-head permeability data, obtained from testing a (-4)-material compacted in a standard permeability testing mold at 12.0% moisture content.

Diameter of soil sample: $D = 10.12$ cm.
Thickness (length of sample): $L = 11.84$ cm.
Inside diameter of tube: $d = 1.08$ cm.
Specific gravity of soil particles: $G = 2.65$.
Volume of sample: $V = 952.0$ cm³.
Weight of dry sample: $W_d = 1804$ g.

Trial Nos.	Temperature of Water °C	Soil °C	Elapsed Time in s	Head at Start of Test h_1 cm	End h_2 cm
1	21.2	21.2	0	80.0	
2	23.8	23.4	57.6		70.9
3	25.4	25.4	14.0	70.9	70.1

Determine the coefficient of permeability to water of this soil at a standard temperature of 20°C. Give your opinion about the test data as given above. Sketch the test arrangement.

12-6. Given: the permeability test apparatus shown in Fig. Problem 12-6.

Calculate k. $\left(\text{Answer: } k = \dfrac{2Q}{a} \dfrac{L}{h_1{}^2 - h_2{}^2}\right).$

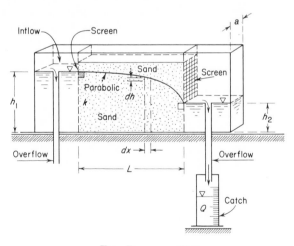

FIG. PROBLEM 12-6.

Chapter 13

HYDRAULICS OF WELLS

13-1. Determination of Permeability Experimentally in the Field.

Pumping of Water out of a Single Well. The method of pumping water out of a test well for the purpose of ascertaining a reasonable value of the coefficient of permeability k can more properly be described as the radial, groundwater gravity flow to a single, central well. In this test, a single test well is installed in a horizontal permeable soil layer. A certain quantity Q of water is continuously pumped out of the well. The pumping takes place for a period lasting from a few days to a fortnight, depending upon soil properties, until the groundwater flow to the well is stabilized, i.e., until a steady state of flow is attained and the depression funnel or cone of the lowered groundwater table around the well is established. The stabilized depression surface, viz., the depression line of the lowered groundwater table, is established by observing the position of the groundwater table and the draw-down s of the groundwater in several observation wells spaced around the test well on two radial lines (Fig. 13-1), one of which, for example, may be selected parallel to the groundwater flow and the other perpendicular to the flow direction. The maximum lowering or draw-down, s_{max}, of the groundwater table is at the well.

A minimum of two observation wells is needed, which then permits the calculation of the coefficient of permeability k of soil to water.

The draw-down decreases with distance from the test well. The depression line dies out gradually and forms, theoretically, a circle around the test well as the circle of influence. Its radius R, in the theory of hydraulics of wells, is termed "the radius of influence of the depression cone."

In water supply engineering the prime problem is to obtain a certain quantity of water out of the ground. The draw-down associated therewith is then secondary in importance. Conversely, in foundation engineering, the important problem is the draw-down of the groundwater table necessary to achieve a dry foundation pit. The amount of pumped water, save for the necessity of determining the pump horsepower, is here otherwise of secondary importance only.

13-2. Ordinary, Perfect, Gravity Wells.

Flow into an Ordinary, Perfect Well. The flow of water into an ordinary, perfect well is a gravity flow where the groundwater table is exposed to atmospheric pressure. Because the radial flowlines to a circular well are three-

180

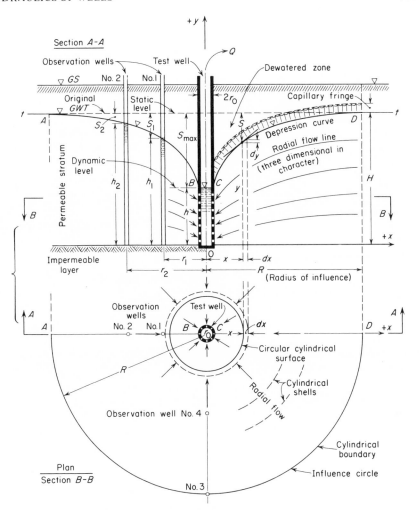

Fig. 13-1.   Ordinary, perfect gravity well.

dimensional in character, this flow problem cannot be treated by means of flow nets, but must be studied analytically.

The rate of flow Q of water into the well at stabilized flow upon pumping, expressed by Darcy's law, is

$$Q = vA = kiA \qquad (m^3/s), \qquad (13\text{-}1)$$

where v = flow velocity in m/s,
$\quad A$ = flow area, in m^2,
$\quad i = dy/dx = \tan \alpha$ = hydraulic gradient,
$\quad dy$ = change in y-coordinate of the depression curve, and
$\quad dx$ = change in x-coordinate of the depression curve.

182   WATER IN SOIL

The area A through which the flow of water to the well takes place is a vertical, circular, cylindrical surface (below the depression curve) with a radius x and height y:

$$A = 2\pi x y. \tag{13-2}$$

While a particle of water approaches the center of the well by an amount dx, the groundwater table experiences a depression dy.

If there exists a continuous, uniform, radial flow over an impermeable stratum, then the rate of flow across any cylindrical area A is equal to the flow Q into the well (and the amount, in turn, pumped out of it):

$$Q = k(dy/dx)2\pi x y. \tag{13-3}$$

Separating variables and integrating, we obtain

$$\int_h^y y\, dy = \frac{Q}{2\pi k} \int_{r_0}^x \frac{dx}{x}, \tag{13-4}$$

or

$$y^2 - h^2 = \frac{Q}{\pi k} \ln \frac{x}{r_0}, \tag{13-5}$$

which is the *general equation of the depression line.* Integrating between $x_1 = r_0$ and $x_2 = R$, and between $y_1 = h$ and $y_2 = H$, obtain

$$\int_h^H y\, dy = \frac{Q}{2\pi k} \int_{r_0}^R \frac{dx}{x}, \tag{13-6}$$

$$H^2 - h^2 = \frac{Q}{\pi k} \ln \frac{R}{r_0}, \tag{13-7}$$

from which the discharge Q can be calculated as

$$Q = \pi k \frac{H^2 - h^2}{\ln(R/r_0)} = \pi k \frac{(H + h)(H - h)}{\ln(R/r_0)}. \tag{13-8}$$

Draw-down. Because draw-down is

$$s = H - y, \tag{13-9}$$

it can now be expressed at any point $(x; y)$ by means of Eq. (13-8):

$$s = H \pm \sqrt{H^2 - \frac{Q}{\pi k} \ln \frac{R}{x}}, \tag{13-10}$$

or, in the system of decimal logarithms,

$$s = H \pm \sqrt{H^2 - \frac{(2.3)Q}{\pi k} \log_{10} \frac{R}{x}}. \tag{13-11}$$

For pumping water out of the well (lowering the groundwater table), use the minus sign before the square root. For recharge of water into the well (and soil) use the plus sign. When $x = R$, then $s = 0$. When $x = r$, $y = h$.

Equations (13-10) and (13-11) also show that the less the thickness of the water-bearing soil stratum H, the greater is the draw-down s. Maximum draw-down at well casing, upon pumping out of the well, is

$$s_{max} = H - h = H - \sqrt{H^2 - \frac{(2.3)Q}{\pi k} \log_{10} \frac{R}{r_0}}. \qquad (13\text{-}12)$$

13-3. Radius of Influence. The radius of influence of the depression cone R is to be estimated from experience, or found by observation in several bore holes made at different distances from the test well. According to Sichardt,[1] for stabilized flow condition, R is given in meters as

$$R = 3000s\sqrt{k}, \qquad (13\text{-}13)$$

where s = maximum draw-down in m and
   k = coefficient of permeability of soil k in m/s.
This equation, giving conservative R-values, has no theoretical support, and dimensionally it is not true. However, in most cases in practice, when R-values are not available, Sichardt's R-values are used with relatively good success, since they exclude large errors.

For larger draw-downs in single wells, Weber's equation,[2]

$$R = c\sqrt{Hk(t)/n} \qquad (m) \qquad (13\text{-}14)$$

gives more precise values.
Here $c \approx 3$, a coefficient;
   H = thickness, in m, of the water-bearing stratum;
   k = coefficient of permeability of soil, in m/s;
   t = time of draw-down, in s; and
   n = porosity of soil, which varies from 0.25 (coarse sand) to 0.34 (fine sand). An average coefficient of porosity of $n = 0.30$ can be used.
Also, Weber's equation has no true dimensions. Although Weber's R does not seem to depend upon the pumping quantity Q, which looks odd, his R-equation is much quoted in the technical literature.

Example. Determine the radius of influence of a depression cone after an ordinary, perfect well has been pumped for 24 h. The thickness of the water-bearing stratum is 7.0 m. The coefficient of permeability is $k=0.005$ m/s. The porosity of the soil is $n = 0.30$.
Solution. The radius of influence is calculated by Weber's Eq. (13-14):

$$R = c\sqrt{Hk(t/n)} = (3)\sqrt{(7)(0.005)(86400/0.30)} = 301.2 \qquad (m).$$

Kozeny[3] gave an expression for the calculation of the radius of influence R in terms of time t during which a yield from the well of Q m³/s has been attained:

$$R = \sqrt{(12t/n)}\sqrt{Qk/\pi} \qquad (m). \qquad (13\text{-}15)$$

Here 12 = a coefficient,
  n = porosity of soil, in decimal fractions,
  k=coefficient of porosity of soil, m/s, and
  $\pi = 3.14$.
The radius of influence increases with the fourth root of discharge Q and permeability k.

As can easily be seen, Kozeny's equation contains true dimensions for R in meters.

Example. Calculate the radius of influence R if the following data were obtained from a pumping test:

yield: $Q = 0.06421$ m^3/s,
permeability: $k = 0.005$ m/s,
porosity: $n = 0.30$,
duration of test: $t = 24$ hr $= 86,400$ s.

Solution. By Kozeny's equation, the radius of influence of the depression cone is calculated as

$$R = \sqrt{\frac{(12)(86400)}{0.30}} \sqrt{\frac{(0.06421)(0.005)}{3.14}} = 186.8 \qquad (m).$$

Example. Given: yield out of well: $Q = 0.06421$ m^3/s,
  thickness of water-bearing stratum: $H = 7.0$ m,
  permeability: k=0.005 m/s,
  hydraulic gradient: $i = 0.00175$.
Determine the radius of influence R.

Solution. The hydraulic gradient suggests that groundwater flows along a slope of an impermeable soil stratum. In such a case the radius of influence can approximately be calculated as

$$R = \frac{Q}{2\pi Hki} = \frac{0.06421}{(2)(3.14)(7)(0.005)(0.00175)} = 166.8 \qquad (m).$$

According to Schoklitsch,[4] the values of the radius of influence of the depression cone for various soils are about as follows:

in coarse gravel $R \le 500$ m $= 1640$ ft,
in fine gravel $R = 100$ m to 500 m $= 330$ ft to 1640 ft,
in sand $R = 50$ m $= 165$ ft, and
in dune sand $R = 5$ m to 10 m $= 15$ ft to 30 ft.

Slichter[5] gives an R-value as 600 ft. Muscat[6] indicates $R = 500$ ft when no specific information is available, the error in the resultant computed value of k being only 10% if the correct magnitude is either half or twice 500 ft. And Tolman[7] suggests $R = 1000$ ft.

Upon the lack of any data for R, in preliminary calculations the R-values can be used as indicated in Table 13-1. The R-values are collected, evaluated and adjusted from many sources.

Whatever the R-values may be, the influence of R on the rate of flow Q is relatively insignificant because it enters into the Q-equation under the sign of logarithm, but logarithms of numbers, particularly of the R/r_0-ratios, vary very slowly. For example, if

$$R/r_0 = 10, 100, 1000, 10000,$$

then $\log_{10}(R/r_0) = 1, 2, 3,$ and 4.

TABLE 13-1. RADIUS OF INFLUENCE IN VARIOUS SOILS

Soil		Radius of Influence R, in meters
Description	Particle Size d in mm	
1	2	3
Coarse gravel	>10	>1500
Medium gravel	2 to 10	500 to 1500
Fine gravel	1 to 2	400 to 500
Coarse sand	0.5 to 1	200 to 400
Medium sand	0.25 to 0.5	100 to 200
Fine sand	0.10 to 0.25	50 to 100
Very fine sand	0.05 to 0.10	10 to 50
Silty sand	0.025 to 0.05	5 to 10

13-4. Coefficient of Permeability. Eq. (13-7) permits one to calculate the coefficient of permeability k of soil:

$$k = \frac{Q}{\pi(H^2 - h^2)} \ln \frac{R}{r_0} \quad \text{(m/s)}, \tag{13-16}$$

or, expressed in decimal logarithms,

$$k = \frac{(2.3)(Q)}{\pi(H^2 - h^2)} \log_{10} \frac{R}{r_0}. \tag{13-17}$$

If the maximum draw-down s_{max} at a certain Q is known, then $s_{max} = H - h$, and

$$H^2 - h^2 = (H + h)(H - h) = (H + h)s_{max} = (2H - s_{max})s_{max},$$

and

$$k = \frac{(2.3)Q}{\pi(2H - s_{max})s_{max}} \log_{10} \frac{R}{r_0}. \tag{13-18}$$

Example. Given: a system consisting of one test well 0.4 m in diameter. The well is installed in a medium sand so that it represents an ordinary, perfect well. The thickness of the groundwater-bearing stratum is 7 m. Upon a draw-down in the well of 3.5 m, the yield of the well is 301 m³/hr. The observed radius of influence is $R = 200$ m. Determine the system's coefficient of permeability.

Solution. By Eq. (13-18),

$$k = (0.732)(301)\frac{\log_{10} 1000}{[(2)(7) - 3.5](3.5)} = 17.99 \text{ (m/hr)} = 0.005 \quad \text{(m/s)}.$$

Note that the coefficient of permeability k represents the overall permeability of the entire water-bearing stratum in the vicinity of the test well and is influenced by the pumping operations. Therefore, k is the "system's" permeability. Some k-values are compiled in Table 13-2.

Example. Calculate the flow Q of groundwater into the well. The well penetrates a 7.0 m-thick water-bearing stratum of medium sand. The coefficient of permeability is $k=0.005$ m/s. The radius of the well is $r_0=0.1$ m. The required maximum drawdown is $s_{max} = 3.5$ m. Also, construct the depression line.

TABLE 13-2. COEFFICIENTS OF PERMEABILITY, k, OF SOIL

Soil Type	k m/s
1	2
Coarse gravel	5×10^{-3} to 1×10^{-2}
Coarse gravel with lenses and pockets of sand	4×10^{-3} to 5×10^{-3}
Medium gravel	3.5×10^{-2}
Fine gravel	3.0×10^{-2}
Coarse river sand	2×10^{-3} to 8.8×10^{-3}
Sand, 4-8 mm	3.5×10^{-2}
2-4 mm	2.5×10^{-2} to 3×10^{-2}
Fine sand + clay	8×10^{-4} to 3×10^{-3}
Fine, clean, sharp sand + some clay	5×10^{-4} to 1×10^{-3}
Dune sand	2×10^{-4}
Very fine sand	1×10^{-4}
Silty fine sand	1×10^{-3} to 1×10^{-4}
Loess, $e = 1.3$	1×10^{-3}
Loess, $e = 0.55$	2×10^{-7}
Clays	2×10^{-7} to 1×10^{-10}

Solution. Radius of influence, by Eq. (13-13):

$$R = 3000s\sqrt{k} = (3000)(3.5)\sqrt{0.005} = 805 \quad \text{(m)}.$$

Flow into a 0.1 m radius well, expressed for any s, and in the system of decimal logarithms:

$$Q_{0.1} = \frac{(1.365)k(2H - s_{max})s_{max}}{\log_{10}(R/r_0)} =$$

$$= \frac{(1.365)(0.005)[(2)(7) - (3.5)]3.5}{\log_{10}(805/0.1)} = 0.06421 \quad (\text{m}^3/\text{s}) =$$

$$= 231.156 \ (\text{m}^3/\text{h}).$$

If the radius of the well were $r_0 = 0.20$ m $= 8''$, and $R = 805$ m, then

$$Q_{0.2} = \frac{0.25082}{\log_{10} 4025} = 0.06958 \quad (\text{m}^3/\text{s}) = 250.488 \quad (\text{m}^3/\text{h}).$$

One sees that the size of the well is of less influence on Q than might be assumed, as can be seen from the following Q-ratio:

$$\frac{Q_{0.2}}{Q_{0.1}} = \frac{250.488}{231.156} = 1.087.$$

Note here that with an increase in the radius of the well by 100%, the increase in discharge into the larger well is only 8.7%.

Assuming a radius of influence for medium sand from Table 13-1 as $R = 200$ m, the discharge into a well of radius $r_0 = 0.1$ m is

$$Q_{200} = \frac{0.25082}{\log_{10}(200/0.1)} = 0.07598 \quad (\text{m}^3/\text{s}) = 273.535 \ (\text{m}^3/\text{h}),$$

and

$$\frac{Q_{805}}{Q_{200}} = \frac{231.156}{273.535} = 0.845.$$

Thus one sees that the magnitude of the radius of influence R has also relatively little effect upon Q: upon increasing the radius of influence four times, the discharge decreases by 15.5%.

For a systematic treatment and discussion on gravity and artesian wells, perfect and imperfect wells, and discharge and recharge wells, the reader is referred to the author's books *Soil Mechanics* and *Mechanics of Soils* (*Fundamentals for Advanced Study*), Ref. 8 and 9, and *Foundation Engineering*, Ref. 10.

188 WATER IN SOIL

REFERENCES

1. W. Kyrieleis and W. Sichardt, *Grundwasserabsenkung bei Fundierarbeiten*, Berlin, Julius Springer, 1930, p. 30.
2. H. Weber, *Die Reichweite von Grundwassersenkungen mittels Rohrbrunnen*, Berlin, Julius Springer, 1928, p. 11.
3. J. Kozeny, "Theorie und Berechung der Brunnen", *Wasserkraft und Wasserwirtschaft*, 1933, vol. 28, p. 104.
4. A. Schoklitsch, *Hydraulic Structures*, trans. S. Shulits, New York, The American Society of Mechanical Engineers, 1937, vol. 1, p. 179.
5. C. Slichter, *19th Annual Report*, 1899, U.S. Geological Survey, Part 2, p. 360.
6. M. Muscat, *Flow of Homogeneous Fluids Through Porous Media*, New York, McGraw-Hill Book Co., Inc., 1937, p. 95.
7. C. F. Tolman, *Ground Water*, New York, McGraw-Hill Book Co., Inc., 1937, p. 387.
8. A. R. Jumikis, *Soil Mechanics*, Princeton, N.J., D. Van Nostrand Company, Inc., 1962, pp. 276-300.
9. A. R. Jumikis, *Mechanics of Soils (Fundamentals for Advanced Study)*, Princeton, N.J., D. Van Nostrand Company, Inc., 1964, pp. 391-414.
10. A.R. Jumikis, "Lowering the Groundwater Table," in *Foundation Engineering*, New York, N.Y., Intext Educational Publishers, 1971, pp. 256-277.

SUGGESTIONS FOR FURTHER READING

1. C.I. Mansur and R.I. Kaufman, "Dewatering," Chapter 3, in Foundation Engineering, G. Leonards, (ed.), McGraw-Hill Book Company, New York, N.Y., 1962, pp. 241-360.
2. Moretrench Corporation, *The Moretrench Wellpoint System*, Rockaway, N.J., 1967.
3. H.R. Cedegren, "Drainage and Dewatering," in *Foundation Engineering Handbook*, edited by H.F. Winterkorn and H.Y. Fang. Van Nostrand Reinhold Company, New York, N.Y., 1975, pp. 221-243.

Chapter 14

SEEPAGE

14-1. Seepage Through Earth Dams. Darcy's law of permeability of water can also be applied to calculate discharge of gravity flow through earth dams. In designing and constructing earth dams the engineer is interested in their stability against sloughing and washing out of slopes. Particularly, he is interested in the loss of water through the earth dam by seepage, as well as in the height of the outcrop point of the uppermost flow or seepage line. This uppermost flow line is also called the saturation line, or the phreatic line.

The uppermost flow line is a free-water surface forming the upper boundary of flow by seepage. Above the saturation line there exists atmospheric pressure. Below this line there exists hydraulic pressure. Below the outcrop point the downstream slope of the earth dam must be protected from washing out.

14-2. Graphical Determination of the Seepage Line. If the shape and position of the uppermost flow line $B_1 B_2 RS$ in the cross section of an earth dam is known (Fig. 14-1), then the discharge quantity of seepage water through the dam can be calculated.

The shape of the seepage line can be determined analytically. It can also be constructed graphically or established in the laboratory—experimenting with a model dam of its prototype, as well as by the method of electrical analogy.

Parabolic Seepage Line. Because the seepage line for most of its length resembles a parabolic curve, A. Casagrande suggests for practical purposes that the real seepage line can be replaced by a parabola[1]. However, the substitute curve deviates from the true seepage line at the upstream and downstream faces of the dam. The assumed parabolically shaped seepage line, $BB_2 ESAV$, is termed the *basic parabola*. The parabola is a curve whose every point is equidistant from a fixed point, termed the focus, and a line, termed the directrix.

14-3. Construction of Parabolic Seepage Line. The graphical construction of the parabolic seepage line is based on the properties of the parabola. For that purpose one must know a point on the parabola, for instance, point B, and the position of the focus F of the parabola.

According to A. Casagrande, the location of the parabolic point B, with its coordinates $(x; y = H)$, is at the surface of the impounded water and is distant 0.3 times the projection, $D_1 B_1$, of the upstream slope $B_1 D$, of the dam and away from point B_1 as shown in Fig. 14-1: $\overline{BB_1} = (0.3)(\overline{D_1 B_1})$.

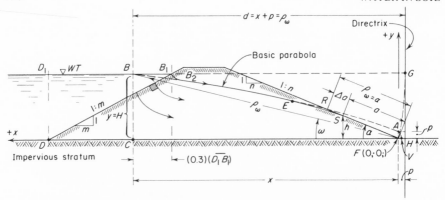

FIG. 14-1.   Basic parabola. Adapted after A. Casagrande, Ref. .1

The position of the focus F of the basic parabola is usually chosen at the intersecting point of the lower boundary flowline (horizontal in this case) and the discharge face, which is the downsteam slope of the dam.

Note that before the parabola can be constructed, the half-parameter p of the parabola must be known. From geometry (Fig. 14-1), $\rho_\omega = d$, or

$$\sqrt{x^2 + y^2} = x + p, \qquad (14\text{-}1)$$

and

$$p = \sqrt{x^2 + y^2} - x. \qquad (14\text{-}2)$$

14-4. Construction of a Parabola for $\alpha > 30°$. The half-parameter p can now be constructed. With the radius, ρ_ω from point B on the parabola as the center, swing an arc, FG, to intersect the line, d, at point G drawn from point B parallel to the x-axis. Then draw through point G a line perpendicular to the x-axis (parallel to y-axis). Line GH is the directrix of the parabola. Section FH is the half-parameter p of the parabola.

An ordinate p, at F, gives point A on the parabola. The bisecting point of FH on the x-axis gives the position of the vertex V of the parabola.

Now that p is known, other points which would lie on the parabola can be found graphically by means of the property of the parabola: namely, that every point on the curve is equidistant from the focus and from the directrix. One proceeds as follows: Draw an ordinate y at any arbitrary abscissa-point (C) on the x-axis. Take the distance $(x + p)$ as a radius ρ_ω and draw from $F(0; 0)$ an arc, FB, for example. The intersection of $(x + p)$ with the y-ordinate gives point B, which lies on the parabola. Repetition of this method with other values of ρ will give enough points to trace out the parabola.

14-5. Outcrop of Seepage Line. The intersection of the basic parabola with the downstream face of the dam at point R (Fig. 14-1) is calculated according to A. Casagrande as $(a + \Delta a)$, where $a = VS$ is the wetted part of the downstream face and point S is the intersection of the actual seepage line with the downstream

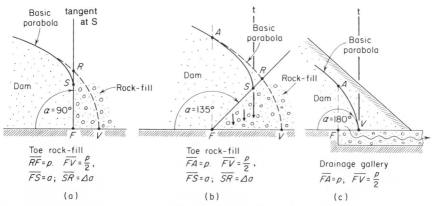

Fig. 14-2. Slope angles for various drainage structures. After A. Casagrande, Ref. 1.

face (or the outcrop point of the seepage line). Note that the quantity $(a + \Delta a)$ is nothing else than a special radius vector ρ, the amplitude ω of which is equal to the angle of slope α of the downstream face. Thus,

$$a + \Delta a = \rho_{\omega = \alpha}, \qquad (14\text{-}3)$$

where Δa is the distance SR above the wetted part of the downstream face. The ratio

$$\frac{RS}{RF} = \frac{\Delta a}{a + \Delta a} = c \qquad (14\text{-}4)$$

is a function of α, where α is the angle of the discharge face of the dam.

14-6. Slope Angles of Downstream Slopes. The dam as shown in Fig. 14-1 has no drainage structure or gallery at the downstream discharge. If the drainage structure at the toe of the dam is as illustrated in Figs. 14-2a and b, then the slope angles of the discharge face are $\alpha = 90°$ and $\alpha = 135°$, respectively. If there is a discharge gallery (Fig. 14-2c), then the slope angle is $\alpha = 180°$. The slope angle is, by convention, the clockwise angle between the base of the dam and the face of discharge. Note that in each case the intersection F of the base line of the dam (bottom flow line) with the discharge face is used as the focus of the basic parabola.

The c-values for various α's are given by A. Casagrande in Fig. 14-3 for any slope from 30° to 180°. Knowing α, which is given by construction of the

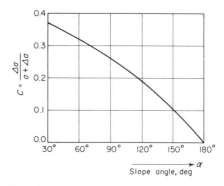

Fig. 14-3. $c = f(\alpha)$. After A. Casagrande, Ref. 1.

dam, determine from Fig. 14-3 the c-value, which then permits one to calculate Δa:

$$\Delta a = (a + \Delta a)c. \qquad (14\text{-}5)$$

This quantity Δa, in turn, permits the determination of the position of point S at which the seepage line crops out of the downstream face of the dam. The outcrop ordinate is h.

The outcrop point S is connected to the basic parabola by sketching a short transition curve ES. Point E on the curve is selected by eye.

Point B_1—intersection of the upstream water level with the face of the upstream slope of the dam—is also connected to the basic parabola, viz., the seepage line at point B_2, by sketching a transition curve between points B_1 and B_2. This transition curve, being the uppermost flow line, must be perpendicular to the upstream slope at point B_1. This is because the slope is an equipotential line. According to the flow net theory, the tangents at point B_1 drawn to the equipotential and flow line intersections must be mutually perpendicular.

14-7. Determination of the Outcrop Point Graphically for $\alpha < 30°$. The position of the outcrop point S, viz., discharge length a, can be determined graphically based on Eq. (14-11) as follows (Fig. 14-4).

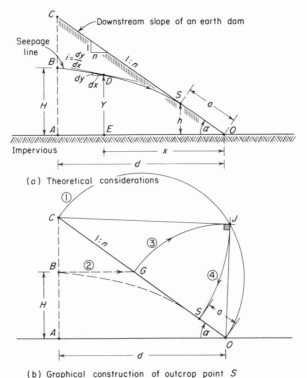

(a) Theoretical considerations

(b) Graphical construction of outcrop point S

FIG. 14-4.   Determination of the outcrop point S, for $\alpha < 30°$.

Extend the H-ordinate above point B (which is a point on the seepage line), and intersect it at point C with the downstream slope of the dam. On OC as a diameter, draw a semicircle. Find point G on the downstream slope by intersecting it with a line from point B drawn parallel to the base AO of the dam.

With point O as a center, and with a radius of OG, point G is transferred onto the semicircle, obtaining point J. Then, from point C as center and with a radius CJ, point J is transferred onto the downstream slope, viz., diameter, to give the outcrop point S of the seepage line.

Note that $\sphericalangle CJO$ is $90°$: $OG = OJ$, and $CJ = CS$. Then the proof for the graphical construction of the discharge length a is, from geometry as in Fig. 14-4b,

$$(OJ)^2 + (CJ)^2 = (OC)^2. \tag{14-6}$$

But

$$OJ = OG = H/(\sin \alpha), \tag{14-7}$$

$$CJ = CS = \frac{d}{\cos \alpha} - a, \tag{14-8}$$

and

$$OC = \frac{d}{\cos \alpha}; \tag{14-9}$$

therefore

$$\left(\frac{H}{\sin \alpha}\right)^2 + \left(\frac{d}{\cos \alpha} - a\right)^2 = \left(\frac{d}{\cos \alpha}\right)^2. \tag{14-10}$$

The solution of this equation for a yields:[1]

$$a = \frac{d}{\cos \alpha} - \sqrt{\frac{d^2}{\cos^2 \alpha} - \frac{H^2}{\sin^2 \alpha}}. \tag{14-11}$$

14-8. Construction of Parabola for $\alpha < 30°$. Now that d, H, and a are known, the parabolic seepage line can be constructed as shown in Fig. 14-5.

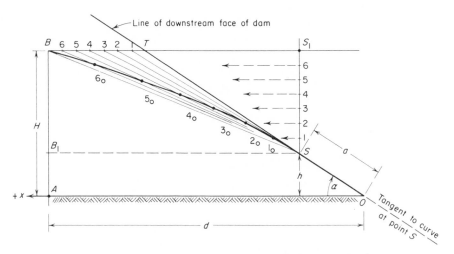

FIG. 14-5. Construction of seepage line for $\alpha < 30°$.

14-9. The Hydrodynamic Flow Net.

Flow Net. Once the position of the uppermost flow line has been established, seepage studies through earth dams can also be performed by means of a flow net.

The pure mathematical theory of potential flow proves basically nothing else than that the flow and equipotential lines form an orthogonal network - the so-called rectangular flow net.

A flow net is a system consisting of two sets or families of mutually orthogonally intersecting curves (Fig. 14-6). One set of these curves, designated as ψ-curves, are the so-called *flow lines*, or *stream lines*. The other set of curves, designated as ϕ-curves, are the so-called *equipotential lines*.

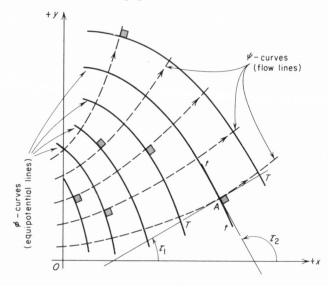

FIG. 14-6.   Flow net.

A flow net can be obtained mathematically, experimentally, or by the method of sketching by trial and adjustment. Flow nets in seepage studies are usually applicable to two-dimensional flow (flow in plane).

Flow Line. The locus of the path which a particle of flowing water takes in its course of seepage through a porous medium, such as soil, is termed a flow line. Thus, a flow line defines the direction and pattern of flow. The space between two adjacent flow lines is called the *flow channel*. Experimentally, it is practical to select not more than 4-6 flow lines.

Experimentally, the flow lines through a hydraulic model dam, confined in a tank with a transparent wall, can be made visible by injecting through the dam from its upstream face and from selected points a dye, fluorescein. The flow lines formed by the dye follow the same path as a particle of water which enters the dam at the same selected points where the dye is introduced.

The complete flow lines are traced on the transparent face of the seepage tank with a colored (white) china-marking pencil. Such experimentally obtained flow nets are shown in Figs. 14-7 and 14-10.

FIG. 14-7.   Experimentally obtained flow lines.

Theoretically, there can be an infinitely large number of flow lines.

As can be understood, the advantage of obtaining the uppermost flow (seepage) line by modeling a dam is that the seepage line can be obtained directly. However, the capillarity in soil above the seepage line may not reveal sharply the true position of the uppermost seepage line.

One thing to remember is that in any flow net, whatever the seepage problem, *flow lines do not intersect*. This means that the flow lines should be drawn such as to avoid violation of continuity of flow through each of the flow channels.

Equipotential Line. An equipotential line is one which is passed through all points of equal piezometric head. Piezometers installed anywhere along an equipotential line should show equal total head (Fig. 14-8).

The total head is the sum of the pressure head, geodetic or elevation head, and a neglible velocity head. Thus, equipotential lines can be considered potential contours.

There is an infinitely large number of equipotential lines present. An arbitrary number of equipotential lines can be chosen.

Over the distance ΔL, between two adjacent equipotential lines ϕ_1 and ϕ_2 in the direction of flow, there takes place a drop in hydraulic head Δh, viz., a loss in driving pressure, or a drop in potential. It is generally understood that water translocates from higher elevations to lower ones; or, in other words, it drops from higher energy levels to lower ones, and hence along the direction of the maximum energy gradient—the shortest path from one position to another one. Note that the excess hydrostatic pressure $\gamma_w \Delta h$ is the force which drives the water through the soil.

Because the hydraulic gradient is expressed as $i = (\Delta h)/(\Delta L)$ (i.e., the gradient equals the loss in hydraulic head divided by the distance ΔL a water particle travelled), the gradient has a maximum value along a flow line perpendicular to the equipotential lines owing to the shortest ΔL (the smaller is ΔL, the greater is i at same Δh. Hence, the *flow lines must intersect equipotential lines at right angles* (see point A, Fig. 14-6 and Fig. 14-8). Because the intersecting lines are curves, the clause of right angles means that the tangent T-T to the flow curve at the point of intersection (point A, Fig. 14-6) and the tangent t-t to the equipotential curve at the same point A should be mutually perpendicular.

14-10. Short Description of Flow Net Theory. Because in most cases seepage problems of water in soil and through earthworks can be treated two-dimensionally, the description of the flow net theory will be limited here to a two-dimensional flow.

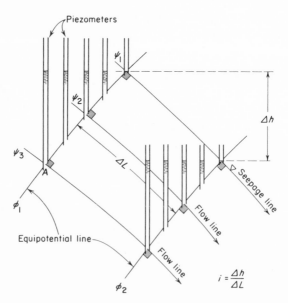

FIG. 14-8.   Hydraulic gradient i.

The flow net theory is based on the following assumptions:
   a) the soil is a homogeneous material (soil properties at every point in the soil mass are the same);
   b) the soil is an isotropic material (permeability in all directions in the soil mass is the same);
   c) all voids in the soil are completely filled with water;
   d) the flow of water is laminar, steady, and continuous;
   e) the soil is incompressible (no volume change in soil mass nor in its voids);
   f) the water is incompressible (the volume occupied by water remains constant);
   g) the fluid (water) is assumed to be ideal and of constant density;

h) the flow of water through the soil mass follows Darcy's law, and

i) the flow of water is not rotational.

The properties of a hydrodynamic flow net are as follows:

1) The two sets of curves (the equipotential and the flow curves) are orthogonal. From the orthogonality of the flow net, it follows that the velocity vector of filtration flow is directed normal to the equipotential line.

2) In an orthogonal, quadratic flow net, the drop in pressure head Δh between any two adjacent equipotential lines (if they are equally spaced) is the same and constant. This drop in pressure head equals a fraction of the total drop in head h between the entrance and exit of the seepage system of the soil:

$$\Delta h = h/N, \qquad (14\text{-}12)$$

where N is the number of equal potential drops along a flow channel, or the number of squares between two neighboring flow lines.

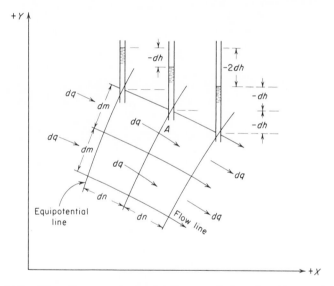

FIG. 14-9.   Flow lines, equipotential lines, and drop in piezometric head.

3) The hydrostatic head h_n at any point under consideration can be determined from the flow net, or calculated as

$$h_n = n(h/N) = n(\Delta h), \qquad (14\text{-}13)$$

where $h/N = \Delta h$ is the equal drop in pressure head between two equipotential lines, and $n = $ number of equal potential drops between the point under consideration and zero potential.

4) The discharge quantity of water flowing between any two adjacent flow lines is constant.

If the pressure difference between any two equipotential lines of a square is the same, for example, dh, then the hydraulic gradient for a square, say at point A, Fig. 14-9, is

$$i = dh/dn.$$ (14-14)

The discharge dq, between two parallel flow lines spaced at a distance dm apart and two parallel planes parallel to the drawing plane spaced one unit of length apart, is, according to Darcy's law,

$$dq = v\,dA = ki\,dA = k(dh/dn)(dm)(1),$$ (14-15)

where v = flow velocity,

$\quad dA$ = differential area perpendicular to flow,

$\quad k$ = coefficient of permeability of soil to water, and

$\quad dh$, dn, and dm are elements as in Fig. 14-9.

If the flow lines are drawn so that the discharge between adjacent flow lines is everywhere the same, and if the equipotential lines are drawn so that the pressure difference between successive lines is likewise everywhere the same, then

$$dq = (\text{const})(dm/dn) = \text{const}.$$ (14-16)

This means that in the flow net of rectangles the ratio of the sides (dm/dn) must be constant.[2]

If the ratio is made $dm/dn = 1$, then the rectangles become squares. Hence, from the above reasoning it is concluded that in an orthogonal system of squares the discharge q between any two equally spaced, adjacent flow lines (or through every flow channel) is a constant quantity throughout the flow net. The discharge is thereby a constant fraction of the total seepage through the soil: $q = Q/M$, where M is the number of flow channels.

5) Forchheimer[3] has shown that the network of squares can be used to determine seepage under dams, sheet piling, cofferdams, and other earth structures. For example, if there are N squares in a strip between two adjacent flowlines (number of equal drops in potential), the head loss, or loss of potential (drop in pressure) along the flow line side of a square is $dh = h/N$, where h is the difference between headwater and tailwater levels, or more generally, h is the total hydrostatic head. The hydraulic gradient along a *square* whose sides are equal to ($dn =$) dm is

$$i = \frac{dh}{dn} = \frac{dh}{dm} = \frac{h/N}{dm}.$$ (14-17)

The discharge through such a strip of one flow channel is

$$dq = v\,dA = k\,\frac{h}{N\,dm}\,dm = k\,\frac{h}{N}.$$ (14-18)

If there are M such strips (number of flow channels) in the dam (also = number of squares between two adjacent equipotential lines), the total discharge per unit length of dam along the shoreline is

$$Q = M \, dq = M(kh/N) = kh(M/N), \qquad (14\text{-}19)$$

as has been shown by Forchheimer.[3]

SEEPAGE PRESSURE

If water within a soil mass is at rest, its effect upon the soil particles is limited to the hydrostatic uplift. However, if water flows or seeps through a mass of soil, the flowing water exerts upon the soil particles a hydrodynamic seepage pressure which acts in the direction of flow and tangentially to a flow line. The magnitude of the seepage pressure is a function of the prevailing hydraulic gradient.

14-11. Derivation of Seepage Pressure Equation. Assume in a saturated soil mass such as an earth dam a differential flow channel whose length is dL and whose net cross-sectional area is dA (Fig. 14-10). The driving pressure, expressed as a function of head dh, is

$$dp = \gamma_w \, dh \, dA, \qquad (14\text{-}20)$$

where γ_w = unit weight of water.

Pressure, dp, is the total hydrodynamic pressure of seepage flow, known also as seepage pressure.

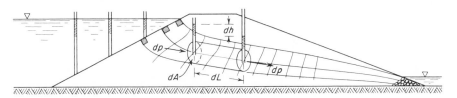

FIG. 14-10. Seepage pressure.

This pressure can be related to a unit volume:

$$\frac{dp}{dV} = \frac{dp}{dA \, dL} = \frac{\gamma_w \, dh \, dA}{dA \, dL}. \qquad (14\text{-}21)$$

Because ordinarily the seepage velocities in soils are low, the inertia force of the moving water is here neglected.

Designating $(dp)/(dA \, dL)$ by D, obtain the equation of seepage force per one unit of volume as

$$D = \gamma_w i \quad \text{(in tons/m}^3\text{, or in kN/m}^3\text{, for example),} \qquad (14\text{-}22)$$

where $i = dh/dL$ is the hydraulic gradient. Note that the seepage force is a mass or body force, distributed over the volume of the body of the soil mass, with the dimensions of a unit weight $(tons/m^3, kN/m^3, g/cm^3, or lb/ft^3)$, depending upon the system of units of measurements used. The hydrodynamic pressure D acts along the direction of flow of water.

Seepage Force Obtained From a Flow Net. By Eq. (14-22), the seepage pressure acting upon a volume made up of a square area, $A = abcd$, in a flow net, times one unit of length of shoreline perpendicular to the drawing plane, Fig. 14-11, is

$$D_s = DA(1) = \gamma_w i A(1) = \gamma_w (\Delta h/\Delta n)(\Delta n \Delta m)(1) = \gamma_w \Delta h \Delta m \quad \text{(tons)}, \quad (14\text{-}23)$$

where Δh = difference in head between the entrance and exit of a differential
            volume $[A(1)]$ formed by a square, $A = abcd$, in a flow net;
      Δn = dimension of square, $A = abcd$, in the direction of flow;
$\Delta h/(\Delta n) = i$ = hydraulic gradient across the square, and
      Δm = dimension of square (ab) perpendicular to flow.

Hence the flow net permits the calculation of the hydrodynamic pressure, i.e., seepage force, exerted by water flowing through an earth mass.

Seepage forces must not be forgotten when stability analyses are made of earth structures through which seepage of water takes place.

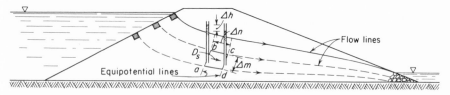

FIG. 14-11. Seepage force in a flow net.

14-12. Effect of Hydrodynamic Pressure Upon Stability of Soil.

Hydrodynamic pressure has a great influence upon the stability of soil. Depending upon the direction of the flow of water through the soil, the hydrodynamic pressure can be thought of as being able to alter considerably the unit weight of the soil.

The effect of D upon a unit weight of soil through which seepage takes place is illustrated in Fig. 14-12. At point 1, or at any point where the flow line is downward and vertical, the effective unit weight of the soil is

$$\gamma_{eff} = \gamma_{sub} + D, \quad (14\text{-}24)$$

indicating densification of soil. This fact, plus the effect of the surface tension forces acting in soil, explains the excellent beach sand conditions at Daytona Beach, Florida, on which heavy autoraces are run.

At point 2, or anywhere on a horizontal flow line, the two vectors, D and γ_{sub}, act perpendicularly to each other, resulting in an obliquely inclined resultant vector.

At point 3, where the flow is upward and vertical, the hydrodynamic pressure acts vertically upward against the submerged unit weight of soil γ_{sub}:

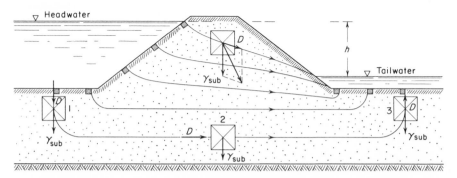

FIG. 14-12. Hydrodynamic pressure conditions of seeping water in soil.

$$\gamma_{eff} = \gamma_{sub} - D. \tag{14-25}$$

Here, when $D = \gamma_{sub}$, the soil appears weightless, and instability of the soil mass is impending. In such a case a special hydraulic condition prevails, termed *critical*, at which there is a *critical hydraulic gradient* i_c and consequently, a critical flow velocity v_c; then

$$D = \gamma_w i_c. \tag{14-26}$$

When the flow velocity v exceeds the critical velocity v_c, i.e., when $v > v_c$, then $D > \gamma_{sub}$ and γ_{eff} (in Eq. 14-25) becomes negative. This means that the soil particles are loosened, buoyed, and lifted up, resulting in a "boiling" or "quick" condition, the phenomenon known as quicksand. The reader is cautioned to remember that quicksand is not a type of sand. Rather, quicksand is a hydraulic condition in soil when there is an upward flow of water at a critical velocity.

The discussion of the hydrodynamic pressure conditions of seeping water in soil at points 1, 2, and 3 reveals that a sand mass may be very stable or may become "quick," depending upon the direction of the seepage flow.

14-13. Position of Hydrodynamic Force in a Ruptured Seeping Slope. If a rupture of a seeping slope of an earthwork should occur, as in Fig. 14-13, the hydrodynamic force D is one of the driving forces, among others, tending to cause the ruptured soil wedge $ABCDA$ to slide out and down.

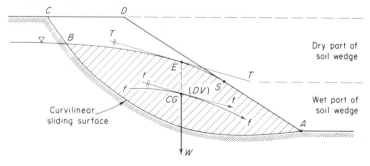

FIG. 14-13. Position of hydrodynamic force in a ruptured seeping slope.

Because D is a mass force, the point of its application is the center of gravity CG of the wet part of the sliding soil wedge $ABESA$. The direction of D is assumed variously: some engineers take it in the direction of the tangent t-t drawn to the flow line at point CG; some, in the direction of the tangent T-T.

The resultant hydrodynamic force to be applied at CG is in magnitude equal to (DV), where V is the volume of the wet part of the soil wedge, i.e., part $ABESA$.

THEORY OF QUICK CONDITION OF SAND

14-14. Quick Condition.

Critical Hydraulic Gradient. In the foregoing discussion on hydrodynamic pressure it was pointed out that this pressure can change the equilibrium of a soil mass. At equilibrium, the downward-acting force $W = \gamma_{sub}$, which is the weight of one unit of volume of the submerged soil, is equal to the upward-acting seepage force $D = \gamma_w i_c$, i.e.,

$$W\downarrow - D\uparrow = 0, \tag{14-27}$$

where i_c = critical hydraulic gradient at the above force equilibrium.

The magnitude of the weight of the submerged soil is calculated as

$$W = \gamma_{sub} = (1-n)(G-1)\gamma_w = \frac{G-1}{1+e}\gamma_w, \text{ (say in lb/ft}^3 \text{ or in kN/m}^3) \tag{14-28}$$

where n = porosity of soil,
G = specific gravity of soil particles,
e = void ratio of soil, and
γ_w = unit weight of water.

Substitution of the γ_{sub} and $D = \gamma_w i_c$ values into Eq. (14-27) yields:

$$\frac{G-1}{1+e}\gamma_w - \gamma_w i_c = 0, \tag{14-29}$$

and the critical hydraulic gradient i_c is calculated as

$$i_c = \frac{G-1}{1+e}. \tag{14-30}$$

The "critical hydraulic gradient" is defined as the minimum hydraulic gradient which will cause a quick condition within a certain type of soil.

With $G = 2.65$ for quartz sand, and an average value of the void ratio of $e = 0.65$ (or $n = 0.393$) for a relatively medium-dense state of packing of the soil, the critical hydraulic gradient has an average value equal to unity:

$$i_c = \frac{G-1}{1+e} = \frac{2.65-1}{1+0.65} = 1.00. \tag{14-31}$$

Factor of Safety. With a factor of safety of $\eta = 3$ to 4, the prevailing hydraulic gradient in a soil mass through which seepage of water takes place should be

$$i \leq i_c/\eta, \tag{14-32}$$

i.e., less than the critical hydraulic gradient i_c.

Example. Given: a sand mass the void ratio of which is $e = 0.70$, and the solid particles the specific gravity of which is $G = 2.66$. Calculate the critical hydraulic gradient for that soil. Also, with a factor of safety $\eta = 3$, compute the safe hydraulic gradient for the given flow system.

Solution. By Eq. (14-30), the critical hydraulic gradient is

$$i_c = \frac{G - 1}{1 + e} = \frac{(2.66) - (1)}{(1) + (0.70)} = 0.976.$$

Safe hydraulic gradient: $i = i_c/\eta = (0.976)/3 = 0.325$.

14-15. "Quicksand" Apparatus. The quicksand phenomenon can be studied most effectively in the laboratory by means of an apparatus called the "quicksand tank," illustrated in Fig. 14-14. For the purpose of visibility such a tank is made of transparent lucite. The tank, 18″ x 18″ x 18″, or 45.7 cm x 45.7 cm x 45.7 cm is connected with inlet and outlet pipes and control globe valves and provided with seven piezometers to measure the loss of pressure head. To create the quicksand phenomenon, an upward flow of water is introduced into the tank under pressure from the space below the filter stone.

Qualitative Description. Upon creating an upward flow through the sand, the water has a certain velocity. For a certain upward flow velocity, there is in the

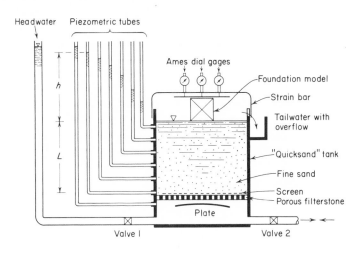

FIG. 14-14. Diagram of quicksand condition tank.

composite soil a certain size of particle which has a similar downward terminal velocity and which will therefore stay suspended, or float, in the upward stream. All finer-sized particles than those suspended will be carried by the stream up and away, whereas all coarser ones will sink and settle out. Thus, for the floating particles a critical flow velocity v_c, viz., critical hydraulic gradient i_c, is attained in the upward flow of water through the sand.

Upon further increase of the hydraulic gradient, one observes through the transparent walls of the apparatus that the sand starts to "boil" violently (Fig. 14-15), piping, channeling, and funneling up from bottom to top.

FIG. 14-15. Violent "boiling" and a "ground-break."

The process of internal, progressive erosion of soil beneath a massive dam founded on sand through which seepage takes place, or erosion around a sheet-piling wall system installed in a seeping soil, is called *piping*. Occasionally, at high flow pressures, a ground-break (water gap) in the sand occurs. Also, because of the upward flow pressure F and the weight G of the soil particle, a rotational motion of asymmetrical sand particles can be observed, causing a total rearrangement of the sand particles. The rotational motion is caused by the mechanical moment applied to an asymmetrical soil particle, as illustrated in Fig. 14-16.

Fine sand can start to "boil" in any open foundation pit if the groundwater rises toward the bottom of the pit at a hydraulic gradient greater than its critical value.

14.16. Other Uses of Quicksand Condition Apparatus. The quicksand appara-
tus is useful for demonstrating several other kinds of phenomena associated with the quick hydraulic phenomenon in soil. For example, a study can be made of the effect of a quicksand condition due to varying hydraulic gradients upon the stability of various model foundations with different contact pressures on the surface of the sand. Also, the behavior of a small concrete cofferdam can easily be studied by means of this apparatus. The cofferdam is placed in position so that the sand surface inside the cofferdam is a few inches below the surface of

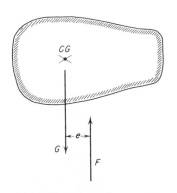

FIG. 14-16. Rotation of an asymmetrical particle of sand.

the sand outside the model. Figure 14-17 shows a failure when the quicksand condition develops inside the cofferdam, and a sand suspension boils over its top onto the relatively stable outside. As the quick condition continues, the degree

FIG. 14-17. Failure of a cofferdam model.

of instability of the cofferdam increases, and at final failure the model sinks into the tank below the ground surface. In this experiment, for instance, it is interesting to note that the upward boiling within the cofferdam starts in its corners, then approximately at the middle of the outside edge, then through the entire bottom of the model, until finally the cofferdam model disappears below the surface.

A model structure can be supported on footings or on a mat, set on the sand,

and caused to fail by a quick hydraulic condition. The same model can be set on piles and also caused to fail by the same agency. Observe that in both cases the critical hydraulic gradients are the same. The lesson from this experiment is that piles are of no value in fine-particled soils where quicksand conditions prevail. If piles are used, and it is economically feasible, they have to be driven down through the quicksand zone to and into a firm stratum. Under varying hydraulic conditions in sandy soil surveyors' bench marks may rise or settle.

The phenomenon of liquefaction of sand can also be demonstrated by means of the quicksand apparatus. A 2-kg (19.61 N) weight is placed on a loosely packed and saturated, but yet barely stable, soil in the tank. Then the hydraulic gradient is slowly applied and gradually increased until its critical value is attained, so as not to disturb the weight. A rod is then quickly thrust into the sand, causing the weight immediately to sink (Fig. 14-18). This phenomenon would occur in

FIG. 14-18. Liquefaction of sand by a sudden shock.

practice where the action of heavy machinery, such as a pile driver, causes a sudden shock to the soil; or where vibrations and/or blasting takes place; or where other dynamic forces such as earthquakes act—each can induce the structure to sink into the quick soil.

The liquefaction in fine, open-structure, and saturated sand, induced by a sudden shock, is explained as follows: the sudden shock means a suddenly applied shearing stress to the soil mass. Upon receiving the shock, the sand tends to decrease rapidly in volume. Simultaneously, the water in the voids of the sand—termed pore water—receives a suddenly applied pressure, or stress. In soil mechanics, stress carried by water is termed *neutral stress*. Upon the increase in neutral stress, some of the weight of the soil mass, which might be considered as furnishing the normal effect or intergranular stress entering into the shearing process of soil, is transmitted to the pore water pressure. According to Coulomb, the shear strength τ of a noncohesive soil can be expressed in an analytical form as

$$\tau = (\sigma_n - u)\tan \phi, \tag{14-33}$$

where $(\sigma_n - u)$ = normal effective (intergranular) stress, in kg/cm^2, or kN/m^2, or $lb/in.^2$, whichever system of units of measurement is used;

σ_n = total normal stress;

u = pore water pressure, or neutral stress, and

$\tan \phi$ = coefficient of internal friction of a noncohesive soil, which for one and the same material is considered to be constant.

From this equation, it can easily be seen that upon the increase in neutral stress u, the effective or intergranular stress of the soil $(\sigma_n - u)$ decreases and the shear strength of the soil τ decreases. The decrease in shear strength means decrease in bearing capacity of the soil.

14-17. Remedial Measures Against a Quick Condition. Concerning the critical hydraulic gradient in connection with the quicksand phenomenon,

$$i_c = h_c/L, \tag{14-34}$$

where h_c = critical hydraulic head, and L = length of seepage path, the problems of the foundation engineer center around two factors: 1) he may vary the value of the length of the seepage path L by means of engineering operations in the field; 2) nature, or the engineer, may vary the value of the pressure head h during construction or after construction is completed.

Thus the methods used to prevent a quicksand condition are based directly upon the fundamental i_c equation (14-34). The larger is L, the smaller is i_c. The smaller is h_c, the smaller is i_c.

The increase in length of the seepage path L is achieved by enclosing the excavation with one or two rows of sheet piling driven to some distance below the grade of excavation. By this increase in L the velocity of seepage, as well as the hydraulic gradient, are decreased.

The prolongation of the length of the seepage path can also be achieved by placing at the bottom of the excavation, where seepage lines converge, a clay blanket or other impermeable material according to the principle as illustrated in Fig. 14-19. However, the effect of such a blanket in decreasing the amount of seepage is small—about 20%.[4]

The hydrostatic pressure head h can be decreased by means of relief wells, as has been done along the levees of the Mississippi River.[5] Seepage can also be intercepted and reduced inside an excavation by means of a wellpoint system. Besides many other field methods, a quicksand condition may be prevented by increasing the downward-acting force. This is achieved by placing a load on the surface of the soil at the place of seepage discharge. Metal or timber mats can be loaded for this purpose in open excavations.

For analytical treatment of seepage and flow nets, the reader is referred to the author's books *Soil Mechanics*, and *Mechanics of Soils* [*Fundamentals for Advanced Study*], References 6 and 7.

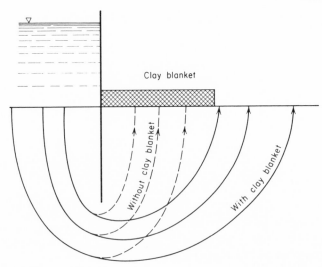

FIG. 14-19. Prolongation of the length of the seepage path.

14-18. Seepage Models. Experimental models can be used to great advantage for the student to visualize and understand the theory of seepage through earth dams and other earthworks, as well as for the purpose of training in obtaining flow lines on laboratory scale models.

The equipotential lines are sketched in the report drawing by the students according to Forchheimer's method of trial and error. In his instruction the author also assigns to students a seepage tank such as illustrated in Fig. 14-20.

FIG. 14-20. Model dam with an underdrain carpet.

Its size is 74″ x 24″ x 6″ (188 cm x 61 cm x 15 cm), and it is equipped with intake and outflow, adjustable overflow devices at both the upstream and downstream sides, and with dye injection points.

With such a seepage tank, experiments can be performed on dam models with homogeneous cross sections, on dam models provided with drainage galleries, on dams with permeable shells on the downstream slope, or with sheet piling or clay cores in the dam. Experimental results from models are evaluated to the natural scale of prototype dams by means of the theory of similitude.

The advantage of the hydraulic model over an electric one is that in the hydraulic model the Q-quantities can be clocked and the system's permeability k calculated. Besides, the hydraulic model permits observation of erosion and sloughing of the slopes of the dam should they occur. The electrical analog device, however, renders the flow net quickly, but does not give discharge, i.e., permeability.

14-19. Flow Nets by Electrical Analogy. The use of an electrical analogy is one of several ways for obtaining flow nets.

In the flow of electricity the current is proportional to the voltage drop. There is an analogy to the flow of water through soils, wherein seepage is proportional to the hydraulic head dissipated, the conductivity in the analogy corresponding to the permeability of the soil.

The analogy between Darcy's law and Ohm's law is as follows:

Darcy's Law   *Ohm's Law*
(*Hydraulic System*)   (*Electric System*)

$$Q = kiA = k\frac{h}{L}A, \qquad\qquad I = E/R = \lambda\frac{E}{L}A, \qquad (14\text{-}35)$$

or   or

$$Q = \left(\frac{kA}{L}\right)h, \qquad\qquad I = \left(\frac{\lambda A}{L}\right)E, \qquad (14\text{-}36)$$

where $(kA)/L$ = resistance of the soil   where $(\lambda A)/L$ = resistance of the
         to flow of water,   electrical conductivity,
Q = seepage or discharge, I = electrical current,
h = potential (pressure) E = voltage, and
         head, λ = electrical conductivity.
A = cross-sectional area, and
k = Darcy's coefficient of
         permeability.

By means of the electrical analogy method, the equipotential lines are traced and plotted, and the flow lines are then sketched in by the method of trial and adjustment. An electrical analog device for tracing equipotential lines is shown in Fig. 14-21.

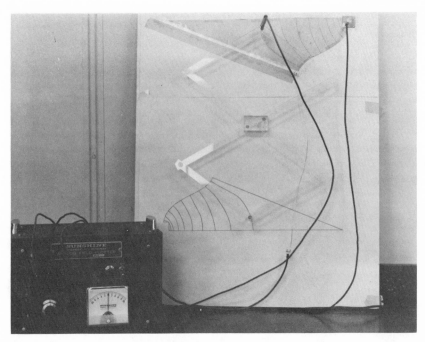

FIG. 14-21. An electrical analog device for tracing of equipotential lines. The pantograph is made of plastic.

14-20. Seepage Analysis by Method of Trial and Adjustment. Because in many cases it is very difficult to comprehend the given seepage system's boundary conditions analytically, seepage flow problems for practical purposes are usually solved by method of trial and adjustment. This method consists of sketching flow and equipotential lines after the uppermost flow line has been established mathematically, experimentally, or graphically by constructing the seepage parabola.

In applying the sketching method in seepage analysis, it is satisfactory enough to use only 5 to 6 flow lines. No improvement in precision is attained in using more than the indicated number of flow lines, because the method of sketching is not a precise one anyway.

A system's flow net affords the solution of the following hydraulic problems:
1) hydrostatic pressure head, h_n, for any point along the base of the dam
2) uplift pressure distribution, p_u, on the base of the dam
3) hydraulic gradient, i, at any point
4) seepage flow veloicty, v
5) amount of seepage, Q
6) seepage pressure, $D = \gamma_w \cdot i$
7) factor of safety against piping, η

Example 1. The application of the flow net theory to hydraulic structures on permeable soils is illustrated by a seepage problem around a sheet piling driven into the

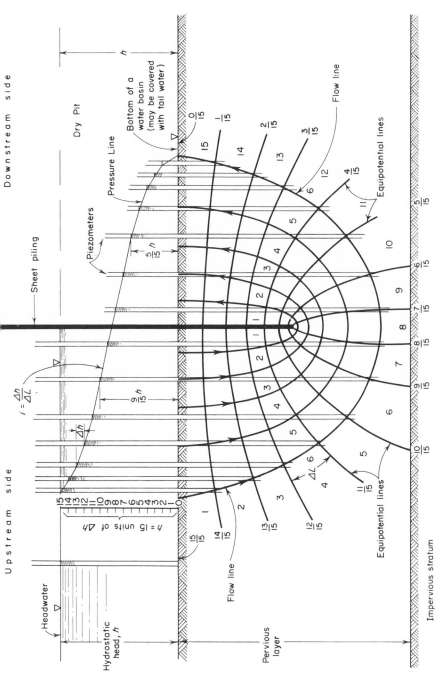

FIG. 14-22. Seepage around sheet piling.

bottom of a water basin, for example, a river, for the purpose of obtaining a pit with a reasonable dry bottom by pumping out the enclosure (Fig. 14-22). The seepage water flowing through the soil around the sheet piling is collected in a sump from which it is pumped out.

In this example, the total drop in head is $h = 15$ ft, and the coefficient of the system's permeability in this example is given as $k = 0.125$ ft/day. The system's flow net is also given. It is required to calculate seepage flow into the enclosure in cubic feet per day per running foot of the wall of sheet piling.

Solution. There are a total of $M = 6$ flow channels in this flow net, and $N = 15$ equal drops in head. The discharge quantity of seepage from the upstream side to the downstream side (pit) is, by Eq. (14-19),

$$Q = kh(M/N) = (0.125)(15)(6/15) = 0.75 \qquad (\text{ft}^3/\text{day})$$

per running foot of wall of sheet piling, a quantity which may be considered small or large, depending upon the length of the perimeter of the enclosure by sheet piling.

In the SI units, this problem is solved as follows:
$h = 15$ ft. $= 4.60$ m
$k = 0.125$ ft/day $= 0.0381$ m/day
$M = 6; \quad N = 15;$
$q = kh(M/N) = (0.0381)(4.60)(6/15) = 0.0701$ m^3/(day)(m)
$\quad = 0.75$ (ft^3/(day)(ft)).

Example 2. In Fig. 14-23 is shown a massive dam resting on the horizontal upper surface of a homogeneous soil (bottom of water basin) underlain by an impervious stratum. On the downstream side, at point A, the dam is provided with a sheet piling at the end of the spilway. The net hydraulic head of water on the upstream side of the dam effective in bringing about seepage flow is $h = 10.0$ m. On the upstream side, the dam is provided with a shear key embedded into the soil $a = 2.0$ m deep. The coefficient of permeability of the soil is $k = 0.500$ m/day.

Assume that after several trials, the flow net is adjusted as shown in Fig. 14-23. In this flow net, the number of flow channels is $M = 5$, and the number of equipotential drops is $N = 13$.

1) *Pressure head.* The pressure head $h = 10.0$ m is divided into 13 equal parts (see right-side of figure). This permits one to vizualize the loss of pressure head between equipotential lines. For example, if the total drop in head is $h = 10.0$ m, then the drop in head across each square is

$$\Delta h = h/N = \frac{10}{13} = \underline{0.77 \ [m]}$$

At the standpipe (imagine one) through the concrete at the No. 4 equipotential line ($n = 4$; here n is the number of equal equipotential drops between the point of consideration and zero potential) the loss in pressure head is

$$\frac{h}{N} \cdot n = n \cdot \Delta h = (\frac{4}{13}) \cdot h = \frac{(4)\,(10)}{13} = \underline{3.08 \ [m]}.$$

The remaining pressure head is here

$$h_{n=4} = h - (\frac{4}{13})\,h = (\frac{9}{13}) \cdot h = \frac{(9) \cdot (10)}{13} = \underline{6.92 \ [m]}$$

and the still available driving pressure at this point is

$$p_{n=4} = \gamma_w \cdot h_{n=4} = (9.81)\,(\frac{9}{13}) \cdot h = (9.81) \cdot \frac{(9) \cdot (10)}{13} = (9.81)\,(6.92)$$

$$= \underline{67.89 \ [kN/m^2]} = \underline{67.89 \ [Pa]}$$

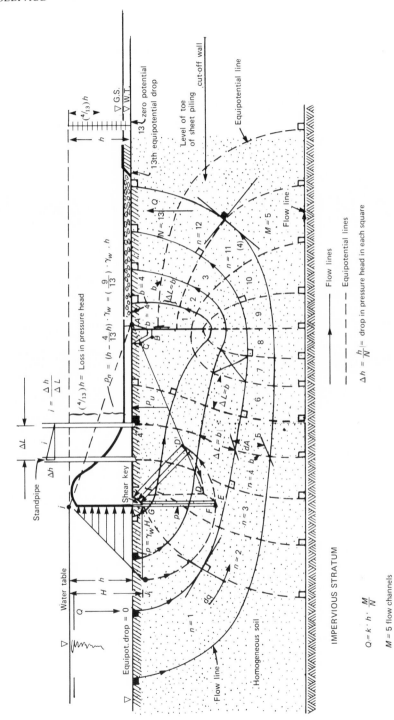

FIG. 14-23. Flow lines and equipotential lines for seepage under a massive dam.

$Q = k \cdot h \cdot \dfrac{M}{N}$

M = 5 flow channels

N = 13 equipotential drop

——— Flow lines

– – – Equipotential lines

$\Delta h = \dfrac{h}{N}$ = drop in pressure head in each square

2. *Uplift pressure.* The uplift pressure p_u at this point No. 4 is the remaining pressure head $h_{n=4}$ time the unit weight of water γ_w:

$$p_{u_{n=4}} = (\frac{9}{13}) \cdot \gamma_w \cdot h = \underline{67.89 \ [kN/m^2]}$$

Notice that this result is independent of the number of squares in the flow net.

3. *Hydraulic gradient.* Consider any square in the flow net. Let the length of the side of the square by $\Delta L = b$. Then the drop in pressure head across the square is

$$\Delta h = \frac{h}{N} = 0.77 \ [m]$$

and the hydraulic gradient i for the square at point A is

$$i = \frac{\text{loss in head}}{\text{distance traversed}} = \frac{\Delta h}{\Delta L} = \frac{\Delta h}{b} = \frac{h}{N \cdot b} = \frac{10.0}{(13)(4.0)}$$

$$= \underline{0.1925 \ [\text{dimensionless}]}$$

This is also the actual exit hydraulic gradient at A (See Fig. 14-23), where $b = 4.0$ m.

4. *Seepage velocity.* Seepage velocity v is expressed as

$$v = k \cdot i = k \cdot \frac{h}{N \cdot b} = \frac{\Delta q}{(\Delta A)(t)} = (0.500) \frac{(10.0)}{(13)(4.0)} = \underline{0.096 \ [m/day]},$$

where $k =$ Darcy's coefficient of permeability, given here as

$$k = 0.500 \ m/day,$$
$$\Delta q = \text{flow through one flow channel per unit time,}$$
$$\Delta A = b \ x \ 1 = 4 \ x \ 1 = 4 \ m^2, \text{ and}$$
$$t = \text{time.}$$

Thus, velocity v at any point in the flow channel varies inversely proportional with the spacing b of the adjacent flow lines.

5. *Amount of seepage.* The total amount of seepage flow Q through all flow channels (M in number) per unit time is

$$Q = k \cdot i \cdot A \ [\text{volume}/(\text{time})(\text{unit length of run of dam})]$$
$$= k \cdot \frac{h}{N \cdot b} \cdot (b \times 1) \cdot M = k \cdot h \cdot \frac{M}{N} = (0.500)(10.0)(\frac{5}{13}) = \underline{1.92 \ m^3/(\text{day})(m),}$$

where M/N is *independent* of the size of the squares.

6. *Seepage pressure.* Refer to Section 14-11 about the derivation of seepage pressure $D = \gamma_w \cdot i$. It should be noticed that seepage pressure is a body-force, and acts along the direction of flow of water. Knowing the hydraulic gradient at any point in the flow net, the seepage pressure D can be calculated:

$$D = \gamma_w \cdot i = (9.81)(0.1925) = \underline{1.888 \ [kN/m^3]}$$

7. *Factor of Safety Against Piping (Quick Condition of Sand) or Hydraulic Ground-break.* The factor of safety η against piping is expressed as the ratio of the critical

hydraulic gradient i_c at exit of the flow system (usually taken as point A, Fig. 14-23). Piping will occur at point A when the upward force of water issuing at A is greater than the weight of the soil particles. The upward seepage force per unit volume of the upward flowing water at point A is

$$D = \gamma_w \cdot i = 1.888 \; [\text{kN}/\text{m}^3]$$

The weight W of the submerged soil particles is

$$W_{sub} = \frac{G - 1}{1 + e} \cdot \gamma_w = \frac{2.65 - 1.00}{1 + 0.50} \cdot (9.81) = \frac{(1.65)\,(9.81)}{1.50} =$$

$$= 16.18 \; [\text{kN}/\text{m}^3]$$

At force equilibrium, $D = W_{sub}$, or

$$\gamma_w \cdot i = \frac{G - 1}{1 + e} \cdot \gamma_w$$

Therefore piping (quick condition) occurs when

$$i = \frac{G - 1}{1 + e} = i_c,$$

where $i_c = \dfrac{G - 1}{1 + e} = \dfrac{1.65}{1.50} = \underline{1.10}$ is the critical hydraulic gradient

in the soil material under consideration.
The factor of safety against piping:

$$\eta = \frac{i_c}{i} = \frac{1.10}{0.1925} = \underline{5.71} \geqq \eta_{all}$$

where η_{all} is the allowable factor of safety, usually of the order of magnitude from $\eta_{all} = 3.00$ to $\eta_{all} = 5.00$.

WATER IN SOIL

REFERENCES

1. A. Casagrande, *Seepage Through Earth Dams*, New England Water Works Association, vol. 51, no. 2, June 1937, pp. 136, 137.
2. A. Schoklitsch, *Graphische Hydraulik*, Leipzig und Berlin, B. G. Teubner, 1923, p. 16.
3. Ph. Forchheimer, *Hydraulik*, Leipzig, B. G. Teubner, 1914, p. 448.
4. L. White and E. A. Prentis, *Cofferdams*, New York, Columbia University Press, 1950, p. 35.
5. W. J. Turnbull and C. I. Mansur, "Relief Well Systems for Dams and Levees," *Proceedings, ASCE*, vol. 79, New York, September 1953.
6. A. R. Jumikis, *Soil Mechanics*, Princeton, N.J., D. Van Nostrand Company, Inc., 1962, pp. 307-349.
7. A. R. Jumikis, *Mechanics of Soils (Fundamentals for Advanced Study)*, Princeton, N.J., D. Van Nostrand Company, Inc., 1964, pp. 415-435.

SUGGESTIONS FOR FURTHER READING

1. U.S. Bureau of Reclamation, *Design of Small Dams*, Denver, Colorado, 1960.
2. H.R. Cedegren, *Seepage, Drainage and Flow Nets*. John Wiley and Sons, Inc., New York, N.Y., 1967.
3. R.J.M. De Wiest, *Geohydrology*, John Wiley and Sons, Inc., New York, N.Y., 1965.
4. P.A. Domenico, Concepts and Models in Groundwater Hydrology, New York, N.Y., McGraw-Hill Book Company, 1972.
5. F.W. Hanna and R.C. Kennedy, *The Design of Dams*, New York, N.Y., McGraw-Hill Book Co., 1931.
6. M.K. Hubert, *The Theory of Groundwater Motion and Related Papers,* Hafner Publishing Co., Inc., New York, N.Y., 1969. Contains Henry Darcy's 1856 paper entitled "Les Fontaines Publiques de la Ville de Dijon," pp. 303-311.
7. International Association for Hydraulics Research, *Fundamentals of Transport Phenomena in Porous Media* (Development in Soil Science 2). Elsevier Publishing Company, Amsterdam/New York, 1972.
8. A.E. Morgan, *Dams and Other Disasters*. P. Sargent, Boston, 1971.
9. P.Y. Polubarinova-Kochina, *Theory of Groundwater Movement*, translated from the Russian by J.M.R. De Wiest. Princeton, N.J.: Princeton University Press, 1962.
10. J.L. Sherrard, R.J. Woodward, S.F. Gizienski and W.A. Clevenger, *Earth and Earth-Rock Dams*, John Wiley and Sons, Inc., New York, N.Y., 1963.
11. E.E. Wahlstrom, *Dams, Dam Foundations and Reservoir Sites*. Amsterdam/New York, N.Y., Elsevier Scientific, 1974.
12. C.W. Boast and D. Kirkham, "Auger Hole Seepage Theory." Proceedings of the Soil Science Society of America, vol. 35, 1971, p. 365.
13. Bureau of Reclamation, "Field Permeability, Tests in Boreholes;" in *Earth Manual* (2nd ed.), Washington, D.C., U.S. Department of the Interior, Bureau of Reclamation, 1974, pp. 573-593.
14. M.E. Harr, *Groundwater and Seepage,* New York, N.Y., McGraw-Hill Book Company, 1962, pp. 15-26; 50-59.

QUESTIONS AND PROBLEMS

14- 1. Of what value are flow nets?

14- 2. Estimate the amount of seepage of the homogenous earth dam sketched in Fig. Problem 14-2 per foot of shore line. Use customary and SI units.
  Given: unit weight of saturated soil mass $\gamma_{sat} = 120$ lb/ft^3 = 18.82 kN/m^3,
  unit weight of water $\gamma_w = 62.4$ lb/ft^3 = 9.81 kN/m^3,
  average coefficient of permeability $k_{ave} = 0.15$ ft/day = 0.04572 m/day.

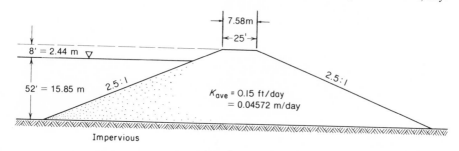

FIG. PROBLEM 14-2.

14- 3. For the earth dam shown in Fig. Problem 14-2, develop analytically an expression for seepage discharge. After you have established the uppermost flow line, calculate discharge in cubic feet per day per foot of shore line and in m^3/(day·m). The coefficients of permeabilities at a standard temperature of 20°C are $k_h = 0.1350$ ft/day = 0.0411 m/day, and k_v=0.0500 ft/day=0.0152 m/day.

14- 4. Given a homogenous earth dam as sketched in Fig. Problem 14-4. $G = 2.70$; $e = 0.75$.

  a) Construct the basic parabola and determine the uppermost flow line when $h = 0$ m.

  b) Construct a flow net and compute seepage in cubic feet per day per 100 m shoreline: k_v=0.0002 cm/min; k_h=0.0008 cm/min when h=0 m.

  c) If there were no drainage gallery and if the uppermost flow line would leave the dam at pont E, what are the hydraulic and stability conditions of the dam at that point? Use here $h = 5$ ft = 1.524 m (tailwater).

  d) Determine the factor of safety η of the dam relative to a quick condition at point E.

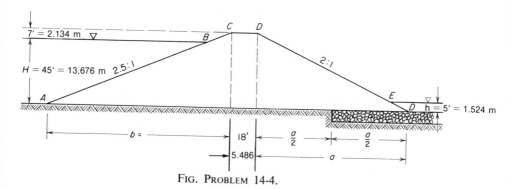

FIG. PROBLEM 14-4.

14- 5. What is the function of the drainage gallery in an earth dam?

14- 6. Given: an earth dam as shown on Fig. Problem 14-6. The difference of head in upstream ana downstream levels is 85 ft or 25.91 m. The coefficients of permeability to water of the dam material are: $k_h = 200$ ft/day or 60.96 m/day, and $k_v=(0.5)k_h$. Porosity of dam: $n = 30\%$. Specific gravity of the soil particles: $G = 2.68$.

Required:

    1) The amount of loss of water from the reservoir by seepage in cubic feet per day per 100 ft or 30.48 m of run of the dam.

    2) From your flow lines in the flow net drawn to scale of the dam (establish a linear scale!) determine:

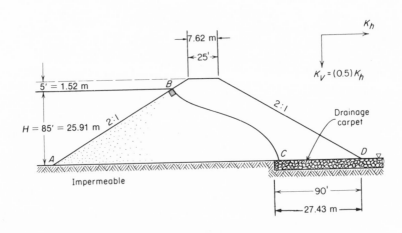

FIG. PROBLEM 14-6.

    a) the actual hydraulic gradient which exists in your first (or upper) flow channel between the first two flow lines and for each of your consecutive equipotential drops;

    b) the critical hydraulic gradient of the system, and

    c) the factor of safety η against the possibility of developing a quick condition in the area of the head of the filter gallery (point C).

    3) Prepare a separate sketch similar to the one shown here, and indicate by vectors all the forces, and their points of application, necessary to be considered in a stability analysis of a slope of an earth bank, relative to rupture along a circularly curved sliding surface. Describe briefly the nature of the various forces pertaining to such a stability or instability problem.

14- 7. What is the effect of a rapid draw-down of water on the upstream side relative to the stability of the dam?

14- 8. Given: a 60-ft-long overflow weir, resting on a pervious layer of soil as shown in Fig. Problem 14-8. The overall coefficient of permeability of the soil is $k = 3.0 \times 10^{-3}$ cm/sec. Calculate discharge Q in cubic centimeters per second per meter of shoreline of the weir. Also, prepare an uplift pressure diagram underneath the weir.

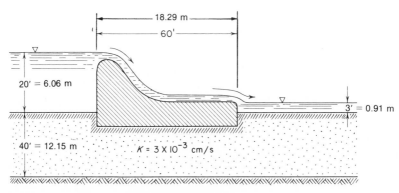

FIG. PROBLEM 14-8.

14- 9. What is the technical meaning of the term "quicksand"?

14-10. Plot a critical hydraulic gradient curve as a function of the void ratio of the soil, $i_c = f(e)$, and discuss what inferences can be drawn from the plotted curve. The specific gravity of the soil in question is $G = 2.65$.

14-11. 1) Derive the equation expressing the critical hydraulic gradient in terms of G and n.

2) Derive this gradient as a function of G and e.

3) Explain what physical conditions govern the i_c-relationship.

4) Does i_c depend upon the system's coefficient of permeability?

6) What does it mean mathematically and physically if $i_c = 1$?

14-12. What is the critical hydraulic gradient to cause a quick condition in a soil mass, the void ratio of which is 0.80, if the specific gravity of the soil particles is 2.66?

14.13. Given a sheet-piled cofferdam as shown in Fig. Problem 14-13.

Required:

a) Establish an orthogonal hydrodynamic flow net.

b) What is the hydraulic gradient at points A and B?

c) What is the critical hydraulic gradient at points A and B?

d) What is the factor of safety η against erosive piping?

e) Calculate the total influx of water into this cofferdam per 100 m of run of excavation.

Required:

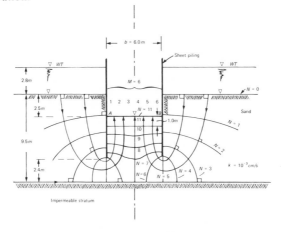

PART IV

Consolidation of Soil
and Settlement of Structures

Chapter 15

PERFORMANCE OF SOIL
UNDER COMPRESSIVE LOAD

15-1. Introduction. If a clayey, saturated soil is subjected to a structural compressive load, then the volume change in the soil is attributed mainly to the expulsion of water out of the voids of the cohesive soil. Volume changes in the vertical direction bring about a settlement of the soil, viz., settlement or a compressive deformation of the soil structure. Thus, settlement of soil may be defined as the vertical, downward displacement of soil, or movement of structure on that soil, brought about by a volume change in the soil due to a decrease in the volume of the voids in the soil, occurring after the beginning of construction.

The settlement of a foundation, in turn, may be defined as the change in elevation of the base of the footing. As the soil settles, so does the foundation. Thus the magnitude of the settlement of the foundation is the same as for the soil upon which the foundation rests. In other words, settlement is the sinking of a structure due to a compressive deformation of the underlying soil.

If the contact pressure at the base of the footing on the soil is uniform, and uniformly distributed, settlements may be tolerable if the type of structure and/ or its exploitation can withstand such settlements. In contradistinction, non-uniform, or differential, settlement of a structure may be disastrous, leading to cracking of the structural members, impairment of the structural rigidity of the building, and eventually to the collapse of the structure. This is particularly true with statically indeterminate structures such as continuous beams on more than two supports, frames, arches, vaults, and others. In these structures, settlement of a support induces supplemental moments, and if these additional bending moments are not taken into account in proportioning the structural members, the structure may turn out to be too weak to resist the additional moments, and may start to crack. A tall building may lean because of unequal, or differential settlements of the soil, and so would two adjacent structures as for example, two oil storage tanks or two towers (Fig. 2-1) built next to each other: these tanks would lean toward each other because of the pressure distribution overlap in soil from these two tanks.

However, a uniform, tolerable settlement should not be construed as a failure because settlement of a soil as a function of load is a normal physical phenomenon. Uniform settlement is settlement which is brought about when the entire structure, under uniform pressure distribution on a uniform, homogeneous soil material, settles evenly without causing additional stresses in the structure.

The term "differential settlement" is used then when some parts of a structure settle more than others.

15-2. Causes of Settlements. Some of the main factors contributing to settlement of soils are as follows:

1) Static loads on soil.
2) Dynamic forces from vibrations excited by machinery, traffic, pile driving operations, explosions, earthquakes, and various impacts on soil due to collapse of structures and/or earthworks. These factors loosen the structural strength of the soil, particularly the strength of noncohesive soils.
3) Fluctuations in the elevation of the groundwater table. This factor can be further subdivided into
   a) normal natural fluctuation and drought;
   b) artificial lowering of the groundwater table as, for example, for providing a dry foundation pit, river regulation or operations for drainage of an area, through radiation of heat from blast and other furnaces (drying, shrinking of soil);
   c) raising the groundwater table artificially by impounding water in a reservoir, by tides, floods (may cause heave of soil), breaks in water mains;
   d) subsidence of soil caused by mining and tunneling operations (subways and vibrations);
4) Settlement from frost-heaved soils:
   a) natural: from thawing;
   b) artificial: under refrigeration houses;
5) Other possible factors.

Figure 15-1 illustrates schematically the nature of the course of uniform consolidation settlement of structures founded on noncohesive and cohesive soils. On noncohesive soils, the settlement almost ceases during and at the end of the time of construction, whereas full settlement of a structure founded on a cohesive soil is attained after a very long time. The latter is due to the long time needed for the expulsion and draining of water out of the voids of the cohesive soil at a certain load intensity (contact pressure) transmitted to the soil by the foundation of the structure.

According to Terzaghi:[1] "Every process involving a decrease in the water content of a saturated soil without replacement of the water by air is called a process of *consolidation*. The opposite process is called a process of swelling, which involves an increase in the water content due to an increase in the volume of the voids." Any intermediate stage in the consolidation process is termed the *degree of consolidation*, and is expressed in percents of the full consolidation.

Likewise, in respect to the stress, in soil mechanics the compressive stress externally applied to a mass of a soil is termed the *total stress*, p. Part of this total stress, which during the consolidation process (drainage process) of a soil

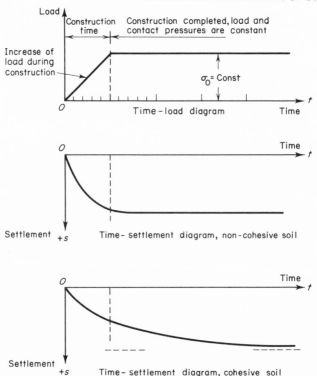

FIG. 15-1.   Nature of course of settlement of a structure of non-cohesive and cohesive soil.   Note that the amount of settlement is not the same for the two kinds of soil.

is taken up by water, is termed the *neutral stress, u*. The other part of the total stress, which is transferred intergranularly on the soil particles, is termed the *effective stress, p_e*. Then

$$p = p_e + u. \tag{15-1}$$

It is obvious that within the process of consolidation, a gradual decrease in neutral pressure takes place, along with a gradual increase in effective pressure. Their sum, however, is at all times constant and equal to the total pressure in magnitude, and is

$$p = p_e + u = p'_e + u' = p''_e + u'' = \cdots = \text{const.} \tag{15-2}$$

The magnitude of constancy, of course, depends upon the total stress *p*.

Equation (15-1) is the fundamental, general equation governing the stress conditions in the consolidation process of a saturated clay.

The consolidation theory of clays is due to Terzaghi and Fröhlich.[2]

Some Reasons for Intolerable Settlements.   From soil mechanics theory on settlement of soils it is known that the magnitude of the settlement depends not only on the compressibility of the soil, but also upon the size and shape of the footings of foundations, upon the stresses in the soil underneath the foundations, water regimen in the soil, and other factors. Compression of soil is manifested in settlement of foundations.

Some of the reasons for differential and/or intolerable settlements follow:

1) Geologic and physical nonuniformity, or anomalies, in type, structure, thickness, and density of the soil medium (alluvial soils, clay, gravel, pockets of sand in clay, clay lenses in sand, wedge-like soil strata, ice lenses in soil, and effects of thawing of such ice lenses); admixture of organic matter; peat; muck.

2) Nonuniform pressure distribution from foundation to soil due to non-uniform loading, and consequent differential performance of soil under the given configuration and structure of the works (part of structure is founded on piles, and part on shallow foundations).

3) Water regimen at the construction site.

4) Overstressing of soil at adjacent site by heavy structures built next to light ones (towers, spires, skyscrapers, silos).

5) Overlap of stress distribution in soil from adjoining structures.

6) Other possible factors.

From the above discussion it can be inferred that foundation design is a very complex problem, in the solution of which one must consider many factors involved and also some "possible impossible conditions."

The prevailing trend in the engineering profession now is to require that plans of every important structure designed on compressible clay should be accompanied by an estimate of the possible settlements which may occur at various points under the foundations, the rate of settlement, and the magnitude of the final settlement.

15-3. Consolidometer. The compressive properties of a soil are usually studied by means of a device termed the consolidometer, Fig. 15-2.

A consolidometer consists of a ring (1), into which is placed a soil sample (2), undisturbed or remolded, whichever may be the assigned problem. Here the soil sample is in a laterally confined state. On top and at the bottom of the soil sample there are porous filter stones (3), one on each side of the sample, to permit a two-way drainage of water expelled out of the voids from the soil sample under a vertical load P. The axial, vertical load is applied on the soil sample by means of a loading yoke (4). The load is transmitted centrally from the loading yoke through a steel ball bearing (5) which rests on a circular loading plate (6), providing a uniform pressure distribution on the soil sample. The soil sample is subjected to predetermined load increments.

The load externally applied on the soil sample compresses the soil, squeezes some water out from the voids of the soil, and the soil sample thus decreases in thickness. This volume change is measured by an Ames dial gage (7). The volume change readings are made at definite time intervals for each load increment.

Depending upon the thickness of the ring, soil samples 1 cm to about 4.5 cm thick (or high) may be subjected to such a laterally confined compression or consolidation test depending upon the thickness of the consolidation ring (1).

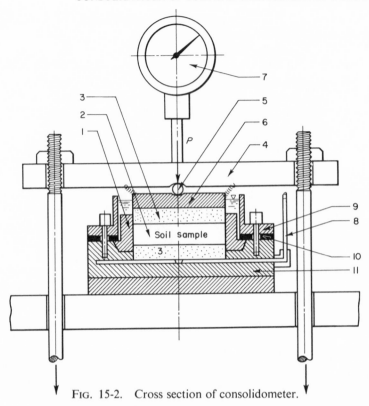

Fig. 15-2. Cross section of consolidometer.

Because drainage of thick layers of clay requires a relatively long period of time, consolidation tests in the laboratory are usually performed on thin samples, 1 to 2.5 cm in thickness. Consolidation of such samples under a certain intensity of load usually is accomplished within a few days, and sometimes even within 24 hours. Consolidation is brought about by effective pressures.

At the bottom of the soil sample, the water expelled from the soil flows through the filter stone and is forced into the standpipe (8).

At the top, a well-jacket (a brass ring) (9), filled with water, is placed around the porous filter stone in order to prevent excessive evaporation from the soil sample during the test. Water is forced into this well-jacket through the upper filter stone upon compression of the soil. Thus, during the consolidation test the soil sample is kept submerged in a saturated condition. This is so practiced because soils have their lowest strength and greatest compressibility when they are in a fully saturated condition. Inundation of the soil would also exclude the resistance to compression by the apparent cohesion (surface tension forces). Besides, the Terzaghi-Fröhlich consolidation theory of clays is devised for a fully saturated condition of the soil; hence, the consolidation test must be performed accordingly.

Theoretically, the standpipe permits the performance of a direct soil permeability test to water during the progress of the consolidation test. In essence, this standpipe is a falling (or rising) head permeameter. However, it is much simpler to calculate k by data as obtained from the consolidation test.

15-4. Consolidation Test. From the description of the consolidation apparatus, it can be inferred that the consolidation test of a soil is in essence a compression test on a laterally confined soil sample, and in a way also a drainage or permeability test under load. It is a model test, not a destructive test like the shear test.

The main purpose of the consolidation test is to obtain information on the compressible properties of a saturated soil for use in determining the magnitude and rate of settlement of structures.

Some detailed description of consolidation tests of soils can be found in Reference 3.

To summarize, the consolidation test of a soil should furnish the following information:

1) the relationship between time and percent consolidation, represented by the time-consolidation diagram;

2) the relationship between the increasing or decreasing load on the soil and the change in the void ratio of the soil, represented by the pressure-void ratio diagram (expansion diagram); and

3) data on permeability of the soil as a function of that particular load.

15-5. Stress-Strain Diagrams. Soils, although they undergo compression like solid bodies, actually follow Hooke's law of deformation only within a relatively narrow load interval (compare the stress-strain diagrams for metal and for soil in Fig. 15-3),

where $P.L.$ = proportional limit,

$\quad\quad p_p$ = stress at proportional limit,

$\quad\quad E.L.$ = elastic limit,

$\quad\quad p_y$ = yield point stress,

$\quad\quad U.S.$ = ultimate strength (p_u),

$\quad\quad L$ = length of steel bar,

$\quad\quad \Delta L$ = deformation of steel bar,

$\quad\quad \varepsilon = \Delta L/L$ = relative deformation, or strain,

$\quad\quad H$ = thickness of layer of soil,

$\quad\quad \Delta H$ = absolute deformation (settlement) of soil,

$\quad\quad \varepsilon = \Delta H/H$ = relative settlement of soil.

The stress-strain curve for soil departs from the straight line as for steel, for example, indicating that soil departs from Hooke's law and that the deformation increases at a great rate after the so-called proportional limit, $P.L.$, is passed. At the yield point $Y.P.$, the strain approaches an infinitely large value, i.e., the soil settles rapidly.

Water in the Voids of Soil. The voids of the soil may be filled with water. Upon compressing such a soil, water is expelled out of the voids of the soil. The loading of saturated clays is thus always accompanied, at ordinary temperatures, by a decrease in soil moisture content, and thus by a decrease in volume of

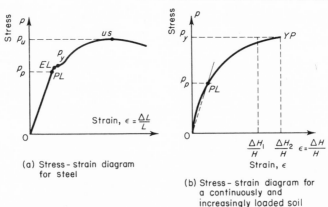

(a) Stress- strain diagram
for steel

Strain, ϵ

(b) Stress- strain diagram for
a continuously and
increasingly loaded soil

FIG. 15-3.   Sketches of the shapes of stress-strain diagrams, (a) for steel and (b) for soil.

the soil. The process of expulsion of water from the voids of the soil is in itself a process of permeability of the clay to water, under the influence of the compressive load externally applied to the soil mass.

The water drains out of the voids of cohesive soils very slowly because of their low permeability.

Resistance to expulsion of water from the voids increases with the decrease in moisture content in the soil during the process of compression. It can now be inferred that with an increase in the compressive load on a clay soil its resistance to compression increases.

Effect of Temperature on Consolidation. Because consolidation of soil is essentially a drainage process involving the concept of permeability, and per- meability is affected by temperature, then, obviously, temperature must logically also have an effect upon the process of consolidation.

The dynamic viscosity tables in the Appendix of this book show that a change in temperature from 0°C to 25°C brings about a corresponding change in the values of dynamic viscosity of about double, i.e., from 0.01790 to 0.00894 (g)/(cm sec) = poises, respectively.

Hence, the higher the temperature of the soil under a consolidation test, the greater its drainage, the higher the compressibility, and the higher the rate of consolidation.

Therefore, upon subjecting a soil to a consolidation test, the soil temperature should be measured, test results corrected, and reported at a standard tempera- ture, say, of +20°C.

Effect of Noncohesive Soil Layers on a Sandwiched Cohesive Soil. If a cohesive soil layer is enclosed between two permeable layers of granular noncohesive material, this condition facilitates drainage of water out of the soil by the fact that the clay has now two drainage faces through which to empty, as compared with one-way drainage. Hence drainage and consolidation with two drainage faces can take place at a much more rapid rate than through one drainage face, assuming that all other conditions in both cases are the same.

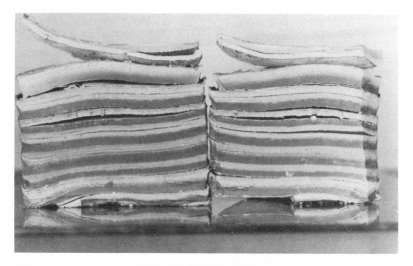

FIG. 15-4. Varved clay.

Likewise, varved clays containing sandwiched layers of silt (Fig. 15-4) drain and consolidate faster and more effectively than a mass of solid clay of the same thickness.

15-6. Preconsolidation. It may have happened that in geological times past, a soil in nature has been previously loaded with a certain pressure (a sheet of glacial ice, for example[4]), p_{pr}, under which the soil had time to consolidate (point 2 on branch 1-2 of the pressure-void ratio curve, Fig. 15-5). In this example the compressive stress is $p_{pr} = 4.0$ kg/cm$^2 \sim 392$ kN/m^2. It also could have happened that after the consolidation time elapsed, the load on the soil was removed to zero, branch 2-3. Some time after the unloading it could be that a sample of this unloaded soil was taken and subjected to a consolidation test under loads from $p = 0$ to $p = p_t = 9.5$ kg/cm$^2 \approx 932$ kN/m^2, reloading branch 3-4-5, past the previous preconsolidation stress, $p_{pr} =$ kg/cm$^2 \sim 392$ kN/m^2, that existed on the soil earlier. Branch 5-6 shows that the soil sample was unloaded to zero (point 6), resulting in a void ratio of $e_6 = 0.23$.

The amount of swelling, or rebound, or *elastic deformation* in terms of void ratio is from $e_5 = 0.10$ to $e_6 = 0.23$, or $\Delta e_{el} = 0.23 - 0.10 = 0.13$. The amount of permanent or *plastic deformation* in terms of void ratio is from $e_3 = 0.35$ to $e_6 = 0.23$, or $\Delta e_{pl} = 0.35 - 0.23 = 0.12$.

This pressure-void ratio relationship as shown in Fig. 15-5 thus indicates that, before the consolidation test, the soil had once before been subjected to a preconsolidation load the pressure intensity of which was $p_{pr} = 4.0$ kg/cm$^2 \approx 392$ kN/m^2.

Note that up to the preconsolidation stress p_{pr}, from zero to p_{pr}, the stress-void ratio curve (*p-e* curve) has a relatively flat slope, whereas past the preconsolidation stress the curve has a relatively steep slope. Such a graph is typical for preconsolidated and reloaded clays. In soil engineering the nature of

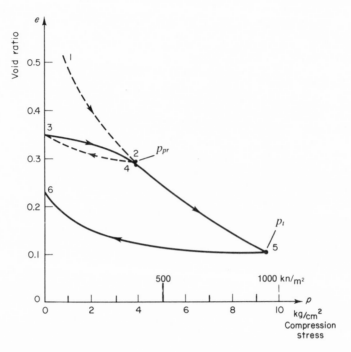

FIG. 15-5.   Pressure-void ratio curve of a precompressed soil. Arithmetic scale.

the slopes of the p-e curve on both sides of the preconsolidation stress indicates the following: up to the preconsolidation load this soil is less compressible than past the preconsolidation load. To illustrate this point simply, assume that on this soil a foundation is to be laid transmitting to the soil a contact pressure of $\sigma_o = 2$ kg/cm$^2 \approx 196$ kN/m^2. Because in our illustration the contact pressure σ_o is less than the given preconsolidation pressure p_{pr}, i.e., $\sigma_o = 2$ kg/cm$^2 < p_{pr} = 4$ kg/cm^2, or $\sigma_o = 196$ kN/m$^2 < p_{pr} \approx 392$ kN/m^2, the magnitude of the settlement s of this clay soil can be expected to be small. If, however, the contact pressure σ_o at the base of the footing were, say $\sigma_o = 7$ kg/cm$^2 \sim 686$ kN/m^2, a case where the contact pressure is larger than the preconsolidation pressure $p_{pr} = 4$ kg/cm$^2 \approx 392$ kN/m^2, then much larger settlement of the clay can be expected than at contact pressures below the preconsolidation pressure.

To find the point representing the preconsolidation pressure on such curves, A. Casagrande[5] suggested the following empirical method which locates the point in question approximately (Fig. 15-6). The p-e curve is usually drawn to a semi-logarithmic scale. Locate by eye the point of the greatest curvature (point A on the recompression branch, for example). Through this point draw a horizontal line A-h and a tangent A-t to the curve. Bisect the angle ∡ hAt thus formed by the bisector Ab. Then draw backwards, from point $5'$, the straight line part of the compression curve 5-$5'$ (straight dotted line, a-a) until it intersects the bisector line Ab to give point p_{pr}. This point then approximately determines the preconsolidation pressure.

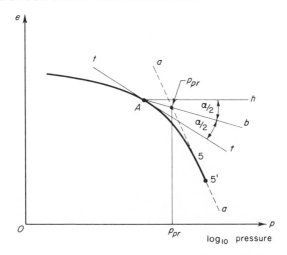

Fɪɢ. 15-6. Determination of preconsolidation pressure p_{pr}. After A. Casagrande.

A soil may have been preconsolidated during the geologic past by the weight of an ice sheet or glacier which has melted away, or by other geologic overburden and structural loads which no longer exist. For example, thick layers of over-burdened soil may have been eroded or excavated away, or heavy structures may have been torn down. Also, capillary pressures which may have acted on the clay layers in the past may have been removed for one reason or another. Preconsolidation may also be caused by evaporation of water from the clay.

The practical significance of the preconsolidation load appears in calculating settlements of structures and in geological studies of unsolidified sediments which at some time in the geologic past may have been subjected to an over-burden load.

As to the pressure history of loaded compressible soils one distinguishes between three kinds of such soils, namely:
  1. normally consolidated soils
  2. overconsolidated or preconsolidated soils, and
  3. underconsolidated soils.

A *normally consolidated soil* is one whose present effective overburden pressure $\bar{p}_o$ on the in-situ prototype soil deposit from which an undisturbed soil sample is subjected to consolidation test is the maximum pressure p_{pr} to which the soil has ever been subjected at any time in its past history. In other words, the normally consolidated soil is one whose preconsolidation pressure p_{pr} is equal to its present effective overburden pressure $\bar{p}_o$:

$$\bar{p}_o = p_{pr}$$

An *overconsolidated or preconsolidated soil* is one which has been completely consolidated under a large overburden pressure p_{pr} in times past which pressure is larger than the present effective overburden pressure:

$$p_{pr} > \bar{p}_o$$

An *underconsolidated soil* is one which is not fully consolidated under the present effective overburden pressure $\bar{p}_o$:

$$\bar{p}_o > p_{pr}$$

Examples of underconsolidated clays are some geologically recently sedimented clay deposits in river deltas; some types of loess,[6] and some undisturbed extra sensitive clays whose loose structure breaks down or collapses upon pressure increase in excess of preconsolidation pressure p_{pr}.[7] One speaks here then about collapsible soils.

As to remolded soils, because a remolded soil has lost its structural characteristics as compared with its structure in its natural conditions, it is inferred that a remolded soil is unsuitable for evaluating its preconsolidation pressure.

15-7. Simplified Pressure-Void Ratio Relationships. In consolidation analysis of a soil, all applied pressures bringing about settlement are effective pressures. When the external compressive effective load $\bar{p}$ is applied to the soil in small increments $\Delta \bar{p}$, then the decrement in void ratio Δe is also small. In such a case the soil compression curve AB can be approximately replaced by a straight line, or chord, AB (Fig. 15-7).

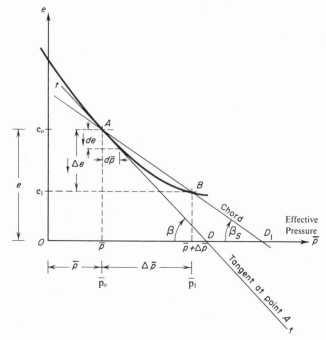

FIG. 15-7.   Pressure-void ratio curve (compression branch, $\downarrow \Delta e$).

The slope of the chord with respect to the $\bar{p}$-axis is:

$$\Delta e / \Delta \bar{p} = -\tan \beta_s. \tag{15-3}$$

When the chord AB rotates through point A in the clockwise direction, then it approaches the tangent (at point A) AD as a limit. The limiting value of the $(\Delta e)/(\Delta \bar{p})$ expression, when $\Delta \bar{p} \to 0$, is

$$\lim_{\Delta \bar{p} \to 0} \frac{e_o - e_1}{(\bar{p} + \Delta \bar{p}) - \bar{p}} = \lim_{\Delta p \to 0} \frac{-(e_o - e_1)}{\Delta \bar{p}} = \lim_{\Delta p \to 0} \frac{-(\Delta e)}{\Delta \bar{p}} = -\frac{d(e)}{d(\bar{p})} =$$

$$\beta = -tan\beta = a_v \qquad (cm^2/g, \text{ or } cm^2/kN), \tag{15-4}$$

which is termed the *coefficient of compressibility*. The minus sign indicates that with increasing effective pressure p the void ratio e decreases. Geometrically this means that the tangent goes through the second and fourth quarters.

The slope of the tangent to the $(\bar{p}\text{-}e)$-curve is a measure of the soil compressibility or its relative deformation.

Equation (15-4) expresses the differential change in void ratio $d(e)$ as a function of differential pressure $d(\bar{p})$, causing the differential change $d(e)$ in e:

$$d(e) = -(a_v) \cdot d(\bar{p}), \tag{15-5}$$

and it means that the change in void ratio e is directly proportional to the change in effective pressure $\bar{p}$.

$$a_v = -\frac{de}{d\bar{p}} = -\frac{\Delta e}{\Delta \bar{p}} = \frac{e_o - e_1}{\bar{p}_1 - \bar{p}_o}$$

$$= m_v (1 + e_o) = (1 + e_o) \cdot \frac{\Delta \epsilon_v}{\Delta \bar{p}} \ [cm^2/g, \text{ or } cm^2/N]$$

$$\tag{15-6}$$

see Fig. 15-7.

Here e_o = initial void ratio
   e_1 = final void ratio
   $\bar{p}_o$ = initial effective pressure
   $\bar{p}_1$ = final effective pressure

$m_v = a_v/(1 + e_o)$ = *coefficient of volume compressibility* or decrease in volume, in cm^2/g or in cm^2/N

$\epsilon_v = \frac{\Delta V}{V} = m_v \cdot \bar{p}$ = volumetric strain or relative deformation of soil

   ΔV = volume change of soil or absolute deformation, and
   V = initial volume of soil

The volume chance ΔV is a function of the increase in effective stress $\Delta \bar{p}$.

The $d(e)$-equation is analogous to Hooke's law of proportionality between stress σ and strain ϵ for solid, elastic materials:

$$\epsilon = \frac{\Delta L}{L} = \frac{\sigma}{E} \quad [\frac{cm}{cm}], \tag{15-7}$$

where $\epsilon = \Delta L / L =$ strain or relative deformation of the elastic, solid material tested, dimensionless

ΔL = absolute axial deformation of a stressed bar, in cm

L = initial length of the stressed element, in cm

σ = axial stress in the stressed element of the solid, kg/cm^2 or kN/cm^2, and

E = Young's modulus of elasticity of the elastic solid material, in kg/cm^2 or kN/cm^2.

Young's modulus of elasticity E indicates the capability of deformation in tension and compression of the elastic solid material. The modulus of elasticity E of materials that follow Hooke's law is constant. However for soils the so-called modulus of elasticity E_s, or stiffness modulus, is a variable quantity as it may be seen by the curvilinear nature of the pressure-relative settlement curve in Fig. 15-8: E_s varies with pressure $\bar{p}$, and indicates the capability of compression deformation of a soil.

If E_s is determined by compression of a soil in a confined condition, in a consolidometer, for example, then the so obtained stiffness modulus of the soil is called the constrained stiffness modulus, or constrained modulus of elasticity of the soil; Then $E_s = M_v$,

where

$$M_v = \frac{1}{m_v} = (1 + e_o)/a_v = -(d\bar{p}/de) (1+e_o) \tag{15-8}$$

is also sometimes called the constrained *compression modulus*, or *deformation modulus*, or modulus of elasticity of soil, commonly used to describe stress-strain relationship of a soil.

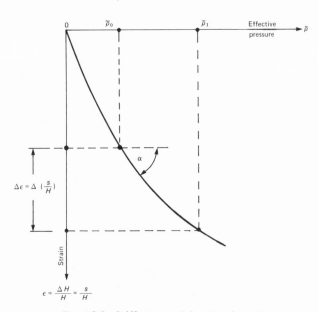

FIG. 15-8. Stiffness modulus E_s of a soil

The modulus of elasticity, or rather stiffness modulus, E_s, of a soil is determined from its compression diagram (Fig. 15-8):

$$E_s = cot\alpha = \frac{\Delta\bar{p}}{\Delta\epsilon} \quad [\frac{kg}{cm^2} \text{ or } \frac{kN}{cm^2}], \tag{15-9}$$

where

$$\epsilon = \frac{\Delta H}{H} = \frac{s}{H} \tag{15-10}$$

is the compressive strain, or relative settlement

$\Delta H = s =$ change (compression, viz., settlement) in thickness of a compressible soil layer, in cm

$H =$ initial thickness of a compressible soil layer, in cm

$s = \Delta H =$ amount of absolute settlement of soil layer H units thick, in cm.

Because the course of the soil compression diagram is a curvilinear one, it indicates that soils generally do not follow Hooke's law. Therefore the so determined E_s-value for a soil is valid only for that pressure range $\Delta\bar{p}$ of the primary compression curve as obtained from a laterally confined soil compression (consolidation) test. For this $\Delta\bar{p}$-range the E_s-value may then be assumed as constant.

For the same reason, it should also be noticed that neither a_v nor $m_v = 1/M_v$ are constants: both quantities decrease with increasing effective pressure, and they are affected by the past stress history of the soil.

The amount of settlement s of a soil using the simplified pressure-void ratio theory is then calculated from Fig. 15-9 as

$$\frac{s}{H} = \frac{\Delta e}{1 + e_o}, \tag{15-11a}$$

or

$$s = \frac{\Delta e}{1 + e_o} \cdot H = m_v \cdot H \cdot \bar{p} = \frac{1}{M_v} \cdot H \cdot \bar{p} = \frac{a_v}{1 + e_o} \cdot H \cdot \bar{p} \quad [cm] \tag{15-11}$$

where all symbols are as before.

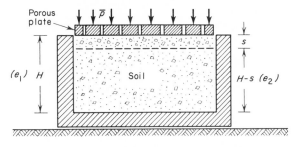

FIG. 15-9. Settlement consideration. One-way drainage (upward).

This solution may be applicable to a practical problem if no lateral expulsion of soil from underneath the base of a footing can take place.

It is advised that the E-values, viz. M_v-values for soils be determined for each particular soil in question, in situ and in the laboratory, respectively.

For one's orientation, the appropriate range of variation in the average stiffness modulus E_s for various soils is shown in Table 15-1 after Kögler and Scheidig.[8]

TABLE 15-1. MODULUS OF ELASTICITY E_s OF SOILS*

Soil Material	Approximate Compression Modulus Values E_s kg/cm^2		N/cm^2	
1	2		3	
Peat	1 to	5	10 to	50
Clay, plastic	5 to	40	50 to	390
Clay, stiff	40 to	80	390 to	790
Clay, medium hard	80 to	150	790 to	1470
Sand, loose	100 to	200	980 to	1960
Sand, dense	500 to	800	4910 to	7850
Gravel, sandy gravel, dense	1000 to	2000	9806 to	19620
Rock, fissured, jointed	1500 to	30000	14710 to	294200
Rock, sound	30000 to	∞	294200 to	∞

*Compiled and prepared after F. Kögler und A. Scheidig: Baugrund und Bauwerk, see Ref. 8.

15-8. The Pressure-Void Ratio Curve. The pressure-void ratio curve can be presented graphically as illustrated in Fig. 15-10. To help to appreciate the involved change in void ratio with pressure, the volumetric relationship between solids and the water-saturated void ratio e is shown to the left of the ordinate axis by the familiar soil phase diagram, which represents here a two-phase soil.

The change in void ratio Δe is obtained by subtracting from the initial void ratio e_o, the final void ratio e_1. The latter is brought about by the load increment $\Delta \bar{p}$.

Example. From the curve, Fig. 15-10, the magnitude of the settlement s of the soil represented on the graph is calculated as follows:

Coefficient of compressibility (slope of chord) a_v:

$$a_v = \left| \frac{-\Delta e}{\Delta \bar{p}} \right| = \frac{e_o - e_1}{\bar{p}_1 - \bar{p}_o} = \frac{1.30 - 0.75}{4.70 - 2.20} = 0.22 \quad (cm^2/kg).$$

Compression modulus, M_v:

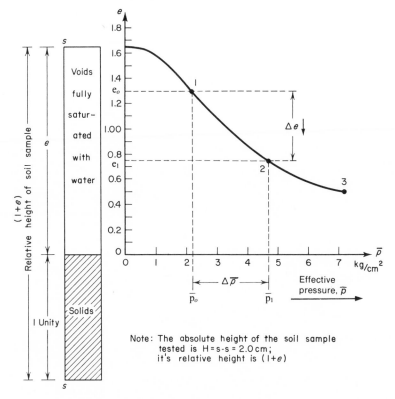

FIG. 15-10.   Pressure-void ratio curve based on change in void ratio.

$$M_v = \frac{1 + e_o}{a_v} = \frac{1 + 1.30}{0.22} = 10.45 \qquad (\text{kg/cm}^2).$$

This low value of M_v indicates a very compressible soil. In Fig. 15-10, the absolute height of the soil sample tested is $(s\text{-}s) = H = 2.0$ cm. (Note on the soil phase diagram that its relative height is $(1 + e)$. Also, at $\bar{p} = 0$, the volume of voids in the soil was 1.65 times greater than that of the solids.)

The pressure causing the change in void ratio is

$$\bar{p} = \Delta\bar{p} = \bar{p}_1 - \bar{p}_o = 4.7 - 2.2 = 2.5 \qquad (\text{kg/cm}^2).$$

Settlement s, by Eq. (15-11):

$$s = (1/M_v) \cdot H \cdot \bar{p} = (1/10.45)\,(2.0)\,(2.50) = 0.48 \quad (\text{cm}).$$

15.9. Compression Index. Because empirically the pressure-void ratio plot resembles approximately a logarithmic curve showing that the void ratio decreases (or increases, whichever the case is) in proportion to the logarithm of the pressure, the void ratio e may be expressed by an empirical equation as a function of initial void ratio e_o and pressure ratio p/p_o as follows:

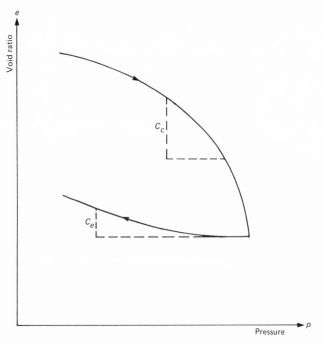

FIG. 5-11. Compression indexes.

a) for the compression branch of the curve:

$$e = e_o - C_c \cdot \log_{10} \left(\frac{p}{p_o} \right) \qquad (15\text{-}12)$$

b) for the expansion branch:

$$e = e_o - C_e \cdot \log_{10} \left(\frac{p}{p_o} \right) \qquad (15\text{-}13)$$

Herein, e = void ratio at pressure p
  e_o = initial void ratio at known initial pressure p_o on soil
  p = externally applied pressure on soil
  C_c = compression index (dimensionless)
  C_e = expansion or swelling index (dimensionless).

The expansion index C_e is always less than the compression index C_c.
If $e = e_1$ and $p = p_1$, rearrangement of Eq. (15-12) gives

$$\Delta e = e_o - e_1 = C_c \cdot \log_{10} \left(\frac{p_1}{p_o} \right) \qquad (15\text{-}12a)$$

or

$$\Delta e = C_c \cdot \log_{10} \left(\frac{p_o + \Delta p}{p_o} \right) \qquad (15\text{-}12b)$$

From here, the approximative compression index is

$$C_c = \frac{\Delta e}{\log_{10}\left(\dfrac{p_o + \Delta p}{p_o}\right)} \qquad (15\text{-}14)$$

Thus, the compression index C_c defines the relationship between change in void ratio Δe and applied pressure Δp. Practically, the compression index C_c is the slope of the linear part of the $(e\text{-}\log_{10}p)$-curve:

$$C_c = \frac{e_0 - e_1}{\log_{10}\left(\dfrac{p_1}{p_o}\right)} \qquad (15\text{-}14a)$$

Because mathematically $C_c = -\dfrac{de}{d(\log_{10}p)}$, $\qquad (15\text{-}14b)$

the C_c-value can be found by determining the slope of the $(e\text{ - }p)$-curve, Fig. 15-11.

With the C_c value for a given layer so determined, the compression, viz., total settlement of that clay layer brought about by a pressure Δp can now be calculated as

$$s = \frac{\Delta e}{1 + e_o} \cdot H = H \cdot \frac{C_c}{1 + e_o} \cdot \log_{10}\left(\frac{p_o + \Delta p}{p_o}\right) \quad [\text{cm}]. \qquad (15\text{-}15)$$

Example. If the initial void ratio of a clay is $e_o = 0.900$ at initial pressure $p_o = 95.8$ kN/m^2, and the compression index of that soil is $C_c = 0.052$, then the void ratio e_1 at $p_1 = p_o + \Delta p = 383.3$ kN/m^2 is

$$e_1 = e_o - C_c \, \log_{10}\left(\frac{p_1}{p_o}\right)$$

$$= 0.900 - (0.052) \cdot \log_{10}\left(\frac{383.3}{95.8}\right) = \underline{0.869}$$

Based on Skempton's experimental data about clay moisture content and compression index relationship as tabulated in Reference 9 as well as on data of others, Terzaghi and Peck[10] (See also Ref. 11) show that the compression index C_c of normally consolidated clays with low to moderate sensitivity may be estimated approximately by means of the following empirical relationship:

$$C_c = 0.009 \; (LL - 10), \qquad (15\text{-}16)$$

where LL = liquid limit of clay in percent.

With this C_c, the total settlement calculates then as

$$s = H \, \frac{(0.009)\,(LL - 10)}{1 + e_o} \cdot \log_{10}\left(\frac{p_o + \Delta p}{p_o}\right) \quad [\text{cm}]. \qquad (15\text{-}17)$$

Thus the order of magnitude of the total amount of compression of such a clay, viz., the total approximative settlement of a structure founded on such a clay may be calculated by means of liquid limit test of the clay without resorting to any consolidation test.

For other methods of estimating compression index refer to References 12, 13, 14 and 15.

Example. Given: a compressible layer of normally consolidated clay $H = 4.0$ m thick. The value of liquid limit of the clay was determined to be $LL = 42\%$. The initial void ratio of the clay was $e_o = 0.900$ at an initial pressure of $p_o = 95.8$ kN/m^2. If the clay layer is loaded with $p = 287.5$ kN/m^2, calculate the amount of total settlement of the clay.

$$s = H \cdot \frac{(0.009)\,(LL\text{-}10)}{1 + e_o} \cdot \log_{10}\left(\frac{p_o + p}{p_o}\right)$$

$$= (4.0) \cdot \frac{(0.009)\,(42\text{-}10)}{1 + 0.900} \cdot \log_{10}\left(\frac{383.3}{95.8}\right)$$

$$= \underline{0.3650}\ [\text{m}] \approx \underline{36.5}\ [\text{cm}]$$

15-10. Time-Settlement Diagrams. The effect of time on the settlement of a laterally confined clay can best be studied by keeping the load on the soil sample constant. On a time-settlement curve of a cohesive soil, such as illustrated in Fig. 15-12, three distinct parts may be observed, parts I, II, and III, each falling within a certain time interval:

Part I: Time from 0 to t_1, during which air is expelled from the voids of the soil after the external load has been applied. The presence of air in the voids of a clay is a very serious problem in the consolidation process, because air cushions retard permeability of soil to water.

Part II: Time from t_1 to t_2, during which the pore water is stressed (or pore water pressure is induced) and expelled due to the applied load, resulting in the so-called main settlement or *primary consolidation* of the soil. The pore water becomes stressed because the application of a load of a certain magnitude usually takes place faster than the pore water can drain out of the voids and equalize within the voids, so the water in the voids is said to be under *excess hydrostatic pressure*.

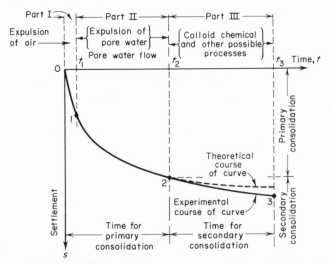

FIG. 15-12.   Elements of a time-settlement curve of a cohesive soil at a constant load.

Thus, the pressure which is induced in the water because of the load increment is called the hydraulic excess pressure. When, after some time, the excess water has been drained out, the soil reaches a state of equilibrium for that load. After the load is increased, the process of drainage from the soil begins again and continues under the new load until a new state of equilibrium is attained.

Part III: Time from t_2 to t_3, during which colloid-chemical processes and surface phenomena become active, such as the stressed moisture films around the soil particles, the moisture surface tension in the corners of the soil particles, viscosity and density changes in the stressed moisture films, molecular attractive forces between soil particles and moisture films, induced electrokinetic potentials, and other processes. All these processes are very slow by their very nature. This is to say, among other things, that the effect of the electric, diffuse double layer upon the draining flow of water now becomes more pronounced than before. The settlement brought about during the period of time of such processes is called the post-settlement or the *secondary consolidation.*

Because of the colloidal-chemical processes, the secondary consolidation process in nature requires long geologic periods of time, and therefore the secondary consolidation process also requires a long time to consolidate the soil fully in the laboratory. Thus one factor in the impossibility of simulating in the laboratory long, natural consolidation processes (into secondary consolidation) comes to the fore.

During the time of secondary consolidation, and because of the reasons mentioned before, the actual experimental, time-settlement curve is offset from its theoretical course, Fig. 15-12.

Secondary consolidation of mineral soils is usually negligible, but in the case of organic soils it may be considerable because of their colloidal nature.

A possible disintegration of clayey soil particles and other possible reasons and processes are also mentioned in the technical literature as probably contributing to secondary consolidation.

The possibility of the disintegration and the mechanical breakdown of the soil particles, however, is somewhat in contradiction to one of the assumptions underlying the consolidation theory, namely, that soil particles are incompressible.

Much research, therefore, is still needed to elucidate the real nature of the process of secondary consolidation in clayey soils, and to determine how to cope with it analytically when describing the consolidation process mathematically.

15-11. Determination of Zero and 100% Consolidation. In practice, only the primary consolidation is usually reckoned with. In this connection there arises a certain difficulty in determining when and where on the time-settlement, i.e., time-consolidation, graph the points of zero percent and that of 100% primary consolidation are located.

A. Casagrande's Method. Because the first part (upper branch of the time-percent consolidation curve) is approximately parabolic in shape when plotted to an arithmetical scale, the zero percent consolidation coordinate may be found, according to A. Casagrande and Fadum[16] in the following way (Fig. 15-13). Select a point P_1 on the time-percent consolidation curve (drawn to semilogarithmic scale) corresponding to a certain time t_1. Through this point (P_1/t_1) draw a horizontal line A-P_1. Select point A so that it corresponds to time $t = (\frac{1}{4})t_1$. Ascertain the ordinate $d = AP_2$, between the horizontal line A-P_1 and the curve. Then lay off this d-value above the curve from point P_2 to give point P_3: $P_2 - P_3 = d$. Through point P_3 should go the horizontally directed, theoretical, zero percent consolidation line. This construction should be repeated for 3 or 4 other arbitrary t-values on the curve, obtaining 3 or 4 other points, such as P_7, P_8, P_9. Points P_3, P_7, P_8, P_9 so found above the curve should line up very closely in the horizontal line P_3-P_9. This horizontal line, then, represents the theoretical zero percent consolidation.

The point of 100% consolidation is arbitrarily found by Ref. 16 by intersecting two tangents, one of which is drawn to the time-percent consolidation curve of the primary branch, and the other to the straight-line part of the secondary consolidation branch, Fig. 15-13. The point of intersection S of the two tangents determines the position of the horizontal line on the graph of the 100% consolidation of the soil sample for any one load on the sample tested for its consolidation properties.

The distance between the zero percent and the 100% line is then divided into ten equal parts, each part meaning 10% consolidation.

The concept of percent, or degree, of consolidation is the ratio of settlement of a clay sample in the consolidometer s_t to its full or 100% settlement s, after

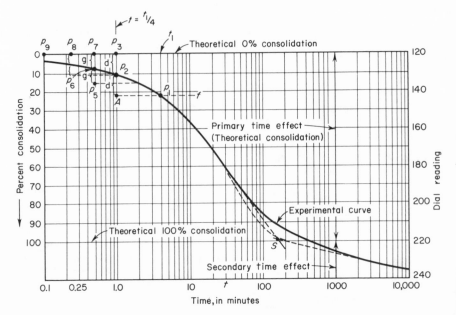

Fig. 15-13. Time-percent consolidation curve.

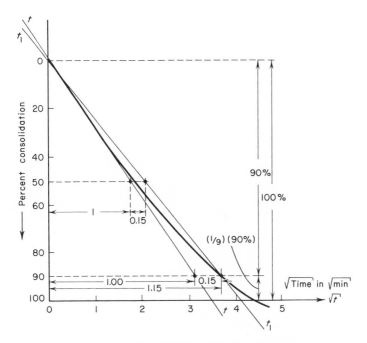

FIG. 15-14. Square root of time fitting method.

full consolidation at a certain pressure has been attained:

$$s_t/s \times 100. \qquad (15\text{-}18)$$

The dial readings indicated on the vertical scale to the right of the time-percent consolidation curve, Fig. 15-13, are the record of the deformation in height of thickness of the soil sample. For convenience, in its turn, the dial readings are then converted into percent consolidation of the soil sample (which in effect means changes in void ratios), as indicated on the left-side ordinate axis (Fig. 15-13).

Taylor's Square Root of Time Fitting Method. The zero percent and the 100% consolidation can also be determined by the so-called square root of time fitting method devised by Taylor.[17] In this method, all dial readings are plotted on the ordinate axis, and the corresponding square roots of time are plotted on the abscissa axis, Fig. 15-14.

Taylor observed that on the theoretical $\sqrt{t}$-percent consolidation curve a straight line exists to beyond 50% consolidation, while at 90% consolidation the abscissa is 1.15 times the abscissa of the straight line produced. Using Taylor's method, first the straight line t-t is drawn which fits best the early part of the experimental curve. The intersection of the t-t line with the ordinate axis yields the "corrected" point of zero percent consolidation. Then a straight line t_1-t_1 is drawn which at all points has abscissas 1.15 times as great as those of the first line (t-t). The intersection of this second line with the experimental curve is taken as the 90% consolidation point. Its time value is t_{90}. One ninth of the vertical distance between the corrected zero point and the 90% point is added below the 90% point, to give the 100% consolidation point of primary consolidation.

15-12. Coefficient of Consolidation. A factor involved in characterizing the rate of consolidation of a soil is the one called the *coefficient of consolidation*, c_v, expressed as

$$c_v = \frac{(1 + e)k}{a_v \cdot \gamma_w} = \frac{k}{m_v \cdot \gamma_w} \quad \left[\frac{cm^2}{s}, \text{ or } \frac{m^2}{s} \right] , \tag{15-19}$$

where k = coefficient of permeability, in cm/s or in m/s. Because during the process of conolidation k and m_v are assumed to be constant, the coefficient of consolidation cv during the process of consolidation of the clay is constant.

The coefficient of consolidation c_v as determined by Casagrande's semilogarithmic plot method, Fig. 15-13, and referring to Fig. 16-3, is

$$c_v = \frac{(0.196) \cdot H^2}{t_{50}} \quad \left[\frac{cm^2}{s} \right] , \tag{15-20}$$

where $0.196 = \tau =$ the so-called time factor for 50% consolidation,
$H =$ length of drainage path, and
$t_{50} =$ time during which 50% of consolidation takes place.
The c_v-value as determined by Taylor's square root of time fitting method is

$$c_v = \frac{(0.848)(H^2)}{t_{90}} , \quad [cm^2/s] \tag{15-21}$$

where $0.848 = \tau =$ time factor corresponding to 90% consolidation
$H =$ length of drainage path, and
$t_{90} =$ time during which 90% of consolidation occurs.
Another method for computing the coefficient of consolidation c_v called the "inflection point method" has been suggested by Cour,[18] namely:

$$c_v = \frac{(0.405) \cdot H^2}{t_i} , \quad [cm^2/s] \tag{15-22}$$

where $t_i =$ time corresponding to the inflection point on the consolidation curve.

REFERENCES

1. K. Terzaghi, *Theoretical Soil Mechanics,* New York, John Wiley and Sons, Inc., 1948, p. 265.
2. K. Terzaghi and O.K. Fröhlich, *Theorie der Setzung von Tonschichten,* Leipzig und Wien, Franz Deuticke, 1936, p. 2.
3. *1976 Annual Book of ASTM Standards, Part 19.* Designation: D 2435-70. Standard Method of Test for One-Dimensional Consolidation Properties of Soils, Philadelphia, Pa., 1976, pp. 305-308.

4. E. Antevs, "The Last Glaciation," Research Series no. 17, New York, *American Geographical Society*, 1928, p. 107.
5. A. Casagrande, "The Determination of the Pre-consolidation Load and its Practical Significance," *Proceedings, First International Conference on Soil Mechanics and Foundation Engineering*, Cambridge, Mass., June 1936, vol. 3, pp. 60-64.
6. R.L. Handy, "Collapsible Loess in Iowa," *Proceedings* of the Soil Science Society of America, vol. 37, 1973, pp. 281-284.
7. H.J. Gibbs and J.P. Bara, "Stability Problems of Collapsible Soils." *Proc. ASCE*, Journal of the Soil Mechanics and Foundation Division, vol. 93, No. SM4, 1967, pp. 577-594.
8. F. Kögler and A. Scheidig, *Baugrund und Bauwerk*, Berlin, Wilhelm Ernst und Sohn, 1948, p. 59.
9. A.W. Skempton, "Notes on the Compressibility of Clays." *Quarterly Journal of the Geological Society London*, vol. 100, 1944, pp. 119-135.
10. K. Terzaghi and R.B. Peck, *Soil Mechanics in Engineering Practice* (2nd ed.), John Wiley and Sons, Inc., New York, N.Y., 1967, p. 73.
11. R.B. Peck, W.E. Hanson, and T.H. Thurnburn, *Foundation Engineering*, (2nd ed.), John Wiley and Sons, Inc., New York, N.Y., 1974, p. 62.
12. J.H. Schmertman, "Estimating the True Consolidation Behavior of Clay From Laboratory Test Results," *Proc. ASCE*, Journal of the Soil Mechanics and Foundations Division, vol. 79, Proc. Separate No. 311, September, 1953.
13. Y. Nishida, "A Brief Note on Compression Index of Soil," *Proc. ASCE*, Journal of the Soil Mechanics and Foundations Division, vol. 82, No. SM3, 1956, pp. 1-14.
14. B.K. Hough, *Basic Soils Engineering*, 2nd ed., The Ronald Press Co., New York, N.Y., 1969 p. 134.
15. G.B. Sowers and G.F. Sowers, *Introductory Soil Mechanics and Foundations* (3rd ed.), the Macmillan Company, New York, N.Y., 1970, p. 102.
16. A. Casagrande and R.E. Fadum, *Notes on Soil Testing for Engineering Purposes*, Soil Mechanics Series, no. 8, Publication from the Graduate School of Engineering, Harvard University, Cambridge, Mass., 1939/40, no. 268, p. 37.
17. D.W. Taylor, *Research on Consolidation of Clays*, Publications from the Department of Civil and Sanitary Engineering, Massachusetts Institute of Technology, Cambridge, Mass., 1942, pp. 17-18.
18. F.R. Cour, "Inflection Point Method for Computing c_v," *Proc. ASCE*, Journal of the Soil Mechanics and Foundations Division, vol. 97, No. SM5, 1971, pp. 827-831.

QUESTIONS AND PROBLEMS

15- 1. Distinguish between the concepts of
a) compaction, b) compression, and c) consolidation.
15- 2. What is the objective of a consolidation test of a cohesive soil?
15- 3. Upon what does the magnitude of settlement of a cohesive soil depend?
15- 4. What is the basic equation used in the consolidation theory?
15- 5. What is the meaning of the term "compressibility"?
15- 6. What is the coefficient of compressibility?
15- 7. What is the modulus of volume change?
15- 8. What is the compression index?
15- 9. How does the compression index differ from the coefficient of compressibility?
15-10. What is the compression modulus?
15-11. What is primary consolidation of soil?
15-12. Explain what is understood by secondary consolidation, and the possible factors causing it.
15-13. What is the "degree of consolidation"?
15-14. Under what conditions, and how, should a prototype clay sample be subjected

to the consolidation test in the laboratory?

15-15. Which are the factors determining the settlement of structures founded on clay?

15-16. What does a steep compression curve indicate?

15-17. What does a low value of M_v of a clay indicate?

15-18. What is precompression pressure?

15-19. How is the precompression pressure determined?

15-20. What is one-way drainage?

15-21. What is two-way drainage?

15-22. The initial void ratio of a 6-m-thick layer of cohesive soil is $e_o = 0.900$, and the final void ratio is $e_1 = 0.800$ after the structure has been completed. What is the probable settlement of this structure?

15-23. Given three pressure-void ratio curves of a loess soil, Fig. Problem 15-23. Curves Nos. 1 and 2 (solid lines) represent two different types of undisturbed loess soil. Curve No. 3 (dotted line) represents a disturbed wind-borne loess.

   Required. Analyze thoroughly the subject of pressure-void ratio curves.

   Particularly:

   a) Describe the curves.

   b) Locate precompression pressure on the diagrams and report their magnitudes.

   c) Plot the three given curves on semilogarithmic graph paper. Locate preconsolidation pressure and compare with those obtained under b).

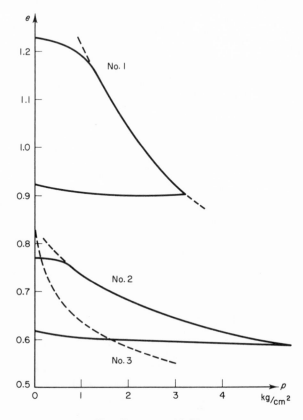

FIG. PROBLEM 15-23.

d) If, on curve No. 1, under a compression process, the void ratio at $p = 1.5$ kg/cm² is $e_1 = ..$, what is the void ratio e_2 at $p = 2.5$ kg/cm²?

e) What is the expected soil performance if soil No. 1 were loaded by a contact pressure of a foundation with $p_0 = 0.5$ kg/cm², and with $p_0 = 2.0$ kg/cm²?

f) Work out Problem d) using soil No. 3.

g) Upon what does the magnitude of change in void ratio depend
 i) in cohesive soils?
 ii) in noncohesive soils?

h) What do compression curves of soils characterize?
 i) Report, in terms of void ratios, the magnitudes of plastic, elastic, and total deformations of soils Nos. 1, 2, and 3.
 ii) Can or cannot plastic and elastic deformations be reported for soil No. 3, and why?

i) Determine a_v, m_v, M_v and C_c values for stresses from 1.5 kg/cm² to 2.5 kg/cm² for loading and unloading branches of the pressure-void ratio curves 1, 2 and 3.

j) Calculate secant modulus E_s for these curves.

k) Calculate tangent modulus E_s for these soils at 1 kg/cm² on the first loading branches.

15-24. Given pressure-void ratio data. Plot the curve to a semilogarithmic scale.

Loading cycle (time = 1440 min):
Pressure, kN/m²:

0.00	32.5	93.6	218.6	468.2	786.1
0.7500	0.7425	0.7091	0.6596	0.6103	0.5620

Unloading cycle (time = 1440 min):

Pressure, kN/m²: 468.2	218.6	93.6	32.5
0.5760	0.5981	0.6319	0.6775

Reloading cycle (time = 1440 min):
Pressure, kN/m²:

93.6	218.6	468.2	786.1	1965.0
0.6500	0.6180	0.5814	0.5503	0.4955

Determine a_v, m_v, M_v and C_c for a chosen pressure interval.

15-25. Replot the compression curve as in Fig. 15-10, and add to it an unloading (expansion) branch defined by the following coordinates (for points on this curve following the course from right to left as the soil sample was unloaded):

Points	p kg/cm²	e
3	7.5	0.50
4	4.0	0.60
5	2.0	0.75
6	0.0	0.95

Calculate the amount of rebound (or swelling) of this soil when it is unloaded from $p_o = 4.7$ kg/cm² to $p_1 = 2.2$ kg/cm². . Report the coefficient of expansion in cm²/kg, and in cm²/g. Also, report the magnitudes of plastic and elastic deformations after the soil sample is unloaded to $p = 0$ kg/cm².

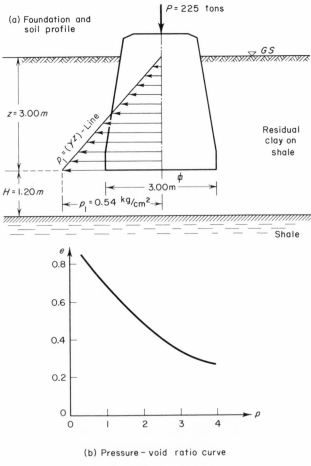

(b) Pressure – void ratio curve

FIG. PROBLEM 15-26.

15-26. Given a squared foundation as shown in Fig. Problem 15-26a. A pressure-void ratio curve is also given for the soil upon which the foundation is to rest. The base of the footing is to be at an elevation of three meters below the ground surface. Because the consolidation theory is developed in units of the metric system, the problem here will be given and is to be solved in the metric system. The load on the foundation is 225 metric tons. The unit weight of soil is $\gamma = 1800$ kg/m³. Find the amount of compression of the layer of clay 1.20 m thick between the hard shale and the base of the footing.

Hint for solution.

1) The vertical pressure of the weight of the soil before excavation at 3.00 m = 300 cm depth ($\gamma = 1800$ kg/m³ $= 0.0018$ kg/cm³):

$$p_1 = \gamma z = (0.0018)(300) = 0.54 \quad (\text{kg/cm}^2).$$

2) The contact pressure on the soil from the foundation:

$$p_2 = \frac{P}{A} = \frac{(225)(1000)}{(300)^2} = 2.5 \quad (kg/cm^2),$$

where A = area of base of footing.

3) $\Delta e =$ 6) $a_v =$ 9) $C_c =$

4) $e =$ 7) $M_v =$

5) $\Delta p =$ 8) $s =$

Note: consider whether it might be more practical to carry the foundation down to the hard shale.

15-27. A consolidation test on varved clay from Moonachie, New Jersey, gave the data in the following table. Plot the pressure-void ratio graph.

Point Nos.	Pressure, kg/cm²	Void Ratio, e
1	0.625	1.088
2	1.250	1.045
3	2.500	0.936
4	5.000	0.777
5	10.000	0.672
6	0.625	0.774
7	1.250	0.761
8	2.500	0.736
9	5.000	0.706
10	10.000	0.660
11	20.000	0.592
12	0.625	0.722
13	1.250	0.710
14	2.500	0.685
15	5.000	0.655
16	10.000	0.622
17	20.000	0.580
18	0.625	0.694

TABLE PROBLEM 15-27.

15-28. Study and discuss the pressure-void ratio curve, Fig. Problem 15-28, obtained from a consolidation test on Moonachie varved clay.

    a) Has the varved clay ever been preconsolidated?

    b) If this clay should occur in a glaciated area, what are the reasons for preconsolidation?

    c) If a preconsolidated clay should occur in a nonglaciated area, what may be the reasons for causing a preconsolidation load?

    d) Present your opinion as to the potential danger to the structural rigidity of a large city water tower founded on varved clay. The tower exerts by its round mat foundation, 6.1 m in diameter, a contact pressure of 24.4 t/m^2 on the clay. The structure is a multiple-story reinforced concrete frame, with solid walls, 27.4 m high. The tolerable settlement for this structure is 0.64 cm.

    e) Determine a_v, m_v and C_c for the pressure range between 2 kg/cm² and 5 kg/cm² on the three compression branches as shown in Fig. Problem 15-28.

f) If the thickness of the compressible soil layer is H = 6 m, what is the amount of total settlement s of the structure as given under (d) above? The initial void ratio is $e_o = 1.030$ at an initial pressure of $p_o = 1.5$ kg/cm^2.

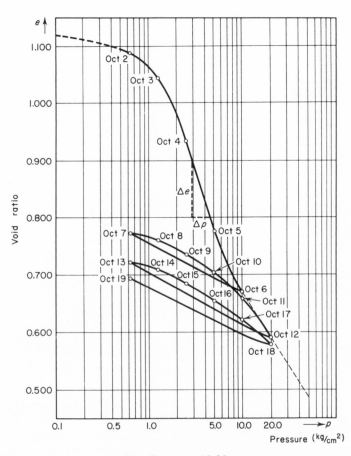

FIG. PROBLEM 15-28

Chapter 16

ONE-DIMENSIONAL CONSOLIDATION; THE CONSOLIDATION PROCESS

For reasons of practical expediency in performing consolidation tests, the consolidation theory in this Chapter is presented in the technical metric units like that in which units the consolidation theory of clays was originally devised by Terzaghi and Fröhlich.[1]

16-1. The Consolidation Process-Hydraulic Problem. The expulsion of water from the voids of the saturated clay soil by an externally applied load in the consolidation process, and the change in volume associated with such a process, are essentially a hydraulic problem. More specifically, it is a problem of permeability of a soil to water. It is, therefore, expedient to supplement here the consolidation theory with the permeability aspect of soil, because permeability, besides compressibility, is one of the principal factors relative to settlement of a soil, viz., settlement of structure. By logic then, concerning the discussion on the theory of consolidation, it can be said that the magnitude of settlement depends upon the compressibility of the soil, whereas the rate of consolidation depends on both permeability and compressibility. The combined effect of permeability and compressibility is usually comprehended in one resulting factor, termed the *coefficient of consolidation:* $c_v = k/(m_v \cdot \gamma_w)$, in cm^2/s.

16-2. Assumptions Underlying the Consolidation Theory. Taking into consideration the permeability factor in soil consolidation, the following are the assumptions underlying the unidimensional consolidation theory of saturated, laterally confined clay soils subjected to axial, vertical loading.

1) The soil is a homogeneous material.
2) The voids in the soil are fully saturated with water and free of air.
3) Water in voids, and the solids of the soil, are incompressible; therefore the change in volume of the soil, when loaded, is effected by the change in volume of the voids.
4) The drainage in laterally confined soil brought about by an externally applied load on the soil takes place in a vertical direction only.
5) The coefficient of permeability of the soil to water is constant throughout the soil.
6) Darcy's law of permeability is applicable.

In reality of course, these assumptions, are not fully met. The results from consolidation studies, however, reveal that large discrepancies between theory and nature are brought about by the presence of a large volume of air in the voids of the soil.

16-3. The Clay System for Analysis. With reference to Terzaghi-Fröhlich consolidation theory of clays,[1] the partial differential equation for a one-dimensional consolidation process of clay involving one-dimensional two-way drainage of variable flow of soil pore water is given as

$$\frac{\partial u}{\partial t} = c_v \frac{\partial^2 u}{\partial z^2}, \qquad (16\text{-}1)$$

where $\partial u/\partial t =$ rate of change of the hydrostatic excess pore water pressure, in $[g/(cm^2 s)]$,

$$c_v = \frac{k}{m_v \gamma_w} = \frac{k}{[a_v/(1 + e)]\gamma_w} = \frac{k(1 + e)}{a_v \gamma_w} = \text{coefficient of consolidation} \quad (16\text{-}2)$$
$$(cm^2/s),$$

$\partial^2 u/\partial z^2 =$ change in hydraulic pressure gradient (g/cm^4),

$c_v(\partial^2 u/\partial z^2) =$ amount of water expelled from the voids of the clay through 1 cm² area and during a time element dt $[g/(cm^2 s)]$, and

$e =$ variable void ratio.

For derivation and solution of Eq. (16-1), the reader is referred to Reference 2.

Permeability. By Eq. (16-2), the relationship between the coefficient of permeability k and the coefficient of consolidation c_v is

$$k = c_v m_v \gamma_w = c_v \frac{1}{M_v} \gamma_w = c_v \frac{a_v}{1 + e} \gamma_w \qquad (cm/s). \qquad (16\text{-}3)$$

This relationship indicates that the coefficient of permeability k can be calculated from the experimental data obtained from the consolidation test. The coefficient of permeability, however, as seen from the above equation and inferred by the logic of the problem, is a function of the variable void ratio e. Also, considering that $a_v = (-de)/(dp)$, it can be observed that k decreases with an increasing consolidation load dp. Thus, k depends upon the degree or percent of consolidation.

16-4. Solution of the Consolidation Equation. The solution of the consolidation equation, Eq. (16-1),

$$\frac{\partial u}{\partial t} = c_v \frac{\partial^2 u}{\partial z^2} \qquad (16\text{-}1)$$

for the neutral pressure, $u = f(z; t)$, is based on the solution of Fourier's equation in one dimension, a solution or integral which must also satisfy the given boundary conditions.

The general integral u, as the general solution of the partial differential equation characterizing a two-way pore water flow and neutral pressures, is

$$u(z; t) = \frac{1}{H} \sum_{n=1}^{n=\infty} (e^{-n^2 Nt}) \left[\sin\left(\frac{n\pi z}{2H}\right) \right] \int_0^{2H} \underbrace{f(z; 0) \sin\left(\frac{n\pi z}{2H}\right)}_{\mu_i} dz, \qquad (16\text{-}4)$$

or, substituting $N = \dfrac{\pi^2 c_v}{4H^2}$, obtain

$$u(z; t) = \frac{1}{H} \sum_{n=1}^{n=\infty} \left[\exp\left(-\frac{n^2\pi^2}{4} \frac{c_v t}{H^2} \right) \right] \left[\sin\left(\frac{n\pi z}{2H} \right) \right] \int_0^{2H} f(z; 0) \sin\left(\frac{n\pi z}{2H} \right) dz.$$

$$(16\text{-}5)$$

The quantity $f(z; 0) = \mu_i$ is the initial neutral pressure.

By means of this equation, the hydrostatic excess pressure, u, can be calculated in clay under any initial stress condition, $f(z; 0) = u_{\text{initial}}$, and thereby at any time, t, and any depth, z, below the top drainage face of the clay. By analogy to Eq. (15-6),

$$s = m_v p_e H \qquad (\text{cm}), \tag{16-6}$$

or

$$ds_t = m_v(\Delta p - u_t) \, dz, \tag{16-7}$$

where $m_v = a_v/(1 + e) =$ amount of linear compression, in cm^2/g,

$p_e = \Delta p - u_t =$ effective pressure,

$\Delta p =$ total pressure increment

$ds_t =$ differential settlement during time t,

$u_t =$ neutral pressure at time t, and

$dz =$ differential thickness of a layer of clay.

Integration of Eq. (16-7) between limits $z = 0$ and $z = H$ gives the total settlement s_t of the clay layer H units of length thick after elapsed time t:

$$s_t = \frac{a_v}{1 + e_i} \int_0^H [\Delta p - u(z; t)] \, dz, \tag{16-8}$$

or

$$s_t = \frac{e_i - e_f}{\Delta p(1 + e_i)} \left[(\Delta p)H - \int_0^H u(z; t) \, dz \right], \tag{16-9}$$

where a_v and e_i (initial void ratio) may be considered to be constant;

$e_f =$ final void ratio at effective pressure p_e.

Note that, geometrically, the quantity in the brackets, Eq. (16-9), is the hatched area A_{et}. This area A_{et} is the effective pressure area A_e at time t, Fig. 16-1. Again, note that at time $t = 0$ the effective area A_{e0} is zero. At time $t = \infty$, the magnitude of the effective area is expressed as

$$A_{e\infty} = p_e H = \Delta p H = A_\circ, \tag{16-10}$$

where the effective pressure area $A_\circ =$ area $OABCO +$ area $CBA'O'C$ for a two-way drainage.

Eq. (16-9), expressing settlement at any time t, can be rewritten as

$$s_t = \frac{e_i - e_f}{1 + e_i} \frac{A_{et}}{\Delta p}. \tag{16-11}$$

The degree of consolidation (or percent of consolidation) μ at any instant of elapsed time may also be written in an abbreviated form as

$$\mu = 1 - u/u_i, \qquad (16\text{-}12)$$

or

$$\mu = 1 - \frac{\text{hydrostatic excess pressure at time } t \text{ and depth } z}{\text{initial hydrostatic excess pressure at time } t = 0 \text{ and depth } z}.$$

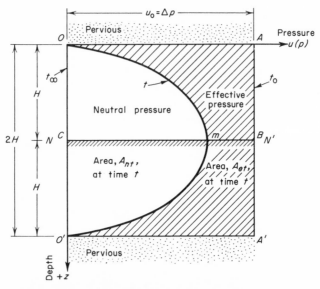

FIG. 16-1.   Effective and neutral pressure areas, A_{et} and A_{nt}, respectively, for a clay system with a two-way drainage.

Immediately after application of the pressure increment (Δp) on the clay, the hydrostatic excess pressure (at time $t = 0$ and depth $z = z$) equals the initial neutral (pore water) pressure u_i, i.e., $(\Delta p) = u_i$.

When $u = u_i$, then $\mu = 0$ ($= 0\%$ consolidation).

When the hydrostatic excess pressure u decreases to zero (after time $t = \infty$), i.e., when $u = 0$, then $\mu = 1$ ($= 100\%$ consolidation).

From the foregoing discussion it can be inferred that the pressure distribution area is, in a way, a measure of the compression which the clay undergoes during the course of consolidation.

Analytically,

$$\mu = 1 - \frac{\displaystyle\int_0^H u(z\,;\,t)\,dz}{(\Delta p)H} \qquad (16\text{-}13)$$

is a dimensionless coefficient expressing the degree of consolidation of the clay at time t and thickness H. Here, thickness H means also the shortest drainage path in one-way drainage of the clay layer.

If $(\Delta p)H = A_o$, total pressure area at time $t = 0$, then Eq. (16-13), expressing the coefficient of the degree of consolidation, may be rewritten as

$$\mu = \frac{A_o - \int_0^H u(z;t)\,dz}{A_o} = \frac{A_o - A_{nt}}{A_o} = \frac{A_{et}}{A_o}, \tag{16-14}$$

where A_{nt} is the neutral pressure area at time t, which is the integral in Eq. (16-14).

The numerator,

$$A_o - \int_0^H u(z;t)\,dz = A_{et}, \tag{16-15}$$

expresses the effective pressure area A_{et} at time t, an area which is a fraction of the total pressure area A_o.

The effective pressure area A_{et} at time t is obtained by subtracting the neutral pressure

$$\int_0^H u(z;t)\,dz \tag{16-16}$$

at time t from the total pressure area A_o.

Thus, the coefficient of degree of consolidation may be defined as the ratio of the instantaneous effective pressure area A_{et} at time t to the total pressure area A_o.

The average value of the coefficient of consolidation μ_{ave}, for a clay layer $2H$ units thick at any time t, is

$$\mu_{ave} = \frac{1}{2H}\int_0^{2H}\left(1 - \frac{u}{u_i}\right)dz = 1 - \frac{1}{2H}\int_0^{2H}\frac{u}{u_i}\,dz = \tag{16-17}$$

$$= 1 - \frac{8}{\pi^2}\left(e^{-Nt} + \tfrac{1}{9}e^{-9Nt} + \tfrac{1}{25}e^{-25Nt} + \cdots\right). \tag{16-18}$$

This equation is good for two-way drainage as it is encountered in the consolidation test, with a porous material on top and at the bottom of the clay sample in the consolidometer.

Check. At time $t = 0$, μ_{ave} must be equal to zero. Inserting $t = 0$ in the μ_{ave}-equation, obtain

$$\mu_{ave_{t=0}} = 1 - \frac{8}{\pi^2}\underbrace{\left(1 + \tfrac{1}{9} + \tfrac{1}{25} + \tfrac{1}{49} + \cdots\right)}_{\to \pi^2/8} = 1 - \left(\frac{8}{\pi^2}\right)\left(\frac{\pi^2}{8}\right) = 0,$$

$$\text{Q.E.D.}$$

Because $N = (\pi^2/4)(c_v/H^2)$, one notes that the degree of consolidation μ, being a function of N, t, H, and z, depends upon:

a) the coefficient of the consolidation of the soil, $c_v = k/(m_v \gamma_w)$; which, in turn, depends upon

    i) the coefficient of permeability k of the soil under the instantaneous load;

ii) the specific loss of pore water, $m_v = a_v/(1+e)$, where
$a_v = (-de)/(dp) =$ coefficient of compressibility, and
$e =$ initial void ratio before applying dp; and

iii) the unit weight of water γ_w, which is a function of temperature;

b) time t of consolidation;

c) thickness of the layer of clay in one-way drainage, or the length of the shortest drainage path H;

d) whether the clay layer is bound by a drainage face at the top, or at the bottom, or at the top and bottom simultaneously, and

e) the position z below the top of the clay layer.

16-5. Time Factor. The coefficient $\tau = c_v t/H^2$ in one-way drainage, in the negative e-exponent, Eq. (16-5), is termed by Fröhlich,[2] for the sake of brevity, the *time factor*:

$$\frac{c_v t}{H^2} = \tau \qquad \left[\frac{(\text{cm}^2/\text{s})(\text{s})}{(\text{cm})^2} \right] = (1). \qquad (16\text{-}19)$$

Here H means one-way drainage.

The time factor is dimensionless, and depends upon

a) the coefficient of consolidation c_v,

b) the elapsed time t, and

c) the length of the shortest drainage path H.

For two-way drainage ($H_2 = H/2$), the time factor τ_2 is,

$$\tau_2 = \frac{c_v t}{H_2{}^2} = \frac{c_v t}{(H/2)^2}, \qquad (16\text{-}20)$$

i.e., the time factor τ_2 is *four times as large* as it is in the case of one-way drainage (refer to Fig. 16-2). For example, if in one-way drainage $H = 120$ cm, then in two-way drainage $H_2 = H/2 = 120/2 = 60$ (cm).

16-6. Model Law. One of the important laws the theory of consolidation of clays has given to the engineering sciences is the so-called *model law of settlement*. It is here understood that the concept of consolidation is equivalent to the settlement concept. If two layers of the same clay of different thickness, say, h and H, where $h < H$, have the same number of drainage faces, and have attained the same degree of consolidation during time t and T, respectively—generally where $t \neq T$ —then their coefficients of consolidation c_v must theoretically be equal, and so must be their time factors τ:

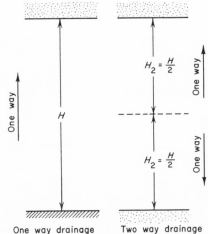

One way drainage   Two way drainage

FIG. 16-2. Length of drainage path.

$$\tau = \frac{c_v t}{h^2}; \qquad \tau = \frac{c_v T}{H^2}. \qquad\qquad (16\text{-}21); (16\text{-}22)$$

Equating both time factors, obtain the following model law:

$$t/T = h^2/H^2. \qquad\qquad (16\text{-}23)$$

This model law of similitude of the consolidation process of a clay reads that the ratio of times, t and T, necessary to attain a certain degree of consolidation in two clay layers of the same material and the same number of drainage faces but different thicknesses h and H, equals the ratio of the squares of the corresponding thicknesses of these layers. Thus, by the way in which t and T are related in the model law, it can be observed that, all other things being equal, to attain the same degree of consolidation of a layer of clay of twice the thickness ($H = 2h$), the time for consolidation would be four times that needed for h:

$$t/T = h^2/(2h)^2, \qquad\qquad (16\text{-}23\text{a})$$

or

$$T = 4t. \qquad\qquad (16\text{-}24)$$

Hence, the consolidation test of soils is a model test, not a destructive test.

For example, if a laboratory sample, $h = 2$ cm thick, has attained in two-way drainage a 60% consolidation during $t = 6$ hours, then its prototype clay layer $H = 3$ m $= 300$ cm thick will attain a 60% consolidation in two-way drainage within a time of

$$T = 6\,\frac{(300)^2}{(2)^2} = 135{,}000 \text{ (hours)} = 5625 \text{ (days)} = 15.4 \quad \text{(years)}.$$

In nature, intermediate sand layers between clay layers greatly facilitate the process of consolidation.

16-7. The Theoretical Time Factor-Percent Consolidation Curve. Because $\mu_{ave} = f(Nt)$, but

$$N = \frac{\pi^2}{4}\frac{c_v}{H^2} \qquad\qquad (16\text{-}25)$$

and

$$\tau = \frac{c_v t}{H^2}, \qquad\qquad (16\text{-}19)$$

it can be written that

$$Nt = \frac{\pi^2}{4}\frac{c_v}{H^2}t = \frac{\pi^2}{4}\,\tau, \qquad\qquad (16\text{-}26)$$

where τ is the time factor. Thus, it is seen that at any time t the coefficient of the average degree of consolidation μ_{ave} of a clay with two drainage faces, and initially with a constant, pore water pressure distribution, is a function of the time factor τ, or

$$\mu_{ave} = f(\tau). \qquad (16\text{-}27)$$

Of course it must be remembered that in general μ_{ave}, viz., $f(\tau)$, depends upon the initial pore water pressure distribution in the clay layer, viz., the shape of the area A_o of the initial pore water pressure diagram and the number of free drainage faces.

Knowing the coefficient of consolidation c_v from testing, and the thickness of the soil sample H in the consolidometer, and assuming consecutive time intervals Δt, viz., time t, one can determine the time factor τ, and thus the degree of the average consolidation of the clay calculated. These results can then be tabulated, or plotted in a graph showing $\mu = f(\tau)$. Therefore, it can be inferred that the degree (percent) of consolidation-time factor graph (the μ-τ graph) is indirectly merely a time-percent consolidation curve for the area of a particular shape of the pressure distribution diagram. This graph, in soil mechanics, is referred to as the *theoretical time-consolidation curve*, which differs in its lower branch, as was discussed previously, from the experimentally obtained time-consolidation curve. Such theoretical curves for variously shaped pressure diagrams are shown in Fig. 16-3.

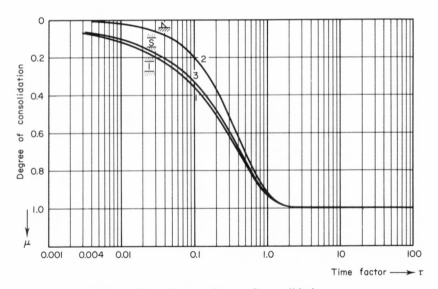

FIG. 16-3.   Time factor – degree of consolidation curves.

16-8. Theoretical Time Factor-Consolidation Tables. To facilitate calculations of the coefficients of degrees of consolidation of soil as a function of the time factor, Terzaghi and Fröhlich published the μ-τ tables for various pressure distribution diagrams. These tables give for certain values, such as $\tau = 0.004$, 0.008, 0.012, the corresponding μ-values, i.e., $\mu = f(\tau)$ (see, for example, Table 16-1).

The τ-μ tables give the degree of consolidation, in decimal fractions, as a function of the time factor τ, for rectangular pressure distribution areas based on the rigorous method of solution of the time consolidation process of a layer of clay embedded between two very pervious layers of sand. The μ-values given in Column 2 of Table 16-1 are the Terzaghi-Fröhlich Table No. 12 for a rectangular area. They are also good for any other arbitrary, linear, initial distribution of the hydrostatic excess pressures, for example, triangular and trapezoidal pressure diagrams, if they have two drainage faces—one on the top and one at the bottom of the clay layer. The drainage length is $L = 2H$.

TABLE 16-1. TIME FACTOR-DEGREE OF CONSOLIDATION VALUES
FOR TWO-WAY DRAINAGE*

Time Factor, τ	Degree of Consolidation, μ		
		Sinusoid 2H 2	Sinusoid 2H 3
1	2	3	4
0.000	0.0000	0.0000	0.0000
0.004	0.0795	0.0649	0.0098
0.008	0.1038	0.0862	0.0195
0.012	0.1248	0.1049	0.0292
0.020	0.1598	0.1367	0.0481
0.028	0.1889	0.1638	0.0667
0.036	0.2141	0.1876	0.0850
0.048	0.2464	0.2196	0.1117
0.060	0.2764	0.2481	0.1376
0.072	0.3028	0.2743	0.1628
0.083	0.3233	0.2967	0.1852
0.100	0.3562	0.3288	0.2187
0.125	0.3989	0.3719	0.2654
0.150	0.4370	0.4112	0.3093
0.167	0.4610	0.4361	0.3377
0.175	0.4718	0.4473	0.3507
0.200	0.5041	0.4809	0.3895
0.250	0.5622	0.5417	0.4603
0.300	0.6132	0.5950	0.5230
0.350	0.6582	0.6421	0.5783
0.40	0.6973	0.6836	0.6273
0.50	0.7640	0.7528	0.7088
0.60	0.8156	0.8069	0.7725
0.70	0.8559	0.8491	0.8222
0.80	0.8874	0.8821	0.8611
0.90	0.9119	0.9079	0.8915
1.00	0.9313	0.9280	0.9152
2.00	0.9942	—	—
∞	1.0000	1.0000	1.0000

* Compiled by permission of Franz Deuticke, Publisher, Vienna, from *Theorie der Setzung von Tonschichten*, by K. Terzaghi and O. K. Fröhlich, Ref. 2, Chapter 15.

Column 3 of Table 16-1 gives μ-values for a quarter-wave, and Column 4 gives μ-values for a half-wave of a sinusoidal, initial pressure distribution for two-way drainage. These values are from the Terzaghi-Fröhlich Tables Nos. 13 and 14, respectively. The drainage length is $L = 2H$. Fig. 16-3 illustrates the courses of the $\mu = f(\tau)$ graphs in Columns 1, 2, and 3. Such graphs are convenient in laboratory work, and in calculating time of certain predetermined

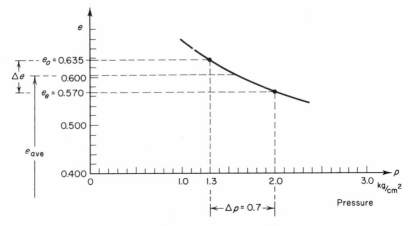

FIG. 16-4.   Pressure – void ratio diagram.

degrees of consolidation of given layers of clay for which the time factor τ is needed.

For one-way drainage the $\mu = f(\tau)$ values are based upon the following considerations.

Rectangular Pressure Diagram. At the center line N-N' of a layer of clay $2H$ thick, embedded between two pervious sand layers, the velocity of the pore water flow, by reasons of symmetry, must be equal to zero. Therefore the boundary layer through the plane of symmetry can be considered as an impervious boundary face. Hence, in one-way drainage the height $H = (2H)/2$ is one half of that in two-way drainage. Hence, the μ-values in one-way drainage are the same as those in the two-way drainage (Table 16-1).

16-9. Illustrative Example. Assume a layer of clay 5 m thick, the bottom of which lies on a sand deposit, and on whose top surface there is also a pervious layer of sand. After the clay has consolidated at a load of 1.3 kg/cm², the load on the surface of the clay has now been increased from 1.3 kg/cm² to 2.0 kg/cm². The unit weight of water is given as $\gamma_w = 1$ g/cm³.

The properties of the clay are:
coefficient of permeability: $k = (1.6)(10^{-6})$ cm/min.
The pressure-void ratio diagram of the clay is given in Fig. 16-4.
Compute:
   a) the magnitude of total settlement;
   b) settlement at 30%, 50%, 70%, 90% consolidation;
   c) degree of consolidation after 1 year, 2 years, and 5 years;
   d) settlement after 1 year, 2 years, and 5 years;

e) length of time required for the total settlement, and

f) length of time needed for 30%, 50%, 70%, 90%, and 100% consolidation.

Solution.

A. Auxiliary Calculations.

i) The given clay system has two-way drainage. Hence, the *shortest drainage path* is $H = 500/2 = 250$ cm.

ii) The *settlement equation* at any time t is

$$s_t = (\mu_\square)(m_v A_o). \qquad (16\text{-}28)$$

iii) The *pressure area* (it is a rectangle) is

$$A_o = (\Delta p)(2H), \qquad (15\text{-}6)$$

$$\Delta p = 2.0 - 1.3 = 0.7 \quad (\text{kg/cm}^2),$$

$$2H = 500 \text{ cm}.$$

$$A_o = (0.7)(500) = 350 \text{ (kg/cm)}.$$

iv) The *specific loss of pore water* m_v is:

$$m_v = \frac{a_v}{1 + e_{ave}} = \frac{\Delta e}{(\Delta p)(1 + e_{ave})} = \frac{e_i - e_f}{(\Delta p)(1 + e_{ave})} =$$

$$= \frac{0.635 - 0.570}{(0.7)\left(1 + \dfrac{0.635 + 0.570}{2}\right)} = 0.0579 \text{ (cm}^2/\text{kg)}.$$

Here, instead of the initial void ratio e_i an average void ratio e_{ave} is used. The use of an average void ratio results in a larger calculated settlement than working with an initial void ratio.

v) The *coefficient of consolidation* c_v is

$$c_v = \frac{k}{m_v \gamma_w} = \frac{(1.6)(10^{-6})}{(0.0579)(0.001)} = 0.02763 \quad (\text{cm}^2/\text{min}),$$

or

$$c_v = (0.02763)(60)(24)(365) = 14,522 \quad (\text{cm}^2/\text{year}).$$

B. Answers.

a) *Total settlement* ($\mu = 1.0$):

$$s = \mu m_v A_o = (1.0)(0.0579)(350) = 20.3 \quad (\text{cm}).$$

b) *Settlement* at 30%, 50%, 70%, and 90% consolidation:

$$s_{30} = (20.3)(0.3) = 6.1 \quad (\text{cm})$$
$$s_{50} = (20.3)(0.5) = 10.2 \quad (\text{cm})$$
$$s_{70} = (20.3)(0.7) = 14.2 \quad (\text{cm})$$
$$s_{90} = (20.3)(0.9) = 18.3 \quad (\text{cm}).$$

c) *Degree of consolidation* after $t = 1$ year, 2 years, and 5 years:
For 1 year:

$$\text{Time factor: } \tau = \frac{c_v t}{H^2} = \frac{(14,522)(1)}{(250)^2} = 0.232.$$

The corresponding degree of consolidation μ, from Table 16-1 by interpolation: at $\tau = 0.200$, $\mu = 0.5041$.

$$\mu_{t=1} = 0.5041 + \frac{0.232 - 0.200}{0.250 - 0.200}(0.5622 - 0.5041) = 0.5413.$$

For 2 years: $t = 2$, $\tau_2 = 2\tau_1 = (2)(0.232) = 0.464$, and $\mu_2 = 0.7404$.
For 5 years: $t = 5$, $\tau_5 = (5)(0.232) = 1.160$, and $\mu_5 = 0.9414$.

d) *Settlement* after 1 year, 2 years, and 5 years:

$$s_t = (20.3)\mu_t.$$

$$\begin{aligned} s_{t=1} &= (20.3)(0.54) = 11.0 & \text{(cm)} \\ s_{t=2} &= (20.3)(0.74) = 15.0 & \text{(cm)} \\ s_{t=5} &= (20.3)(0.94) = 19.1 & \text{(cm)}. \end{aligned}$$

Settlement after a very long time ($t \to \infty$; $\tau \to \infty$; $\mu_\infty = 1.00$):

$$s_{t \to \infty} = (20.3)(1.00) = 20.3 \qquad \text{(cm)}.$$

A settlement of the magnitude of $s = 5.52$ cm, for example, will take place within t years:

$$\mu = (5.52)/20.3 = 0.271 \to \tau \approx 0.06,$$

and

$$t = \frac{\tau H^2}{c_v} = \frac{(0.06)(250)^2}{14{,}522} = 0.258 \text{ years} = 93 \text{ days}.$$

e) The total settlement of 20.3 cm will take place theoretically after a very long time (> 8.6 years).

If the clay sample used in the consolidation test was 2.0 cm thick, with two drainage faces, and 100% consolidation took place within 24 hours $= 0.00273$ years, then the 500-cm-thick prototype layer of clay would consolidate after

$$t/T = h^2/H^2,$$

or

$$T = t(H^2/h^2) = 0.00273(500/2)^2 = 170.62 \qquad \text{(years)},$$

which is a long period of time.

f) *Time for consolidation*:

for $\mu = 30\%$ ($\tau = 0.072$),

$$t_{30} = \frac{\tau H^2}{c_v} = \frac{(0.072)(250)^2}{14{,}522} = 0.31 \qquad \text{(years)};$$

for $\mu = 50\%$ ($\tau = 0.200$),

$$t_{50} = \frac{(0.200)(250)^2}{14{,}522} = 0.86 \qquad \text{(years)};$$

for $\mu = 70\%$ ($\tau = 0.40$),

$$t_{70} = \frac{(0.40)(250)^2}{14{,}522} = 1.72 \qquad \text{(years)};$$

for $\mu = 90\%$ ($\tau = 0.85$),

$$t_{90} = \frac{(0.85)(250)^2}{14{,}522} = 3.66 \qquad \text{(years)};$$

for $\mu = 99.42\%$ ($\tau = 2.00$),

$$t_{99.42} = \frac{(2)(250)^2}{14,522} = 8.6 \quad \text{(years)};$$

for $\mu = 1.00 \approx 0.9999$ ($\tau \approx \to \infty$),

$$t_{99.99} \to \frac{(\infty)(250)^2}{14,522} \to \infty \quad \text{(a very long period of time)}.$$

16-10. Illustrative Example. All data are as in the preceding problem, but the clay layer, 500 cm thick, rests on an artesian aquifer from which water is flowing upwards through the clay. Because it is assumed in this problem that pore water cannot be expelled from the clay through its bottom face against the artesian pressure, then the only way for the pore water to escape is upward into the sand. Therefore the contact surface between the layer of clay and the artesian aquifer may be considered impervious at the bottom of the clay, thus presenting a clay system with one-way drainage upward. Here $H = 500$ cm. Settlement:

$$s_t = \mu m_v A_o = (20.3).$$

a) The *total settlement* is the same as before:

$$s = (1.0)(20.3) = 20.3 \quad \text{(cm)}.$$

b) *Settlement* at 30%, 50%, 70%, and 90% consolidation (same as before):

$$s_{30} = 6.1 \quad \text{(cm)}$$
$$s_{50} = 10.2 \quad \text{(cm)}$$
$$s_{70} = 14.2 \quad \text{(cm)}$$
$$s_{90} = 18.3 \quad \text{(cm)}.$$

c) *Degree of Consolidation* after 1 year, 2 years, and 5 years. Because of the longer drainage path, $H = 500$ cm, the degree of consolidation in this one-way drainage system is less than in a two-way drainage system.
For 1 year:

$$\text{Time factor } \tau_1 = \frac{c_v t}{H^2} = \frac{(14,522)(1)}{(500)^2} = 0.058.$$

The corresponding degree of consolidation: $\mu_1 = 0.2720$.
For 2 years:
$$\tau_2 = 2\tau_1 = (2)(0.058) = 0.116,$$
$$\mu_2 = 0.3735.$$
For 5 years:
$$\tau_5 = (5)(0.058) = 0.290,$$
$$\mu_5 = 0.6030.$$

d) *Settlement*:
After 1 year: $s_1 = \mu_1(20.3) = (0.2720)(20.3) = 5.52 \quad \text{(cm)}.$
After 2 years: $s_2 = \mu_2(20.3) = (0.3735)(20.3) = 7.58 \quad \text{(cm)}.$
After 5 years: $s_5 = \mu_5(20.3) = (0.6030)(20.3) = 12.24 \quad \text{(cm)}.$

e) *Total settlement of the prototype clay layer*, for one way drainage:

$$T = t\frac{H^2}{(h/2)^2} = (0.00273)\frac{500^2}{(1)^2} = 682.5 \quad \text{(years)}.$$

Check: in one-way drainage, the settlement takes place four times longer than in two-way drainage, i.e., $4 \times 170.62 = 682.48$ (years), which checks with the calculation above.

f) *Time for consolidation*:
   for $\mu = 30\%$ ($\tau = 0.072$)

$$t_{30} = \frac{\tau H^2}{c_v} = \frac{(0.072)(500)^2}{14,522} = 1.24 \qquad \text{(years)}.$$

For $\mu = 50\%$: $t_{50} = 3.44$ (years).

Note again that in one-way drainage consolidation takes place: $(500^2)/(250^2) =$ 4—four times longer than in two-way drainage.

$$t_{99.42\%} = \frac{(2)(500)^2}{14,522} = 34.43 \qquad \text{(years)}.$$

As a matter of exercise, 11 cm settlement takes place within t_{11} years time:

$$11.0 = \mu(20.3),$$

or

$$\mu = (11.0)/20.3) = 0.5418,$$

for which there is a corresponding time factor of $\tau = 0.2325$, and

$$t_{11} = \frac{\tau H^2}{c_v} = \frac{(0.2325)(500^2)}{14,522} = 4.00 \qquad \text{(years)}.$$

16-11. Conclusion.

It appears that the consolidation theory of clays is good for water in bulk in the voids of the soil (this pertains to primary consolidation). The theory, how-ever, does not take into account the film moisture adsorbed to the surfaces of the soil particles—moisture migration mechanism by way of water film flow.[3,4] (This pertains to secondary consolidation). Nor is the consolidation theory satisfactory for unsaturated soils (air cushions, gas, and/or vapor pressure). Only comprehensive comparison of actually measured settlements of structures with the predicted or calculated ones may permit evaluation of the usefulness of the method of settlement analysis, based on the consolidation theory of clays, where it is assumed that all voids are totally filled with water, and that Darcy's law is valid.

In the technical literature many publications on consolidations of soils and settlement of structures on such soils show that the measured magnitudes of settlement agree reasonably with those calculated by means of the consolidation theory. For example, it has been reported at the Second International Congress on Bridge Construction, held in 1936 in Berlin and at Munich, that, based on many settlement measurements of bridge piers and abutments, the measured or observed magnitudes of settlement were less than the calculated ones.

If the shear stress in a mass of soil underneath a foundation exceeds the shear strength of the soil, the soil may then fail in shear, causing large settlements and resulting in a tilting or collapse of the structure. Shear failure takes place quickly as soon as the bearing capacity of the soil is exceeded, whereas consolidation settlements continue over a long period of years after the structure has been completed (Figs. 15-1, 18-2 and 18-4).

As consolidation proceeds, more water is expelled from the soil. Thus, consolidation increases the shear strength of the soil with time.

REFERENCES

1. K. Terzaghi and O.K. Fröhlich, *Theorie der Setzung von Tonschichten*, Leipzig und Wien, Franz Deuticke, 1936.
2. A. R. Jumikis, *Soil Mechanics*, Princeton, N.J., D. Van Nostrand Company, Inc., 1962, pp. 353-397.
3. A. R. Jumikis, *Thermal Soil Mechanics*, New Brunswick, N.J., Rutgers University Press, 1966, pp. 87-92.
4. A. R. Jumikis, *Thermal Geotechnics*, New Brunswick, N.J. Rutgers University Press, 1977.

SUGGESTIONS FOR FURTHER READINGS

1. J. Lowe, III, P.F. Zaccheo, and H.S. Feldman, "Consolidation Testing with Back Pressure," *Proc. ASCE*, Journal of the Social Mechanics and Foundations Division, vol. 90, No. SM5, 1964, pp. 69-86.
2. R.F. Scott, "New Method of Consolidation Coefficient Evaluation," *Proc. ASCE*, Journal of the Soil Mechanics and Foundations Division, vol. 87, No. SM1, 1961, pp. 29-39.
3. A.W. Skempton and L. Bjerrum, "A Contribution to the Settlement Analysis of Foundations on Clay," Géotechnique (London), vol. 7, No. 4, 1957, pp. 168.

QUESTIONS

16- 1. What is the "coefficient of consolidation"?

16- 2. How can the coefficient of consolidation be determined?

16- 3. What is understood by excess hydrostatic pressure?

16- 4. What are the assumptions underlying the consolidation theory of clays?

16- 5. Distinguish between the use of the term "consolidation" by geologists and by engineers.

16- 6. Upon what does the rate of consolidation of a clay depend?

16- 7. Upon what does the rate of settlement depend?

16- 8. What basic law has the consolidation theory contributed to the compression of clays?

16- 9. In which direction does the course of the consolidation process in clay proceed: from the center towards the drainage face (towards the outside), or from the drainage face in the direction of the interior of the clay? Illustrate your explanation by an appropriate sketch.

16-10. What is the fundamental, general equation governing the stress conditions in the consolidation process of a cohesive soil? Explain the physical contents this equation represents.

16-11. What is the "pressure distribution area"?

16-12. What is understood by "fitting the time curve" in consolidation theory?

PROBLEMS

16- 1. Plot time-consolidation curves of the Moonachie varved clay, and determine 0% and 100% consolidation by the Casagrande and Taylor methods.

Elapsed Time (minutes)	Time of Initial and Vertical Dial Readings					
	Oct. 2, 3:00 p.m.	Oct. 3, 3:00 p.m.	Oct. 4, 3:00 p.m.	Oct. 5, 3:00 p.m.	Oct. 6, 3:00 p.m.	Oct. 7, 3:00 p.m·
	Dial Readings (inches)					
1	2	3	4	5	6	7
0	0.9100	0.9343	0.9513	0.9943	1.0569	1.0979
0.25	0.9132	0.9380	0.9571	1.0022	1.0674	1.0751
0.5	0.9150	0.9390	0.9590	1.0056	1.0708	1.0749
1	0.9174	0.9405	0.9622	1.0120	1.0721	1.0740
2	0.9207	0.9425	0.9668	1.0207	1.0767	1.0729
3	0.9233	0.9436	0.9700	1.0275	1.0801	1.0711
5	0.9267	0.9453	0.9740	1.0361	1.0845	1.0695
8	0.9295	0.9465	0.9776	1.0417	1.0878	1.0670
10	0.9302	0.9470	0.9788	1.0440	1.0890	1.0650
15	0.9312	0.9477	0.9815	1.0477	1.0908	1.0635
30	0.9323	0.9487	0.9850	1.0514	1.0929	1.0619
60	0.9334	0.9493	0.9876	1.0529	1.0944	1.0600
120	0.9338	0.9498	0.9898	1.0543	1.0955	—
1440	0.9343	0.9513	0.9943	1.0569	1.0979	1.0584
Pressure on soil (kg/cm²)	0.625	1.250	2.500	5.000	10.000	0.625

Note. The readings of the vertical dial used in this test increased as the soil sample was compressed. One revolution = 200 small divisions; 1 division = 0.0001 in.

16- 2. Given time-dial reading data as tabulated.

Elapsed Time (minutes)	Dial Readings (inches)	Cumulative Compression h (inches)	Consolidation (%)	Void Ratio
1	2	3	4	5
0	0.24930	0.00000	0.00	0.6596
0.25	5540			
0.5	5630			
1	5776			
2	5969			
4	6245			
8	6600			
15	6929			
30	7183			
60	7300			
120	7360			
240	7406			
480	7442			
1440	7511		100.00	

Total pressure on soil sample, $p = 67.9$ lb/in.^{2} during a loading cycle. The soil is Raritan clay. Void ratio at time $= 0$ minutes is $e_o = 0.6596$, and at time t_{1440}, the void ratio is $e = 0.6103$. Relative height of solids at time t_o is 1.000. Absolute height of solids at time t_o is $h = 0.448$ inches. Prepare the time-consolidation curve. Plot this data to a semilogarithmic scale on 5-cycle paper. Plot the dial reading (consolidation) curve. Calculate and fill in columns 3, 4 and 5. Determine 0% and 100% consolidation.

16- 3. Using Eq. 16-3, calculate the value of the time factor τ at 90% consolidation ($\tau = 0.848$).

16- 4. Calculate the degree of consolidation μ for a time factor of $\tau = 0.200$ for two-way drainage and for a rectangular excess pressure distribution area ($\mu = 0.5041$).

16- 5. Prepare time factor-degree of consolidation tables for the various cases (by straight-line interpolation) from Table 16-1 in 5% intervals, i.e., $\tau = f(\mu)$, arranging data as follows:

μ	τ
0.00	0.000
0.05	
0.10	
0.15	
...	
0.90	
0.95	
1.00	

16- 6. What is the value of $\mu_{ave} = f(z; t)$ in the rigorous solution for a clay system with one-way drainage?

16- 7. Derive the expression for the coefficient of permeability of clay k, in centimeters per second, from the consolidation test:

$$k = c_v \cdot m_v \cdot \gamma_w = \frac{\gamma_w a_v \tau H^2}{(1+e)t},$$

where $c_v = \dfrac{\tau \cdot H^2}{t}$ = coefficient of consolidation

   $m_v = \dfrac{a_v}{1+e}$ = coefficient of volume change

   γ_w = unit weight of water;
   a_v = coefficient of compressibility, cm^2/kg;
   τ = dimensionless factor, termed the time factor;
   H = half the thickness of the layer of clay in one-way drainage, or the shortest path of drainage of clay;
   e = initial void ratio under a pressure increment $\overline{\Delta p}$;
   t = time in seconds.

16- 8. If the coefficient of compressibility is $a_v = 0.1071$ cm^2/kg, the coefficient of consolidation is $c_v = 12960$ $cm^2/year$, the initial void ratio is $e = 0.680$, and the temperature during the tests is $+ 25°C$, calculate the coefficient of permeability k in centimeters per second, in centimeters per minute, and in centimeters per year at $+20°C$.

16- 9. If the coefficient of consolidation of a 3.0-m-thick layer of clay is $c_v = 0.0003$ cm^2/s, what is the average consolidation of that layer of clay in one year with two-way drainage?   (0.71)
The same as above, for one-way drainage system?   (0.37)

16-10. Given on the compression curve, Fig. 16-4, $p_1 = 1.5$ kg/cm^2 and $p_2 = 2.00$ kg/cm^2; $c_v = 0.025$ (cm^2/min) for a silty clay layer draining on both sides. The thickness of the clay sample in the consolidometer was 2.0 cm. The thickness of the prototype layer of the soil was 10 ft. Under the given pressure and test conditions, the clay sample gave a 50% consolidation within a period of 7.2 minutes. Experimental 100% consolidation was reached in 1.2 hours.
Determine: a) Coefficient of compressibility.
        b) Specific loss of pore water.
        c) Permeability of clay for the given test conditions, in centimeters per second, and in centimeters per year.
        d) How long will it take for the layer of clay 10 ft thick to reach a 50% consolidation?
        e) How large is the settlement of the clay layer at 50% consolidation?
        f) What is the magnitude of the total settlement?
        g) After how long a time will the 100% settlement be attained?
        h) How large will be the settlement after one month? One year?
        i) What are the corresponding degrees of consolidation in h)?
        j) Calculate and show all time factors involved.

16-11. Given a square footing, $6' \times 6'$, as shown in Fig. Problem 16-11, founded 4' below the ground surface. The footing is loaded centrally with a load of $P = 43.2$ tons. The profile of the soil is also shown. The pressure-void ratio curves are shown in Problem Figs. 16-11a, b, c, and d, respectively. The four soil samples attained 100% consolidation from 0 kg/cm^2 to 1.2 kg/cm^2 in two-way drainage in the following times:
sample No. 1: thickness of sample $2H = 2.54$ cm; in 66 h 00 min
sample No. 2: thickness of sample $2H = 2.54$ cm; in 71 h 00 min
sample No. 3: thickness of sample $2H = 2.54$ cm; in 79 h 06 min
sample No. 4: thickness of sample $2H = 2.54$ cm; in 125 minutes.

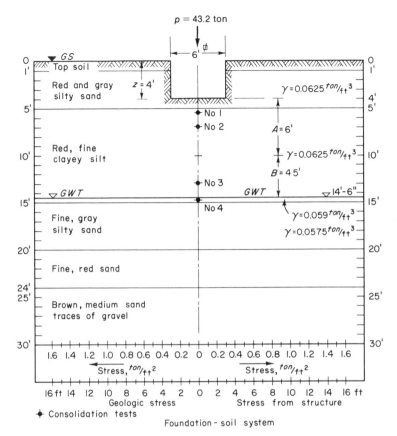

FIG. PROBLEM 16-11.

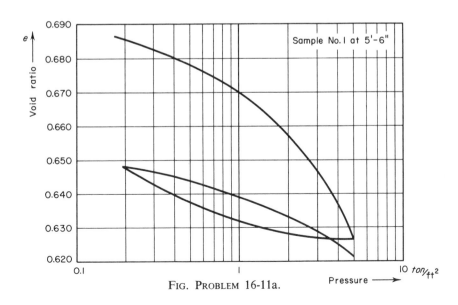

FIG. PROBLEM 16-11a.

Required:

a) Explain the nature of the given four pressure-void ratio curves.

b) Calculate the total settlement of the given structure.

c) In how long a time, approximately, will the soil attain 50%, 80%, and 100% consolidation?

d) Estimate the percent of consolidation 2, 5, 10, 20, and 50 years after the erection of the structure.

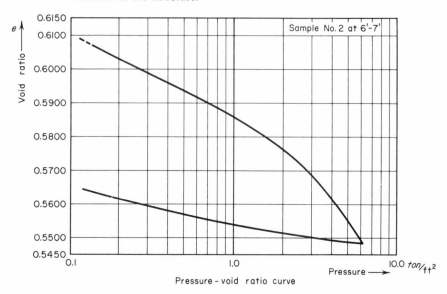

FIG. PROBLEM 16-11b.

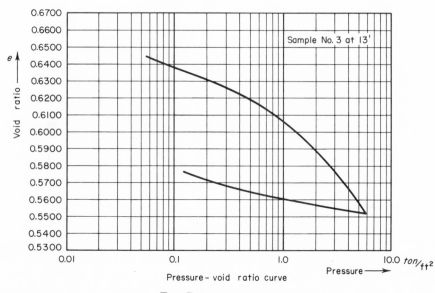

FIG. PROBLEM 16-11c.

Chapter 17

VERTICAL SAND DRAINS

17-1. Principle of Function of Sand Drains. The principle of the functioning of a sand drain is based on the consolidation theory of radially and centrally dewatered clay systems.

The normally slow process of consolidation of clays, silt, muck, and other native, compressible, saturated materials may be accelerated by means of vertical sand drains which aid in the expulsion of the pore water from the soil. Essentially, a sand drain consists of a vertical bore hole put down through the saturated, fine-particled soil, and extending to a relatively firm bottom—an impervious layer of rock, such as shale, or basalt, or any other practically impervious geological formation, and backfilled with a pervious material such as carefully graded sand Fig. 17-1.

Because, by the model law of consolidation, time varies as the square of the length of the drainage path, the distance that a particle of pore water must travel upon expulsion from H to $H/2$ increases the rate of consolidation fourfold. Thus, a vertical sand drain brings about a more than two-fold decrease in the length of the drainage path because of the radial drainage of water towards the vertical drain. The horizontal distance for drainage, in this case of sand drains, is many times shorter than the distance for draining vertically, i.e., $R < H$. Besides, the horizontal permeability of a cohesive soil is usually larger than its vertical permeability because of the shape of the clay particles.

The weight of the fill compresses the soft material, forcing the water into the sand drain and up into the lateral drainage blanket provided from the base of the fill by a layer of pervious sand, from which the pore water, expelled from the sand drains, rapidly drains out laterally. The greater the load on the native, compressible material, the faster the process of consolidation.

Sometimes the sand drains are allowed to puncture an impervious layer (Fig. 17-2) if there is a layer of pervious sand beneath. Such a condition would provide for another drainage outlet below the impervious course, thus creating a two-way drainage system and speeding the process of consolidation of the compressible material—stabilizing the fill considerably.

Sometimes an overload fill is placed on top of the permanent fill to bring about the desired amount of settlement. When the settlement of the whole fill over the sand drains exceeds the expected settlement, and settlement is proceeding at a very low rate, the overload fill may then be removed. The overload is usually removed after a waiting period, say, of about 30 days, and can be reused on

271

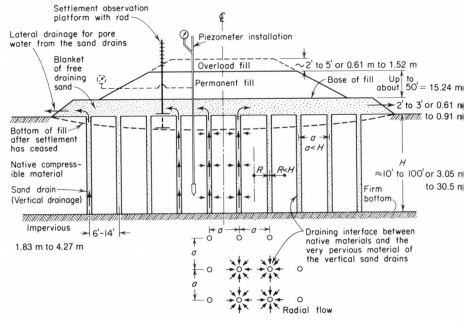

FIG. 17-1.   The function of vertical sand drains.

adjacent projects. The 30 days, of course, is not a standard; the waiting period can be any necessary period of time other than 30 days.

The practical application of the sand drain method for accelerating the consolidation of soil in the United States is credited to O. J. Porter.[1]

17-2. Purpose of Sand Drains. The purpose of a sand drain system is to accelerate the expulsion and draining away of the pore water squeezed out of the voids of the soft soil by the earth fill, or by a structural load. This speeds up the rate of consolidation and, thus, the settlement of the soil. Sand drains are also used, under some circumstances, to drain and control land slides. Sand drains also relieve the hydrostatic excess pressure induced in the voids of the soil by the application of the weight of the fill material on the ground surface of the compressible soil.

Sand drains, providing supplementary outlets for the expelled pore water, also accelerate the increase in shear strength of the native soil to be consolidated.

17-3. Diameter of Drains. The diameter of sand drains varies in practice from about 18 in. to about 24 in. or ∼ 46 cm to 61 cm. Too small a diameter is not desirable because of difficulty in filling the mandrel pipe with sand and the danger of an arching of the sand because of the friction between the column of sand and the wall of the metal tube (mandrel). The sand drain need be only large enough to drain away the expelled quantity of pore water, and to allow for a safety margin against clogging up the drainage interface between the native material and the pervious material in the sand drain by infiltration of fine material.

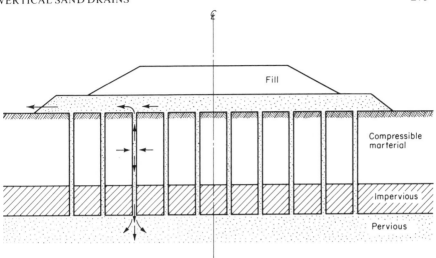

FIG. 17-2. Sand drains puncture an impervious layer.

17-4. Spacing of Sand Drains. The spacing of sand drains depends upon the type and permeability of the soil. For these and other possible reasons the sand drains are, in practice, spaced from 6 to 14 ft or from ~ 1.83 m to 4.27 m center to center. Sand drains are effective for their purpose if their spacing a is less than their depth H, i.e., if $a < H$. Economy requires a study of the effect of spacing the sand drains on the rate of consolidation. Terzaghi[2] recommends choosing the spacing so that 80% of the total consolidation is brought about during the time of construction of the fill. In practice, spacing for 20 in. (~ 50.8 cm) diameter sand drains varies on the average from 6 to 10 ft, or from 1.83 m to ~ 3.05 m.

17-5. Depth of Sand Drains. The depth of the sand drains is dictated by the geology, i.e., by the depth of the firm layer below the ground surface. Sand drains have been placed to a depth of from 10 ft to 60, 70, 90 (or 3.05 m to 1.83 m, 21.34 m, 27.43 m), and in some cases even to 100 and 135 ft (30.5 m to 41.15 m). Sometimes, where "mud" depths are less than 20 ft (6.10 m), it is more economical to strip the "mud" before filling the embankment.

17-6. Installation of Sand Drains. A sand drain is now usually installed by means of a hollow steel pipe, called the mandrel, which acts as a casing during the filling of the sand drain. The lower end of the mandrel is provided with a flat, hinged bottom plate. The empty pipe, with the bottom plate closed, is driven vertically through the native soil material by means of a pile driver having a guide frame. At the top of the pipe there is a sand skip attached to fill the hollow plugged mandrel. The skip can slide up and down the guide frame. After the mandrel has been driven to the proper depth, the mandrel is pulled out during backfilling with sand. The sand is filled under a pressure of about 100 lb/in.^{2} (6.89 kN/m^2). The pressure is admitted into the mandrel at its top. As the mandrel is withdrawn from the ground, the backfill sand is forced out of the mandrel through its lower end by the weight of the sand and the applied pressure (compressed air, or steam) past the now-opened and free-hanging bottom plate into the vertical hole left in the ground by driving the mandrel. The bottom plate is thus recovered and reused.

The rate of withdrawal of the mandrel and the application of pressure must, of course, be very carefully regulated. The pressure is intended to prevent developing of arching of sand in the tube, and to make a reasonably strong sand column.

Upon withdrawal of the mandrel the backfill sand is left as a vertical sand cylinder to function as a vertical sand drain.

The sand drains may also be installed by jetting a hole in the soil, or by driving an open casing into the soil, washing the soil out of the casing, and filling the hole with draining sand afterward.

17-7. Sand for Drains. The sand used as a draining medium is usually a very carefully selected and clean material. Sometimes not more than 5% of the (-100) material is allowed. To be consistent with economy and availability of materials, no specially prepared graded sand, as applied in the construction of filters, is used. The only requirement for sand to be used in vertical drains is that it should carry away the pore water unobstructed and not permit the fine, native soil to be washed in. The permeability requirements are that the drain sand should be approximately 1000 times more permeable than that of the consolidating native soil. The order of magnitude of the permeability of the various consolidated soils is between $k = 10^{-5}$ cm/s and $k = 10^{-6}$ cm/s.

However, the California Department of Highways, according to Stanton,[3] has used the following typical specifications on several of their vertical sand drain projects.

Grading Requirements for Sand Drains[3]

U.S. Standard Sieve[4]		
Series	Mesh Opening mm	Percent Passing Sieve
$1/2''$	12.7	90 - 100
No. 8	2.38	25 - 100
No. 30	0.590	5 - 50
No. 50	0.297	0 - 20
No. 100	0.149	0 - 3

17-8. Blanket. After the installation of the vertical sand drains, a blanket of free-draining sand, one to three feet in thickness, is spread over the entire sand-drain area. The blanket should extend to the outer, initial slope, or toe of the slope of the embankment. The sand blanket provides for lateral drainage at the base of the fill for pore water from the vertical sand drains. The sand and gravel used as a blanket should be clean. It is sometimes specified that the blanket material should contain not more than 5% to 10% of (−200) material (<0.074 mm).

The grading of a blanket material established by the California Department of Highways for some of its projects, and also used on some New Jersey sand drain projects, is:

Grading of Blanket Material[4]
(Clean, coarse sand and gravel)

U.S. Standard Sieve[4]		
Series	Mesh Opening mm	Percent Passing
3/8″	9.52	80 - 100
No. 8	2.38	5 - 50
No. 30	0.590	0 - 20
No. 50	0.297	0 - 5

Permanent Fill. Permanent fill is constructed on top of the drainage blanket. Fills as high as 50 to 70 ft (15.24 m to 21.34 m) have been stabilized by the vertical sand drain method.

17-9. Rate of Loading. The rate of loading is one of the most important processes in making the fill. Too fast a rate of loading may cause a failure of the earthwork. Rapid loading may induce high hydrostatic excess pressures. These neutral pressures in the early stage of the consolidation process do not contribute to the shear strength of the soil. Therefore, a careful loading control must be practiced.

Control. The purpose of controlling the rate of the construction of an earth embankment is to prevent the rupture of the native soil and the shearing off of the sand drains—deformations which result in lateral displacement or slide failures of the earth mass and/or in the formation of "mud waves," or earth heaves.

The devices for controlling the rate of the settlement of the fill and the developed pore water pressures at various depths in the soil underneath the fill are the settlement observation platforms and the piezometers, such as shown in Fig. 17-1.

A settlement observation platform is a platform made of timber, to which a vertical rod is attached (Fig. 17-1). The platforms are installed at the base of the fill, and periodic settlement measurements of the platforms (the platforms settle as the fill settles) permit one to gain an insight into the settlement, i.e., consolidation process.

The order or magnitude of induced pore water pressures while filling the embankment is up to 12 or 15 lb/in.² (82.68 kN/m² to 130.35 kN/m²), depending upon the type of soil and rate of loading. As time goes on, the pore water pressure indicating gauges show that pore water pressures gradually decrease to normal because the pressure of the pore water is relieved by the establishment of the drainage flow through the vertical sand drains and the lateral drainage blanket.

By correlation of the rate of consolidation of the native soil with the pore water pressures at various depths in that native soil, it is possible to estimate the rate of loading, viz., rate of application of the next safe lift of the fill material.

The amounts of settlement of soil of from 4 to 20 ft (1.22 m to 6.07 m) have been attained in various instances without failure in shear and without displacing the adjacent mass of soil,[5] thus proving in many instances the safe and economic value of the sand drain method for stabilizing native, compressible soil materials.

There are, however, instances known where the sand drains were not functioning successfully.[6]

17-10. Applications of Sand Drains. Sand drains have been used extensively in California, as well as on the east coast of the United States, for stabilizing compressible soils for highways and railroad yards. They have been used extensively also for airfield and port development work in the metropolitan areas of New York, N.Y. and Newark, N.J.; for highway projects in Connecticut; for the northern part of the New Jersey Turnpike and the Garden State Parkway, also in New Jersey; as well as in Europe for improving the soil properties suitable for foundation engineering purposes.

REFERENCES

1. O. J. Porter, "Studies of Fill Construction over Mud Flats Including a Description of Experimental Construction Using Vertical Sand Drains to Hasten Stabilization," *Proceedings*, First International Conference on Soil Mechanics and Foundation Engineering, held in June 1936 at Cambridge, Mass., vol. 1, pp. 229-235.
2. K. Terzaghi, "Drainage of Clay Strata by Filter Wells," *Civil Engineer*, no. 10, October 1945, p. 463.
3. F. E. Stanton, "Vertical Sand Drains as a Means of Foundation Consolidation on Accelerating Settlement of Embankment over Marsh Land," *Proceedings*, Second International Conference on Soil Mechanics and Foundation Engineering, held in 1948, in Rotterdam, vol. 5, p. 273-278.
4. ASTM, *1976 Annual Book of ASTM Standards, Part 41*. Designation E 11-70, Standard Specification for Wire-cloth Sieves for Testing Purposes. ASTM, Philadelphia, PA., 1976, pp. 7-11.
5. H. A. Simard, "Sand Piles Hasten Completion of California Expressway," *Roads and Streets*, December 1947.
6. W. S. Housel, *Checking up on Vertical Sand Drains*, Highway Research Board Bulletin, no. 90, 1954, pp. 1-16.

SUGGESTIONS FOR FURTHER READING

1. R.A. Barron, "Consolidation Settlement of Fine-Grained Soils by Drain Wells," *Transactions ASCE*, vol. 113,1948, pp. 718-742.
2. L. Casagrande and S. Poulos, "On the Effectiveness of Sand Drains," *Canadian Geotechnical Journal*, vol. 6, No. 3, 1969.
3. S.J. Johnson, "Foundation Precompression with Vertical Sand Drains," *Proc. ASCE*, Journal of the Soil Mechanics and Foundations Division, vol. 96, No. SM1, 1970.
4. F.E. Richart, Jr., "Review of the Theories for Sand Drains," *Transactions ASCE*, vol. 124, 1959, p. 709.

Chapter 18

SETTLEMENT

18-1. The Washington Monument, Washington, D.C. The Washington monument, according to the 1933 report mentioned in Ref. 1, affords the longest settlement record available in the United States. The monument is founded on a "sandy mound" (Fig. 18-1). Borings in 1931 disclosed an irregular bed of compressible clay 10 to 40 ft (3.05 m to 12.20 m) thick overlying rock. The size of the original footing was 80 ft square (24.38 m²). The construction work on the monument, begun in 1848, was interrupted in 1854, when the structure was 150 ft (45.64 m) high and the total weight was about 31,152 tons (277.14 MN), giving a contact pressure on the soil of $p_o = 5$ tons/ft² $= 478.8$ kN/m².

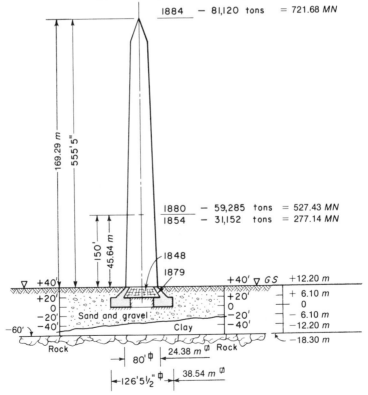

FIG. 18-1. Washington monument. Years, weights, and soil profile.

277

There are no settlement records available for this monument prior to 1879. After that year, the original foundation of the monument was underpinned to a size of 126 ft 5½ in. square (38.54 m²). Then building of the monument was continued, and it attained its full height by 1884. During the process of increasing the load to 5 ton/ft² (478.8 kN/m²) again, the monument settled 4½ in. (11.43 cm); subsequently to 1885, it settled another inch (2.54 cm), and it is probably still slowly settling quite uniformly. According to the 1933 report, the structure is nearly plumb. It was the opinion of the committee in Ref. 1 that the compresison of the 10- to 40-ft-thick (3.05 m to 12.20 m) clay layer is probably responsible for most of the observed settlements.

The course of the construction of the monument can be followed from the time-settlement diagram, Fig. 18-2.

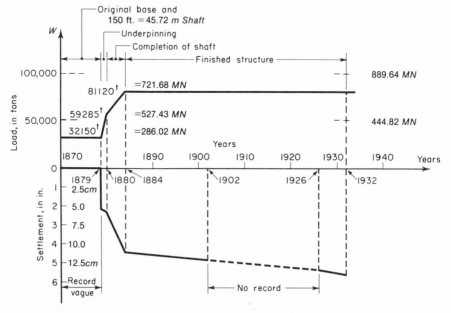

FIG. 18-2. Time-settlement diagram, Washington monument.

18-2. The Leaning Tower of Pisa. A world-renowned example of differential settlement is the classical leaning tower of Pisa, Italy. Based on his studies on the settlement of the tower, Imbeaux[2] in 1927 published an article in which he put forward a theory that the principal cause of leaning of the bell tower is the subterranean water (*erosion theory*).

In Italian circles the opinion prevails that the hypothesis relative to the instability of the tower is *the low bearing capacity of the layer of sand* (Fig. 18-3). According to Krynine,[3] "since 1932 more than 1000 tons of high-strength cement in the form of grout has been injected into the soil through 361 holes, 2 in. (5.08 cm) in diameter."

In 1934, Terzaghi[4] published a diagram showing stress distribution in soil

(a) Vertical section

(b) Plan of base of footing

(c) Linear distribution of contact pressure on soil

(d) Curvilinear pressure distribution on top surface of clay, c-c 8.0 m below the base of footing.

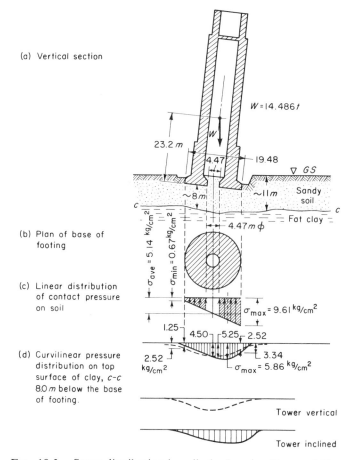

$W = 14.486 t$

23.2 m

4.47

19.48

∇ GS

~8 m   ~11 m   Sandy soil

c — Fat clay — c

4.47 m ϕ

$\sigma_{ave} = 5.14$ kg/cm^2

$\sigma_{min} = 0.67$ kg/cm^2

$\sigma_{max} = 9.61$ kg/cm^2

1.25

4.50   5.25   2.52

2.52 kg/cm^2

3.34

$\sigma_{max} = 5.86$ kg/cm^2

Tower vertical

Tower inclined

FIG. 18-3. Stress distribution in soil, the Leaning Tower of Pisa.

under the leaning tower (Fig. 18-3) and, based on soil mechanics considerations that the settlement and the leaning of the tower are attributable probably and almost exclusively to the gradual consolidation of the clayey soil situated 8 m underneath the footing of the foundation of the tower, also published a time-settlement diagram for the tower (Fig. 18-4).

On the horizontal time axis are plotted the years of the various construction stages, and on the vertical load axis (up) are designated the corresponding loads of the galleries erected. On the vertical settlement axis (down) is indicated the relative settlement of the southern side of the tower. The settlements indicated are differences in elevation between the highest and deepest point of the base of the footing. The horizontal parts in the steps of the time-load diagram indicate the years during which construction of the tower was interrupted because of the pronounced settlements. The magnitude of the absolute settlement of the tower at the door is reported by Terzaghi as being 2.4 m $\approx$ 7.87 ft. After the intermediate settlements ceased, construction of the tower was resumed by adding one or two more galleries. The diagram also shows that the bell gallery was erected in A.D. 1350. The total load of the tower was then 14,486 metric tons, resulting in a settlement of 70 cm ≈ 27.5 in. This diagram also shows that from 1174 to 1933, a period of 759 years, the resulting settlement of the point in question attained 150 cm ≈ 59.0 in., and that most of the settlement has already

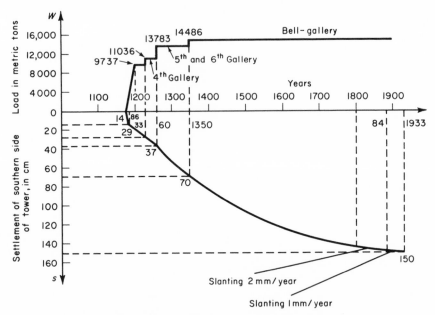

FIG. 18-4. Time-settlement diagram for the Leaning Tower of Pisa.

reached a state of rest (the time-settlement curve approaches a horizontal line asymptotically). Thus, Terzaghi estimated that the center of the footing settled about 0.8 m ≈ 2.62 ft, which means that the lowest point of this footing settled about 3.2 m ≈ 10.5 ft, whereas the highest point settled about 1.6 m ≈ 5.25 ft.

The stress distribution diagram, Fig. 18-3, shows the conventional stress distribution according to a trapezoid underneath the base of the round footing:

$$\left.\begin{array}{l}\sigma_{max} = 9.61 \text{ kg/cm}^2 \\ \sigma_{min} = 0.67 \text{ kg/cm}^2\end{array}\right\} \text{ tower in leaning position.}$$

$$\sigma_{ave} = 5.14 \text{ kg/cm}^2 \quad \text{tower in vertical position.}$$

The stress distribution diagram due to the weight of the tower at 8 m depth shows a maximum pressure of $\sigma_{max} = 5.86$ kg/cm^2 on the surface of the clay.

Terzaghi also calculated, by comparison with another structure and using the model law, that 95% of the total settlement of the tower would be attained after

$$t_2 = t_1 \frac{k_1}{k_2} \frac{H_2^2}{H_1^2} = (17)(10)(2)^2 = 680 \quad \text{(years)}, \tag{18-1}$$

where $H_1 = 15$ m thickness of clay underneath another structure used for comparison;

$t_1 = 17$ years to bring about 95% consolidation of the layer of clay $H_1 = 15$ m thick;

$H_2 = 30$ m $= 2H_1 =$ thickness of clay layer in question underneath the leaning tower of Pisa;

$k_2 = (k_1)/(10) =$ permeability relationship of clay to water between layers H_2 and H_1.

The 100% consolidation will, of course, require a very long period of time.

C.B. Spencer[5] reported in 1954 after a visit to Pisa that the tower was still leaning some 0.04 in. (1.016 mm) per year. The question, therefore, arises whether consolidation is the only reason for the settlement of the Leaning Tower of Pisa.

The historical, classical example in soil mechanics, namely that of the Leaning Tower of Pisa, renders ever again new problems in geotechnical engineering. Here the problems of groundbreak and stability of the tower come to the fore.

Fig. 18-5 shows an up-to-date soil profile, ring foundation of the Leaning Tower of Pisa, soil contact pressure distribution under the ring foundation, and a table of average values of soil physical properties after Dr. E. Schultze.[6,7]

Dr. Schultze was one of the consultants to the Italian comission* for working out stabilization proposals of remedy and underpinning to save the Tower of Pisa from further movement and eventual collapse. Based on results of soil investigation and stability analyses on hand, Dr. Schultze answered in the affirmative the following question: "Can the Leaning Tower of Pisa still be saved?" The answer is:[8]

"Under the conditions as they prevail today the Tower of Pisa will not collapse because

1) there just still exists safety of stability, and
2) the observed time-tilting line approaches a final value which is less than the critical one."

By 1967, the said commission received 2700 proposals for making fast of the tower. However the fundamental difficulty in working out stabilization methods lies in the low factor of safety against tilting, viz., groundbreak, the relatively low coefficient of compressibility of the soil materials at the site, and the great sensitivity of the tower to any external encroachment effects. Another important problem of stabilization is to secure the tower during the construction work. The supporting auxiliary structures which may be temporarily required may turn out to be much more expensive than the final underpinning work of the foundation of the tower itself.

18-3. The Subsidence of Mexico City. The settlements of soil and structures and the subsidence of this modern Mexican metropolis, the Federal District of Mexico City—a city of four million people and one of the largest cities in North America—are very well known. They are very celebrated and spectacular examples of large-scale soil consolidation frequently cited by soil and founda-

*Commissione per il Consolidamento della Torre Pendente di Pisa.

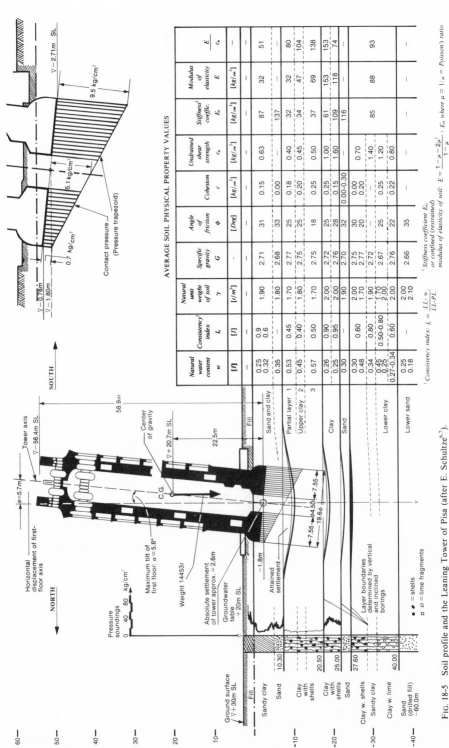

AVERAGE SOIL PHYSICAL PROPERTY VALUES

Soil layer	Natural water content w [1]	Consistency index[1] I_c [1]	Natural unit weight of soil γ [t/m³]	Specific gravity G	Angle of friction ϕ [Deg]	Cohesion c [kg/cm²]	Undrained shear strength c_u [kg/cm²]	Stiffness[2] coeffic. E_s [kg/cm²]	Modulus of elasticity E [kg/cm²]	$\dfrac{E}{c_u}$
Fill	—	—	—	—	—	—	—	—	—	—
Sand and clay	0.25 / 0.32	0.9 / 0.6	1.90	2.71	31	0.15	0.63	87	32	51
	0.35	0.45	1.80	2.68	33	0.00	—	137	—	—
Partial layer 1 / Upper clay 2	0.45	0.40	1.80	2.77 / 2.75	25 / 25	0.18 / 0.20	0.40 / 0.45	32 / 34	32 / 47	80 / 104
3 Clay	0.57	0.50	1.70	2.75	18	0.25	0.50	37	69	138
Clay with shells	0.26 / 0.25	0.90 / 0.95	2.00 / 2.00	2.72 / 2.76	25 / 28	0.25 / 0.15	1.00 / 1.60	61 / 109	153 / 118	153 / 74
Sand	0.30	—	1.90	2.70	32	0.00–0.30	—	116	—	—
Lower clay	0.30 / 0.48 / 0.34	0.60 / 0.80 / 1.00	2.00 / 1.70 / 1.90	2.75 / 2.77 / 2.72	30 / 20	0.00 / 0.20	0.70 / 1.40 / 1.20	85	88	93
Sandy clay	0.45	0.50–0.80	2.00	2.67	25	0.25				
Clay w. lime	0.25	0.60	2.00	2.76	22	0.22	0.80			
Lower sand	0.27–0.34 / 0.25 / 0.18	—	2.00 / 2.10	2.66	35	—	—	—	—	—

[1] Consistency index: $I_c = \dfrac{LL - w}{LL - PL}$

[2] Stiffness coefficient E_s, or confined (restrained) modulus of elasticity of soil: $E = \dfrac{1-\mu-2\mu^2}{1-\mu} \cdot E_s$, where $\mu = 1/m$ = Poisson's ratio

FIG. 18-5 Soil profile and the Leaning Tower of Pisa (after E. Schultze[6,7]).

tion engineers.

Mexico City, called by the Aztecs Tenochtitlán, and founded by them in 1325 on a small island in Lake Texcoco, is situated in a large valley basin of about 3110 square miles (8054 km^2). The surface of this elliptical plateau is about 7400 ft $= 2255.52$ m above sea level. The deepest point of the basin is about 7225 ft (2202.18 m) above sea level.[9]

The general process of subsidence of this area began long ago in pre-Spanish and Spanish times after the installation of dikes and drainage canals to cope with floods in that city. To protect the city from floods, the Aztecs in 1449, under the rule of Montezuma I, began to build a dam 10 miles long (16.09 km). After the conquest of Mexico by the Spaniards, the latter, too, were engaged in flood protection work, mainly by means of canals. There occurred extensive floods in Mexico City in 1555, 1580, 1607, 1629, and later.

The subsiding process of Mexico City was accelerated about 1789 when the plateau was drained. The subsidence still takes place at an alarming rate caused by the installation and pumping of about 3500 subartesian wells throughout the Federal District of Mexico City starting about 1910 to increase the water supply. The depth of these wells is 50 to about 500 ft (15.24 m to 152.4 m). Some of them are supposed to be 700 ft (213.36 m) deep. Since 1900, when the new sewerage system was installed, and when the settlement of the soil had attained about three-quarters of an inch, Mexico City has sunk more than 16 ft (4.88 m). In 1944, the rate of pumping of the wells was 7 m^3/s $\approx$ 1850 gallons per s or about 237 ft^3/s (according to Mexican engineers). Mexico city settles now at an unbelievable rate of 2 ft (0.61 m) a year, or more than 1 mm per day. From 1900 to about 1957 buildings have settled in some places about 25 ft (7.62 m) below the ground surface. Speaking in hyperbole, there is no talk about the rate of settlement of the city, but rather about the rate of disappearance of it.

Actually, the settlement, viz., subsidence, of Mexico City began with the erection of the old Spanish City. Although the structures in the old Spanish City in Mexico City are generally neither high nor heavy (save for a few cathedrals), the great settlements in this part of the city took place during the many centuries that passed since the application of the city load on the very compressible soil. The development of the modern Mexico City took place around the old Spanish city. Fig. 18-6 illustrates the concept of the subsidence of Mexico City. The tall and heavy structures inevitably settle whether or not they are founded on piles.

The reason for the subsiding of Mexico City is in part the load of the city and the nature of the soil deposit in the large, flat Mexico Valley surrounded by mountains. Borings in the city indicate that the soil consists of a layered system of gravel, sand, silt, and clay, the latter of which is mostly of volcanic origin, containing montmorillonite. This clay ranges in depth from 30 to 600 ft (9.14 m to 182.88 m).

The particularly conspicuous characteristics of this "gelantine-like" clay are:
a) the very low unit weight in moist condition,
b) the high moisture content, and
c) a very low coefficient of permeability.

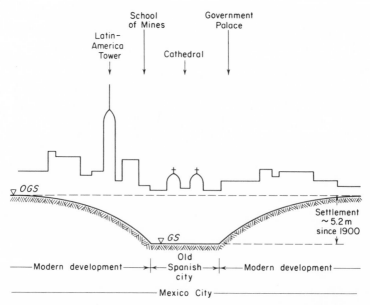

FIG. 18-6.   Illustrating the concept of the subsidence of Mexico City.

This clay contains commonly about 200% to 500% of moisture by dry weight in undisturbed samples. Some soil samples have a void ratio as high as $e = 15$. The soft clays form confined aquifers. The coefficient of permeability of this soft clay is of the order of magnitude of $k = 10^{-7}$ cm/s. Rabe[10] gives a figure of $k = 2 \times 10^{-9}$ cm/min. The clay is often interspersed with thin sand layers and pockets of sand lenses.

When asked the reason for these aggravating settlements, the Mexican replies: "Jaboncillo," meaning a mass of soap, i.e., the soap-like, slippery, oily soil. This term was introduced by the Aztecs to denote the extensive lake of mud—the soil, meaning the bentonite clay when wet.

Another factor contributing to the subsidence is the increased rate of pumping of the wells which extend down through the clay into the coarse, permeable soil materials, as well as the weight of the buildings expelling water out of the voids of the soil. The intensive evaporation of soil moisture through the ground surface in this valley at such a high elevation also causes the soil to consolidate and to settle.

18-4. Soil Profile and Soil Properties. Soil exploration borings have penetrated the soil of Mexico City to nearly 2000 ft. (609.6 m) without hitting bedrock. Dependable soil material, in the usually accepted sense, exists in Mexico City only at great depth. Some reasonably satisfactory bearing material can be found at depths of from 110 to 230 ft (33.53 m to 70.1 m) (Fig. 18-7). At a depth of about 165 ft (50.29 m) there is a layer of gravel and sand cemented with fine clay. Other sediments in the soil profile of Mexico City are volcanic ashes and water-deposited layers (lacustrine volcanic clay). The volcanic ashes, fine in

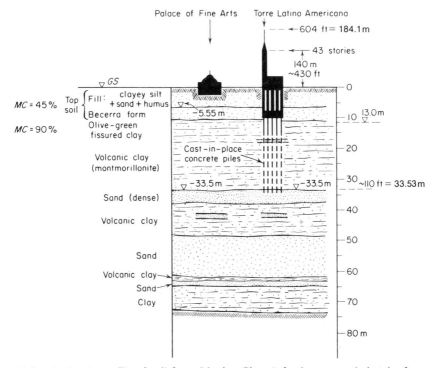

FIG. 18-7.   A sketch profile of soil from Mexico City. A freely prepared sketch after
Zeevaert, Ref. 13.

texture, settled in the lake basin very slowly, thus forming a very spongy textural
structure. These volcanic ash clays, a 33- to 66-ft-thick (10.06 m to 20.12 m) layer,
overlie the cemented sand and gravel. On top of the volcanic clay, a layer about
16 ft (4.88 m) thick of volcanic sand is deposited, and on top of this more volcanic
ash is deposited (about 100 ft or 30.48 m thick). This clay layer possesses
bentonite characteristics. Above these expansive clays, there exists a layer about
35 ft (10.67 m) thick of transported clay and artificial fill. This was filled by
Aztecs and Spaniards as a flood protective measure.

According to Cuevas,[11] Carillo,[12] Gonzalez,[13] Albin[14] and Zeevaert,[15,16,17] the
soil properties underneath Mexico City can be approximately described as
follows.

The upper layer—the top soil—varies in thickness from a few inches to several
yards. The unit weight of this soil ranges from about 88 lb/ft³ to 150 lb/ft³ (~ 1400
kg/m³ to ~2400kg/m³). The next layer (Fig. 18-7) consists of clay and marl,
about 32 ft to 105 ft thick, and is classed as a clayey silt. It is bright in color,
turning to gray or brown on being exposed to the oxidation of air.

The clay shrinks in air by an amount of $\frac{1}{8}$ of its original volume. The porosity,
or void ratio e, of this clay is high: it varies from $e = 2$ to $e = 12$, and in some
cases to $e = 15$. Such large void ratios result in very low submerged unit weights
of the soil. The unit weight of this soil is about 38 lb/ft³ (≈ 609 kg/m³). This

explains the high compressibility of the volcanic ash. The fine volcanic ash in the Mexico Valley has decomposed into thixotropic bentonite clay containing about 20% of the mineral montmorillonite, about 50% ashes, diatoms, and minute marine crustacea, about 10% organic colloids, and other substances. The clay is about 40% finer than 2 microns.

Then follows a thin layer of sand, about 5 ft (1.52 m) thick, and then another clay layer 65 ft (19.81 m) thick, another sand layer 13 ft (3.96 m) thick, and another layer of compressible volcanic clay of very great thickness.

The *seat of settlement* of the upper clay layer is in its lower part at a depth between 92 ft and 108 ft (28 and 33 m). The second clay layer contributes the largest part of the soil settlement in Mexico City. Both clay layers gave between 1949 and 1953 a total settlement of 36 in. (≈ 93 cm).

18-5. Nature of Damage. The subsidence of Mexico City has brought with it many engineering problems. Under settlement conditions the benchmarks become unreliable. Hence, it is difficult to perform precise settlement studies in the field. Also, the settlement of Mexico City's soil results in disastrous breakage of the city's sewer system and pipe lines; in undulating streets (Avenida Juarez, Avenida Tenochtitlán, for example) and cracking pavements and structures; tilting and settlement of monumental buildings such as churches, cathedrals (among them the Guadalupe National Shrine and the cathedral on the Plaza de la Constitucion), monuments, museums, theaters, the former School of Mines, Fig. 18-8, and the Palace of Fine Arts, the first floor of which is now the basement. The Y.M.C.A. building settles because of the pumping from several adjacent wells 700 ft (213.36 m) deep. Even the most modern buildings in Mexico City, such as the Department of Hydraulic Resources Building, and the building which housed the United States Embassy on the Paseo de la Reforma, are victims of the subsidence.

Figure 18-9 shows a three-stage pavement and the position of the streetlight pole erected on the original (first) pavement.

Figure 18-10 shows the titled Guadalupe National Shrine before its recent repair. This indicates how difficult it is to design and construct foundations on soils and areas previously described. The settlement of the soil of Mexico City can thus be regarded as a large-scale consolidation test.

18-6. Recent Development. To cope with the unfavorable soil conditions in Mexico City engineers are now trying to build "floating foundations"—hollow, cellular, concrete boxes—which are placed in the upper clay stratum. The term "floating (or compensating) foundation" carries the idea of compensating the weight of the excavated soil by an equivalent, total weight of the new structure. This principle has been applied to the building of the National Lottery of Mexico,[18] and several other structures. Where the structures are lighter than the excavated soil, they are lifted up, as for example the pumping station "La Condesa." Also, cases are known where in that city the casings of the sub-artesian wells were lifted up above the ground surface, so that the projecting tops, to assure the proper operation of the wells, had to be cut off. Sometimes,

FIG. 18-8.   The building of the former
National Engineers' School, School of
Mines, Mexico City.

FIG. 18-9.   Three-stage pavement and
the position of the street-light pole
indicate settlement of this street in
Mexico City.

FIG. 18-10. The tilted Guadalupe National Shrine, Mexico. Author.

because of the hydrostatic pressure and swelling pressure of the soil, the bottoms of excavations of foundation pits burst through.

Lately, tilting and settlement of floating structures are controlled, among other methods, by pumping water into and out of the cells which settled less than the other end of the structure.

The partly floating foundation of the Tower Latino Americana, Fig. 18-11, consists of a reinforced concrete mat supported on 361 concrete point-bearing piles driven to a depth of 33.5 m into a firm layer of sand.

18-7. Remedial Measures Against Harmful Settlements. In general, settlements of soil, since they are natural phenomena, are unavoidable. However, the engineer should make provision for keeping down large, intolerable, and non-uniform settlements.

To attain uniform settlements it is not necessary to achieve the same contact pressure intensities σ_o under all footings of the foundations of one structure, say $\sigma_o = W/A$, where $W =$ weight of the structure and foundation and $A =$ contact area. However, it is necessary to bring into accord the shape and the size of the footings so that all foundations of one and the same structure attain one and the same amount of settlement. Every nonuniform load distribution leads to unequal, or differential, settlement.

The following is a list of some remedial measures against large settlements:

FIG. 18-11. Torre Latino Americana, Mexico City.

a) removal of soft layers of soil, such as peat, muck, or other material, consistent with economy;

b) the use of properly designed and constructed pile foundations;

c) provision for lateral restraint or counterweight against lateral expulsion of a soil mass from underneath the footing of a foundation, or from underneath the base of an earth fill;

d) reduction of the contact pressure on the soil in some instances; the problem here is more that of the proper adjustment between pressure, shape, and size of the foundation in order to attain uniform settlements underneath the structure;

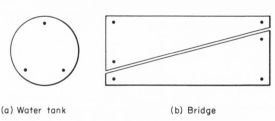

(a) Water tank   (b) Bridge

FIG. 18-12. Three-point support of structures.

e) preconsolidation of a building site long enough for the envisioned load and tolerable settlements (dams, bridges, highway or airfields fills);

f) building slowly on cohesive soils to avoid lateral expulsion of a soil mass, and to give time for the pore water to be expelled by the surcharge load and drained away;

g) chemical or mechanical stabilization of soil at a building site.

To achieve uniform settlements, one would

a) design foundations by observing the "area law" of the loaded footing;

b) use artificial cushions of soil underneath the less settling foundation parts of the structure;

c) build different parts of foundations of different weight and on different soil at different depths;

d) build the heavier parts of the structure first (such as towers and spires, for example) and the lighter parts later.

To make intolerable settlements harmless, sometimes the following constructive measures are applied:

a) structures are supported on foundations designed as statically determined structural systems;

b) structures and their foundations are designed as a rigid, stereometric unit (for example silos on continuous slab);

c) long structures are subdivided and built as separate units;

d) a structure, the parts of which are nonuniformly loaded, is subdivided.

Sometimes, to obviate undesirable stress at any stage of differential settlement, structures like bridges, water towers, reservoirs, and swimming pools are supported on three points,[19] Fig. 18-12. The three-point supporting system permits jacking up the structure at each individual support so that the structure may be raised and leveled as settlement takes place.

To accomplish these objectives, the need for thorough soil exploration and soil testing comes to the fore.

18-8. Allowable Settlement of Foundations. Because soil is a porous medium, all structures founded on soil will more or less settle. Therefore, for purpose of rational foundation design there exists a need for a knowledge about the magnitude of allowable or tolerable, harmless settlement of structures. Usually, uniform settlements may be tolerated without a great objection. However, depending upon the technological, architectural or functional significance of the structure and upon the nature of its service and operation, differential settlements may be more difficult to tolerate than uniform ones.

In classifying structures by their allowable settlements, Thornley[20] indicates the following allowable settlements:

a) for monumental structures; cathedrals; large power plants; foundations for heavy machinery; grain elevators; large concrete tanks; office buildings; hotels, and stores of 10 or more stories in height and all of structural steel or reinforced concrete; multiple-story warehouses; retaining walls; concrete arches for bridges, and hangars - the requirement relative to *differential settlement* under working load must be held within a maximum limit of $\frac{1}{8}''$ (= 0.3175 cm), and *gross settlement* under working load to a maximum of $\frac{1}{2}''$ (= 1.27 cm);

b) for suspension bridges of structural steel; steel frame buildings, piers and

TABLE 18-1
TOLERABLE DIFFERENTIAL SETTLEMENTS OF STRUCTURES

Type of structure	Tolerable differential settlement	Qualifying conditions
Circular steel petroleum or fluid storage tanks: Fixed top: Floating top:	(Units of radians of slope of settlement profile) 0.008 0.002 to 0.003 (depending on details of floating top).	Values apply to tanks on floor base. Rigid slabs for base will not permit such settlements without cracking and local backing.
Tracks for overhead traveling crane.	0.003	Value taken longitudinally along track. Settlement between tracks generally does not control.
Rigid circular mat or ring footing for tall and slender rigid structures such as stacks, silos, or water tanks.	0.002 (cross slope of rigid foundation)	
Jointed rigid concrete pressure pipe conduit.	0.015 (radians of angle change at joint)	Maximum angle change at joint is generally 2 to 4 times average slope of settlement profile. Damage to joint also depends on longitudinal extension.
One- or two-story steel frame, truss roof, warehouse with flexible siding.	0.006 to 0.008	Presence of overhead crane, utility lines, or operation of forklifts on warehouse floor would limit tolerable settlement.
One- or two-story houses with plain brick bearing walls and light structural frame.	0.002 to 0.003	Larger value is tolerable if significant portion of settlement occurs before interior finish is complete.
Structures with sensitive interior or exterior finish such as plaster, ornamental stone, or tile facing.	0.001 to 0.002	Larger value is tolerable if significant portion of settlement occurs before finish is complete.
Structures with relatively insensitive interior or exterior finish such as dry wall, movable panels, glass panels.	0.002 to 0.003	Damage to structural frame may limit tolerable settlements.
Multistory heavy concrete rigid frame on structural mat foundation 4 ft ± thick.	0.0015	Damage to interior or exterior finish may limit tolerable settlements.

STRUCTURE

SETTLEMENT PROFILE

AVERAGE SLOPE OF
SETTLEMENT PROFILE

DIFFERENTIAL
SETTLEMENT
EDGE TO
CENTER

Tolerable differential settlement is expressed in terms of slope of settlement profile

Value of 0.001 = ¼-in. differential settlement in 20-ft distance

Value of 0.008 = 2-in. differential settlement in 20-ft distance

SETTLEMENT 291

docks, the differential settlement under working load should be kept
within a maximum of ¼″ (= 0.635 cm), and

c) for factories, stores, apartment buildings, hotels, churches, warehouses,
machine shops, and highway structures, the differential settlement under
working load should be not more than ½″ (= 1.27 cm).

Because of the nature of soil properties which may vary at the construction site
from foot to foot, and which properties are affected very much by the moisture
content in soil, it is very difficult indeed to set any standards for allowable
magnitudes of settlement of structures on soil.

Table 18-1 contains NAVFAC tolerable differential settlements of structures.
This table is the reproduced Table 6-1 on page 7-6-8 from the NAVFAC Design
Manual.[21]

One should be cognizant that the various magnitudes of allowable settlement
suggested hitherto by various authors, agencies and other sources should be
considered as guides only. Some foreign building ordinances indicate the
following allowable settlement of various types of structures:[22]

Auxiliary structures for industrial plants	20 to 40 cm
Statically determinate structures with massive foundation	12 to 20 cm
Apartment houses of bricks, and structures with statically determined girders	8 to 12 cm
Apartment houses and industrial structures of statically indetermined systems	5 to 8 cm
Sensitive industrial structures subjected to dynamic stresses	3 to 5 cm

REFERENCES

1. "Earths and Foundations"—A Progress Report of Special Committee, presented at
the Annual Meeting of the ASCE, New York, January 18, 1933. *Proceedings
ASCE*, 1933, vol. 59, pp. 777-820, 813-814.
2. E. Imbeaux, "Les eaux souterraines, cause principale de l'inclinaison du campanil
de Pisé," Académie des Sciences—Comptes Rendus, Paris, Nov. 7, 1927, vol. 185,
no. 19, pp. 995-998.
3. D. P. Krynine, *Soil Mechanics*, New York, McGraw-Hill Book Co., Inc., 1947,
p. 410.
4. K. Terzaghi, "Die Ursachen der Schiefstellung des Turmes von Pisa," *Der Bauingenieur*, January 5, 1934, no. 1/2, pp. 1-4. Hereto, a mathematical discussion by
O. K. Fröhlich on pressure distribution, consolidation and similitude; March 16,
1934, no. 11/12, pp. 112-113.
5. C. B. Spencer, "Leaning Tower of Pisa—an Engineering Absurdity," *Columbia
Research News in Engineering and Science 1954 Annual*, Columbia University
Engineering Center, New York, pp. 8-9.
6. E. Schultze, "Erfahrungen als Gutachter beim Turm von Pisa," *Mitteilungen aus
dem Institut für Verkehrswasserbau, Grundbau und Bodenmechanik (VGB) der
Technischen Hochschule Aachen*, VGB-Baugrundtagung, 1972, p. 56.
7. E. Schultze, "Das Problem des Turms von Pisa." *Mededelingen van de Koninklijke
Academie voor Wetenschappen, Letteren en Schone Kunsten van Belgie*. Brussel,

1972, p. 4.

8. E. Schultze, "Ist der Turm von Pisa noch zu retten," *Mitteilungen aus dem Institut für Verkehrswasserbau, Grundbau und Bodenmechanik (VGB) der Technischen Hochschule Aachen,* Aachen, 1971.

9. W. H. Rabe, "Die Geschichte der Hochwassersicherung der Stadt Mexico," *Die Bautechnik,* no. 17/18, April 8, 1941, p. 192.

10. W. H. Rabe, "Der Baugrund der Stadt Mexico und die Senkungen ihrer Gebäude," *Die Bautechnik,* no. 28, 1941, p. 300.

11. J. A. Cuevas, "Foundation Conditions in Mexico City," *Proceedings,* First International Conference on Soil Mechanics and Foundation Engineering, vol. 3, June 22-26, 1936, Cambridge, Mass., p. 233.

12. N. Carillo, "Influence of Artesian Wells in the Sinking of Mexico City," *Proceedings,* Second International Conference on Soil Mechanics and Foundation Engineering, June 21-30, 1948, Rotterdam, vol. 7, p. 157.

13. M. Gonzalez, "Level Control in Buildings by Means of Adjustable Piling," *Proceedings,* Second International Conference on Soil Mechanics and Foundation Engineering, June 21-30, 1948, Rotterdam, vol. 4, pp. 152-156.

14. P. Albin, Jr., "Special Foundations Support Mexico City's Buildings on Highly Compressible Clay," *Civil Engineering,* 1949, vol. 19, no. 8, pp. 25-28.

15. L. Zeevaert, "Pore Pressure Measurements to Investigate the Main Source of Surface Subsidence in Mexico City" (Disc.), *Proceedings,* Third International Conference on Soil Mechanics and Foundation Engineering, August 16-27, 1953, Zürich, vol. 2, pp. 299-304.

16. L. Zeevaert, "Foundation Design and Behaviour of Tower Latino Americana in Mexico City," *Géotechnique,* vol. 7, no. 3, September 1957, pp. 115-133.

17. L. Zeevaert, *Foundation Engineering for Difficult Subsoil Conditions,* New York, N.Y., Van Nostrand Reinhold Company, 1973.

18. J.A. Cuevas, "The Floating Foundation of the New Building for the National Lottery of Mexico: An Actual Size Study of the Deformations of a Flocculent-Structured Deep Soil," *Proceedings,* First International Conference on Soil Mechanics and Foundation Engineering, June 22-26, 1936, Cambridge, Mass., vol. 1, pp. 294-301.

19. P.H. Ogden, "Adjustable Water Tanks at Heanor," *Civil Engineering* (London), 1948, vol. 33, p. 131.

20. J.H. Thornley, *Foundation Design and Practice,* New York, N.Y., Columbia University Press, 1959, pp. 29-32.

21. *NAVFAC Design Manual - Soil Mechanics, Foundations, and Earth Structures (NAVFAC DM-7),* Washington, D.C., Department of the Navy, Naval Facilities, Engineering Command, March, 1971, Table 6-1, p. 7-6-8-.

22. A.R. Jumikis, *Soil Mechanics,* Princton, N.J. D. Van Nostrand Company, Inc., 1962, p. 358.

PART V

Strength Properties of Soil

Chapter 19

SHEAR STRENGTH OF SOIL

In all stability calculations of earth masses of all kinds involving plastic shear failure (groundbreak, stability of earth slopes, earth pressures on earth retaining structures, for example) shear strength of soil is one of the most important mechanical property.

19-1. Definition. The shear strength of soil is the resistance to deformation by continuous shear displacement of soil particles or en masse upon the action of a tangential (shear) stress.

The shear strength of a soil is basically made up of

1) the structural resistance to displacement of the soil because of the interlocking of the soil particles,
2) the frictional resistance to translocation between the individual soil particles at their contact points, and
3) cohesion (adhesion) between the surfaces of the soil particles.

19-2. Determination of Shear Strength of Soil. The shear strength of a soil is usually determined experimentally by one of the following methods:

1) direct shear test;
2) laterally confined compression test, known also as the triaxial compression test; and
3) unconfined compression test.

All shear tests of soils are essentially destructive tests in contradistinction to consolidation tests which, by their nature, are model tests.

Depending upon the type of shear test devices producing shear planes, soils can be tested in single shear, double shear, torsional shear, and punch shear. In this book only the single type of shear will be dealt with.

The shear strength τ as represented by the τ-line on the graph in Fig. 19-1, is given analytically by the following straight-line equation, known as Coulomb's shear strength equation:[1]

$$\tau = \sigma_{n_{eff}} \tan \phi + c \qquad (\text{kg/cm}^2), \qquad (19\text{-}1)$$

where the intercept c is a test parameter termed the cohesion of the soil,
the slope of the τ-line, $\tan \phi$, is termed the coefficient of internal friction of that soil,

ϕ = angle of internal friction of the soil, or a test parameter, also termed the angle of shearing resistance, and

$\sigma_{n_{eff}}$ = effective normal stress on the rupture plane.

Equation (19-1) reads that the shear strength τ of a frictional-cohesive soil varies as a straight line function of the applied effective, normal stress $\sigma_{n_{eff}}$. In other words, the shear strength of a soil is proportional to the normal stress on the shear plane.

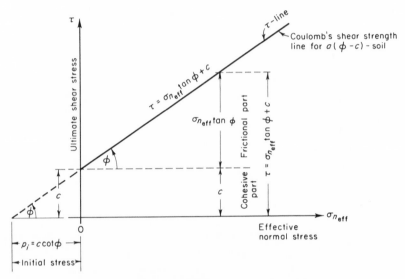

FIG. 19-1   Shear strength factors, shown graphically.

To exclude from the shear test results the effect of apparent cohesion, the shear test must be performed under an inundated condition (surface tension of water is eliminated).

The shear strength of noncohesive soil is

$$\tau = \sigma_{n_{eff}} \tan \phi, \tag{19-1a}$$

because $c = 0$.

The shear strength of a pure cohesive soil whose coefficient of friction is $\tan \phi = 0$, is mathematically expressed as

$$\tau = c. \tag{19-1b}$$

Fig. 19-2 shows plots of Coulomb's shear strength lines of a moist, cohesive soil at various preloadings p_1, p_2, and p_3. The soil test specimens were prepared with a various moisture content corresponding to its liquid limit. After the predetermined preloading p of a soil specimen has been attained the soil specimen is sheared off resulting in a pair of stress coordinates:

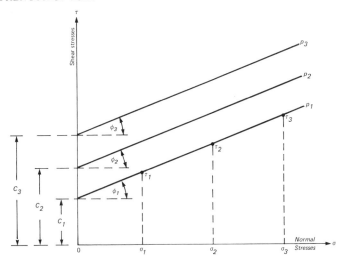

FIG. 19-2. Shear strength τ as a function of preloading p.

at preloading p_1: σ_1; τ_1

σ_2; τ_2

σ_3; τ_3

– – – –

σ_n; τ_n

at preloading p_2: σ_1; τ_1

σ_2; τ_2

σ_3; τ_3

– – – –

σ_n; τ_n,

and so on.

Here σ, σ_1, σ_2. . .σ_n are normal stresses, and

τ, τ_1, τ_2. . .τ_n are shear stresses.

The cut-off ordinates c on the τ-axis for each preloading p show that c (cohesion) depends upon preloading of the soil specimen. Hence, the c-value (or cohesion) of soil are test parameters.

19-3. Types of Shear Tests. Among the types of testing the shear strength of soil the following ones are the most common:

a) *unconsolidated-undrained* shear test (uu), also known by some agencies as the "quick" shear test (Q),[2,3]

b) *consolidated-undrained* shear test (cu), also known by some agencies by the term "consolidated quick" shear test (Q_c),[2] and

c) *consolidated-drained* shear test (cd), also known simply as the "drained" or "consolidated slow" shear test (S).[2]

Fig. 19-3 shows general graphic representation of undrained, partly drained and drained shear strength of a cohesive soil.

These shear tests provide information about the range of variation of soil shear resistance and for many practical soil engineering problems are adequate for the required solutions.

The type of shear test and its procedure to use for a soil depends upon what is considered to be the most representative behavior of the soil in the prototype. The chosen shear test method should simulate natural conditions as closely as possible.

a) *The Unconsolidated-Undrained (uu), or Quick, Shear Test (Q).* An unconsolidated-undrained, or quick, shear test is one where the shear resistance of a soil sample is measured immediately after application of the normal load (perpendicular to shear plane). The test is made on the soil sample in its natural condition or initial state of compaction. To assure that during the test the void ratio of the soil would change as little as possible, the load on the test sample is applied so quickly that no time is allowed for consolidation of, or fully to drain out of the water from the voids of the soil specimen either before or during the shear test.

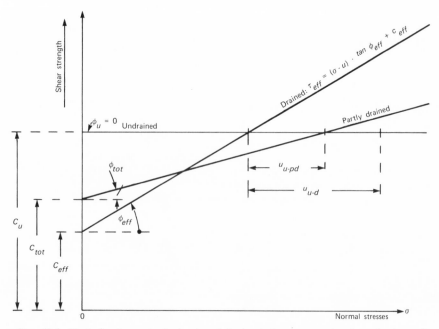

FIG. 19-3. Undrained, partly drained and drained shear strength of a cohesive soil; u = neutral or pore water pressure.

Upon quick application of the load on the saturated soil test specimen, neutral stress (pore water pressure), u, is induced. The neutral pressure thus carries all the load, because the duration of time of test is too short to dissipate this hydrostatic excess of neutral pressure by water being drained out of the soil specimen at any stage of the test.

Fig. 19-4 shows graphical representation of unconsolidated-undrained triaxial tests of a saturated clay.

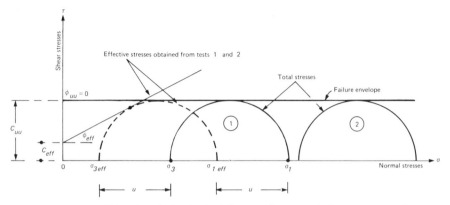

FIG. 19-4. Unconsolidated undrained triaxial tests of saturated clay; u = neutral or pore water pressure.

Usually, the entire quick or unconsolidated-undrained shear test can be completed till failure in about 5 to 10 minutes.

The standard method of test for the unconsolidated-undrained (quick) (Q) shear strength of soils uu is referred to Reference 3.

In the engineering practice one usually has to deal with a relatively quick shear loading when the excess pore water has no time to drain, or when there is no time to adjust or equalize the pore water pressure. Under such conditions the resistance of an earth mass to shear (sliding) under certain conditions results in smaller values than those obtained from the usual tests. Therefore, the most unfavorable condition is to be considered - the sudden loading of a soil mass till failure. Accordingly, the shear test in the laboratory is to be performed quickly on unconsolidated-undrained soil specimens; hence the term "quick" test.

.b) *The Consolidated-Undrained (cu) Test (Q_c).* This kind of a quick shear strength test is similar to the preceding one, except that here the test is performed in two phases, namely: the consolidation phase, and the quick shear phase.

In the consolidation phase, the soil specimen is allowed slowly to consolidate completely under a certain all-around confining pressure. During consolidation, the drainage of soil pore water out of the voids of the soil specimen is thus permitted.

In the second phase, after the desired consolidation under the effective pressure has been attained, the axial load is applied on the soil specimen at a quick rate to bring about shear. During the quick application of the shear stress no drainage is allowed. Hence, during this phase of test, excess pore water pressure (or neutral pressure) is induced carrying the axial load, virtually unaccompanied by further consolidation, viz., increase in effective stress. Usually the second phase of this Q_c-test can be accomplished in 5 to 10 minutes.

c) *The Consolidated-Drained (cd) or Slow Shear Test (S_c).* In this kind of test, the soil specimen is allowed slowly to consolidate completely under a certain lateral confining pressure before the axial pressure is applied on

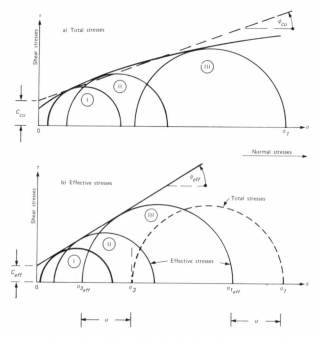

FIG. 19-5. Consolidated drained tests of saturated clay.

the sample. Throughout the duration of the slow consolidation process
under the applied lateral confining pressure drainage of the pore water
out of the soil specimen is allowed. Hence, there is practically no excess
pore water pressure (neutral pressure) in the soil specimen, i.e., $u = 0$.
Because of the slow loading the excess pore water pressure induced by the
lateral loading is dissipated by consolidation, viz., drainage. Therefore all
stresses acting on the tested soil specimen are effective stresses (σ_{eff}), Fig.
19-5).

After this phase of consolidation, the axial load is applied on the soil
specimen. In order to bring about dissipation or pore water pressure the
application of the axial load, too, must take place very slowly so that the
soil specimen would consolidate slowly. For cohesive soils, therefore, the
axial load, viz., shear force must be applied in very small increments, and
after a sufficient time lapse to allow for complete consolidation before the
next axial load increment is applied. Again, here all pressures on the soil
specimen are effective pressures. Often it may require 4 to 6 weeks to
complete a single consolidated-drained (slow) test.

In a way, these three methods of shear strength test of soils reflect best the true
shear properties of a soil material.

Of course, it is possible to devise shear strength testing methods for soils other
than those as described above.[4]

The measurement of shear strength of soil in the laboratory is accomplished
either by the direct shear test or by the triaxial compression test.

DIRECT SHEAR TESTING OF SOIL

19-4. Controlled Strain Shear Testing of Soil. The shear strength of soil can be tested by a direct shear apparatus of the controlled stress type or of the controlled strain type.

The principle of the two types of direct shear test devices is illustrated in Fig. 19-6. In the controlled stress shear apparatus the shear stress is applied at a constant rate or in equal increments by means of a dead weight, for instance, till failure occurs. The shear displacement is measured by a dial gage, such as an Ames dial gage, which indicates the amount of displacement.

The controlled stress type shear test is used for most practical purposes in soil engineering. The controlled strain type shear test is primarily used in research but can also be used for solving practical problems. The controlled strain (shear displacement) is applied to the shear box horizontally at a constant rate by means of a screw (manually operated or motorized) and a calibrated testing ring. The constant rate of shear displacement is observed on the Ames dial gage. The testing ring with a calibrated force dial gage shows the shear resistance of the soil at any rate of horizontal strain applied to the soil through the shear box.

The direct shear testing method is one which is most widely used in practice. Its advantage is the simplicity to perform, but the so obtained results are sensitively affected by test procedure.

19-5. Shear Strength of Sand. The principal advantage of the shear test apparatus of the controlled strain type is that in this test of a dense sand the peak shear resistance, as well as the ultimate shear resistances smaller than the peak,

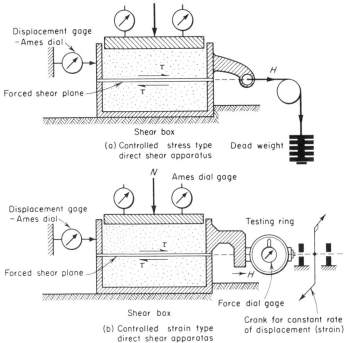

FIG. 19-6. Two types of direct shear testing devices.

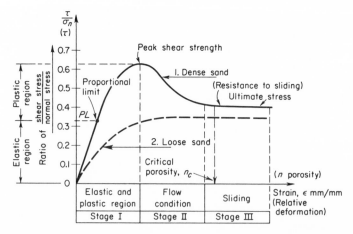

FIG. 19-7. Shear strength as a function of strain at constant normal stress σ_n.

can be observed and plotted. Such a plot, the shear-strain diagram of a soil, is illustrated in Fig. 19-7. By this method of test, not only the magnitudes of shear resistance can be measured, but, as Fig. 19-7 illustrates, such test results plotted on a graph also indicate how the soil behaves during the process of shear, particularly as the shear process approaches failure. In this figure, the stress-strain curves for a dense sand and for a loose sand are shown, namely, the shear stress τ, or the ratio of τ/σ_n, is represented as a function of unit displacement (unit deformation), or strain ϵ of soil along its forced shear plane.

Here $\sigma_n = N/A$ = pressure normal to the shear plane

N = normal load on soil specimen in the shear box, and

A = shear area of soil in the shear box.

At the beginning of the shear process, up to the so-called proportional limit (*P.L.*) within stage I, Fig. 19-7, the stress necessary for shearing the densely packed soil increases proportionally with the increase in strain. This can be explained by the higher density and greater pressure with which the soil particles are pressed against each other during the initial stage of shear deformation, and consequently also by the increased number of contacts between the soil particles compared with a loose structure of sand.

Point *P.L.* is also termed the critical shear stress. The region between point *P.L.* and the greatest τ-ordinate, or τ/σ_n-ordinate, in stage I depends very much upon the petrographic properties of the sand such as the shape and the surface topography of the particles.

Note that after all of the shear strength of the dense sand is exhausted, the τ-ϵ curve (shear/shear displacement curve) of the dense sand has a maximum value known as the *peak shear stress*, which is the shear strength of the soil sample at that normal load in that test. Past the peak in stage II, with further continuous increase in shear displacement (strain), the resistance to shear stresses τ, overcoming some of the cohesive forces at points of contact between soil particles, and possible distortion of individual soil particles, are decreasing—

attaining a continuously sliding, ultimate stress, stage III.

In the last stage (III) of the process of continuous shear displacement, the phenomenon of resistance to sliding is brought out. The resistance to sliding is less than the resistance to shear of dense sand as well as loose sand (compare with peak shear). The resistance to sliding is governed mainly by mutual friction between the translocating soil particles. The interlocking of soil particles in this stage can be considered absent.

Loose sands in the controlled strain shear test usually do not exhibit a peak shear stress on a graph as the dense sands do. Here with increase in shear strain the shear stress increases curvilinearly until an ultimate (failure) shear stress is attained. After this, a continuous, unlimited shear displacement may prevail without any change in the shear stress.

The density of sand at which no change in volume is brought about upon the application of shear strains is called the critical density. The porosity and void ratio corresponding to the critical density are called the *critical porosity* and the *critical void ratio*, respectively.

The critical density, i.e., porosity, or void ratio, is calculated from the vertical changes in the volume of the sand in the shear box. For these quantities the corresponding shear stresses are plotted in a density–shear stress graph, or in a porosity–shear stress graph. The critical density and/or critical porosity (n_c) are read and scaled off the graph at the numerical value of the ultimate shear stress (stress at continuously sliding shear deformation in Fig. 19-7).

Every sand has a certain critical density.[5] Sandy soils having a porosity less than critical loosen up, or expand, upon shear but loosely packed sands densify, i.e., reduce their volume, Fig. 19-8.

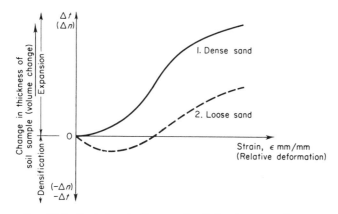

FIG. 19-8. Variation in degree of soil density upon shear.

From a series of the strain-shear strength graphs such as shown in Fig. 19-7, the peak and ultimate strength graphs for noncohesive soils, Fig. 19-8, can be plotted. One notices from Fig. 19-9 that the angle of internal friction ϕ_{max} for peak strength is larger than that for ultimate strength ϕ.

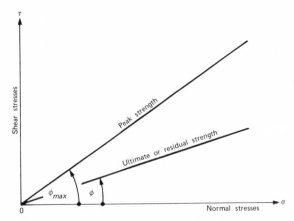

FIG. 19-9. Peak and ultimate strength graphs of a noncohesive soil.

19-6. Shear Strength of Clay. The shear process of cohesive soils is more complicated than with sands because of the pore water present. The frictional resistance of cohesive soils is less than that of noncohesive soils because the fine clay particles are easily deformable. The cohesion of clays is considerably larger than that of sands because in clays the sum of the internal surfaces of the clay particles is very large (large specific surface): this promotes the increase in true cohesion which depends upon the action of the surface tension forces. Also, the capillary system in cohesive soils is much finer, thus contributing considerably to the magnitude of the apparent cohesion.

The shear test results of an undisturbed clay usually exhibit, too, a peak of shear strength on the deformation-shear stress graph. However, when the undisturbed clay is remolded, the peak point in many instances no longer exists. These conditions are illustrated in Fig. 19-10.

Sensitivity of Clay. The ratio of the peak shear strength of the undisturbed clay τ_u to the maximum value of the remolded shear strength of the same clay τ_r is

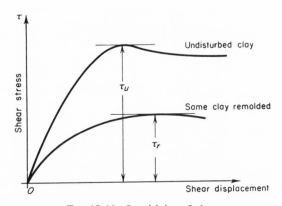

FIG. 19-10. Sensitivity of clay.

called the *coefficient of sensitivity*, s, of that clay:

$$s = \tau_u / \tau_r. \qquad (19\text{-}2)$$

The sensitivity s may also be expressed as a ratio of unconfined compressive strength q_{uu} in its undisturbed condition to compressive strength q_{ur} in remolded condition:

$$s = \frac{\tau_u}{\tau_r} = \frac{q_{uu}}{q_{ur}} \qquad (19\text{-}2a)$$

The rating of sensitivity of most clays usually varies from $s = 2$ to $s = 4$, and may be as high as $s = 8$ or more.

A typical rating of sensitivity may have the following values:

s	Sensitivity rating
<1	insensitive
1-2	slight
2-4	medium
>4	high

The larger the coefficient of sensitivity, the less is the remolded shear strength of the clay, and consequently the more sensitive is that clay. The sensitivity of some clays is great, but the sensitivity of shear strength to remolding is less great in others. Hence, the shear strength of the soil depends very much upon whether its natural structure is disturbed or not.

DIRECT SHEAR TESTING OF CLAY

19-7. Unconsolidated-Undrained, or Unconsolidated-Quick Direct Shear Test of Clay. Clays usually contain a certain amount of free water. Under certain conditions the degree of saturation S of clays may be practically $S = 100\%$. Because clays, due to their low coefficient of permeability, drain slowly, upon the application of a normal stress to the clay in a shear box, the water has no time to drain out of the voids of the clay. Thus *the normal stress induces a balanced pore-water pressure.* This pore water, until intergranular pressure is established later after some of the water has drained out, carries the normal stress (viz., structural load on clay soil) during the initial period of time. If, at this point, a clay sample is subjected to shear, and the drainage of the water from the voids of the clay soil does not take place effectively, the shear is independent of the normal stress because of the pore water. Such a shear test is termed the unconsolidated-undrained, or unconsolidated-quick shear test. In such a test, the applied total normal stress is σ_n, and the induced pore water pressure u is equal in magnitude to the total normal stress, i.e.,

$$u = \sigma_n. \qquad (19\text{-}3)$$

Hence, the effective normal stress is

$$\sigma_{n_{eff}} = \sigma_n - u = 0, \qquad (19\text{-}4)$$

and the measured shear strength of the clay in this test is

$$\tau = c, \qquad\qquad (19\text{-}5)$$

which, analytically, represents a straight line parallel to the σ_n-axis and at a distance c from the latter.

From the undrained, unconsolidated, quick shear test results of a clay, one should not immediately draw the conclusion that when $\tau = c$, it should also be true that $\tan \phi = 0$. This would be incorrect, because the soil tested may have frictional properties; however, because of the ineffective drainage, the intergranular pressure $\sigma_{n_{eff}}$ does not start to act immediately (it is counterbalanced during the initial stage of loading by the pore water pressure), because there is no time for consolidation. In other words, time is needed for consolidating the clay sample to bring into play the intergranular pressure, and it may appear that $\phi = 0$. However, it is more correct to say that $\phi = 0$ is the angle of shear resistance because of this particular method of testing the clay under quick, undrained, and unconsolidated conditions.

The unconsolidated quick shear test of clay may in practice find its application to a stability problem of a foundation. If the foundation load is transmitted to an unconsolidated clay, the following question arises: what is the factor of safety of the clayey soil mass against shear immediately after laying the foundation?

In the course of time, as the clay consolidates more and more, the strength of the soil increases, and so does the factor of safety against shear.

19-8. Consolidated-Undrained, or Consolidated Quick Direct Shear Test of Clay. The principle of the consolidated-undrained (quick) direct shear test of a clay is that the clay sample in the shear box is subjected to an appropriate normal stress. Under this stress a certain amount of water will drain out of the voids of the clay, bringing about a certain degree of consolidation of the clay. The consolidation brings about a greater density, and, hence, a greater shear strength of the clay. After the appropriate degree of consolidation has been attained, the clay sample is subjected to a quick process of shear, similar to that in the unconsolidated, quick shear test. Because the permeability of clay is usually low, it is assumed that during the quick shear in the consolidated, quick shear test no drainage of water out of the voids of the clay takes place during the period of shear. Therefore, this type of test is sometimes also called the consolidated, undrained shear test of soil.

The testing procedure of clay in this test is to subject a certain number of clay samples of the same type of clay to normal consolidation stress. Each consecutive soil sample out of, say, 5 or 6 samples is subjected to a larger normal stress (or to a smaller normal stress) than the previous one until consolidation is attained, and then sheared off. During the shear, pore water pressure is built up. When each consecutive soil sample is subjected to a larger normal stress than the previous one, for example, $\sigma_1 < \sigma_2$, the attained void ratio e in each following soil sample consolidated is less than in the previous consolidated soil sample. The densities of each soil sample after consolidation γ, in their turn, increase. Thus soil samples subjected to smaller, normal consolidation stresses, contain more water in their voids than those subjected to larger, normal consolidation stresses.

When the shear test results of the clay at various consolidation pressures are plotted in a shear strength graph of the clay, the plot usually results in a line the first part of which (at smaller normal consolidation stresses) is curved, a-1-2-b, Fig. 19-11. The curved part of the plot is then adjoined at point b by a straight line. Over a certain range of normal, consolidation stresses $\sigma_{n_{eff}}$, the shear strength of the clay can be approximately expressed analytically as

$$\tau = \sigma_{n_{eff}} \tan \phi + c. \qquad (19\text{-}1)$$

It can be understood, therefore, that the curved part of the shear strength

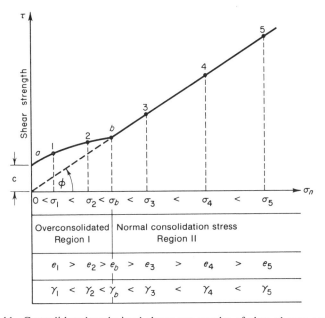

FIG. 19-11. Consolidated-undrained shear test results of clay, shown graphically.

curve is the effect of the amount of water, or the effect of the neutral stress, in the voids of the soil.

Within region I, represented by the curved part of the shear strength diagram a-1-2-b, there is more water in the voids of the clay than within region II; in region I the effect of neutral stress is very pronounced compared with that within region II. Within region II, the intergranular stress is more pronounced than in region I, but the pore water pressure is still present, although to a smaller magnitude than in I.

It can be understood that the angle ϕ, and the cut-off c, on the consolidated, quick shear strength graph are parameters of these particular *test conditions*, and not the properties of the soil. The uncertain factor in this test is the magnitude of the neutral stress.

The consolidated, quick shear test is applicable, for example, for stability calculations against failure in shear of consolidated dams, slopes, and other earthworks made of cohesive soil material under conditions of rapid draw-down of water, where the water has not time to drain out of the voids.

19-9. Consolidated-Drained or Consolidated Slow Direct Shear Test of Clay.[3,6] The consolidated-drained (slow) shear test (*cd*) on clays is performed by first consolidating the various clay samples to appropriate consolidation stresses and then by shearing the consolidated soil samples very slowly. The slow process of shear affords time enough for the water to drain out of the voids of the soil under the consolidation stress. Therefore, during the shear process in this kind of test, pore water pressures do not build up to any significant degree. This means that the effective, normal stress on the soil sample during shear is equal to the applied, normal consolidation stress. The shear strength diagram obtained from the consolidated-drained (slow) shear test of clay is similar in appearance to that obtained from the consolidated-undrained (quick) shear test. The difference, however, between the two curves is that in the consolidated-drained (slow) shear test of clays the ultimate shear resistances τ are plotted against the effective, normal stresses $\sigma_{n_{eff}}$, Fig. 19-12.

The shear strength of the clay can be expressed analytically over a certain range of effective normal stress as

$$\tau = \sigma_{n_{eff}} \tan \phi + c. \tag{19-1}$$

In this test, the value of the parameter ϕ is larger than that obtained for the same soil from the consolidated, quick shear test, because the neutral stress in the slow (drained) test is practically zero, and the intergranular friction between the soil particles acts in its full magnitude.

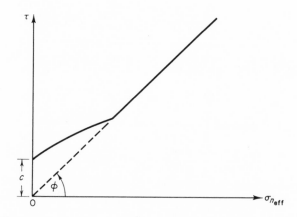

FIG. 19-12. Consolidated-drained (slow) shear test results of clay, shown graphically.

From the aforegoing discussion one gets the notion that the direct shear testing method, though simple as it appears to perform, is also afflicted with some disadvantages, namely:

1) the soil drainage conditions during the direct shear test cannot be controlled; hence variations in pore water (neutral) pressure in the soil specimen cannot be measured. However, if the neutral pressure is zero, the normal pressure on the shear plane is the effective normal pressure;

2) the shearing of the soil specimen takes place over a forced, predetermined shear plane. This forced plane is not necessarily the weakest one;

3) the area of the forced shear plane is not constant during the direct shear test;

4) the normal load N on the shear plane does not remain constant during the direct shear test because of variation of the shear area. Therefore, upon shearing, an unequal pressure distribution sets in over the shear plane;

5) also, during the direct shear test there occur large pressure concentrations at the edges of the soil specimen and small pressures at the center.

TRIAXIAL COMPRESSION OF SOIL

The triaxial compression test method for determining soil shear strength is generally suitable for all types of soil - noncohesive and cohesive ones. Fig. 19-13 shows a sand specimen tested in triaxial compression. The main advantage of the triaxial testing method lies in

1) the possibility of controlling drainage conditions during the entire testing;

2) the possibility of measuring pore water pressures during the test;

3) the freedom of the soil specimen to fail in shear on the weakest shear plane;

4) the fairly uniform pressure distribution on the developing shear plane during continued, progressive testing;

FIG. 19-13. Triaxial compression test specimen of sand after failure in shear.

The main disadvantage of the triaxial test method is the necessary, relatively elaborate triaxial testing device with all the needed accessories for measuring total and neutral pressures in and volume changes of the soil specimen subjected to a triaxial test.

19-10. Stress Conditions on the Shear Plane. The stress conditions on the shearing plane of a cylindrically shaped soil sample can be determined grapho-analytically and analyzed conveniently by Mohr's[7] stress circles, Fig. 19-14.

In the triaxial compression test the lateral stresses, σ_2 and σ_3, on the soil sample cylindrical in shape are same (fluid pressure, liquid or gas). Hence, $\sigma_2 = \sigma_3$.

In this method, the normal stresses $(\sigma_1, \sigma_3, \sigma_n)$, acting on a soil sample subjected to a triaxial compression test, are plotted as abscissas and the shear stresses (τ) as ordinates. With the difference in major normal stresses, $(\sigma_1 - \sigma_3)$, as a diameter, a circle is drawn. The radius of the stress circle is $(\sigma_1 - \sigma_3)/2$.

Remember from strength of materials that for major principal stresses σ_1, the corresponding shear on the same plane is $\tau = 0$, and $\tau = 0$ for σ_3. Thus, the ends of the stress diameter on Mohr's stress circle have the coordinates $(\sigma_1; 0)$ and $(\sigma_3; 0)$.

The normal stress σ_n, and the shear stress τ, on an inclined shear plane can be geometrically demonstrated on Mohr's graph to be as follows:

$$\sigma_n = OB = \frac{\sigma_1 + \sigma_3}{2} + \frac{\sigma_1 - \sigma_3}{2} \cos 2\alpha, \tag{19-6}$$

$$\tau = BE = (CE) \sin 2\alpha = \frac{\sigma_1 - \sigma_3}{2} \sin 2\alpha. \tag{19-7}$$

It follows that each point on the circle gives the pair of stresses acting on a rupture plane of specific inclination α.

A tangent t-t, drawn to the stress circle at point E, has the equation

$$\tau = \sigma_n \tan \phi + c, \tag{19-8}$$

an equation which characterizes the shear strength of the soil. The slope of this line, $\tan \phi$, physically means the coefficient of internal friction of the soil; ϕ is the angle of internal friction, and c is the cohesion.

For future application, ϕ and c are rather test parameters obtained by special apparatus and by special methods of testing. Being a test parameter, the angle ϕ, as obtained from various kinds of instruments and by various methods of tests is termed the angle of shearing resistance.

The cutoff, $OF = p_i = c \cot \phi$, Fig. 19-14 made on the normal stress axis by the tangent t-t, indicates an initial normal stress in the cohesive soil brought about by surface tension forces.

The magnitude of the resultant stress σ_r can also be scaled off, or calculated from Mohr's stress diagram.

Again, as was discussed in the section on the direct shear test of soil, for noncohesive soils $c = 0$,

$$\tau = \sigma_n \tan \phi, \qquad (19\text{-}9)$$

and for pure cohesive soils, when $\phi = 0$,

$$\tau = c, \qquad (19\text{-}10)$$

i.e., the tangent takes a course parallel to the σ-axis, Figs. 19-15a and b, respectively.

The discussion above reveals that shear strength of soils is a function of the lateral confining pressure σ_3.

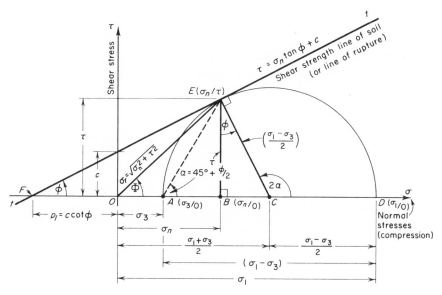

FIG. 19-14. Mohr's stress circle.

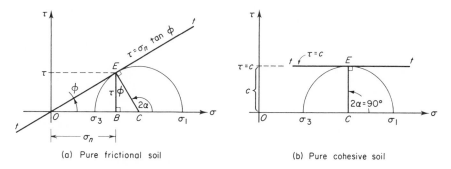

(a) Pure frictional soil

(b) Pure cohesive soil

FIG. 19-15. Stress circles for various types of soil.

19-11. Purpose of Triaxial Compression Test. The purpose of the triaxial compression test of soils is to provide basic data on:

1) the ultimate, laterally confined, compressive strength;
2) the angle of internal friction;
3) the cohesion; } test or shear strength parameters
4) the shear strength;
5) the so-called modulus of elasticity, and
6) the pore water pressure.

The results obtained from the triaxial compression test are used for:
1) making estimates of the probable bearing capacity of a soil;
2) stability calculations of earthworks, earth-retaining structures, and foundations;
3) analyzing stress-strain relationships of loaded soils, and
4) estimating settlements of soil under load.

19-12. Types of Tests. Fundamentally, there are two types of tests which can be performed by means of the triaxial compression apparatus, namely: 1) open-system test, and 2) closed-system test.

In the open-system triaxial test, sometimes called the drained, or slow, test, the pore water is allowed to drain out of the soil sample.

In the closed-system test, sometimes called the undrained, or quick, test, no drainage is allowed. The water content of the soil sample is assumed to be constant throughout the test.

Consolidation under lateral stress in the open-system test may be allowed to any degree desired. During the process of lateral consolidation, water is allowed

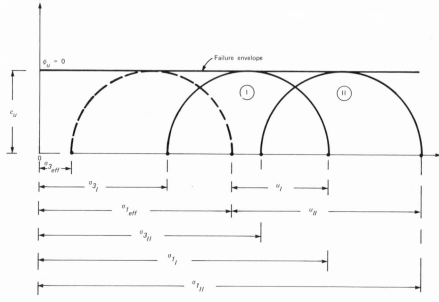

FIG. 19-16. Mohr's stress circles for total and effective stresses as obtained from unconsolidated undrained triaxial compression tests on a saturated clay.

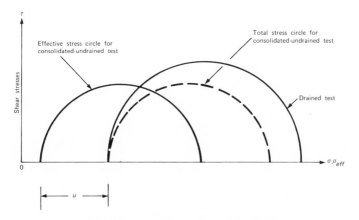

FIG. 19-17. Mohr's stress circles for saturated clay.

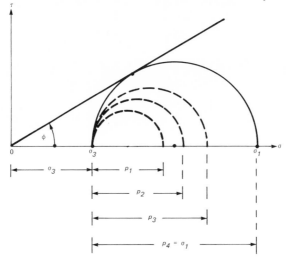

FIG. 19-18. Representation of states of stress during a drained triaxial test.

to drain. Then the soil sample is subjected to axial stress (σ_1). During the application of the axial stress, the system may be either open or closed. If it is closed, the shear stress develops at a constant water content which remains in the soil sample after the consolidation under the lateral stress (σ_3).

Tests may also be performed on a soil sample in which no consolidation is allowed prior to the application of the axial stress. Drainage may or may not be allowed to take place. Therefore, as discussed before, one distinguishes between:

    a) unconsolidated-undrained triaxial compression test (Fig. 19-16)

    b) consolidated-undrained triaxial compression test (Fig. 19-17) and

    c) consolidated-drained triaxial compression test (Fig. 19-18).

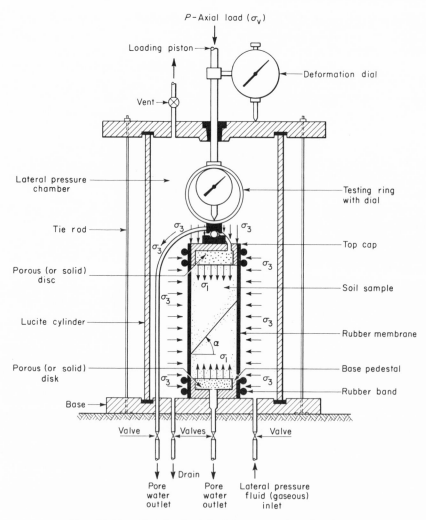

P-Axial load (σ_v)

Loading piston

Deformation dial

Vent

Lateral pressure chamber

Testing ring with dial

Tie rod

σ_3 σ_3
σ_3

Top cap

Porous (or solid) disc

σ_3

σ_1

Soil sample

σ_3

Lucite cylinder

σ_3

Rubber membrane

α
σ_1

Porous (or solid) disk

σ_3 σ_3

Base pedestal

Rubber band

Base

Valve   Valves   Valve

Drain

Pore water outlet

Pore water outlet

Lateral pressure fluid (gaseous) inlet

FIG. 19-19.   Sketch of a triaxial compression chamber.

19-13. Apparatus. A sketch of a triaxial compression chamber is given in Fig. 19-19. The vertical, axial stress σ_1 can be applied to the soil sample manually by turning the gear-wheel (or by dead weights), or mechanically by means of an electric motor, or by compressed gas pressure. The soil sample of a cohesive soil is trimmed to size to fit the apparatus. The height of the soil sample, usually cylindrical in shape, is customarily 2 to 3 times its diameter.

19-14. Pore Water Pressure. Generally, the shear strength of a soil depends primarily upon the externally applied normal or confining pressure on the soil mass. This pressure forces the soil particles into a more close contact. Hence, the volume of the soil mass becomes somewhat reduced. This volume change is attributed mainly to the reduction in the voids or pores of the soil. If the soil is completely saturated, that is, if all the voids are completely filled with water, the volume of voids can be decreased only if some of the water pressure will be induced. This induced water pressure resists the externally applied pressure. This resisting water pressure is termed the pore water pressure, or neutral pressure. In triaxial compression tests of saturated soils, and in consolidation tests, the pore water pressure or neutral pressure must be measured and recorded.

Generally, pore water pressure means the pressure (gage pressure) exerted by water occupying the voids of the soil. Pore water pressure is a natural force which is present not only in cohesive soils, but may be also in granular soils. However, in granular soils the voids are large; therefore, pore water pressure has a negligible effect on the testing process and its results: because of ease to drain, pore water pressures dissipate quickly. In cohesive soils the voids are minute and pore water pressure exerts an additional, all-directional pressure of considerable magnitude.

Relative to undisturbed saturated soils, Terzaghi[8] recognized the pore water pressure as being the neutral stress u which "is equal to the product of the unit weight of the water γ_w and the height h_w to which the water rises in a piezometric tube at the point under consideration. . . ."

Soil mechanics has demonstrated that water within the voids of a mass of a soil has a significant mechanical effect upon the strength of the soil, particularly upon its shear strength. Also, pore water pressure retards consolidation of a cohesive soil.

Pore water pressure measurement installations are used in the application of vertical sand drains to consolidate fills rapidly, as well as during the construction of earth dams.

In conclusion, it must be said that the greatest difficulty in applying the shear test results to practical design problems in soil engineering is the correct evaluation of the field conditions under which the soil has to perform, namely, soil type, loading, and the degree of consolidation. For the proper field evaluation the soil should be tested in an attempt to simulate conditions as they might occur in the field, and consequently the proper test values of ϕ and c should be used in stability calculations of earth masses.

19-15. Example. A triaxial compression test on a cohesive soil sample, cylindrical in shape, yielded the following effective stresses:
   a) major principal stress—1000 lb/in.^{2} = 800 lb/in.^{2} + 200 lb/in.^{2},
   b) minor principal stress—200 lb/in.^{2},
   c) the angle of inclination of the rupture plane: 60° with the horizontal.
Requirements
   a) Present all of the information pertaining to this problem in the form of Mohr's stress diagram.
   b) Determine analytically normal stress, shear stress, and resultant stress on the rupture plane through a point. Also determine the angle of obliquity of the resultant stress with the shear plane.
   c) What is the magnitude of the cohesion?
   d) What is the value of the coefficient of internal friction?
   e) What is the magnitude of the initial stress in the soil?
   f) Write the Coulomb's shear strength equation

i) in the algebraic form, and

ii) for the particular case of the given soil test.

g) How is Coulomb's equation of shear strength of soil used in practice?

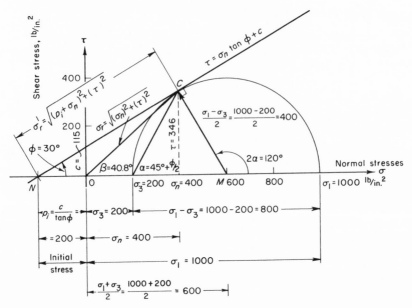

FIG. 19-20. Graphical representation of stress conditions in soil, Example 19-15.

Answers

a) *Mohr's stress diagram* is constructed as shown in Fig. 19-20.

$\sigma_1 = 1000$ lb/in.^{2}; $\sigma_3 = 200$ lb/in.^{2}; $\sigma_{n_{eff}} = 400$ lb/in.^{2};

$\sigma_r = 530$ lb/in.^{2}; $c = 115$ lb/in.^{2}; $\phi = 30°$; $p_i = 200$ lb/in.^{2}.

b) i) *Normal stress*: with $\alpha = 60°$, $\cos^2 60° = 0.25$, and $\sin^2 60° = 0.75$.

$\sigma_n = \sigma_1 \cos^2 \alpha + \sigma_3 \sin^2 \alpha = (1000)(0.250) + (200)(0.750) = 400$ lb/in.^{2}.

ii) *Shear stress*: with $\sin 2\alpha = \sin 120° = \cos 30° = 0.866$,

$$\tau = \frac{\sigma_1 - \sigma_3}{2} \sin 2\alpha = \frac{1000 - 200}{2}(0.866) = 346.4 \text{ lb/in.}^2.$$

iii) *Resultant stress*:

$$\sigma_r = \sqrt{(\sigma_n)^2 + (\tau)^2} = \sqrt{(400)^2 + (346)^2} = 530 \text{ lb/in.}^2.$$

iv) *Angle of obliquity* (Fig. 19-20):

$$\beta = \arctan\frac{\tau}{\sigma_n} = \arctan\frac{346}{400} = \arctan(0.864) = 40°50'.$$

Angle of obliquity of σ_r with shear plane:

$$90° - \beta = 90° - 40°50' = 49°10'.$$

c) $\tan\phi$: with $\alpha = 60°$, from geometry: $2\alpha = 90° + \phi$,
or $\phi = 120° - 90° = 30°$; $\tan\phi = \tan 30° = 0.577$.

d) *Cohesion*: From τ-equation: $\tau = \sigma_n\tan\phi + c$,

$$c = \tau - \sigma_n\tan\phi = 346.4 - (400)(0.577) = 115.6 \text{ lb/in.}^2.$$

e) *Initial stress*:

$$p_i = \frac{c}{\tan\phi} = \frac{115.6}{0.577} = 200 \text{ lb/in.}^2.$$

f) *Coulomb's shear strength equation*:
   i) algebraically:

$$\tau = \sigma_{n_{eff}}\tan\phi + c$$

   ii) for the particular case:

$$\tau = (0.577)\sigma_{n_{eff}} + 115.6.$$

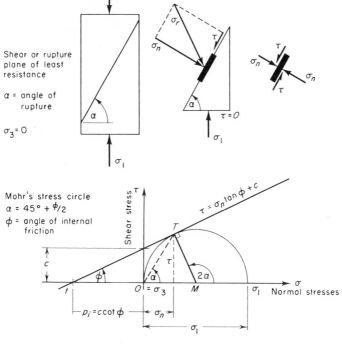

FIG. 19-21. Principle of unconfined compression test.

g) Coulomb's shear strength equation is used in practice in its modified form, namely, that the normal stress in that equation should be the effective normal stress: $\sigma_{n_{eff}} = \sigma_n - u$, where u is the neutral stress.

19-16. Unconfined Compression Test.[9] Essentially, the unconfined compression test is a special case of the triaxial compression test of soils where the compressive and shear strengths of a soil prism, or cylinder, are measured under zero lateral stress ($\sigma_2 = \sigma_3 = 0$), see Fig. 19-21. The test is based on the assumption that there is no moisture loss during the test.

In this test, carefully prepared prisms, or cylinders, of soils are subjected to gradually increasing vertical pressure, and simultaneous measurements of the deformations of the soil samples are made. One of the features of the unconfined compression test is the ability to cause failure in a soil sample in a weak zone.

The unconfined compression test is applicable to unweathered, slightly disturbed, disturbed (remolded), and undisturbed cohesive soils. Cohesionless soils (sands and gravels) cannot be subjected to this kind of test, because they do not form unsupported prisms and cylinders.

The unconfined compression test is one of the simplest and quickest tests used for the determination of the shear strength of cohesive soils, and it is also a simple substitute for more cumbersome field tests.

19-17. Apparatus. Any compression device which permits an unconfined, axial loading and the measurement of strain is suitable for unconfined compression tests of soil. The apparatus may be of the controlled stress or controlled strain type. The axial load σ_1 may be applied manually, mechanically, by dead weights, pneumatically, by means of screws, or by other means. A pneumatic, unconfined compression

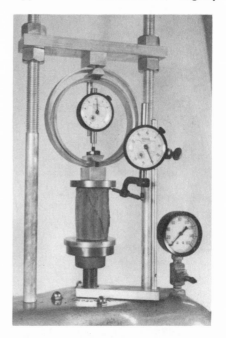

FIG. 19-22. Unconfined compression test device.

apparatus of the controlled strain type is illustrated in Fig. 19-22. The pressure is exerted on the sample and on the testing ring from below. Note in this figure the rupture plane in the tested soil cylinder.

19-18. Purpose and Application of Unconfined Compression Test. The purpose of the unconfined compression test of cohesive soils is to determine:

1) the ultimate, unconfined compressive strength,
2) the approximate, ultimate shear strength,

3) the approximate angle of internal friction ϕ, }
4) cohesion c (from Mohr's stress circle),   } test parameters, and
5) the so-called modulus of elasticity E of soil.

The results obtained from unconfined compression tests are approximate. However,

1) they serve as a direct, quantitative measure of the consistency of cohesive soils, giving a clue as to the danger of rupture of embankment slopes or other earth masses;
2) they provide basic information on the strength properties, thus permitting us to estimate the possible bearing capacity of the soil in foundations and earthworks;
3) they give the stress-strain relationship under rapid failure conditions, and
4) they permit comparison of soil samples taken from various bore holes of approximately similar soil formation, thus saving most of the expensive and time-consuming shear tests.

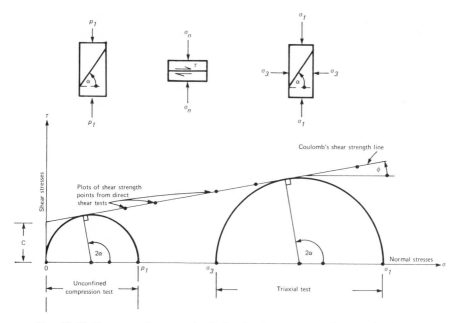

FIG. 19-23 illustrates the general relationship between the three basic kinds of laboratory shear strength tests.

REFERENCES

1. C. A. Coulomb, "Essai sur une application des règles de maximis et minimis à quelques problèmes de statique relatifs à l'architecture", *Mémoires de la mathématique et de physique*, présentés à l'Académie Royale des Sciences, par divers savants, et lûs dans ses Assemblées, Paris, De L'Imprimerie Royale, 1776, vol. 7, Année 1773, pp. 347-348.
2. Bureau of Reclamation, *Earth Manual*, Washington, D.C., U.S. Department of the Interior, 1975, pp. 44-49.
3. *1976 Annual Book of ASTM Standards, Part 19*, Designation D. Standard Method for Test of Unconsolidated-Undrained Strength of Cohesive Soils, ASTM, Philadelphia, Pa., 1976.
4. *1976 Annual Book of ASTM Standards, Part 19*, Designation D 2850-70, Standard Method of Test for Unconsolidated, Drained Strength of Cohesive Soils in Triaxial Compression. ASTM, Philadelphia, Pa., 1976, pp. 348-353.
5. A. Casagrande, "Characteristics of Cohesionless Soils Affecting the Stability of Slopes and Earth Fills", *Contributions to Soil Mechanics, 1925-1940*, Boston, Boston Society of Civil Engineers, 1940, pp. 257-276.
6. 1976 Annual Book of ASTM Standards, Part 19, Designation D 3080-72, Standard Method of Direct Shear Test of Soils Under Consolidated Drained Conditions, ASTM, Philadelphia, Pa., 1976, pp. 399-403.
7. O. Mohr, *Technische Mechanik*, Berlin, Wilhelm Ernst und Sohn, 1906.
8. K. Terzaghi, "The Shearing Resistance of Saturated Soils and the Angle Between the Planes of Shear," *Proceedings* of the (First) International Conference on Soil Mechanics and Foundation Engineering, held at Cambridge, Mass., June 22-26, 1936, vol. 1, Paper no. d-7, pp. 54-56.
9. *1976 Annual Book of ASTM Standards, Part 19*, Designation D 2166-66 (Reapproved 1972), Unconfined Compression Strength of Cohesive Soil, ASTM, Philadelphia, Pa., 1976, pp. 263-266.

OTHER PERTINENT REFERENCES

1. American Society of Civil Engineers (ASCE), Soil Mechanics and Foundations Division, *Research Conference on Shear Strength of Cohesive Soils*, held at the University of Colorado, Boulder, Colo., June 1960. University of Colorado, Boulder, Colo.
2. *Procedures for Testing Soils*, Philadelphia, ASTM, 1958, pp. 357-359.
3. L. Carlson, "Determination in Situ of the Shear Strength of Undisturbed Clay by Means of a Rotating Auger," *Proceedings, Second International Conference on Soil Mechanics and Foundation Engineering, Rotterdam, 1948*, vol. 1, pp. 265-270.
4. A. Casagrande, "A Non-Metallic Piezometer for Measuring Pore Pressures in Clay," an Appendix to his paper entitled "Soil Mechanics in the Design and Construction of the Logan Airport," *Contributions to Soil Mechanics, 1941-1953*, Boston, Boston Society of Civil Engineers, 1953, pp. 198-205.
5. A. Casagrande and S.D. Wilson, Report to Waterways Experiment Station on Triaxial Research Performed During 1950-51, Harvard University, December 1951.
6. A. Casagrande and S.D. Wilson, "Prestress Induced in Consolidated-quick Triaxial Tests," *Proceedings, Third International Conference on Soil Mechanics and Foundation Engineering, Zürich,* August 1953.
7. M. Darienzo and E. Vey, "Consistency Limits of Clay by the Vane Method," *Proceedings, 34th Annual Meeting of the Highway Research Board, Washington, D.C.,* January 11-15, 1955, pp. 559-566.
8. H.J. Gibbs and C.T. Coffey, "Techniques for Pore Pressure Measurements and Shear Testing of Soil." *Proceedings of the 7th International Conference on Soil Mechanics and Foundation Engineering,* vol. 1, 1969, pp. 151-157.

9. A.R. Jumikis, *Soil Mechanics,* Princeton, New Jersey, D. Van Nostrand Company, 1962.
10. R.A. Lohnes, A. Millan and R.L. Handy, "In-situ Measurement of Soil Creep." *Proc. ASCE,* Journal of the Soil Mechanics and Foundations Division, vol. 98, No. SM1, 1972, pp. 143-147.
11. P.L. Newland and G.H. Allely. "Volume Changes in Drained Triaxial Tests on Granular Materials. *Géotechnique* (London), vol. 7, 1957, pp. 17-34.
12. R.H.G. Parry (editor), *Stress-Strain Behaviour of Soils,* Henley-on-Thames, Oxfordshire, G.T. Foulis and Co., Ltd, 1972.
13. D.W. Taylor, "Shearing Strength Determination by Undrained Cylindrical Compression Test with Pore Pressure Measurements," *Proceedings, Second International Conference on Soil Mechanics and Foundation Engineering, Rotterdam,* June 1948.
14. K.A. Turner, Jr., Design and Operation of a Pressure Cell for Measuring Pore Water Pressure (mimeographed), New Brunswick, N.J., Rutgers - The State University, 1955.
15. E. Vey and L. Schlesinger, "Soil Shear Tests by Means of Rotating Vane," *Proceedings, 29th Annual Meeting of the Highway Research Board,* December 13-16, 1949, Washington, D.C., 1950, p. 547.
16. R.N. Yong and B.P. Warkentin, *Soil Properties and Behaviour,* Amsterdam/New York, N.Y., Elsevier Scientific Publishing Company, Chapters 8-10, 1975, pp. 261-381.

PROBLEMS

19- 1. Show graphically that $\alpha = 45° + \phi/2$.

19- 2. Why do engineers need to know the shear strength of a soil?

19- 3. What is the physical law governing failure in shear of a soil?
How does an effective normal stress differ from an applied total normal stress?

19- 4. Explain effective and neutral stress in soil and the significance of considering or not considering neutral stress in performing a shear test of a cohesive soil. Make illustrative sketches.

19- 5. Describe and illustrate how the shear strength of a soil varies with its moisture content. Discuss the deductions concerning the consequences in an earthwork when the moisture content in the soil gradually increases. Under what conditions can moisture content in soil increase in the field as applied to an earthwork?

19- 6. A direct shear test of a ϕ-soil at a normal stress of 4 kg/cm² resulted in a shearing stress of 3 kg/cm².

Determine: a) the angle of internal friction for this noncohesive soil.
b) the shearing resistance at a normal stress of 6 kg/cm².
Represent all of the stresses on a stress diagram.

19-7 . Given direct shear test results on a remolded sandy soil at 13.2% moisture content and 109 lb/ft³ dry density. The test was performed at $\sigma_n = 3.3$ lb/in.². The testing ring dial reading constant is 33 lb per 0.0100 in. deformation of ring. The cross-sectional area of the shear area is 4.0 in.².

Plot and analyze the test results, showing three graphs on one drawing: shear stresses as a function of time, horizontal displacement as a function of time, and vertical displacement of soil as a function of time.

Observe the table. What kind of shear test is this? Report the ultimate shear stress. In what state of density is the sand?

Time in minutes	Testing ring dial readings in inches	Horizontal displacement dial readings in inches	Vertical displacement dial readings in inches	Remarks
1	2	3	4	5
0	0.0000	0.0000	0.0000	The minus sign
0.5	0.0024	0.0012	−0.0010	means decrease
1.0	0.0038	0.0050	−0.0010	of height of
1.5	0.0056	0.0090	−0.0005	soil sample in
2.0	0.0074	0.0120	+0.0005	the shear box
2.5	0.0090	0.0177	+0.0020	upon shearing.
3.0	0.0104	0.0225	+0.0045	
3.5	0.0114	0.0284	+0.0070	
4.0	0.0120	0.0345	+0.0100	Plus sign,
4.5	0.0116	0.0407	+0.0130	in contra-
5.0	0.0110	0.0475	+0.0170	distinction, means increase in height.

TABLE PROBLEM 19-7

19- 8. Given the following test results of a remolded sandy soil with some binder at an optimum moisture content of 13% and dry unit weight of 15.69 kN/m^3. The method of test is the unconsolidated, quick, direct shear test where no time was allowed for the consolidation of the specimen.

σ_n (lb/in.^{2})	σ_n kN/m^2	τ (lb/in.^{2})	τ kN/m^2
3.3	22.75	9.6	66.19
6.7	46.19	11.8	81.36
9.9	68.26	12.7	87.56
13.3	91.70	16.8	115.83
16.5	113.76	20.2	139.27

a) Plot the shear strength curve for this soil and for this test condition.
b) Determine the tests parameters ϕ and c.
c) Analyze and explain the obtained graph.

19- 9. A consolidated-undrained (Q_c) triaxial compression test on a silt soil furnished the following results.

Total normal stresses	Stresses on soil cylinders, in kN/m^2			
	Test numbers			
σ	1	2	3	4
σ_1	131.00	251.66	372.32	496.42
σ_3	68.95	134.45	206.84	275.79
The plot of these stresses gives the apparent angle of internal friction, ϕ_a.				
Pore water pressure, u, in kN/m^2	48.26	93.08	137.90	203.40
Effective normal stresses, $\sigma_{n_{eff}}$, in kN/m^2				
$\sigma_{n_{eff2}}$,		158.58		
$\sigma_{n_{eff3}}$		41.37		
The plot of these stresses gives the effective angle of internal friction, ϕ_e.				

TABLE PROBLEM 19-9.

19-10. A consolidated-drained (slow) s_c test by the method of triaxial compression on a cohesive soil gave the following results.

Effective normal stresses, $\sigma_{n_{eff}}$	Stresses on Soil Cylinders, in kN/m^2	
	Test numbers	
	1	2
$\sigma_{n_{eff}}1$	227.53	448.16
$\sigma_{n_{eff}}3$	68.95	137.90

The plot of these stresses gives the true angle of internal friction ϕ.

    a) Plot the stress circles and Mohr's shear strength envelope for these tests.

    b) What is the magnitude of the true angle of internal friction ϕ in these tests?

    c) Compare ϕ with ϕ_a and ϕ_e.

    d) What is your observation about cohesion?

Note. Bring out the idea that ϕ_a, ϕ_e, ϕ and c are test parameters, rather than soil constants.

19-11. Given the following unconfined compression test results:
unconfined compressive strength - 200 kN/m^2
angle of rupture with the horizontal - 60°

Required: 1) Plot Mohr's stress circle.
2) What are the values of σ_1 and σ_3?
3) Locate position of center of stress circle.
4) What is the value of the initial stress?
5) What are the values of the test parameters ϕ and c?
6) What is the value of the normal stress on the shear plane? Show it on the Mohr's diagram.
7) What is the value of the shear stress in the shear plane?
8) Write the shear strength equation with your parameters involved.

Note: Show all quantities on a neatly drawn figure.

19-12. Given the following data from an unconfined compression test of a cohesive soil. The angle of rupture was measured to be $\alpha = 63°$ with the horizontal. The diameter of the soil specimen is 38.1 mm. The height of the cylindrical soil specimen is 96.8 mm. Type of soil: greensand (Collington). The moisture content of the soil specimen at its rupture was determined to be $w = 24\%$.

Point Nos. on Curve	Axial load, σ_1 (kN/m^2)	Deformation of Soil Specimen Δh (mm)
0	0	0
1	30.41	0.635
2	62.40	1.194
3	106.52	2.362
4	129.62	3.759
5	136.86	4.978
6	121.35	6.426
7	110.32	7.468
8	106.18	8.839

1) Plot the axial load as a function of deformation, i.e., $\sigma_1 = f(\Delta h)$.
2) Determine the ultimate, unconfined compressive load.
3) Plot the axial stress in kN/m^2 as a function of strain $(\Delta h/h)$, and determine the proportional limit.
4) Plot Mohr's stress diagram and determine σ_n, τ, ϕ and c.

19-13. Fig. Problem 19-13a illustrates an angle of shearing resistance ϕ_u of an unconsolidated soil at an excess pore water pressure u. Explain by Fig. Problem 19-13b as to how to determine graphically the effective angle of internal friction ϕ_{eff} and the effective normal pressure $\sigma_{n_{eff}}$ for an unconsolidated soil if the excess pore water pressure u at the instance of rupture of the soil is known.
Hint. The tangent drawn to the unconsolidated Mohr's stress circle should pass through point 0_1, and it should be parallel to the tangent drawn at the consolidated Mohr's stress circle.

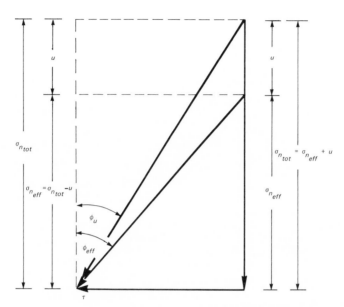

FIG. PROBLEM 19-13a. Angle of shearing resistance at excess pore water pressure u.

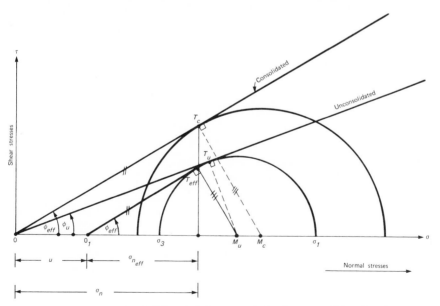

FIG. PROBLEM 19-13b. Mohr's stress circles for consolidated and
unconsolidated soils.

Chapter 20

STRESS DISTRIBUTION IN SOIL

20-1. Contact Stresses. Stresses in soil are caused by two principal factors,
1) *self-weight of the soil,*

$$\sigma_s = \gamma H, \tag{20-1}$$

where σ_s = stress in soil at depth H and
γ = unit weight of soil, and
2) the stress from the *structural load* applied to the soil.

20-2. Boussinesq's Theory: Assumptions. Boussinesq's stress distribution theory is based on the results given by the mathematical theory of elasticity for the simplest case of loading of a solid, homogeneous, elastic-isotropic, semi-infinite medium: namely, the case of a single, vertical, point load applied at a point on the horizontal boundary surface (ground surface).

A semi-infinite body is one bounded from one side with a horizontal boundary plane. In the case of soil, the horizontal boundary plane would be the ground surface, and a semi-infinite medium is the mass of soil below the ground surface.

Point loads in soil mechanics are a) single, concentrated loads, and b) uniformly distributed loads over symmetric polygonal, or circular, areas when stresses in soil are considered only at depths greater than the threefold diameter of the loaded area. In deriving his stress distribution theory for a single, concentrated load, J. V. Boussinesq[1] made the following assumptions:

1) The soil medium[2] is an elastic, homogeneous, isotropic, semi-infinite medium which extends infinitely in all directions from a level surface and which obeys Hooke's law.
2) The soil is weightless.
3) Originally, before the application of the single, concentrated load, the soil is not subjected to any other stress, i.e., the soil is stress-less, or unstressed.
4) The stress distribution from the applied, concentrated load is independent of the type of material of which the homogeneous, elastic-isotropic body is made. Relative to soil the change in volume upon the application of stress to the soil is neglected.
5) In this medium, the law of linear stress distribution is valid.
6) There exists a continuity of stress.
7) In such a system the stresses are distributed symmetrically with respect to the z-axis.

The limitations of the theory based on the above assumptions restrict it to the proportionality between stress and deformation (Hooke's law).

According to Boussinesq's theory, the various stresses caused in the semi-infinite medium by a single, concentrated load have the functions summarized as follows (Fig. 20-1):

$$\sigma_z = \frac{3P}{2\pi}\frac{z^3}{R^5} = \frac{3P}{2\pi R^2}\cos^3\beta \tag{20-2}$$

$$\sigma_x = \frac{P}{2\pi}\left[3\frac{x^2z}{R^5} - \frac{m-2}{m}\left(\frac{x^2-y^2}{Rr^2(R+z)} + \frac{y^2z}{R^3r^2}\right)\right] \tag{20-3}$$

$$\sigma_y = \frac{P}{2\pi}\left[3\frac{y^2z}{R^5} - \frac{m-2}{m}\left(\frac{y^2-x^2}{Rr^2(R+r)} + \frac{x^2z}{R^3r^2}\right)\right] \tag{20-4}$$

$$\sigma_r = \frac{P}{2\pi}\left[3\frac{r^2z}{R^5} - \frac{m-2}{m}\left(\frac{R-z}{Rr^2}\right)\right] \tag{20-5}$$

$$\sigma_t = \frac{P}{2\pi}\left[\frac{m-2}{m}\left(\frac{1}{r^2} - \frac{z}{R^3} - \frac{z}{Rr^2}\right)\right] \tag{20-6}$$

$$\tau_{rt} = \tau_{zt} = 0 \tag{20-7}$$

$$\tau_{rz} = \frac{3P}{2\pi}\frac{rz^2}{R^5} \tag{20-8}$$

$$\tau_{zx} = \frac{3P}{2\pi}\frac{z^2x}{R^5} \tag{20-9}$$

$$\tau_{zy} = \frac{3P}{2\pi}\frac{z^2y}{R^5} \tag{20-10}$$

The stresses in soil at any point $N(R;\beta)$ in polar coordinates are:

$$\sigma_z = \frac{3P}{2\pi R^2}\cos^3\beta, \tag{20-11}$$

$$\sigma_r = \frac{P}{2\pi R^2}\left(3\sin^2\beta\cos\beta - \frac{m-2}{m}\frac{1}{1+\cos\beta}\right), \tag{20-12}$$

$$\sigma_t = -\frac{m-2}{m}\frac{P}{2\pi R^2}\left(\cos\beta - \frac{1}{1+\cos\beta}\right), \tag{20-13}$$

For $m = 2$, $\quad \sigma_t = 0.$ \hfill (20-14)

$$\tau = \frac{3P}{2\pi R^2}\sin\beta\cos^2\beta. \tag{20-15}$$

A volume-stable soil is characterized by Poisson's number or coefficient of $m = 2$, in which the cubal deformation is proportional to $(m-2)$. With $m = 2$, Poisson's ratio is $\mu = 1/m = 0.5$.

For the derivation and practical application of the various Boussinesq's stress components in soil and foundation engineering, see References 3, 4 and 5.

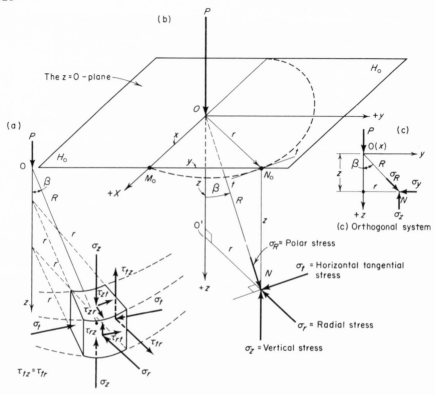

FIG. 20-1.   Load and stresses in the cylindrical coordinate system.

20-3. Vertical Normal Stress.   In foundation engineering, engineers are interested more in the vertical, normal, compressive stress σ_z acting on a horizontal area.

By Eq. (20-2), the Boussinesq's vertical stress component σ_z is

$$\sigma_z = \frac{3}{2}\frac{P}{\pi}\frac{z^3}{R^5}. \tag{20-2}$$

With $R^2 = z^2 + r^2$, and with $r^2 = x^2 + y^2$, where x, y, and z are the coordinates of point N (see Fig. 20-1), the vertical, normal, compressive stress σ_z is calculated as

$$\sigma_z = \frac{3P}{2\pi z^2}\frac{1}{[1 + (r/z)^2]^{5/2}}, \tag{20-16}$$

or

$$\sigma_z = K(P/z^2), \tag{20-17}$$

where

$$K = \frac{3}{2\pi}\frac{1}{[1 + (r/z)^2]^{5/2}} = \frac{0.478}{[1 + (r/z)^2]^{5/2}}, \tag{20-18}$$

is the Boussinesq vertical stress coefficient.

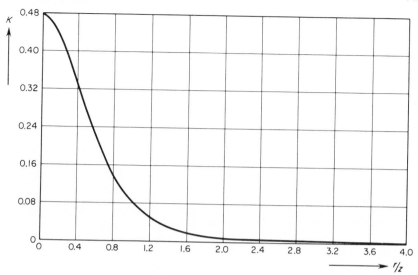

FIG. 20-2. $K = f(r/z)$.

Thus, Eqs. (20-11) and (20-13) permit the calculation of the vertical, normal, compressive stress σ_z caused by a concentrated load P, at any point N below the boundary surface H_o-H_o of a semi-infinite medium (viz., below the ground surface).

When point N is on the z-axis, i.e., on the line of action of P, then $\beta = 0$, $r = 0$, and σ_z has a maximum value of

$$\sigma_z = \frac{3P}{2\pi z^2} = (0.478)\frac{P}{z^2};$$ (20-19)

see Eqs. (20-16) and (20-18).

Note that Boussinesq's equations give the stresses in a semi-infinite medium caused by the surface loads only (refer to the assumption that the medium is weightless and that the load P is a concentrated point load).

20-4. Boussinesq's Vertical Stress Coefficients K. To facilitate vertical stress distribution calculations of single, concentrated loads by means of Boussinesq's theory, there are tables available[6] supplying the K-values for various r/z-ratios in Boussinesq's stress distribution equation, $\sigma_z = K(P/z^2)$; see Table 20-1. The K-values can also be presented in a graph, Fig. 20-2.

Example. The vertical stress σ_z, at a point the coordinates of which are $z = 15.0$ ft, and $r = 7.5$ ft away from the line of action of a single, vertical, concentrated load of $P = 400,000$ lb $= 200$ tons is calculated by means of the K-tables as follows:

$$\frac{r}{z} = \frac{7.50}{15.00} = 0.5; \quad K_{0.5} = 0.2733 \text{ (from the } K\text{-tables)};$$

$$z^2 = (15.0)^2 = 225.0;$$

$$\sigma_z = K(P/z^2) = (0.2733)(200)/(225) = 0.24 \text{ (ton/ft}^2\text{)}.$$

TABLE 20-1. BOUSSINESQ COEFFICIENTS $K = f(r/z)$ (Ref. 6)

r/z	K	r/z	K	r/z	K	r/z	K	r/z	K	r/z	K
.00	.4775	.50	.2733	1.00	.0844	1.50	.0251	2.00	.0085	2.50	.0034
.01	.4773	.51	.2679	1.01	.0823	1.51	.0245	2.01	.0084	2.51	.0033
.02	.4770	.52	.2625	1.02	.0803	1.52	.0240	2.02	.0082	2.52	.0033
.03	.4764	.53	.2571	1.03	.0783	1.53	.0234	2.03	.0081	2.53	.0032
.04	.4756	.54	.2518	1.04	.0764	1.54	.0229	2.04	.0079	2.54	.0032
.05	.4745	.55	.2466	1.05	.0744	1.55	.0224	2.05	.0078	2.55	.0031
.06	.4723	.56	.2414	1.06	.0727	1.56	.0219	2.06	.0076	2.56	.0031
.07	.4717	.57	.2363	1.07	.0709	1.57	.0214	2.07	.0075	2.57	.0030
.08	.4699	.58	.2313	1.08	.0691	1.58	.0209	2.08	.0073	2.58	.0030
.09	.4679	.59	.2263	1.09	.0674	1.59	.0204	2.09	.0072	2.59	.0029
.10	.4657	.60	.2214	1.10	.0658	1.60	.0200	2.10	.0070	2.60	.0029
.11	.4633	.61	.2165	1.11	.0641	1.61	.0195	2.11	.0069	2.61	.0028
.12	.4607	.62	.2117	1.12	.0626	1.62	.0191	2.12	.0068	2.62	.0028
.13	.4579	.63	.2070	1.13	.0610	1.63	.0187	2.13	.0066	2.63	.0027
.14	.4548	.64	.2040	1.14	.0595	1.64	.0183	2.14	.0065	2.64	.0027
.15	.4516	.65	.1978	1.15	.0581	1.65	.0179	2.15	.0064	2.65	.0026
.16	.4482	.66	.1934	1.16	.0567	1.66	.0175	2.16	.0063	2.66	.0026
.17	.4446	.67	.1889	1.17	.0553	1.67	.0171	2.17	.0062	2.67	.0025
.18	.4409	.68	.1846	1.18	.0539	1.68	.0167	2.18	.0060	2.68	.0025
.19	.4370	.69	.1804	1.19	.0526	1.69	.0163	2.19	.0059	2.69	.0025
.20	.4329	.70	.1762	1.20	.0513	1.70	.0160	2.20	.0058	2.70	.0024
.21	.4286	.71	.1721	1.21	.0501	1.71	.0157	2.21	.0057	. .	. .
.22	.4242	.72	.1681	1.22	.0489	1.72	.0153	2.22	.0056	2.72	.0023
.23	.4197	.73	.1641	1.23	.0477	1.73	.0150	2.23	.0055	. .	. .
.24	.4151	.74	.1603	1.24	.0466	1.74	.0147	2.24	.0054	2.74	.0023
.25	.4103	.75	.1565	1.25	.0454	1.75	.0144	2.25	.0053	. .	. .
.26	.4054	.76	.1527	1.26	.0443	1.76	.0141	2.26	.0052	2.76	.0022
.27	.4004	.77	.1491	1.27	.0433	1.77	.0138	2.27	.0051	. .	. .
.28	.3954	.78	.1455	1.28	.0422	1.78	.0135	2.28	.0050	2.78	.0021
.29	.3902	.79	.1420	1.29	.0412	1.79	.0132	2.29	.0049	. .	. .
.30	.3849	.80	.1386	1.30	.0402	1.80	.0129	2.30	.0048	2.80	.0021
.31	.3796	.81	.1353	1.31	.0393	1.81	.0126	2.31	.0047	. .	. .
.32	.3742	.82	.1320	1.32	.0384	1.82	.0124	2.32	.0047	2.84	.0019
.33	.3687	.83	.1288	1.33	.0374	1.83	.0121	2.33	.0046	. .	. .
.34	.3632	.84	.1257	1.34	.0365	1.84	.0119	2.34	.0045	2.91	.0017
.35	.3577	.85	.1226	1.35	.0357	1.85	.0116	2.35	.0044	. .	. .
.36	.3521	.86	.1196	1.36	.0348	1.86	.0114	2.36	.0043	2.99	.0015
.37	.3465	.87	.1166	1.37	.0340	1.87	.0112	2.37	.0043	. .	. .
.38	.3408	.88	.1138	1.38	.0332	1.88	.0109	2.38	.0042	3.08	.0013
.39	.3351	.89	.1110	1.39	.0324	1.89	.0107	2.39	.0041	. .	. .
.40	.3294	.90	.1083	1.40	.0317	1.90	.0105	2.40	.0040	3.19	.0011
.41	.3238	.91	.1057	1.41	.0309	1.91	.0103	2.41	.0040	. .	. .
.42	.3181	.92	.1031	1.42	.0302	1.92	.0101	2.42	.0039	3.31	.0009
.43	.3124	.93	.1005	1.43	.0295	1.93	.0099	2.43	.0038	. .	. .
.44	.3068	.94	.0981	1.44	.0288	1.94	.0097	2.44	.0038	3.50	.0007
.45	.3011	.95	.0956	1.45	.0282	1.95	.0095	2.45	.0037	. .	. .
.46	.2955	.96	.0933	1.46	.0275	1.96	.0093	2.46	.0036	3.75	.0005
.47	.2899	.97	.0910	1.47	.0269	1.97	.0091	2.47	.0036	. .	. .
.48	.2843	.98	.0887	1.48	.0263	1.98	.0089	2.48	.0035	4.13	.0003
.49	.2788	.99	.0865	1.49	.0257	1.99	.0087	2.49	.0034	. .	. .
										4.91	.0001
										6.15	.0001

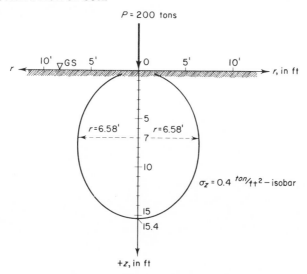

FIG. 20-3.   The $\sigma_z = 0.40$ ton/ft²-isobar.

20-5. Pressure Distribution Diagrams. By means of the Boussinesq vertical stress equation, Eq. (20-17), the following diagrams can be calculated and presented graphically:

1) the stress isobar diagram;
2) the vertical stress distribution on a horizontal plane, z units below the ground surface; and
3) the vertical stress distribution vertically r units away from the line of action of the single, vertical, concentrated load P.

The Stress Isobars. An isobar is a line which connects all points below the ground surface of equal stress, Fig. 20-3. Obviously, for any one load system many isobars can be drawn on one diagram. In other words, an isobar is a stress contour. In the literature such an isobar diagram is termed the "bulb of pressure," or "pressure bulb."

A system of isobars indicates the decrease in stress intensity and reminds one of an onion bulb. The soil mass within the boundaries of the pressure bulb furnishes the support for the bearing, loading plate, or footing of the foundation.

Example. For a single, concentrated load of $P = 200$ tons construct an isobar for $\sigma_z = 0.4$ kg/cm² = 0.4 ton/ft² = 800 lb/ft².
Solution. The calculation is best performed in a tabular form. The problem consists of finding corresponding r-values for various depths z. By Eq. (20-17),

$$K = \sigma_z z^2/P, \qquad (20\text{-}20)$$

or

$$K = (0.4)z^2/200 = z^2/500.$$

Assuming various z-values, calculate their corresponding K-values, and for these determine from the K-tables the respective (r/z)-ratios. Knowing the (r/z)-ratios, calculate r for each of the previously assumed z-values. The σ_z-values for the same radius r are the same on both sides of the axis of symmetry of the pressure bulb. The $\sigma_z = 0.4$ ton/ft² isobar calculation is compiled in Table 20-2.

TABLE 20-2. ISOBAR DATA FOR $\sigma_z = 0.4 \text{ ton/ft}^2 = \text{const}$

Depth z ft	K	$\dfrac{r}{z}$	r in ft	σ_z ton/ft^2
1	2	3	4	5
0.5	0.0005	3.750	1.875	0.40 = const
1	0.002	2.840	2.84	0.40
2	0.008	2.035	4.06	0.40
3	0.018	1.650	4.95	0.40
5	0.050	1.210	6.05	0.40
7	0.098	0.940	6.58	0.40
8	0.128	0.830	6.64	0.40
10	0.200	0.650	6.50	0.40
14	0.392	0.290	4.06	0.40
15	0.450	0.155	2.33	0.40
15.4	0.478	0.000	0.00	0.40

When $r = 0$, then $K = 0.478$, and the isobar crosses the line of action of the load, $P = 200$ tons, at a depth of

$$z = \sqrt{500K} = \sqrt{(500)(0.478)} = 15.4 \qquad \text{(ft)}$$

below the ground surface.

The $\sigma_z = 0.4 \text{ ton/ft}^2$ isobar is illustrated in Fig. 20-3. It lies in the vertical plane passing through the line of action of P. Actually the isobar is a spatial, curved surface because in this case for each z the radii in all directions around the axis of symmetry are equal.

Note from Fig. 20-3 that in general isobars are not circular curves. Rather, their shapes approach the curve of lemniscate.

System of Several Concentrated Loads. If a system of several concentrated loads is given, then for plotting the resulting isobars each of the normal, compressive stresses in the system may be added at any point to obtain the total stresses at that point. Points with equal stresses are connected by a curvilinear line to give isobars (by interpolation).

Vertical Stress Distribution Diagram on a Horizontal Plane. To plot the vertical stress distribution diagram on a horizontal plane, keep the depth z, determining the position of that horizontal plane, below the ground surface constant, i.e., $z = \text{const}$. Then, using various assumed values for r, calculate the (r/z) ratios, and by means of the K-Table determine the corresponding K-values. Also, calculate the (P/z^2) value which for each horizontal plane (for each z) is a constant, and compute the vertical stress σ_z by means of Eq. (20-17):

$$\sigma_z = K(P/z^2).$$

Example. Calculate and plot the vertical stress distribution diagram on a horizontal plane located $z = 7.0$ ft below the ground surface. The concentrated load is $P = 200$ tons.

TABLE 20-3. VERTICAL STRESS ORDINATES FOR DEPTH $z = 7.0$ ft $=$ const

Radius r ft	$\dfrac{r}{z}$	K	$\dfrac{P}{z^2}$	σ_z ton/ft^2
1	2	3	4	5
0	0	0.4775	4.081	1.94
1	0.14	0.4548	4.081	1.86
2	0.28	0.3954	4.081	1.61
3	0.42	0.3181	4.081	1.30
4	0.57	0.2363	4.081	0.96
5	0.71	0.1721	4.081	0.70
6	0.85	0.1226	4.081	0.50
6.58	0.94	0.0980	4.081	0.40
7	1.00	0.0844	4.081	0.34
8	1.14	0.0595	4.081	0.24
9	1.28	0.0422	4.081	0.17
10	1.42	0.0302	4.081	0.12
12	1.71	0.0157	4.081	0.06
15	2.14	0.0065	4.081	0.03
21	3.00	0.0015	4.081	0.006

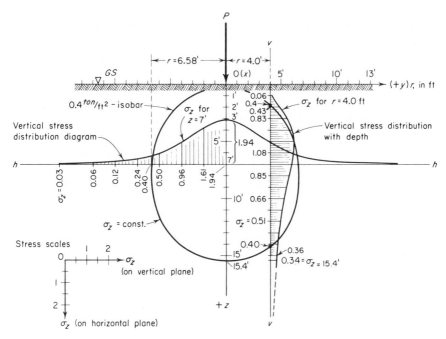

FIG. 20-4. Vertical stress distribution diagrams.

334 STRENGTH PROPERTIES OF SOIL

Solution. The calculation is performed in a tabular form (see Table 20-3). The soil-force system is plotted to a *geometric scale*. The vertical stresses are plotted to a *stress scale*. The diagram is plotted in Fig. 20-4 along the line *h-h*.

Note that the vertical stress distribution diagram due to Boussinesq is bell-shaped, that therefore the vertical stress distribution is nonuniform, and that the maximum stress ordinate (in the example $\sigma_z = 1.94$ ton/ft^2) is located on the line of action of the concentrated load. The stress decrease is an asymptotic one.

Note that the vertical stress distribution diagram on a horizontal plane can be obtained graphically if the isobar diagram is given, containing several isobars. When a horizontal plane *h-h* is passed at a certain *z* through the pressure bulb (isobars), the intersection of the horizontal line with the particular isobar gives the vertical stress ordinate at the point of intersection (read the value of the intersected isobar).

Vertical Stress Distribution Diagram Along a Vertical Plane. Such a diagram shows the variation in magnitude of vertical stress with depth *z* at a constant distance *r* from the *z*-axis. In the diagram these stresses are represented by horizontal ordinates.

TABLE 20-4. VERTICAL STRESS ORDINATES FOR $r = 4.0$ ft = const

Depth, z (ft)	$\frac{r}{z}$	K	z^2	$\frac{P}{z^2}$	σ_z ton/ft^2
1	2	3	4	5	6
0	$\to \infty$	$\to 0$	0	$\to \infty$	Indeterminate
1	4	0.0003	1	200	0.06
2	2	0.0085	4	50	0.43
3	1.33	0.0374	9	22.2	0.83
4	1.00	0.0844	16	12.5	1.06
5	0.8	0.1386	25	8.0	1.11
6	0.66	0.1934	36	5.6	1.08
6.58	0.61	0.2165	43.3	4.6	1.00
7	0.57	0.2363	49	4.08	0.96
8	0.50	0.2733	64	3.12	0.85
9	0.44	0.3068	81	2.47	0.66
10	0.4	0.3294	100	2.00	0.66
12	0.33	0.3687	144	1.39	0.51
15	0.27	0.4004	225	0.89	0.36
15.4	0.26	0.4054	235.2	0.85	0.34

Example. For $P = 200$ tons, and with $r = 4.0$ ft = const, the vertical stresses σ_z for various depths z are computed as follows. Assuming various z-values, calculate the (r/z) ratios, and determine the K-values from the K-Tables. Then calculate for each depth, z, the (P/z^2) values, and calculate the vertical stress, σ_z, by Eq. (20-17):

$$\sigma_z = K(P/z^2).$$

The calculation is performed in a tabular form (see Table 20-4). The vertical stresses are to be plotted to a stress scale. The diagram is shown in Fig. 20-4 plotted along the line *v-v*.

Note from the plot that the magnitude of the vertical stress first increases and then

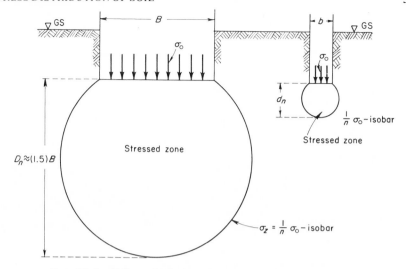

FIG. 20-5.   Effect of width of footings on depth of isobars.

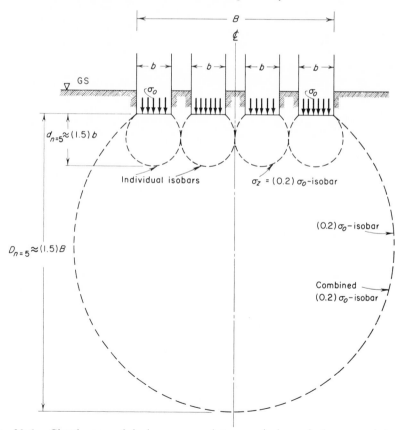

FIG. 20-6.   Closely spaced isobars merge into one isobar of the same intensity, reaching far deeper than the individual isobars.

decreases with depth. The decrease is an asymptotic one. This diagram can also be obtained graphically if the isobar diagram is given. The ordinates are obtained by reading the isobar values at their intersection with the vertical plane v-v.

20-6. Effect of Size of Footing on Depth of Isobar. The two isobars of the same intensity, say of $\sigma_z = (0.2)(\sigma_o)$, in Fig. 20-5 show that the wider the loaded area, the deeper is its effect, i.e., the deeper is the extent of this isobar. If several loaded footings are spaced closely enough, the individual isobars of each footing in question would combine and merge into one large isobar of the same intensity, (see Fig. 20-6), reaching about $D_{n=5} = (1.5)B$ deep below the base of the sum of the closely spaced footings. The meanings of the symbols n, $D_{n=5}$ and $d_{n=5}$ are shown in Figs. 20-5 and 20-6.

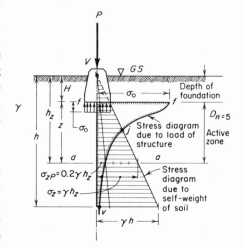

FIG. 20-7.   Active zone.

From Fig. 20-6, it can also be deduced that the settlement of a group of closely spaced friction piles in compressible soil can be expected to be larger than the settlement of a single friction pile.

Note in Fig. 20-7 that the vertical stress diagram from self-weight of soil is of triangular shape, and that its vertex is located at the ground surface, point V. The vertical stress distribution diagram ffv, however, starts at the base elevation f-f of the footing, where the structural load is transmitted to the soil.

Fig. 20-8 shows two widths of loaded foundations, b_1 and b_2, whereby $b_1 < b_2$. The contact pressures of both foundations are the same, namely, $\sigma_{o1} = \sigma_{o2} = \sigma_o$. This figure illustrates that the wider the loaded area, the deeper is its influence. The $(0.5)\sigma_o$-isobar underneath the narrow footing, the width of which is b_1, does not reach the soft layer of soil, whereas underneath the larger footing with a width b_2 the $(0.5)\sigma_o$-isobar intercepts the soft layer. The soft layer receives on its top a compressive stress which is larger than $(0.75)\sigma_o$. Obviously, therefore, if contact pressures are the same, the wider footing b_2 would cause a greater settlement than footing b_1 (disregarding in this discussion the expulsion of soil laterally from underneath the base of the footing). In the latter case the narrow footing may sometimes settle more than the wide footing.

Figure 20-8 also hints that small-scale, soil-bearing tests with small loading or bearing plate areas are of very little use for settlement calculations if a wide foundation is contemplated. This is particularly true when the soil encountered is a cohesive one where expulsion of water from the voids of the soil (settlement) requires a certain amount of time, or if a seam of clay exists in the field at a certain depth. The pressure of interest (isobar) by a small plate would not reach

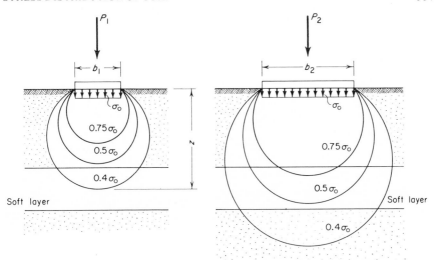

FIG. 20-8. Effect of size of footing on depth of isobar of equal intensity in a layered soil system. The larger the loaded area, the deeper is its influence.

this clay; hence the loading test results with a small loading area, applied to a wide foundation, would even be erratic. Loading tests, therefore, should be made on an area as large as practicable to reflect the combined effects of all of the soil properties to a greater depth at the site.

20-7. Stress Components from Linear Loads. The stress components from a single, uniformly distributed, *vertical,* concentrated linear load p (see Fig. 20-9) applied on the upper, horizontal boundary plane of the elastic semi-infinite medium are:[4,5]

$$\sigma_R = \frac{2p}{\pi R} \cos\beta \qquad (20\text{-}21)$$

$$\sigma_x = \frac{2p}{\pi m R} \cdot \frac{z}{R} = \frac{2p}{\pi m} \cdot \frac{1}{R} \cdot \cos\beta \qquad (20\text{-}22)$$

$$\sigma_y = \frac{2p}{\pi R} \cdot \frac{y^2 z}{R^3} = \frac{2p}{\pi R} \cdot \sin^2\beta \cdot \cos\beta = \frac{2p}{\pi z} \cdot \sin^2\beta \cdot \cos^2\beta \qquad (20\text{-}23)$$

$$\sigma_z = \frac{2p}{\pi R} \cdot \frac{z^3}{R^3} = \frac{2p}{\pi R} \cdot \cos^3\beta = \frac{2p}{\pi z} \cdot \cos^4\beta = \frac{2p}{\pi \cdot z} \cdot \frac{1}{[1+(r/z)^2]^2} \qquad (20\text{-}24)$$

$$T_{yz} = \frac{2p}{\pi R} \cdot \frac{y \cdot z^2}{R^3} = \frac{2p}{\pi R} \cdot \sin\beta \cdot \cos^2\beta = \frac{2p}{\pi z} \cdot \sin\beta \cdot \cos^3\beta \qquad (20\text{-}25)$$

$T_{xz} = 0$, and

$\tau_{yx} = 0$ (because of symmetry).

These stress component equations are good for any Poisson's number $m = 1/\mu$, not only for $m = 2$.

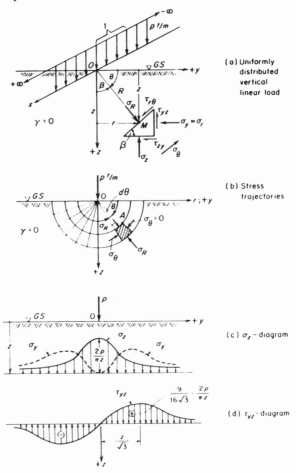

FIG. 20-9. System of vertical, uniformly distributed linear load p.

The stress components of a single, uniformly distributed *horizontal* linear load q (see Fig. 20-10) are:[5]

$$\sigma_x = \mu(\sigma_y + \sigma_z) = \frac{2q}{\pi m \rho^2} \cdot y \qquad (20\text{-}26)$$

$$\sigma_y = \frac{2q}{\pi \rho^4} \cdot y^3 \qquad (20\text{-}27)$$

$$\sigma_z = \frac{2q}{\pi \rho^4} \cdot y \cdot z^2 \qquad (20\text{-}28)$$

$$\tau_{yz} = \tau_{zy} = \frac{2q}{\pi \rho^4} \cdot y^2 \cdot z \qquad (20\text{-}29)$$

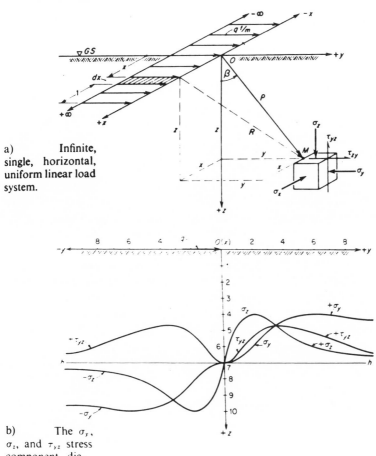

a)   Infinite, single, horizontal, uniform linear load system.

b)   The σ_y, σ_z, and τ_{yz} stress component diagrams from a horizontal load.

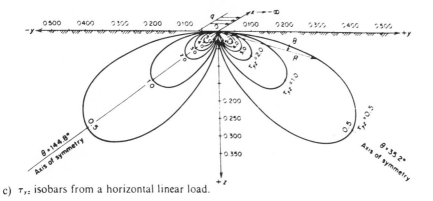

c) τ_{yz} isobars from a horizontal linear load.

FIG. 20-10. System of horizontal, uniformly distributed linear load.

$\tau_{xz} = \tau_{xy} = 0,$

where $\rho = \sqrt{y^2 + z^2}$ (20-30)

20-8. Stress Influence-Value Graphs. Because compressive stresses in cohesive soil beneath the base of a foundation bring about settlement, knowledge of stress distribution in soil is of great importance in foundation design. In particular, the magnitudes of compressive stresses are needed for the determination of the compression of soil, the rate of consolidation of soil, and for the prediction of the total probable settlement of the soil.

To enable one to ascertain quickly stress fields in an elastic medium, viz., soil or rock, the author prepared and published appropriate stress distribution influence value tables and graphs, References 7, 8, and 9. The tables were prepared based on Boussinesq's stress distribution theory. These stress influence value tables and graphs are of value not only in teaching civil engineering students in soil mechanics, rock mechanics, foundation engineering and hydraulic structures-and waterways engineering but they are also of value for actual design as well as for research in the above mentioned geotechnical engineering disciplines.

Reference 7, entitled "Stress Distribution Tables for Soil Under Concentrated Loads" contains stress influence values for single concentrated (vertical, horizontal, inclined) loads and for linear loads applied to the upper, horizontal boundary surface (viz., ground surface) of an elastic, semi-infinite elastic medium and for various Poisson's numbers $m = 1/\mu$ and Fröhlich's stress concentration factors ν.

These tables may be considered an effective means of rationalizing the engineer's work, and their use may result in considerable savings in time and money in those phases of a project to which the stress distribution analyses in soil and rock pertain.

The use of the stress distribution influence value tables may give the design engineer the satisfaction of feeling that his analysis rests on a sound theoretical basis.

Because the influence values in these tables are dimensionless, they are equally applicable for use in any system of units of measurement, whether the British, or the technical metric system, or the SI units.

Author's influence value tables, Reference 8, pertain to Vertical stress influence values for uniformly distributed loads on soil *for any point* under square, rectangular, strip[8] and circular bearing areas on the boundary surface of an elastic, homogeneous, semi-infinite medium. The tables also permit convenient plotting of stress isobars, under either the short side or the long side of the footing of a structural foundation.

For the purpose of illustration, the author prepared influence value graphs for some commonly encountered surface loadings as shown in Figs. 20-11 through 20-20. Notice that these influence value graphs as well as the influence value tables render the sought influence values immediately and directly without any unwieldy intermediate operations with corners and influence meshes.

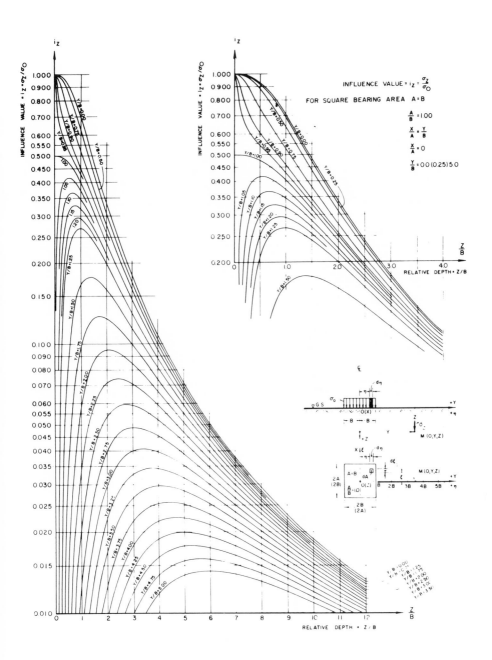

FIG. 20-11. Vertical stress influence value graph for uniformly loaded square bearing area.[8]

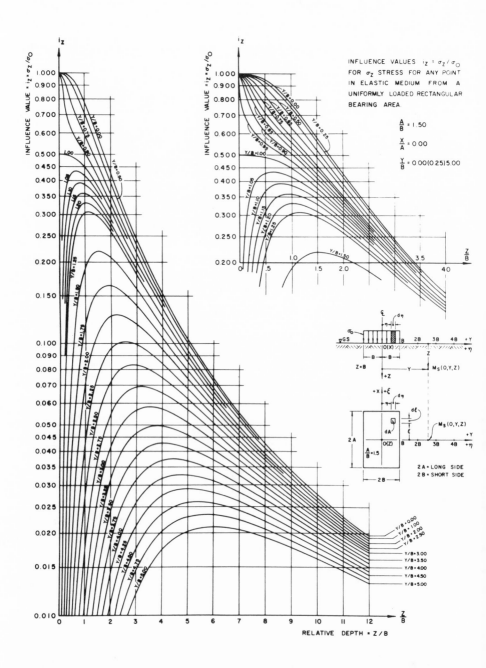

FIG. 20-12. Vertical stress influence value graph for uniformly loaded
rectangular bearing area relative to short side.[8]

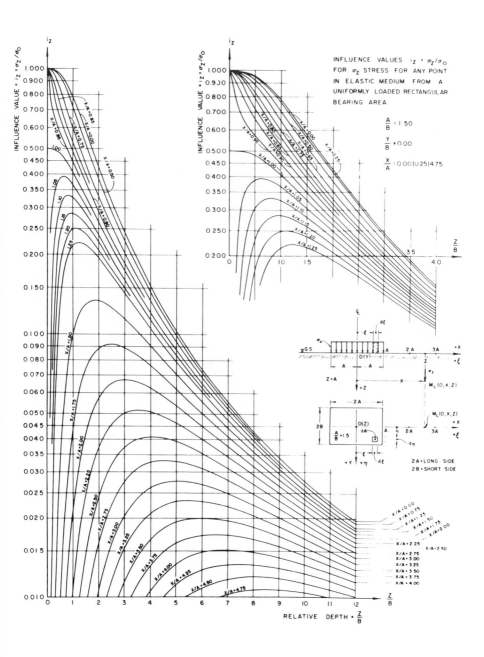

Fɪɢ. 20-13. Vertical stress influence value graph for uniformly loaded rectangular bearing area relative to long side.[8]

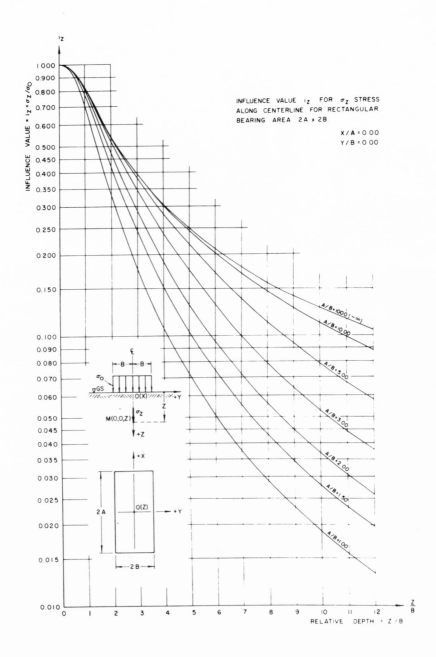

FIG. 20-14. Vertical stress influence value chart for stress along
centerline for rectangular bearing areas.[8]

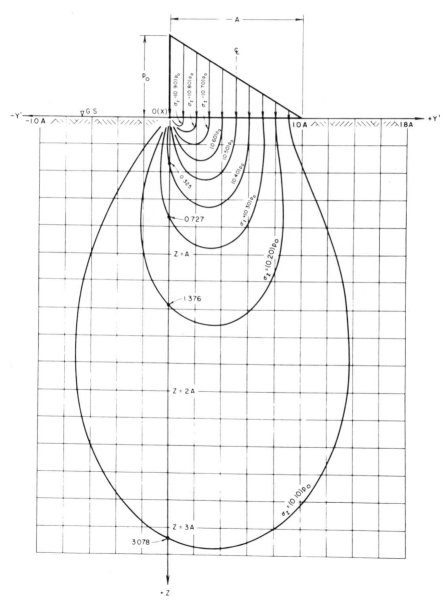

FIG. 20-15. Vertical stress isobars for triangular-strip surface loading.[8]

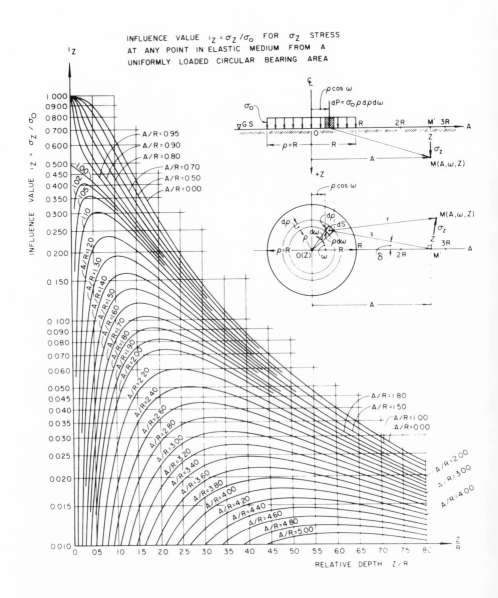

FIG. 20-16. Vertical stress influence value graph for stress at any point in elastic medium from a uniformly loaded circular bearing area.[8,9]

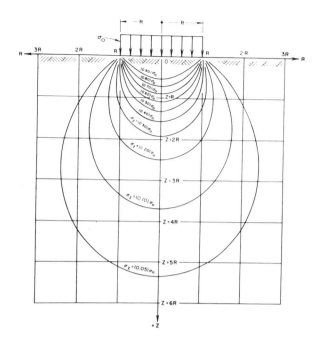

FIG. 20-17. Vertical stress isobars σ_z from a uniformly loaded circular area.[8]

The use of these influence value graphs are now shown by the following examples.

Example 1. Refer to Fig. 20-11. Given a square bearing area: $2A = 2B = 4.00$ m = 400 cm. It exerts on the soil a uniformly distributed contact pressure of $\sigma_o = 300 \text{kN/m}^2$. Determine the σ_z-stress at a point M whose coordinates are: $X = 0.00$, $Y = 2B$, and $Z = 3B$.

Solution. For $A/B = 2.00/2.00 = 1.00$; $X/A = 0.00$; $Y/B = 4.00/2.00 = 2.00$; $Z/B = (3)(2.00)/2.00 = 3.00$, and directly from tables[8] or from the influence value graph in Fig. 20-11, the influence value $i_z = \sigma_z/\sigma_o = 0.08455$, and the stress sought is

$$\sigma_z = i_z \cdot \sigma_o = (0.08455)(300) = \underline{25.4 \text{ [kN/m}^2\text{]}}.$$

Notice that here the given point M lies outside the contour of the uniformly loaded square bearing area.

Example 2. Refer to Figs. 20-12, 20-13 and 20-14. Determine the magnitude of the σ_z stress on the vertical through the center of the uniformly loaded rectangular bearing area at depth $Z = 2.0$ m, if the size of the bearing area is given as 2.0 m x 3.0 m? $\sigma_o = 300 \text{kN/m}^2$.

Solution. The center point coordinates are $X = 0.00$ and $Y = 0.00$. Hence, $A/B = 3.0/2.0 = 1.50$, $X/A = 0.00$, $Y/B = 0.00$, and $Z/B = 2.00/1.00 = 2.00$. The point lies inside the contour.

Therefore the vertical center stress at depth $Z = 2.00$ m (directly from the graphs, Figs. 20-12, 20-13 or 20-14, or from tables, Ref. 8, with no subdivision of the given rectangle into four partial ones) is

$$\sigma_z = i_z \cdot \sigma_o \ (0.42829)(300) = \underline{128.5 \text{ [kN/m}^2\text{]}}.$$

Example 3. Refer to Fig. 12-13. A rectangular bearing area whose dimensions are $2A = 6.00$ m and $2B = 4.00$ m is uniformly loaded with a contact pressure of $\sigma_o = 300$ kN/m^2. Determine the σ_z stress for a point in the soil marked M whose coordinates are $X = 2A$ (long side), $Y = 0.00$, and $Z = 2.00$ m.

Solution. $A = 3.00$ m; $B = 2.00$ m; $A/B = 3.00/2.00 = 1.50$ m; $Y/B = 0.00$; $Z/B = 2.0/2.0 = 1.00$. $X/A = 2A/A = 2.00$. Therefore the given point M lies on the x-axis outside the contour of the rectangle. The pertinent relative values are $Y/B = 0.00$; $X/A = 2.00$, and $Z/B = 2.00/2.00 = 1.00$. Directly from tables,[8] or from the graph in Fig. 12-13 (for the long side of the rectangle), obtain the corresponding influence value $i_z = 0.02134$. Thus the sought stress is

$$\sigma_z = (0.02134)(300) = \underline{\ 6.4\ [\text{kN}/\text{m}^2].}$$

Example 4. Given a uniformly loaded rectangular bearing area whose plan dimensions are $2A = 15.00'$ and $2B = 10.00'$. The intensity of the contact pressure on the soil is given as $\sigma_o = 4.00$ ton/ft^2. Determine the vertical, normal stress σ_z at point M, whose coordinates are $X = (2.25)'$; $B = 11.25'$; $Y = (2)B = 10.00'$ and $Z = (2) \cdot B'$.

Solution. The given X and Y coordinates show that point M lies outside the contour of the rectangle. The dimensionless ratios are: $A/B = 7.50/5.00 = 1.50$; $X/A = 11.25/7.50 = 1.50$; $Y/B = 10.00/5.00 = 2.00$; $Z/B = 10.00/5.00 = 2.00$. For the solution of this problem, the graphs here presented cannot be used because the graphs are here prepared for $\frac{Y}{A} = 0.00$, but in this example $X/A = 1.50$. Therefore, one should resort to tables.[8] From tables, obtain the influence value $i_z = 0.05066$. The sought stress at point M is

$$\sigma_z = (0.05066)(4.00) = \underline{0.203\,[\text{ton}/\text{ft}^2].}$$

Example 5. Determine the magnitude of the vertical normal σ_z stresses in soil at points M_o, M_1, M_2, M_3 and M_4 from a uniformly loaded circular bearing area whose radius is $R = 10.00$ m. The contact pressure on soil is given as $\sigma_o = 400$ kN/m^2. All points M_n are to be determined for depth $Z = 5.00$ m. In this $Z = 5.00$ plane, points M_n are located from the vertical centerline $\mathcal{C}$ of the circle at the following horizontal radial distances A (refer to chart in Fig. 20-16).

M_0: $A = $ O   (on the centerline)
M_1: $A = $ R/2   (at the middle of the radius)
M_2: $A = $ R   (on the rim or circumference of the circle)
M_3: $A = 2R$ (at a radial distance of two radii)
M_4: $A = 3R$ (at a radial distance of three radii).

Solution. Use tables[8] or chart in Fig. 20-16. The dimensionless parameters, the corresponding influence values i_z, and vertical stresses are

For point M_o:

$$A/R = 0.00 \qquad Z/R = 5.00/10.00 = 0.50$$
$$i_z = 0.91056$$
$$\sigma_z = i_z \cdot \sigma_o = (0.91056)(400) = \underline{364.2\,[\text{kN}/\text{m}^2].}$$

For point M_1:

$$A/R = (R/2)/R = 0.50; \qquad Z/R = 0.50$$
$$i_z = 0.83957;$$
$$\sigma_z = i_z \cdot \sigma_o = (0.83957)(400) = \underline{335.8\,[\text{kN}/\text{m}^2].}$$

For point M_2:

$$A/R = R/R = 1.00; \qquad Z/R = 0.50$$

$$i_z = 0.41748;$$
$$\sigma_z = i_z \cdot \sigma_o = (0.41748)\,(400) = \underline{167.0\;[kN/m^2]}.$$

For point M_3:

$$A/R = 2R/R = 2.00; \qquad Z/R = 0.50$$
$$i_z = 0.01047;$$
$$\sigma_z = i_z \cdot \sigma_o = (0.01047)\,(400) = \underline{4.2\;[kN/m^2]}.$$

For point M_4:

$$A/R = 3R/R = 3.00; \qquad Z/R = 0.50$$
$$i_z = 0.00101;$$
$$\sigma_z = i_z \cdot \sigma_o = (0.00101)\,(400) = \underline{0.4\;[kN/m^2]}.$$

The stress influence values as discussed above (Refs. 7-9) are valid for *limply arranged* single uniform Boussinesq's stresses (σ_o) over rectangular, strip, and circular bearing areas on a homogeneous, elastic, hemispatial medium, viz., ground surface, and for their free, unobstructed propagation.

There is no friction between the limply arranged σ_o-stresses. Thus the above discussed stress influence values *do not* pertain to rigid footing systems.

Boussinesq's stress components in an elastic, homogeneous, isotropic medium are valid only if there is free unobstructed stress propagation in the medium. If, however, free propagation of stresses are obstructed by a vertical, rigid, unyielding earth retaining structure, or by a rigid, incompressible horizontal rock formation, for example, Boussinesq's stress components are not directly applicable. In such instances the effect of a wall (rock) on the magnitude of the σ_z and σ_y stresses may be taken into account by applying the method of mirror-images to the Boussinesq's stresses: the lateral pressure σ_y at any point on the backface of a smooth wall, and the vertical pressure σ_z on the (incompressible) rock are then precisely double the Boussinesq's pressures, while the shear stress at the backface of the wall vanishes.

In view of the above, the author's stress influence value tables and graphs are also valid for calculating lateral pressures σ_y on rigid walls, in that the tabular (graph) values are simply multiplied by a factor of 2. The same pertains to vertical stress components σ_z acting on horizontal incompressible layers at some depth z below ground surface.

20-9. Triaxial stress $\bar{\sigma}_z$ and Settlement of Soil Under Rigid Circular Footings. Fig. 20-18 shows a chart for resultant triaxial, vertical normal stress influence values $\bar{\sigma}_z/\sigma_o = (KV)$ as a function of half-angle α and Poisson's number m of soil for a *rigid*, smooth, circular footing,[10,11] laid on the ground surface.

This chart renders $\bar{\sigma}_z$-stresses acting along the centerline $\mathbf{Q}$ or on the z-axis of symmetry of the soil-foundation-load system only. The influence value $(KV) = \bar{\sigma}_z/\sigma_o$ is

$$\bar{\sigma}_z/\sigma_o = (KV) = \frac{1}{2}\left(\frac{m+1}{m}\right)(\sin^2\alpha)\left(\frac{m-2}{m} + 2\cos^2\alpha\right). \qquad (20\text{-}31)$$

Herein,

$$\sigma_o = \frac{V}{A} = \frac{V}{\pi \cdot R_o^2} \ , \tag{20-32}$$

is the average pressure computed from the externally, centrically applied, single concentrated load V acting on the rigid circular footing with a smooth base whose radius is R_o (Fig. 20-18).

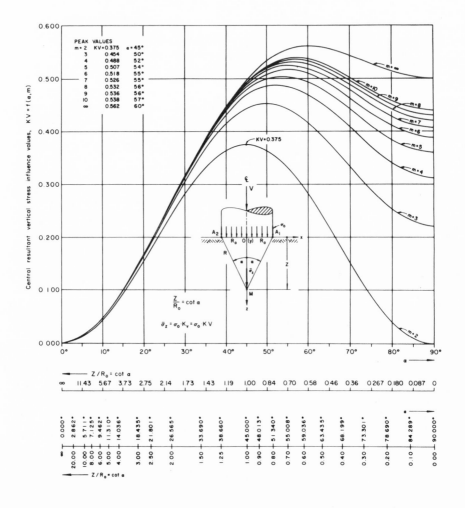

FIG. 20-18. Chart for resultant, triaxial, vertical normal stress influence values $\bar{\sigma}_z / \sigma_o = (KV) = f(\alpha;m)$ for a rigid, smooth circular footing.[10,11]

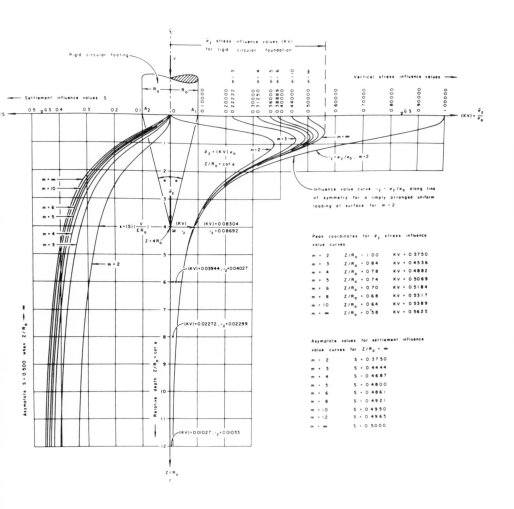

FIG. 20-19. Vertical triaxial stress and settlement influence value chart
for rigid circular foundation.[12]

The dimensionless influence values (KV) were computed for Poisson's numbers of $m = 1/\mu = 2, 3, 4, 5, 6, 7, 8, 9, 10$ and ∞. The chart shows that the vertical, normal, triaxial stress $\bar{\sigma}_z$ increases with increasing Poisson's number.

Example 6. If $m = 2.0$, and $Z/R_0 = \cot\alpha = 1.0$, then $\alpha = 45°$, and the influence value from tables [10] or chart in Fig. 20-18 is

$$f(\alpha; m{=}2) = (KV) = \bar{\sigma}_z/\sigma_o = 0.37500.$$

For average computed pressure $\sigma_o = V/(\pi \cdot R_o) = 200$ kN/m², the vertical triaxial stress $\bar{\sigma}_z$ along the centerline (z-axis) is

$$\bar{\sigma}_z = (\sigma_o)(KV) = (200)(0.37500) = 75.00 \ [\text{kN/m}^2].$$

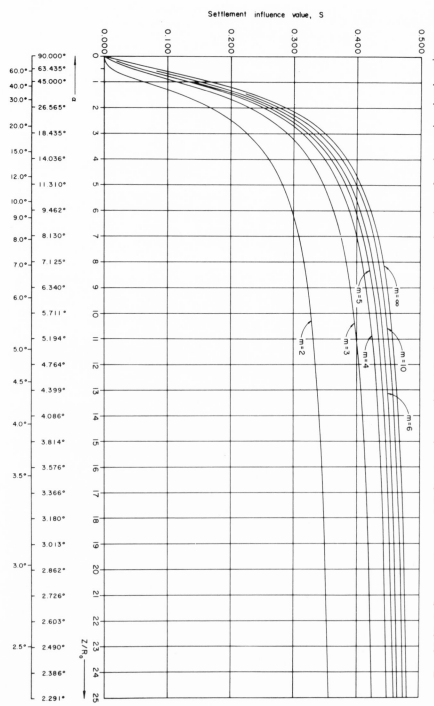

FIG. 20-20. Influence value graph S for stepwise, partial settlement calculations as a function of angle α, viz., depth ratio $z/R_o = Z/RO = \cot\alpha$, for a rigid, centrally loaded circular footing. Shown: S for $Z/RO = 0$ to $Z/RO = 25$.

The nature of the $\bar{\sigma}_z$-stress distribution and dimensionless settlement influence value graphs (S) for total elastic settlement (s) computations of a homogeneous monolayer soil are shown in Fig. 20-19.[12] The settlement influence-value chart may also be used for calculating total elastic settlement of a multilayered soil system.[10,12] The elastic settlement influence value charts (S) are also shown in Fig. 20-20 and 20-21.

The elastic settlement s may be obtained by multiplying the corresponding settlement influence value S by the factor $V/(E \cdot R_o)$:

$$s = (S) \cdot \left(\frac{V}{E \cdot R_o} \right) \quad , \tag{20-33}$$

where

$$E = \frac{1 - \mu - 2\mu^2}{1 - \mu} \cdot E_s \tag{20-34}$$

is the constant modulus of elasticity of soil in situ, in kN/m^2,
$\mu = 1/m =$ Poisson's ratio of soil
$m = 1/\mu =$ Poisson's number, and
$E_s =$ stiffness modulus (constrained modulus of elasticity) of soil obtained from soil test in the laboratory, in kN/m^2.

The uniform elastic settlement influence-value charts derived for a rigid centrically loaded circular foundation may also be used effectively for approximating the settlements of soil imposed by a rigid square foundation whose area is equivalent to that of the circle:

$$(2A)^2 = \pi \cdot R_o^2$$
$$R_o = (2A) \cdot \sqrt{1/\pi} = (1.128) \cdot (A), \tag{20-35}$$

where $2A =$ length of side of the square, and
$R_o =$ radius of circle.

This approximation is thought to be valid also for rectangles with side ratios of up to 1 to 5 only, according to Schleicher.[13]

Elastic settlement of a multilayered soil system under a rigid circular footing is calculated as the sum

$$s = \sum_1^n (\Delta s) = \Delta s_1 + \Delta s_2 + \Delta s_3 + \ldots + \Delta s_n \tag{20-36}$$

$$= \frac{V}{R_o E_1} \cdot S_1 + \frac{V}{R_o \cdot E_2} \cdot (S_2 - S_1) + \frac{V}{R_o \cdot E_3} \cdot (S_3 - S_2) + \ldots$$

$$+ \frac{V}{R_o \cdot E_n} \cdot (S_n - S_{n-1})$$

of settlement of the individual layers Δs, where n is the number of consecutive soil layers, and E_n is the modulus of elasticity of the individual soil layer. Using the settlement influence values $S_1, S_2, S_3, \ldots, S_{n-1}, S_n$, the individual or partial settlement Δs_n of a layer calculates as[10]

$$\Delta s_n = \frac{V}{R_o \cdot E_n} (S_n - S_{n-1}). \tag{20-37}$$

For purpose of orientation, the approximate values of Poisson's number m and in situ modulus of elasticity E for some common geological materials of construction are given in Tables 20-5 and 20-6, respectively.

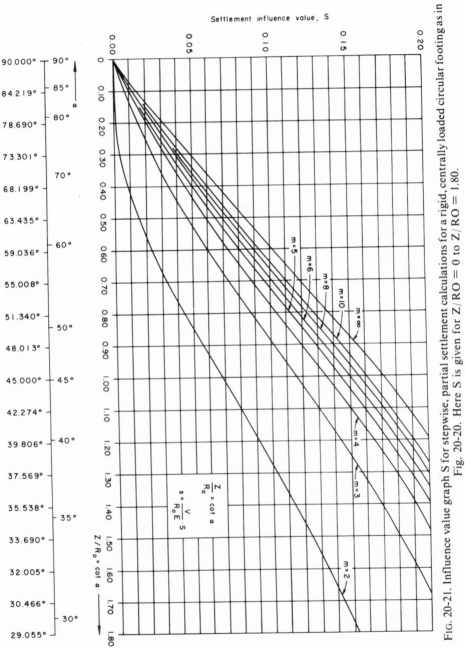

FIG. 20-21. Influence value graph S for stepwise, partial settlement calculations for a rigid, centrally loaded circular footing as in Fig. 20-20. Here S is given for $Z/RO = 0$ to $Z/RO = 1.80$.

TABLE 20-5
POISSON'S RATIO VALUES μ OF SOME
ANISOTROPIC SOILS AND ROCKS

Material	μ	m	Ref.
Basalt	0.200	5.0-7.0	
Diabase	0.333	3.0	
Dolomite	0.200-0.083	5.0-12.0	
Gabbro	0.200-0.125	5.0-8.0	
Granite	0.15-0.24	6.7-4.1	(a)
Gneiss	0.11	9.1	(a)
Gneiss	0.200-0.091	5.0-11.0	
Limestone	0.200-0.100	5-10	
Limestone	0.16-0.23	6.2-4.4	(a)
Limestone	0.333	3.0	
Marble	0.25-0.38	4.0-2.6	(a)
Marble	0.20-0.111	5.0-9.0	
Salt rock	0.333	3.0	
Sandstone	0.125-0.0665	8-15	
Sandstone	0.17	5.9	(a)
Sandstone	0.333	3.0	
Schist	0.17-0.10	6.0-10.0	
Schist	0.08-0.20	12.5-5.0	(a)
Tuff	0.11	9.1	(a)
Snow (fully plastic)	———	~4.0	(b)
Ice, at 0°C	0.360	3.0	(c), (d)
Ice, at -5°C	0.380	3.0	(c), (d)
Ice, at -15°C	0.330	3.0	(c), (d)
Gravelly sand, densely deposited	0.340	3.18	(e)
Gravel	0.14-0.10	7.0-10.0	
Gravel, medium	0.47	2.13	(e)
Sand	0.250-0.125	4.0-8.0	(e)
Sand, coarse	0.15	6.0	(b)
Sand, medium	0.20	5.0	
Sand, medium	0.445	2.20	(e)
Sand, fine	0.25	4.0	
Sand, clayey	0.30	3.33	
Sand, uniform	0.20	5.0	
Silty sand	0.25	4.0	
Silt	0.333	3.0	
Shale, Triassic	0.11-0.54	1.85-9.10	(f)
Loess, dry	0.440	2.27	(e)
Clay	0.400-0.20	2.5-5.0	(b)
Clay, moist	0.455	2.2	(e)

(a) *Physical Properties of Some Typical Foundation Rocks,* U.S. Bureau of Reclamation, Concrete Laboratory Report SP39, 1954.

(b) L. Bendel, *Ingenieurgeologie,* Wien, Springer, Vol. 1, 1948, p. 435, and Vol. 2, 1948, p. 600.

(c) Snow, Ice and Permafrost Establishment, Corps of Engineers, U.S. Army, SIPRE Report No. 4, July, 1951, by Univ. of Minnesota, *Review of the Properties of Snow and Ice,* Minneapolis, Minn., March, 1951.

(d) A.R. Jumikis, *Thermal Soil Mechanics,* New Brunswick, N.J., Rutgers University Press, 1966, p. 153.

(e) H. Lorenz, *Grundbau-Dynamik,* Berlin, Springer, 1960, pp. 248-249.

(f) A.R. Jumikis and A.A. Jumikis, *Red Brunswick Shale and Its Engineering Aspects,* New Brunswick, N.J.: College of Engineering, Rutgers-The State University of New Jersey. Engineering Research Bulletin No. 55, 1975, p. 51

TABLE 20-6
APPROXIMATE RANGES OF MODULUS OF ELASTICITY E
OF SOME SOILS AND ROCKS

Soil Type	Modulus of Elasticity E			
	(kg/cm^2)		(kN/m^2)	
Peat	1 to 5	98.07	-	490.33
Clay, very soft	5 to 15	490.33	-	1470.997
Clay, soft	15 to 30	1470.99	-	2941.995
Clay, medium hard	30 to 100	2941.995	-	9806.65
Clay, hard	100 to 150	9806.65	-	14709.97
Clay, sandy	150 to 300	14709.97	-	29419.95
Loess	70 to 200	6864.655	-	19613.3
Sand, silty	100 to 200	9806.65	-	19613.3
Sand, loose	100 to 300	9806.65	-	29419.95
Sand, dense	400 to 800	39226.6	-	78453.20
Gravel, dense ⎫ Gravel, sandy ⎭	1,000 to 2,000	98066.5	-	196133.0

Rock Type	Modulus of Elasticity E			
	(kg/cm^2)		(MN/m^2)	
Rock	30,000 to	∞		2941.99
Sandstone	50,000 to	800,000	4903.325	- 78453.20
Shale	100,000 to	320,000	9806.650	- 31381.28
Limestone	100,000 to	800,000	9806.65	- 78543.00
Granite	200,000 to	600,000	19613.30	- 58839.00
Basalt	600,000 to	1,000,000	58839.00	- 98066.50

An example of calculating total elastic settlement of a multilayered soil system from $\overline{\sigma}_z$-stress transmitted to the soil through a rigid circular foundation is illustrated by Fig. 20-22 and Tables 20-7 and 20-8.

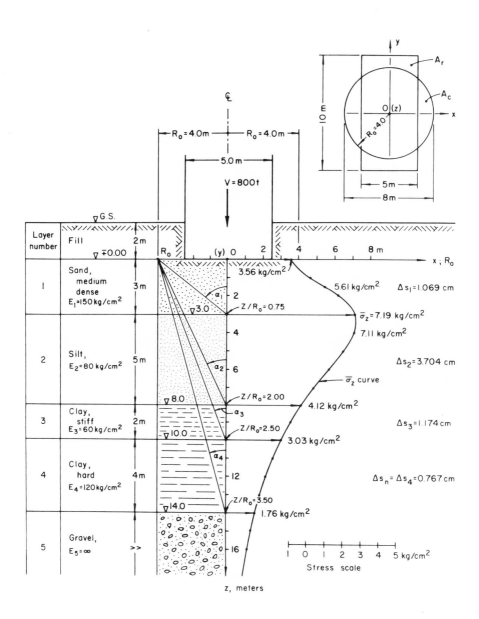

FIG. 20-22. Sketch demonstrating example of resultant vertical stress $\bar{\sigma}_z$ and settlement calculations for a rigid rectangular footing on a multilayered soil system.

TABLE 20-7
COMPILATION OF RESULTANT VERTICAL STRESSES $\overline{\sigma}_z$

Layer No.	At Elevation (m)	Relative Depth $Z/R_o = \cot\alpha$	α (deg.)	Influence Value KV for $m=3$	Stress $\overline{\sigma}_z = (\sigma_o)(KV)$ (t/m^2)
1	2	3	4	5	6
1	▽ 0.00	0.00	90.000	0.22222	3.556
	▽ 1.00	0.25	75.965*	0.28301*	4.528
	▽ 1.60	0.40	68.199	0.35011	5.608
	▽ 2.00	0.50	63.435	0.39111	6.258
	▽ 3.00	0.75	53.132*	0.44937*	7.190
2	▽ 4.00	1.00	45.000	0.44444	7.111
	▽ 5.00	1.25	38.660	0.40399	6.464
	▽ 6.00	1.50	33.690	0.35240	5.638
	▽ 7.00	1.75	29.745	0.30212	4.834
	▽ 8.00	2.00	26.565	0.25778	4.124
3	▽ 9.00	2.25	23.972*	0.22044*	3.527
	▽ 10.00	2.50	21.801	0.18919	3.027
4	▽ 12.00	3.00	18.435	0.14222	2.276
	▽ 14.00	3.50	15.945	0.10981	1.760
5	▽ 16.00	4.00	14.036	0.08689	1.390
	▽ 18.00	4.50	12.529	0.07025	1.153

* α and KV values obtained by linear interpolation.

TABLE 20-8
SETTLEMENT COMPUTATION

Sequence of Layers	Relative Depth Z/R_o	Settlement Influence Value S for $m=3$	Settlement Influence Value Differences (S_n-S_{n-1}) (cm)	E_n (kg/cm²)	Partial Settlement $\Delta s_n = \left[\dfrac{V}{R_o E_n} \cdot (S_n - S_{n-a})\right]$ (cm)
1	2	3	4	5	6
1 Sand	0.75	0.08022	0.08022	$E_1 = 150$	$\Delta s_1 = 1.069$
2 Silt	2.00	0.22838	0.14816	$E_2 = 80$	$\Delta s_2 = 3.704$
3 Clay, stiff	2.50	0.26361	0.03523	$E_3 = 60$	$\Delta s_3 = 1.174$
4 Clay, hard	3.50	0.30965	0.04604	$E_4 = 120$	$\Delta s_4 = 0.767$
5 Gravel				$E_{n=5} = \infty$ Considered incompressible	

Total settlement $s = \overset{4}{\underset{1}{\Sigma}}\ (\Delta s) = 6.714$ cm $\approx$ 6.8 (cm)

20-10. Pressure on Tunnel Roof. Given a tunnel of rectangular (or circular) cross section located h units below the ground surface as shown in Fig. 20-23. The soil is a (ϕ-c) soil, and has a unit weight of γ. The width of the tunnel is a, and its length is b. The perimeter of horizontal projection of the tunnel is U.

Required:

1) Establish algebraically the general σ_z-function expressing vertical compressive stress on the tunnel roof because of the overburden soil. Calculate σ_z for (ϕ-c)-soil, ϕ-soil, and c-soil.

2) Discuss the σ_z-equation.

3) What is the algebraic value for σ_z when the coefficient of internal friction of soil μ is equal to zero, and when cohesion c alone along the sides of the overburden soil above the roof of the tunnel would carry the weight of the soil column $abde$?

4) What is the value of the vertical stress σ_z on the roof of the tunnel ($U = 2a + 2b$) for large h? Is or is not this stress a maximum stress, and why?

5) If $a = 40$ ft, $b = 200$ ft (length of tunnel), $\phi = 30°$, $\gamma = 100$ lb/ft^3, $c = 200$ lb/ft^2, $K_a = \sigma_y/\sigma_z = 0.333$, and $h = 90$ ft, calculate compressive stress on top of the tunnel roof considering

a) a tunnel with $U = 2(a+b)$,

b) a long tunnel with $U = 2b$,

c) a short tunnel with $U = 2a$,

d) an intermediately long tunnel with $a = b/2$ and $U = 2a + (2)(b/2) = 4a$,

e) $b = a/2$, and $U = 2a + 2b = 2a + a = 3a$.

Solution. The principle involved in calculating the compressive stress on the roof of a tunnel (horizontal roof or horizontal projection of circular pipe) is the equilibrium of a horizontal, elemental lamina (a unit long per run of tunnel) of soil of thickness dz and length a. Here, a is the width of the tunnel, Fig. 20-23.

Let σ_z = vertical, compressive stress at depth z below the ground surface (a principal stress);

σ_y = horizontal stress at depth z (a principal stress);

$\sigma_y/\sigma_z = K_a = \tan^2(\pi/4 - \phi/2)$, approximately;

γ = unit weight of soil;

ϕ = angle of internal friction of soil;

$\tan \phi = \mu$ = coefficient of internal friction of soil;

c = cohesion of soil;

$A = ab$ = area of horizontal projection of tunnel roof, and

U = its perimeter: $U = 2a + 2b = 2(a + b)$.

Equilibrium of the elemental soil prism, the thickness of which is dz, along the z-axis gives the following differential equation:

$$d\sigma_z = \frac{\gamma A - \mu U K_a \sigma_z - Uc}{A} dz. \tag{20-38}$$

Integration gives the sought σ_z-stress as

$$\sigma_z = \frac{1}{\mu K_a} (\gamma \frac{A}{U} - c)[1 - e^{-(\mu K_a U/A)h}]. \tag{20-39}$$

This function is now ready for discussion.

Comments. In the case of a ϕ-soil, the soil above the tunnel (or grain in a silo) will probably *arch* itself, and it can be imagined to form a series of arches (or domes) superposed upon each other. The arching effect makes the

360 STRENGTH PROPERTIES OF SOIL

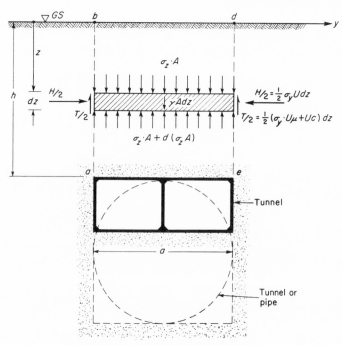

FIG. 20-23. Tunnel.

relationship $\sigma_y = \sigma_x K_a$ very indeterminate. Moreover, the lateral pressure distribution on the vertical sides (faces) of the outside walls of the tunnel cannot be clearly formulated because much of the weight of the soil directly over the tunnel has been transferred by arching to the sides of the adjacent soil (to the left of line ab and to the right of line de). Equation (20-39) does not render the lateral pressure on the tunnel lining, caused by the swelling of the saturated clay.

This theory can probably be applied to ordinary soil, dry or moist, and to soils which do not swell.

REFERENCES

1. J. V. Boussinesq, *Application des potentiels à l'étude de l'equilibre et du mouvement des solides élastiques*, Paris, Gauthier-Villars, 1885.
2. S. Timoshenko, *History of Strength of Materials*, New York, McGraw-Hill Book Co., Inc., 1953, p. 332.
3. A. R. Jumikis, *Soil Mechanics*, Princeton, N.J., D. Van Nostrand Company, Inc., 1962, pp. 516-548.
4. A. R. Jumikis, *Mechanics of Soils* (Fundamentals for Advanced Study), Princeton, N.J., D. Van Nostrand Company, Inc., 1964, pp. 78-142.
5. A.R. Jumikis, *Theoretical Soil Mechanics,* Princeton, N.J., D. Van Nostrand Company, Inc., 1969, pp. 36-257.
6. Progress Report of Special Committee of the American Society of Civil Engineers, "Earths and Foundations," *Proceedings, ASCE,* May 1933, vol. 59, no. 5, p. 781.

STRESS DISTRIBUTION OF SOIL   361

7. A.R. Jumikis, *Stress Distribution Tables for Soil Under Concentrated Loads*, Engineering Research Publication No. 48, New Brunswick, New Jersey. Rutgers University, The State University of New Jersey, College of Engineering, Bureau of Engineering Research, 1969, 233 pages.
8. A.R. Jumikis, *Vertical Stress Tables for Uniformly Distributed Loads on Soil.* Engineering Research Publication No. 52. New Brunswick, New Jersey, College of Engineering, Rutgers University, Bureau of Engineering Research, 1971, 495 pages.
9. A.R. Jumikis, "Influence Value Graphs for Circular Bearing Areas." Highway Research Record No. 405. Highway Research Board, Division of Engineering, National Research Council, Washington, D.C. 1972, pp. 45-50.
10. A.R. Jumikis, *Settlement Tables for Centrically Loaded, Rigid Circular Footings on Multilayered Soil Systems.* Engineering Research Bulletin No. 54. New Brunswick, New Jersey. Rutgers University, The State University of New Jersey, College of Engineering, Bureau of Engineering Research, 1973 (65 pages).
11. A.R. Jumikis, "Vertical Stress Chart for Rigid Circular Foundations." *Proc. ASCE,* Journal of the Soil Mechanics and Foundations Division, vol. 99, No. SM12, Dec., 1973, pp. 1196-1201.
12. A.R. Jumikis, "Settlement Influence-Value Chart for Rigid Circular Foundations." *Highway Research Record No. 457.* National Research Council - National Academy of Sciences - National Academy of Engineering, Washington, D.C., 1973, pp. 27-38.
13. F. Schleicher, "Zur Theorie des Baugrundes," *Der Bauingenieur,* No. 49, 1926, pp. 949-952.

Other Pertinent References

1. H. Hertz, "Über die Berührung fester elastischer Körper," *Journal für Mathematik* (Crelle), 1881, vol. 2.
2. A. E. H. Love, "The Stress Produced in a Semi-infinite Solid by Pressure on Part of the Boundary," *Philosophical Transactions of the Royal Society of London.* Series A, vol. 228, London, Hanison and Sons, Ltd, November 1929, pp. 377-420.
3. H. Lamb, "On Boussinesq's Problem," *Proceedings of the London Mathematical Society,* 1902, vol. 34, p. 276.
4. A. Föppl and L. Föppl, *Drang und Zwang, Eine Höhere Festigkeitslehre für Ingenieure,* München and Berlin, R. Oldenburg, 1944, vol. 2, p. 202.
5. H. Gray, "Stress Distribution in Elastic Solids," *Proceedings,* First International Conference on Soil Mechanics and Foundation Engineering, June 1936, Cambridge, Mass., Paper E-10, vol. 2, pp. 157-168.
6. W. Steinbrenner, Tafeln zur Setzungsberechnung, p. 121, no. 4, Schriftenreihe der Strasse 1, Strasse, 1934.
7. N. M. Newmark, "Influence Charts for Computation of Stresses in Elastic Foundations," *Bulletin,* University of Illinois, Urbana, Ill., November 10, 1942, Bulletin Series no. 338, vol. 40.
8. N. M. Newmark, "Stress Distribution in Soil," *Proceedings,* Purdue Conference on Soil Mechanics and its Applications, September 2-6, 1940, Purdue University, Lafayette, Ind., 1940, pp. 295-303.
9. K. Terzaghi, "Opening Discussion on Settlement of Structures," *Proceedings, First* International Conference on Soil Mechanics and Foundation Engineering, June 1936, Cambridge, Mass., vol. 3, pp. 79-87.
10. M.G. Spangler and J.L. Mickle, "Lateral Pressures on Retaining Walls due to Backfill Surface Loads." Highway Research Bulletin No. 141, Washington, D.C., 1956, pp. 1-15.

QUESTIONS AND PROBLEMS

20- 1. Determine the vertical compressive stress caused by a soil at a depth $z = H = 10.0$ ft. The unit weight of the soil is $\gamma_s = 110$ lf/ft^3. Plot the total stress distribution diagram.

20- 2. The same as in Problem 20-1. At a 4 ft depth below the ground surface there is a groundwater table ($\gamma_w = 62.4$ lb/ft^3). Plot the vertical stress distribution diagram due to the soil and groundwater.

20- 3. Given a layered system of soil as shown in Fig. Problem 20-3. Plot the total stress distribution diagram.

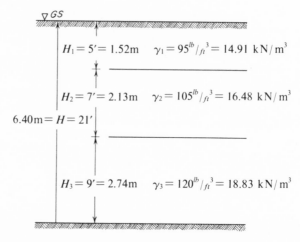

FIG. PROBLEM 20-3.

20- 4. Explain and illustrate the concept of "pressure bulb."

20- 5. Given a single, vertical, concentrated load of $P = 200$ tons $= 1.78$ MN at the ground surface. The area of the foundation is 100 sq. ft. $= 9.29\,m^2$. Calculate and plot isobars for 80%, 60%, 40%, 20%, 10%, 5%, 3%, 2%, and 1% of total contact pressure.

Note. For small, symmetrical bearing areas or footings, when their contact areas may be considered small, the problem may be solved based on the single, concentrated load P. However, when the contact area of the base of the footing is relatively large, the problem must be solved based on load from the footing uniformly distributed on the soil. In this problem, for illustrative purposes, assume that the area 100 sq ft or 9.29 m^2, is small.

20- 6. Given two concentrated loads, $P_1 = 100$ tons (890 kN) and $P_2 = 300$ tons (2.67 MN), spaced 12 ft $= 3.66$ m apart. Draw the 0.5 ton/ft^2-isobar (4.45 kN/m^2). Order of spacing of loads: $P_1 - P_2$.

Hint. First plot the 0.5 ton/ft^2-isobars for each load separately. Then plot 0.4, 0.3, 0.2, and 0.1 ton/ft^2-isobars, and by the principle of superposition combine these isobar values to give intersections to result in the combined 0.5 ton/ft^2-isobar for the given two loads P_1 and P_2.

20- 7. Plot the vertical stress distribution diagram in the example of Sect. 20-5 on a horizontal plane where $z = 1.0$ m.

20- 8. The same problem as 20-7, but for $z = 3.0$, $z = 5.0$, and $z = 10.0$ m.

20- 9. Plot for $P = 200$ tons $= 1.78$ MN the vertical stress distribution diagram for $r = 0$ m, $r = 0.61$, and $r = 2.00$ m.

20-10. The compressive strength of a silty clay at elevation -18.00 is 0.4 ton/ft^2. What is the stress at this elevation transmitted from a 200 ton concentrated load placed at an elevation of − 10.00 on the line of action of the concentrated load?

20-11. A foundation as sketched in Fig. Problem 20-11 transmits a vertical concentrated load of $P = 2.0$ MN.

    a) What is the vertical stress distribution on a horizontal plane at elevation − 12 m?

        Note. 1) Plot this figure to a geometric scale.

              2) Plot stresses to a stress scale.

              3) Elevations are given in feet.

              4) The unit weight of soil is $\gamma = 17.26$ kN/m³.

    b) What is the vertical stress, induced by P, on the crest of the underground utility facility?

    c) Plot the soil vertical stress distribution diagram along a vertical line A-B, drawn through the crest of the underground utility facility.

    d) What is the total vertical stress at point B?

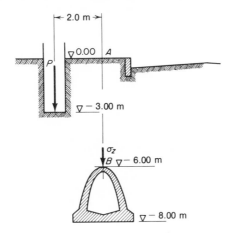

FIG. PROBLEM 20-11.

20-12. Given: two foundation footings the sizes of which are $6' \times 6'$ and $4' \times 4'$, and carrying vertical loads of 108,000 lb and 64,000 lb, respectively. They are founded 10 ft below the ground surface. These footings are spaced 21 ft center to center. Calculate the vertical stress in soil 10 ft below the ground surface midway between the edges of the two foundations. Plot the vertical stress distribution diagram on a horizontal plane at $z = 5$ ft below the base of the footing under both footings throughout.

20-13. Given an incompressible rock formation overlain by a homogeneous layer of soil 3 meters thick. The ground surface is loaded with a vertical concentrated load of $P = 400$ kN. Plot vertical stress distribution diagram on the surface of the rock.

20-14. Given a homogeneous soil of great thickness the ground surface of which is loaded with a vertical concentrated load of $P = 400$ kN. Plot horizontal pressure distribution diagram on a vertical plane spaced 3 m from P. Plot the diagram for a depth of 6 m.

20-15. Given the same soil and load conditions as in Problem 20-14. Three meters away from P, there is a vertical obstruction to free stress distribution in the form of a flexible earth retaining structure of 100 m running length. The retaining structure extended 6 m into soil measured from the ground surface. Construct horizontal pressure distribution diagram along the depth of the earth retaining structure.

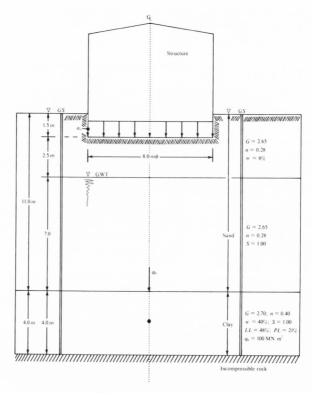

FIG. PROBLEM 20-17.

Plot also a shear stress diagram.
20-16. Redo Problem 20-15 assuming that the earth retaining structure is unyielding, rigid. The backface of the structure is smooth.
20-17. Given a soil profile as shown in Fig. Problem 20-17. The clay layer, 4 m thick, is a homogeneous, normally-consolidated clay. The clay is underlain by an impervious, incompressible rock formation. On top of the clay there is a sand deposit 11.0 m thick. In this sand, 1.5 m below the ground surface a cylindrical oil tank, 8.0 m in diameter is constructed. Assume that its flexible circular mat foundation exerts on the sand a uniform contact pressure of $\sigma_o = 20$ MN/m². The groundwater table is 2.5 m below the base of the foundation, or 4.0 m below the ground surface.

The soil data are as follows:

For sand: $G = 2.65$
                 $n = 0.28$
                 $w = 8\%$ moisture content above GWT
For clay: $G = 2.70$
                 $n = 0.40$
                 $q_u = 100$ MN/m² at top of clay
                 $w = 40\%$;
                 $LL = 48\%$
                 $PL = 21\%$
                 $e_o = w \cdot G \cdot S$ (saturated condition, $S = 1.0$).

Required: 1) plot total and effective geostatic pressure distribution diagram with depth along the vertical centerline of the system;

2) plot vertical pressure distribution diagrams in soil imparted to the soil by the contact pressure σ_o from the tank, along the centerline and along a vertical line at the edge of the foundation.

3) Considering that the settlement of the sand layer is insignificant, it can be omitted from settlement analysis of the problem on hand. Estimate the absolute amount of total consolidation settlement at the center of the base of foundation and

4) at the edge of foundation, and

5) report what is the amount of the final differential settlement of the clay, viz., tank, between the center and edge of its foundation.

Chapter 21

LATERAL EARTH PRESSURE

21-1. Lateral Earth Pressures. Lateral earth pressure is the force which is exerted by the soil mass and which acts upon an earth-retaining structure, for instance, a retaining wall.

The magnitude of the lateral earth pressure is known to vary considerably a) with the displacement of the retaining wall,[1] and b) with the nature of the soil.

If the wall does not translocate but is fixed rigidly, the pressure is termed *earth pressure at rest*. Its value can be ascertained only approximately.

If the wall yields or displaces away from the backfilled soil some of the retained backfill would break away from the rest of the soil mass and slide down, thereby exerting a pressure on the wall. This pressure is termed the *active earth pressure* (the soil mass is active). The value of the active earth pressure is less than the "at rest" value, and attains a limiting or minimum value E_a. The moving away of the wall from the soil mass removes the confinement of the soil wedge. The active earth pressure is thus a force which tends by rotating and/or translation to put the retaining structure out of equilibrium. The active earth pressure indicates the magnitude of the force which can develop upon the motion of a retaining structure away from the earth mass which the structure must resist.

If the inner or back face of the retaining wall is forced against the backfill, the pressure is termed the *passive earth pressure*, or the *passive earth resistance*. Passive earth resistance is encountered, for example, when the supporting toe of an arch bridge transmits its horizontal component of the inclined force through the foundation of the bridge to the soil. One also encounters passive earth resistance in sheet-piling problems.

The magnitude of the passive earth pressure is greater than the "at rest" value, attaining a limiting or maximum value E_p. The passive earth pressure indicates the maximum value of the force which can develop upon the motion of the retaining structure towards the earth mass—a force which the soil must resist before it ruptures. Generally, the surface upon which the broken-away or sheared-off soil slides down is termed the *rupture*, or *sliding surface*. The rupture surface of an ideal, granular material such as dry sand, for example, assumes almost the character of a plane (see Figs. 21-1 and 21-2).

The magnitudes of active and passive earth pressures, E_a and E_p, respectively, can be determined analytically by means of Coulomb's earth pressure theory,[3] as well as graphically.

FIG. 21-1. Approximate plane rupture   FIG. 21-2. Surface of rupture. Photo by
surface in sand. After Müller-Breslau,   author.
Ref. 2.

For an analytical treatment of lateral earth pressures the reader is referred to
the author's books *Soil Mechanics* and *Mechanics of Soils* (*Fundamentals for
Advanced Study*), References 4 and 5, respectively.

Some historical notes about the period of the classical earth pressure theory
may be found in Reference 6.

According to Coulomb's theory, total active earth pressure or thrust E_a per
unit length of run of earth retaining wall is calculated by means of the following
general equation:

$$E_a = (\frac{1}{2}) \cdot \gamma \cdot H^2 \cdot K_a$$

wherein

γ = unit weight of the backfill soil
H = height of wall on which the total earth pressure acts, and
K_a = active earth pressure coefficient, dimensionless.

At this point it should be thoroughly understood that for various kinds of
geometrical configurations of the soil-wall system the active earth pressure
coefficient has a different, its own value. The nine basic kinds of earth
pressure systems and the corresponding K_a-values are shown in Fig. 21-3.[7]

For a vertical backface of a wall and horizontal ground surface (System No. 5),
the K_a-value is

$$K_a = \frac{1-\sin\phi}{1+\sin\phi} = \tan^2[(\pi/4) - (\phi/2)], \qquad (21\text{-}1)$$

and the corresponding magnitude of total active earth pressure for System No. 5 is

$$E_a = (\frac{1}{2})\,(\gamma)\,(H^2)\cdot\tan^2(\pi/4-\phi/2) = (\frac{1}{2})\,(\gamma)\,(H^2)\,(K_a) \qquad (21\text{-}2)$$

Here ϕ = angle of internal friction of backfill soil.

The total earth resistance or passive earth pressure E_p for System No. 5 is

$$E_p = (\frac{1}{2})\cdot(\gamma)\,(H^2)\cdot\tan^2(\pi/4 + \phi/2) = (\frac{1}{2})\,(\gamma)\,(H^2)\,(K_p) \qquad (21\text{-}3)$$

The point of application of E_a and E_p is located at one-third of the height of the wall from the base. The forces E_a and E_p at their point of application act at an angle of wall friction ϕ_1 with the normal to the backface of the wall. If the vertical backface of the wall is smooth, $\phi_1 = 0$, and consequently E_a and E_p act perpendicularly to the wall.

For earth pressure systems other than System No. 5, use K-values with angles α, δ, ϕ, and ϕ_1 with their appropriate signs according to sign convention as shown in Fig. 21-3.

A. FRICTIONAL SOILS

21-2. Active Earth Pressure Function E_a. The total active earth pressure E_a for a ϕ-soil determined by statics from the equilibrium of the three following forces: the weight W of the soil rupture wedge W, sometimes called the sliding soil wedge, the soil reaction R on the rupture plane $\overline{AC}$, and the active earth pressure E_a (Fig. 21-4). In this figure,

> $\overline{AD}$ is the ϕ-line;
> $\overline{AC}$ is the rupture plane;
> T is the friction force in the rupture plane;
> ρ is the angle of rupture ($\rho = \phi + \omega$);
> δ is the angle of slope of the ground surface.

The magnitude of the earth pressure E_a is then determined from equilibrium condition of the free-body representing the soil wedge, $\triangle ABC$, the weight W of which is to be balanced by reaction R on the rupture plane and the reaction caused by E_a (Fig. 21-4b). The true magnitude of the active earth pressure E_a ($\diagup$) exerted by the soil wedge on the wall is then equal to the magnitude of the reaction E_a ($\diagup$) by the wall on the soil wedge.

The magnitude of E_a can be determined either by force projections on any two mutually perpendicular axes, or by means of the force-vector triangle (Fig. 21-4c). If the position or inclination of the plane rupture surface is known (refer to rupture angle ρ), that is, the angle ρ which would give the sought earth pressure E_a, and if the weight W of that soil wedge is also known, then, applying the sine law, the lateral reaction, viz., earth pressure E_a can be established from the vector triangle as

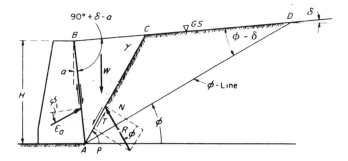

(a) Forces in the wall-soil wedge system

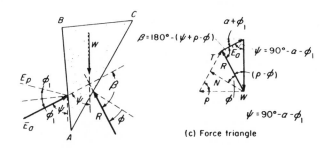

(c) Force triangle

(b) Free body diagram

FIG. 21-4 Active earth pressure.

$$E_a = [W \cdot \frac{\sin(\rho - \phi)}{\sin(\psi + \rho - \phi)}]_{max} \qquad (21\text{-}4)$$

The reaction

$$R = E_a \frac{\sin\psi}{\sin(\rho - \phi)} \qquad (21\text{-}5)$$

is seldom of interest.

The weight W is a function of the rupture angle ρ:

$$W = \frac{1}{2} \cdot \gamma \cdot H^2 \cdot \frac{\cos(\delta - \alpha)}{\cos^2\alpha} \cdot \frac{\cos(\rho - \alpha)}{\sin(\rho - \delta)} = f(\rho) \qquad (21\text{-}6)$$

wherein δ = angle of slope of ground surface GS.

The two unknown quantities ρ and E_a can now be calculated by solving the following system of two equations with two unknowns:

$$E_a = [W \cdot \frac{\sin(\rho - \phi)}{\sin(\psi + \rho - \phi)}]_{max} \qquad (21\text{-}7)$$

Coefficients of

No. and signs of angles relative to system 1	Earth Pressure System	Active Earth Pressure K_a	Passive Earth Pressure (resistance) K_p
1.	2.	3.	4.

①

A: $(+)\alpha$, $(+)\delta$, $(+)\phi$, $(-)\phi_1$
P: $(+)\alpha$, $(-)\delta$, $(-)\phi$, $(-)\phi_1$

$$K_a = \frac{\cos^2(\phi-\alpha)}{\cos^2\alpha\,\cos(\alpha+\phi_1)\left[1+\sqrt{\dfrac{\sin(\phi+\phi_1)\sin(\phi-\delta)}{\cos(\alpha+\phi_1)\cos(\alpha-\delta)}}\,\right]^2}$$

$$K_p = \frac{\cos^2(\phi+\alpha)}{\cos^2\alpha\,\cos(\alpha-\phi_1)\left[1-\sqrt{\dfrac{\sin(\phi+\phi_1)\sin(\phi+\delta)}{\cos(\alpha-\phi_1)\cos(\alpha-\delta)}}\,\right]^2}$$

②

A: $(+)\alpha$, $\delta=0$, $(+)\phi$, $(+)\phi_1$
P: $(+)\alpha$, $\delta=0$, $(-)\phi$, $(-)\phi_1$

$$K_a = \frac{\cos^2(\phi-\alpha)}{\cos^2\alpha\,\cos(\alpha+\phi_1)\left[1+\sqrt{\dfrac{\sin(\phi+\phi_1)\sin\phi}{\cos(\alpha+\phi_1)\cos\alpha}}\,\right]^2}$$

$$K_p = \frac{\cos^2(\phi+\alpha)}{\cos^2\alpha\,\cos(\alpha-\phi_1)\left[1-\sqrt{\dfrac{\sin(\phi+\phi_1)\sin\phi}{\cos(\alpha-\phi_1)\cos\alpha}}\,\right]^2}$$

③

A: $(+)\alpha$, $(-)\delta$, $(+)\phi$, $(+)\phi_1$
P: $(+)\alpha$, $(+)\delta$, $(-)\phi$, $(-)\phi_1$

$$K_a = \frac{\cos^2(\phi-\alpha)}{\cos^2\alpha\,\cos(\alpha+\phi_1)\left[1+\sqrt{\dfrac{\sin(\phi+\phi_1)\sin(\phi+\delta)}{\cos(\alpha+\phi_1)\cos(\alpha+\delta)}}\,\right]^2}$$

$$K_p = \frac{\cos^2(\phi+\alpha)}{\cos^2\alpha\,\cos(\alpha-\phi_1)\left[1-\sqrt{\dfrac{\sin(\phi+\phi_1)\sin(\phi-\delta)}{\cos(\alpha-\phi_1)\cos(\alpha+\delta)}}\,\right]^2}$$

④

A: $\alpha=0$, $(+)\delta$, $(+)\phi$, $(-)\phi_1$
P: $\alpha=0$, $(+)\delta$, $(-)\phi$, $(-)\phi_1$

$$K_a = \frac{\cos^2\phi}{\cos\phi_1\left[1+\sqrt{\dfrac{\sin(\phi+\phi_1)\sin(\phi-\delta)}{\cos\phi_1\cos\delta}}\,\right]^2}$$

$$K_p = \frac{\cos^2\phi}{\cos\phi_1\left[1-\sqrt{\dfrac{\sin(\phi+\phi_1)\sin(\phi+\delta)}{\cos\phi_1\cos\delta}}\,\right]^2}$$

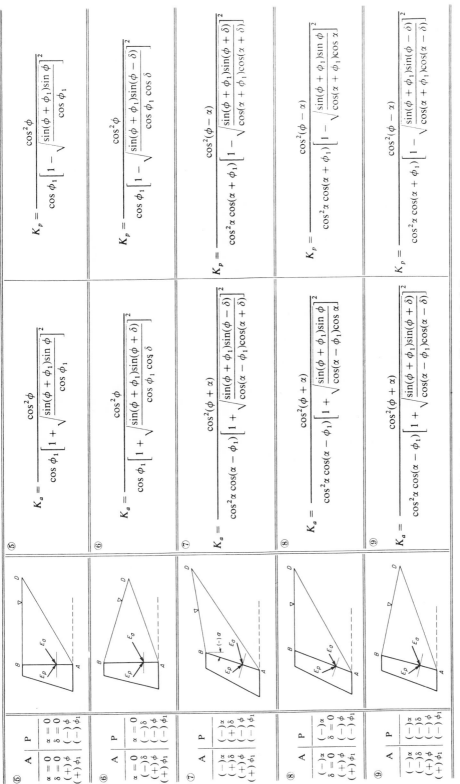

Fig. 21-3 Earth pressure coefficients. Ref. 7.

$$\frac{dE_a}{d\rho} = 0$$

Here $\quad \psi = 90° - \alpha - \phi_1$ $\qquad\qquad\qquad\qquad\qquad$ (21-8)

$$\therefore E_a = E_{max} = \frac{1}{2} \cdot \gamma \cdot H^2 \cdot K_a \qquad\qquad\qquad (21\text{-}9)$$

The solution for E_a renders the active earth pressure coefficients K_a for the nine basic earth pressure systems as shown in Fig. 21-3.

An example of calculating active earth pressure E_a by various units of measurement for earth pressure system No. 5 is shown in the compilation that follows:

Active earth pressure
$E_a = \frac{1}{2} \cdot \gamma \cdot H^2 \cdot K_a$
$K_a = 0.333$
$H = 9.84$ [ft] or $H = 9.84/3.28 = 3.0$ [m]

U.S. units	Technical metric units	SI units
$\gamma = 112.36$ lb/ft^3	$\gamma = 1800$ kg$_f$/m^3	$\gamma = (1.77)(10^4)$ N/m^3
$H = \quad 9.84$ ft	$H = 3.0$ m	$H = 3.0$ m
$E_a = (\frac{1}{2})(112.36)(9.84^2)(0.333)$	$E_a = (\frac{1}{2})(1800)(3.0^2)(0.333)$	$E_a = (\frac{1}{2})(1.77)(10^4)(3.0^2)(0.333)$
$= (1.81)(10^3)$ [ft/lb]	$= (2.7)(10^3)$ [kg$_f$/m]	$= (2.6523)(10^4)$ [N/m]
	$= 2.7$ [t/m]	$\approx (2.7)(10)$[kN/m]
Check	Check	Check
$(1.81)(10^3)(1.488162)(10^{-1})$	$(2.7)(6.71970)(10^2)$	$(2.6523)(10^4)(6.85393)(10^{-2})$
$= 2.7$ [t/m]	$= (1.81)(10^3)$ [lb/ft]	$= (1.817)(10^3)$ [lb/ft]
		or
		$(2.6523)(10^4)(1.01972)(10^{-1})$
		$= (2.7)(10^3)$ [kg$_f$/m]

Here the active earth pressure equation

$$E_a = \frac{1}{2} \cdot \gamma \cdot H^2 \cdot K_a = \frac{1}{2} \cdot (\gamma H K_a) \cdot H \qquad\qquad (21\text{-}10)$$

suggests that the soil lateral pressure distribution diagram on the backface of the wall is a triangular one its base pressure ordinate being $\gamma H K_a$. The physical area of the triangular lateral pressure distribution diagram, $(\frac{1}{2})(\gamma H K_a) \cdot H$ gives the total active earth pressure $E_a = \frac{1}{2} \cdot \gamma \cdot H^2 \cdot K_a$. Its position or point of application on the backface of the wall is determined by the position of the centroid of the triangle, i.e., at a point located at $H/3$ above the base of the wall (viz., triangle).

The corresponding soil lateral pressure distribution diagrams are shown in Fig. 21-5.

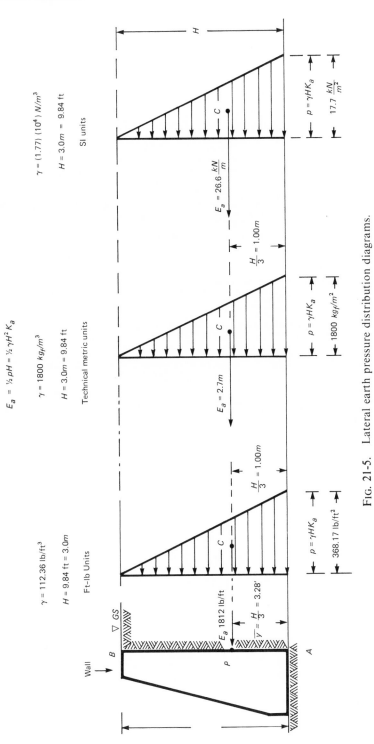

$p = \gamma H K_a$

$K_a = 0.333$

$E_a = \frac{1}{2} p H = \frac{1}{2} \gamma H^2 K_a$

$\gamma = 1800 \ kg_f/m^3$

$H = 3.0m = 9.84 \ ft$

Technical metric units

$\gamma = 112.36 \ lb/ft^3$

$H = 9.84 \ ft = 3.0m$

Ft-lb Units

$\gamma = (1.77)(10^4) \ N/m^3$

$H = 3.0m = 9.84 \ ft$

SI units

FIG. 21-5.   Lateral earth pressure distribution diagrams.

The pressures to use in constructing the soil lateral pressure distribution diagrams are all effective pressures. If in the given earth pressure system there is groundwater present, then the effect of hydrostatic pressure on the wall must be added separately if the total lateral pressure on the wall is required. It is because the K_a-values for soil are less than that for water ($K_{water} = 1.0$)

21-3. Passive Earth Pressure Function E_p. Everything that has been said about determining analytically the magnitude of active earth pressure and the position of the most dangerous rupture surface holds also for calculating the passive earth pressure E_p, except that the signs of the angles of friction ϕ and ϕ_1, have to be changed to the opposite (Fig. 21-6).

Upon sliding of the ruptured soil wedge *upward*, the frictional force T on the rupture plane $\overline{AC}$ acts in the opposite direction of the movement, i.e., down.

Relative to motion, when the soil wedge $\triangle ABC$ slides up, the relative motion of the wall is down, and the friction on the back face of the wall acts up. Hence

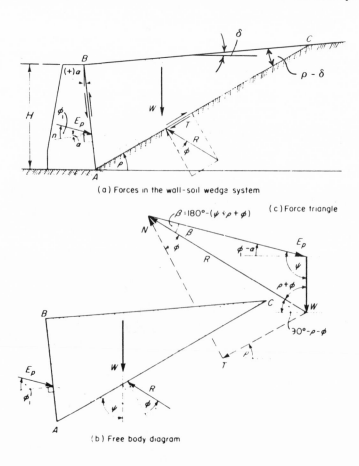

(a) Forces in the wall-soil wedge system

(b) Free body diagram

(c) Force triangle

FIG. 21-6. Passive earth pressure.

the force from the wall against the soil mass for overcoming the resistance of the latter is considerably greater than in the case of active earth pressure.

The system of the two equations for calculating the two unknowns, ρ and E_p, is

$$
\left.
\begin{aligned}
E_p &= \left[W \cdot \frac{\sin (\rho + \phi)}{\sin (\psi + \rho + \phi)} \right] \min \\
\frac{dE_p}{d\rho} &= 0
\end{aligned}
\right\} \qquad (21\text{-}11)
$$

Here $\psi = 90° - \alpha + \phi_1$ (21-12)

$\therefore E_p = E_{min} = \frac{1}{2} \cdot \gamma \cdot H^2 \cdot K_p.$ (21-13)

The K_p-equations resulting from the solution of the system of equations (21-11) for the nine basic earth pressure systems are shown in Fig. 21-3.

21-4. Rupture Angles. The general solution of $dE_a / d\rho = 0$ and $dE_p / d\rho = 0$ renders the angle of rupture ρ which may be written as consisting of two terms, namely:

for the active case:

$$\rho = \phi + \omega, \qquad (21\text{-}14)$$

where ϕ = angle of internal friction of noncohesive soil, and
     ω = auxiliary angle of rupture, measured in counterclockwise direction from the ϕ-line ($= \overline{AD}$);

for the passive case:

$$\rho = \Omega - \phi, \qquad (21\text{-}15)$$

where ϕ = angle of internal friction of noncohesive soil, and
     Ω = auxiliary angle of rupture, measured in counterclockwise direction from the ϕ-line.

The algebraic expressions for tangent values of the ω and Ω angles, $\tan\omega$ and $\tan \Omega$, for earth pressure systems 1 through 9 are tabulated in Figs. 21-7[7] and 21-8[7], respectively. Angles ω and Ω permit one to draw easily the rupture surface lines through the heel-point of the wall (point A).

Some of these omega-equations can be simplified and transformed, or course. However, to afford a visual comparison of the various factors entering into these equations, and to see their effect on the $\tan\omega$- and $\tan \Omega$- values, transformation has not been attempted.

With $\phi_1 = 0$ (smooth backface of wall), and $\phi = 30° = \pi/6$ the angle of rupture ρ for earth pressure system no. 5 is
for the active case:

$$\rho = \phi + \omega = \pi/4 + \phi/2 = \pi/3 = 60° \qquad (21\text{-}16)$$

for the passive case:

$$\rho = \Omega - \phi = \pi/4 - \phi/2 = \pi/6 = 30° \qquad (21\text{-}17)$$

Tangents of Rupture Angles, tan ω

No. and signs of angles relative to system 1	Active Earth Pressure System	Tangents of Rupture Angles, tan ω
1.	2.	3.
① $+\alpha$ $+\delta$ $(+\phi)$ $(+\phi_1)$		$$\tan \omega = \tan(\rho - \phi) = \frac{-\tan(\phi - \delta) + \sqrt{\tan(\phi - \delta)[\tan(\phi - \delta) + \cot(\phi - \alpha)][1 + \tan(\phi_1 + \alpha)\cot(\phi - \alpha)]}}{1 + \tan(\phi_1 + \alpha)[\tan(\phi - \delta) + \cot(\phi - \alpha)]}$$
② $+\alpha$ $\delta = 0$ $(+\phi)$ $(+\phi_1)$		$$\tan \omega = \tan(\rho - \phi) = \frac{-\tan \phi + \sqrt{\tan \phi[\tan \phi + \cot(\phi - \alpha)][1 + \tan(\phi_1 + \alpha)\cot(\phi - \alpha)]}}{1 + \tan(\phi_1 + \alpha)[\tan \phi + \cot(\phi - \alpha)]}$$
③ $+\alpha$ $-\delta$ $(+\phi)$ $(+\phi_1)$		$$\tan \omega = \tan(\rho - \phi) = \frac{-\tan(\phi + \delta) + \sqrt{\tan(\phi + \delta)[\tan(\phi + \delta) + \cot(\phi - \alpha)][1 + \tan(\phi_1 + \alpha)\cot(\phi - \alpha)]}}{1 + \tan(\phi_1 + \alpha)[\tan(\phi + \delta) + \cot(\phi - \alpha)]}$$
④ $\alpha = 0$ $+\delta$ $(+\phi)$ $(+\phi_1)$		$$\tan \omega = \tan(\rho - \phi) = \frac{-\tan(\phi - \delta) + \sqrt{\tan(\phi - \delta)[\tan(\phi - \delta) + \cot \phi][1 + \tan \phi_1 \cot \phi]}}{1 + \tan \phi_1[\tan(\phi - \delta) + \cot \phi]}$$

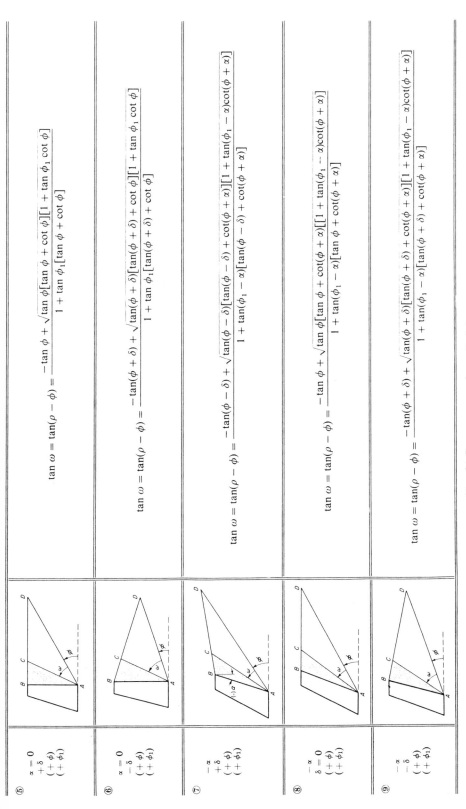

FIG. 21-7. tan ω equations. Ref. 7.

⑤

$\alpha = 0$
$+ \delta$
$(+ \phi)$
$(+ \phi_1)$

$$\tan \omega = \tan(\rho - \phi) = \frac{-\tan \phi + \sqrt{\tan \phi [\tan \phi + \cot \phi][1 + \tan \phi_1 \cot \phi]}}{1 + \tan \phi_1 [\tan \phi + \cot \phi]}$$

⑥

$\alpha = 0$
$- \delta$
$(+ \phi)$
$(+ \phi_1)$

$$\tan \omega = \tan(\rho - \phi) = \frac{-\tan(\phi + \delta) + \sqrt{\tan(\phi + \delta) [\tan(\phi + \delta) + \cot \phi][1 + \tan \phi_1 \cot \phi]}}{1 + \tan \phi_1 [\tan(\phi + \delta) + \cot \phi]}$$

⑦

$- \alpha$
$+ \delta$
$(+ \phi)$
$(+ \phi_1)$

$$\tan \omega = \tan(\rho - \phi) = \frac{-\tan(\phi - \delta) + \sqrt{\tan(\phi - \delta) [\tan(\phi - \delta) + \cot(\phi + \alpha)][1 + \tan(\phi_1 - \alpha)\cot(\phi + \alpha)]}}{1 + \tan(\phi_1 - \alpha) [\tan(\phi - \delta) + \cot(\phi + \alpha)]}$$

⑧

$\delta = 0$
$- \alpha$
$(+ \phi)$
$(+ \phi_1)$

$$\tan \omega = \tan(\rho - \phi) = \frac{-\tan \phi + \sqrt{\tan \phi [\tan \phi + \cot(\phi + \alpha)][1 + \tan(\phi_1 - \alpha)\cot(\phi + \alpha)]}}{1 + \tan(\phi_1 - \alpha) [\tan \phi + \cot(\phi + \alpha)]}$$

⑨

$- \alpha$
$- \delta$
$(+ \phi)$
$(+ \phi_1)$

$$\tan \omega = \tan(\rho - \phi) = \frac{-\tan(\phi + \delta) + \sqrt{\tan(\phi + \delta) [\tan(\phi + \delta) + \cot(\phi + \alpha)][1 + \tan(\phi_1 - \alpha)\cot(\phi + \alpha)]}}{1 + \tan(\phi_1 - \alpha) [\tan(\phi + \delta) + \cot(\phi + \alpha)]}$$

No. and signs of angles relative to system 1	Passive Earth Pressure System	Tangents of Rupture Angles, $\tan \Omega$
1.	2.	3.
① $\begin{aligned} &+\alpha \\ &+\delta \\ &(-\phi) \\ &(-\phi_1) \end{aligned}$		$\tan \Omega = \dfrac{\tan(\phi + \delta) + \sqrt{\tan(\phi + \delta)[\tan(\phi + \delta) + \cot(\phi + \alpha)][1 + \tan(\phi_1 - \alpha)\cot(\phi + \alpha)]}}{1 + \tan(\phi_1 - \alpha)[\tan(\phi + \delta) + \cot(\phi + \alpha)]}$
② $\begin{aligned} &+\alpha \\ &+\delta = 0 \\ &(-\phi) \\ &(-\phi_1) \end{aligned}$		$\tan \Omega = \dfrac{\tan \phi + \sqrt{\tan \phi [\tan \phi + \cot(\phi + \alpha)][1 + \tan(\phi_1 - \alpha)\cot(\phi + \alpha)]}}{1 + \tan(\phi_1 - \alpha)[\tan \phi + \cot(\phi + \alpha)]}$
③ $\begin{aligned} &+\alpha \\ &-\delta \\ &(-\phi) \\ &(-\phi_1) \end{aligned}$		$\tan \Omega = \dfrac{\tan(\phi - \delta) + \sqrt{\tan(\phi - \delta)[\tan(\phi - \delta) + \cot(\phi + \alpha)][1 + \tan(\phi_1 - \alpha)\cot(\phi + \alpha)]}}{1 + \tan(\phi_1 - \alpha)[\tan(\phi - \delta) + \cot(\phi + \alpha)]}$
④ $\begin{aligned} &+\alpha = 0 \\ &+\delta \\ &(-\phi) \\ &(-\phi_1) \end{aligned}$		$\tan \Omega = \dfrac{\tan(\phi + \delta) + \sqrt{\tan(\phi + \delta)[\tan(\phi + \delta) + \cot \phi][1 + \tan \phi_1 \cot \phi]}}{1 + \tan \phi_1[\tan(\phi + \delta) + \cot \phi]}$

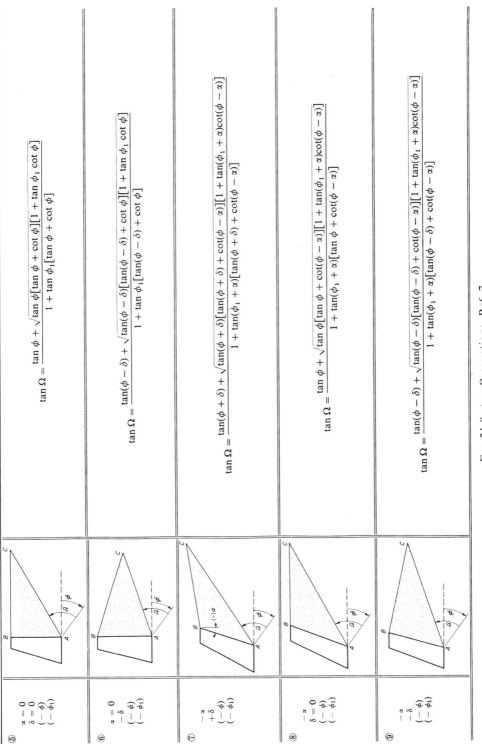

Fig. 21-8. tan Ω equations. Ref. 7.

B. FRICTIONAL-COHESIVE SOILS

21-5. Active Earth Pressure. Consideration of stress condition in soil shows that cohesion of a (ϕ-c)-soil does not affect the position of the rupture surface. Hence the earth pressure of a cohesive (ϕ-c)-soil can be approximately determined by the method used for noncohesive soil (Fig. 21-9). For earth pressure system No. 5, the total active earth pressure E_a of a (ϕ-c)-soil per one unit length of run of wall is

$$E_a = E_A - \Delta E_a = \tfrac{1}{2}\gamma H^2 K_a - 2cH\sqrt{K_a} = \tfrac{1}{2} \cdot \gamma H^2 K_a \left(1 - \frac{4c}{\gamma H \sqrt{K_a}}\right) \qquad (21\text{-}18)$$

where $c =$ over the rupture surface uniformly distributed constant cohesion, in N/m^2; the K_a-values are same as before.

The magnitude of cohesion, viz., shear strength of the soil, must be determined by *test on that soil*. The test should be performed under conditions which would simulate as closely as possible those most likely to occur in nature.

The position of point of application of E_a caused by a cohesive backfill material is determined by the position of the centroid of the resultant lateral earth pressure distribution diagram (Fig. 21-10).

Again, notice for future studies that K_a (K_p) pertains to the geometry of the earth pressure system and frictional coefficients of soil and that of between the material of the earth retaining structure and the soil only. It does not involve any effects of surcharge on the ground surface. One sees that the trigonometric earth pressure coefficients K_a and K_p depend upon the combination of angles, α, δ, ϕ and ϕ_1 in the earth pressure system. Therefore, for each system there is a different - their own - K_a-coefficient, viz., K_p-coefficient (Fig. 21-3).

Example. Determine the magnitude of the total active earth pressure from a frictional-cohesive soil [a (ϕ-c)-soil] against a vertical wall ($\alpha=0$) the height of which is $H = 3.0\,m$. The ground surface is horizontal ($\delta = 0$); $\gamma = 17.7\,kN/m^3$; $\phi = 30°$; $\phi_1 = 0$; $c = 5.0$ kN/m^2.

Solution.

$$K_a = \tan^2(45° - \phi/2) = \tan^2(45° - 30°/2) =$$
$$= \tan^2 30° = (0.578)^2 = \underline{0.333}$$
$$\sqrt{K_a} = \sqrt{0.333} = \underline{0.578}$$
$$E_a = E_A - \Delta E_a = \tfrac{1}{2} \cdot \gamma \cdot H^2 \cdot K_a - 2 \cdot c \cdot H \cdot \sqrt{K_a}$$
$$= (\tfrac{1}{2})\,(17.7)\,(3.0^2)\,(0.333) - (2)\,(5)\,(3)\,(0.578)$$
$$= 26.52 - 17.34 = \underline{9.18\ [kN/m]}.$$

21-6. Passive Earth Pressure. By reasoning similar to that presented for the active earth pressure, the magnitude of total passive earth pressure for a (ϕ-c)-soil for earth pressure system No. 5 is

$$E_p = E_p + \Delta E_p = \tfrac{1}{2} \cdot \gamma \cdot H^2 \cdot K_p + 2cH\sqrt{K_p} \qquad (21\text{-}19)$$

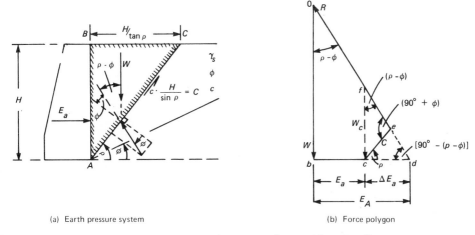

(a) Earth pressure system   (b) Force polygon

FIG. 21-9. Active earth pressure from a $(\phi - c)$-soil.

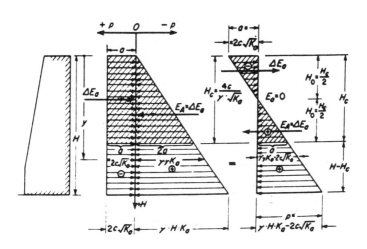

FIG. 21-10. Lateral stress distribution diagram for a $(\phi - c)$-soil; active pressure; no surcharge.

(see Fig. 21-11). Its lateral pressure distribution diagram is shown in Fig. 21-12. The K_p-values are same as before.

Example. Determine the magnitude of passive earth pressure E_p, when $H = 3.0$ m; $\gamma = 17.7$ kN/m^3; $\phi = 30°$; $\phi_1 = 0$; $\alpha = 0$; $\delta = 0$; $c = 5$ kN/m^2.

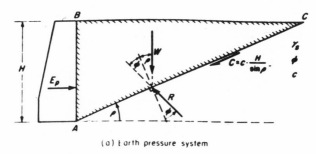

(a) Earth pressure system

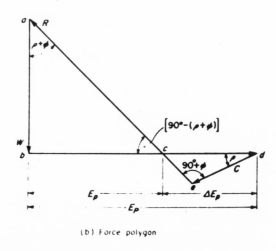

(b) Force polygon

FIG. 21-11. Passive earth pressure from a $(\phi - c)$-soil.

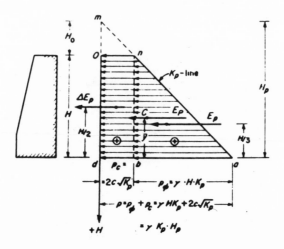

FIG. 21-12. Lateral stress distribution diagram for a $(\phi - c)$-soil; passive pressure; no surcharge.

Solution.

$$K_p = \tan^2(45° + \phi/2) = \tan^2 60° = (\sqrt{3})^2 = \underline{3.00}$$

$$\sqrt{K_p} = \sqrt{3} = \underline{1.73}$$

$$E_p = E_p + \Delta E_p = (\tfrac{1}{2})\ (\gamma)\ (H^2)\ (K_p) + (2)\ (c)\ (H)\ (\sqrt{K_p})$$

$$= (\tfrac{1}{2})\ (17.7)\ (3.0^2)\ (3.00) + (2)\ (5)\ (3.0)\ (1.73)$$

$$= 238.95 + 51.90 = \underline{290.85\ [kN/m]}$$

21-7. Special Cases.

a) When $\phi = 0$, then $\rho_{act} = \rho_{pass} = 45°$,

and

$$E_a = \tfrac{1}{2} \cdot \gamma \cdot H^2 - 2cH \tag{21-15}$$

$$E_p = \tfrac{1}{2} \cdot \gamma \cdot H^2 + 2cH \tag{21-16}$$

i.e., the earth pressures are equal to geostatic pressure, decreased, viz., increased by the double cohesion over the height H of the surface of the backface of the wall.

b) When $c = 0$, then Equations transform into

$$E_a = (\tfrac{1}{2})\ (\gamma)\ (H^2)\ (K_a) \tag{21-2}$$

and

$$E_p = (\tfrac{1}{2})\ (\gamma)\ (H^2)\ (K_p). \tag{21-3}$$

21-8. Active and Passive Earth Pressure Coefficient Tables. To facilitate earth pressure calculations, earth pressure coefficient tables such as given by Reference 7, for example, can be used. These tables are prepared by the author for plane rupture surfaces, and quickly give the numerical values of the K_a and K_p coefficients for various α, δ, ϕ, and ϕ_1 at even five-degree intervals. The batter angles of the wall α vary in these tables between $+25°$ and $-25°$. The angles of inclination δ of the ground surface vary between $+30°$ and $-30°$. The angle of friction ϕ of the soil or any other backfill material is varied in five-degree intervals from $0°$ to $55°$. The angles of friction ϕ_1 between the backfill material and the surface material of the back face of the earth-retaining structure are allowed to vary in five-degree intervals between $-55°$ and $+55°$. For example, if $\alpha = 5°$, $\delta = 10°$, $\phi = 30°$, and $\phi_1 = 20°$, then the earth pressure coefficient for the active earth pressure by Table A-29 is $K_a = 0.386$. Intermediate K-values for angles not given in these tables can be determined with satisfactory precision by linear interpolation from the given K-values in the tables between which the desired K-value is located.

These tables likewise indicate, for each entry value of K_a and K_p, the corresponding tangents of angles of rupture, ω and Ω.[7] The angle designated by small omega, ω, pertains to the most dangerous soil rupture angle for the active earth pressure, whereas the angle designated by capital omega, Ω, pertains to the most dangerous rupture angle for passive earth pressure. These angles are to be measured in the counterclockwise direction from the corresponding ϕ-lines in earth pressure systems where the wall is to the left of the viewer and the backfill material behind the wall to the right.

21-9. Surcharge. Surcharge increases soil lateral pressure on earth retaining structures. If the horizontal ground surface is surcharged with a uniformly distributed load the intensity of which is p_o, the earth pressures are expressed as

$$E_a = (½) \; (\gamma + \frac{2p_o}{H}) \; (H^2) \; (K_a) - 2 \cdot c \cdot H \cdot \sqrt{K_a} \qquad (21\text{-}17)$$

$$E_p = (½) \; (\gamma + \frac{2p_o}{H}) \; (H^2) \; (K_p) + 2 \cdot c \cdot H \cdot \sqrt{K_p} \qquad (21\text{-}18)$$

When $c = 0$, the soil lateral pressure distribution diagram for active earth pressure looks like shown in Fig. 21-13. The soil lateral pressure distribution for passive earth pressure appear like that shown in Fig. 21-14. The coordinate $\bar{y}$ of the centroid of the trapezoidal soil lateral pressure distribution diagram is calculated as

$$\bar{y} = \frac{E_{ap_o} \dfrac{H}{2} + E_{aW} \dfrac{H}{3}}{E_{ap_o} + E_{aW}} \qquad (21\text{-}19)$$

where $E_{ap_o} + E_{aW} = E_a$ is the total active earth pressure on the wall,

$E_{ap_o} = p_1 \cdot H = p_o \cdot K_a \cdot H =$ active earth pressure on wall from surcharge, and

$E_{aW} = ½ \cdot \gamma \cdot H^2 \cdot K_a =$ active earth pressure from backfill soil with no surcharge.

The point of application of E_a on the wall is to be transferred from the centroid of the lateral pressure distribution diagram to the wall. It lies between $H/2$ and $H/3$.

The surcharge raises the point of application of E_a above the heel of the wall and above the one third point of H thus increasing the overturning moment arm. When $\phi_1 = 0$, E_a acts horizontally on a vertical backface of wall.

If the ground surface is inclined and surcharged with a uniformly distributed load p, like earth pressure system No. 4 in Fig. 21-15, then the inclined surcharge p is to be converted into an equivalent surcharge p_o as if it were distributed over a horizontal ground surface:

$$(p) \; (ds) = p_o(dx) \qquad (21\text{-}20)$$

$$\therefore \; p_o = p \cdot \frac{ds}{dx} = p \cdot \frac{1}{dx/ds} = \frac{p}{\cos\delta} \qquad (21\text{-}21)$$

where all quantities are shown in Figure 21-15. From here on, the trapezoidal soil lateral distribution diagram can now be constructed the usual way as before.

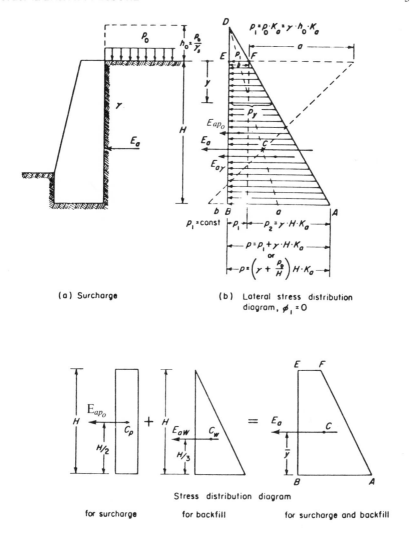

FIG. 21-13. Surcharge on ground surface with lateral stress distribution diagram.

As discussed in Chapter 20, Boussinesq's lateral stress components in soil brought about by a surface loading (surcharge on ground surface) propagate in elastic medium unobstructed. However, if stress propagation is obstructed, for example, by a rigid, unyielding retaining wall with a smooth backface, lateral, normal stresses on the wall are double the values of Boussinesq's stress components in an elastic solid derived from theory of elasticity.

21-10. Graphical Methods for Determining Earth Pressures. The magnitudes of active and passive earth pressures can also be conveniently determined graphically by Poncelet[8] and Culmann[9] methods. The graphical methods are

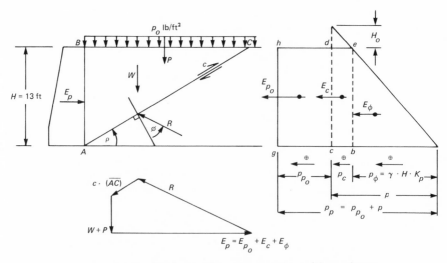

FIG. 21-14. Passive earth pressure system with surcharge.

adequate for most practical purposes. The Poncelet graphical method is one of the most popular.

A graphical method for the direct location of Coulomb's most dangerous rupture surface and for the determination of the lateral earth pressure was given by Poncelet[8] in 1840. The method is derived for a wall with an unbroken, straight, back face and for a plane ground surface, the latter of which may be inclined, Fig. 21-16. The ground surface may or may not contain a uniformly distributed surcharge.

The method of Poncelet construction is suitable for determining active as well as passive earth pressures.

21-11. Active Earth Pressure. Poncelet graphical method for noncohesive soils is based on constructing the triangle

$$\triangle ABC(= \tfrac{1}{2}fn = \triangle ACS = W/\gamma) \text{ to find quantities } n, f, \text{ and } e.$$

The graphical construction starts with drawing the line of natural slope (ϕ-line) AD at an angle of ϕ with the horizontal. Then the position line is drawn through heel A of the wall. The position line makes an angle of $(\phi + \phi_1)$ with the back face of the wall, AB. Through point B, another line, BK, is drawn parallel to the position line to give point K on the line of natural slope AD. Points, B, C, and D must lie on one continuous, unbroken line. The line, BK, forms an angle, $\angle AKB = \psi$, with line AD. By geometry, from $\triangle ABK$, the value of this angle is:

$$\angle AKB = 180° - (\phi + \phi_1) - (90° + \alpha - \phi) = 90° - \alpha - \phi_1 = \psi, \quad (21\text{-}22)$$

which is the angle between the position line and the line of natural slope. Hence, $BK \| CS$. Assuming that the position of point S is known, draw also $SV \| AC$.

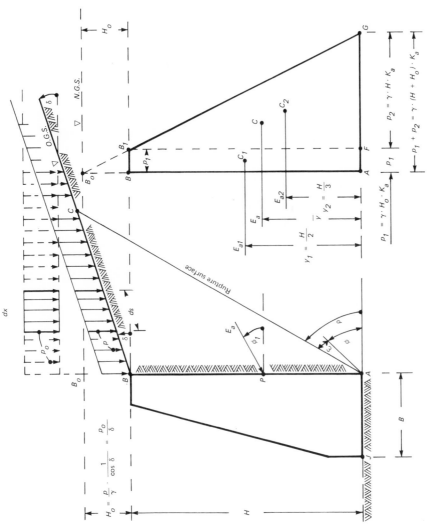

FIG. 21-15. Earth pressure system with surcharge on inclined ground surface.

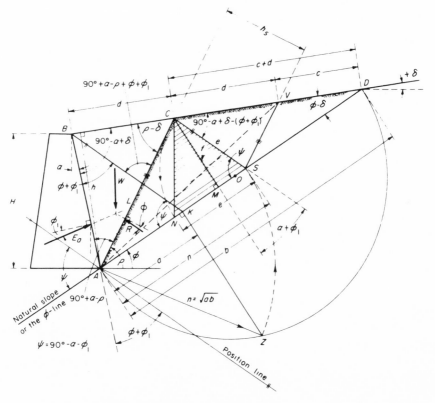

FIG. 21-16. Poncelet construction for active earth pressure. Noncohesive soil.

The $\triangle ACD \sim \triangle SVD$ and $\triangle BDK \sim \triangle CDS$. Besides, $\triangle ACS = \triangle ACV$ because of their common base $AC = L$, and equal height h_s. But, because $\triangle ACS = \triangle ABC$, then also $\triangle ACV = \triangle ABC$.

These latter and equal triangles have the same height h_d, therefore their bases, BC and CV, must be of equal length, i.e.,

$$BC = CV = d. \tag{21-23}$$

Let $AK = a$, and let $AD = b$. Based on the similarity of triangles, $\triangle ACD$ and $\triangle SVD$, Fig. 21-16, the following side ratios can be written:

$$\frac{b}{n} = \frac{c+d}{d}. \tag{21-24}$$

In similar triangles $\triangle KBD$ and $\triangle SCD$, Fig. 21-16, the side ratios are:

$$\frac{b-n}{n-a} = \frac{c+d}{d}. \tag{21-25}$$

The equating of Eqs. (21-24) and (21-25) gives

$$\frac{b}{n} = \frac{b-n}{n-a}, \tag{21-26}$$

yielding

$$n^2 = ab \quad \text{or} \quad n = \sqrt{ab}. \tag{21-27}$$

Hence, if n is known, the position of point S and thus the position of the most dangerous rupture surface AC can be determined and the weight of the sliding soil wedge W and the active earth pressure E_a can be calculated. Thus, Eq. (21-27) is Poncelet's relationship which exists when the lateral earth pressure E_a is maximum. One would draw now through point S a line CS, parallel to the position line to give point C, Fig. 21-16; CS determines the magnitude of e. Then a perpendicular is dropped from point C to AD to give point M on AD. The magnitude of $CM = f$, which is the height of the triangle NCS, is thus determined. With e, f, and n known, the weight W of the rupture wedge of soil is

$$W = \tfrac{1}{2}\gamma fn, \tag{21-28}$$

and the active earth pressure E_a is

$$E_a = \tfrac{1}{2}\gamma fe. \tag{21-29}$$

Note that the quantity $n = \sqrt{ab}$ represents the geometrical mean between the two quantities a and b, which can be constructed graphically. In the discipline of earth pressure theory, the geometric mean, $n = \sqrt{ab}$, is termed the *Poncelet rule*.
   Proof. From geometry, Fig. 21-16,

$$n/a = b/n \tag{21-30}$$

or

$$\underline{n = \sqrt{ab}.} \tag{21-31}$$

21-12. Steps for Graphical Method. To find n and the active earth pressure for a noncohesive soil, proceed by steps as follows (Fig. 21-16):
   1) Draw AB to represent the back face of the wall.
   2) Draw BD to represent the ground surface.
   3) Draw line of natural slope AD at an angle ϕ with the horizontal.
   4) At point B draw the position line BK at an angle of $(\phi+\phi_1)$ with line AB, the back face of the wall. This line cuts line AD at K, and gives $AK = a$.
   5) On $AD = b$ as a diameter, describe a semicircle AZD.
   6) From point K erect a perpendicular KZ to AD, cutting the semicircle at point Z.
   7) With the chord $AZ = n$ as a radius, with its center point at A, draw the arc $\overset{\frown}{ZS}$, cutting line AD at point S. Then $AS = AZ = n$. Here n is the geometric mean of a and b.
   8) Draw SC parallel to line BK, cutting the ground surface line at point C. Then $CS = e$.

9) Join A and C. This line represents Coulomb's most dangerous rupture plane, and it defines the size of the sliding soil wedge. This wedge, ABC, sliding over the rupture plane AC, would give the maximum value of the active earth pressure E_a.

10) From point C erect a perpendicular to AD to give point M. Then $CM = f$. The triangular area $\triangle ACS = \frac{1}{2} fn$, which is the area of the weight of the sliding soil wedge.

11) From point S as a center, and with a radius of $SC = e$, draw the arc $\overparen{CN}$ cutting AD at point N. Thus $NS = e$. Join points C and N to obtain the triangular area $\triangle NCS = \frac{1}{2} fe$.

12) The triangular areas $\frac{1}{2} fn$ and $\frac{1}{2} fe$, when multiplied by the unit weight of soil γ, give the weight of the sliding wedge and active earth pressure, respectively:

$$W = \tfrac{1}{2}\gamma fn, \tag{21-32}$$

$$E_a = \tfrac{1}{2}\gamma fe. \tag{21-33}$$

If the inclined ground surface is surcharged with a uniformly distributed load the intensity of which is p, then

$$W = \tfrac{1}{2}\gamma_1 fn = \tfrac{1}{2}\left(\gamma + \frac{2p\cos\delta}{h}\right)fn, \tag{21-34}$$

and

$$E_a = \tfrac{1}{2}\gamma_1 fe = \tfrac{1}{2}\left(\gamma + \frac{2p\cos\delta}{h}\right)fe, \tag{21-35}$$

where h is the perpendicular distance from the heel point A to the ground surface BC.

21-13. Passive Earth Pressure (Earth Resistance). The determination of Coulomb's earth pressure graphically from a noncohesive soil by Poncelet's graphical method is similar to that in the case of active earth pressure, except that the signs of the angles of friction, ϕ and ϕ_1, have to be changed to the opposite. Graphically this is accomplished by constructing the position line through points A or B at an angle of $(-)(\phi + \phi_1)$ with the line AB, of the back face of the wall. In other words, the angle $(-)(\phi + \phi_1)$ is constructed on the opposite side of the wall-line AB, as compared with the active case; see Fig. 21-17. Likewise, the ϕ-line is to be drawn through point A at the angle $(-)\phi$.

21-14. Steps for Construction for Passive Earth Pressure. The steps to be followed in Poncelet's construction for passive earth pressure are shown in Fig. 21-17. These are:

1) Draw the wall, the back face of which is AB.

2) Draw the ground surface. Extend the ground surface line through point B to the left of wall.

3) Draw the $[(-)\phi]$-line, AD, through A at an angle of $(-)\phi$ with the horizontal.

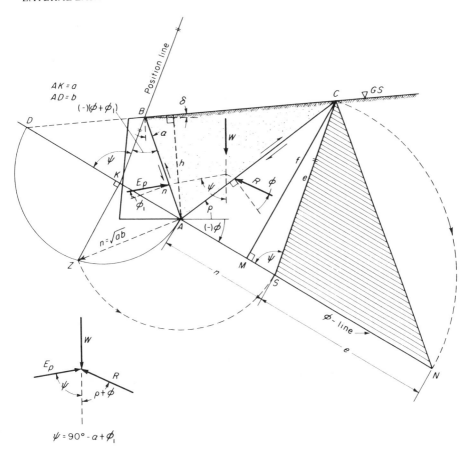

FIG. 21-17. Poncelet construction for passive earth pressure. Noncohesive soil.

4) Intersect the ground surface AD with the $[(-)\phi]$-line, BD, to give point D.

5) Through point B, draw the position line BK at an angle of $(-)(\phi + \phi_1)$ with the line AB. BK cuts AD at point K. Then $AK = a$.

6) On $AD = b$ as a diameter, describe a semicircle AZD.

7) Draw a perpendicular KZ to AD to give point Z on the semicircle.

8) With $AZ = n = \sqrt{ab}$ as a radius whose center is at point A, draw the arc $\overset{\frown}{ZS}$, cutting line AD in point S. Then $AS = AZ = n = \sqrt{ab}$.

9) Draw SC parallel to BK: SC cuts the ground surface line DBC at point C. $CS = e$.

10) Join A and C. Line AC is Coulomb's most dangerous rupture surface, and it defines the size of the sliding soil wedge. This wedge, sliding over the rupture surface AC, would give the values of the earth resistance (passive earth pressure) E_p.

11) From point C, establish a perpendicular, $CM = f$, to line AD to give point M on line AD. Then, the triangular area, $\triangle ACS = \frac{1}{2}fn$, is the area of the weight of the sliding soil wedge ABC. The weight of the sliding wedge is

$$W = \tfrac{1}{2}\gamma fn. \tag{21-36}$$

12) From point S as a center, and with a radius of $SC = e$, draw arc $\overset{\frown}{CN}$, cutting AD at point N: $NS = e$, and by joining C and N, the triangular area $\triangle SCN = \frac{1}{2}fe$, is found. The magnitude of the passive earth pressure is

$$E_p = \tfrac{1}{2}\gamma fe, \tag{21-37}$$

or

$$E_p = \tfrac{1}{2}\gamma e^2 \sin \psi. \tag{21-38}$$

If the ground surface is surcharged, then instead of γ, γ_1 must be used:

$$\gamma_1 = \gamma + \frac{2p \cos \delta}{h}, \tag{21-39}$$

where h is the perpendicular distance from the heel point A to the ground surface BC or its extension BD.

Note that the magnitude of the passive pressure is greater than that in the active case.

The point of application of E_p is determined by the position of the centroid of the soil lateral stress distribution diagram.

21-15. General Earth Pressure Coefficient Equations. Poncelet's graphical constructions permit the establishment of general equations for active and passive earth pressure coefficients K_a and K_p, respectively, for various inclinations α of the back face of the wall, for various slopes δ of the ground surface, and for various values of angle of internal friction ϕ of noncohesive soil, and wall friction ϕ_1. The effect of surcharge must be taken care of by modifying the unit weight of soil from γ to γ_1.

The K_a-Coefficient. Analytically, the active earth pressure is expressed as

$$E_a = \tfrac{1}{2}\gamma e^2 \sin \psi =$$

$$= \tfrac{1}{2}\gamma H^2 \frac{\cos^2(\phi - \alpha)\cos(\alpha + \phi_1)}{\cos^2 \alpha \cos^2(\alpha + \phi_1)\left[1 + \sqrt{\dfrac{\sin(\phi + \phi_1)\sin(\phi - \delta)}{\cos(\alpha + \phi_1)\cos(\delta - \alpha)}}\right]^2}, \tag{21-40}$$

or

$$E_a = \tfrac{1}{2}\gamma H^2 K_a, \tag{21-41}$$

where

$$K_a = \frac{\cos^2(\phi - \alpha)}{\cos^2 \alpha \cos(\alpha + \phi_1)\left[1 + \sqrt{\dfrac{\sin(\phi + \phi_1)\sin(\phi - \delta)}{\cos(\alpha + \phi_1)\cos(\delta - \alpha)}}\right]^2} \qquad (21\text{-}42)$$

is the general trigonometric active earth pressure coefficient for system 1. For other systems, use angles with their appropriate signs according to sign convention as shown in Fig. 21-3.

Note for future studies that K_a pertains to the geometry of the earth pressure system and frictional coefficients of soil and between masonry and soil only. It does not involve any effects of surcharge on the ground surface.

Note that when in system 1 $\delta > \phi$, K_a is unreal.

One sees that the trigonometric pressure coefficient depends upon the combination of angles α, δ, ϕ, and ϕ_1 in the system. Therefore, for each system there is a different K_a-coefficient.

The K_p-Coefficient. By procedure analogous to that followed in deriving the K_a-coefficient, the general trigonometric earth pressure coefficient K_p, for system 1 in Fig. 21-3 is

$$K_p = \frac{\cos^2(\phi + \alpha)}{\cos^2 \alpha \cos(\alpha - \phi_1)\left[1 - \sqrt{\dfrac{\sin(\phi + \phi_1)\sin(\phi + \delta)}{\cos(\alpha - \phi_1)\cos(\delta - \alpha)}}\right]^2}. \qquad (21\text{-}43)$$

The general passive earth pressure equation is then

$$E_p = \tfrac{1}{2}\gamma H^2 K_p. \qquad (21\text{-}44)$$

Specialization of the K_a and K_p equations can be made for any combination of given set of angles governing the configuration of the given retaining wall-earth pressure system as tabulated in Fig. 21-3.

Rupture Angles ω and Ω. The rupture angle for the active case is designated by ω (Fig. 21-7). The rupture angle for the passive case is designated by Ω (Fig. 21-8). Angles ω and Ω are to be measured counterclockwise from the ϕ-line. Angles ω and Ω permit one to draw easily the rupture lines through the heel of the wall.

The algebraic expressions for tan ω and tan Ω are tabulated for various systems in Figs. 21-7 and 21-8, respectively. Some of these equations can be simplified and transformed. However, to afford a visual comparison of the various factors entering into these equations, and to see their effect on the tan ω- and tan Ω-values, transformation has not been attempted.

Example. Calculate the magnitude of the active earth pressure for the following conditions:

$$H = 24 \text{ ft}; \qquad \gamma = 100 \text{ lb/ft}^3; \qquad p = 0;$$

$$\alpha = -10°; \qquad \delta = 8°; \qquad \phi = 30°; \qquad \phi_1 = 20°.$$

Solution. By Eq. (21-42),

$$K_a = \cfrac{\cos^2[30° - (-10°)]}{\cos^2(-10°)\cos(-10° + 20°)\left[1 + \sqrt{\cfrac{\sin(30° + 20°)\sin(30° - 8°)}{\cos(-10° + 20°)\cos[8° - (-10°)]}}\right]^2} =$$

$$= \cfrac{\cos^2 40°}{\cos^2 10° \cos 10°\left[1 + \sqrt{\cfrac{\sin 50° \sin 22°}{\cos 10° \cos 18°}}\right]^2} = 0.255.$$

The magnitude of the active earth pressure is calculated as

$$E_a = \tfrac{1}{2}\gamma H^2 K_a = \tfrac{1}{2}(100)(24^2)(0.255) = 7344 \text{ (lb)}.$$

The horizontal stress ordinate for the triangular stress distribution diagram at the base of the wall is

$$p_a = \gamma H K_a = (100)(24)(0.255) = 612.0 \text{ (lb/ft}^2).$$

Some selected earth pressure coefficients and tangent values of supplementary rupture angles ω and Ω for earth pressure system No. 5 are compiled for various ϕ angles in Table 21-1.

In Table 21-2, angles of wall friction ϕ_1 are summarized.

TABLE 21-1

K_a, tanω, and K_p, tan Ω, VALUES
FOR EARTH PRESSURE SYSTEM NO. 5
$(\alpha = 0°; \quad \delta = 0°; \quad \phi_1 = 0°)^1$

ϕ deg	Active earth pressure		Passive earth pressure	
	K_a	tanω	K_p	tanΩ
1	2	3	4	5
0	1.000	1.000	1.000	1.000
5	0.840	0.918	1.191	1.091
10	0.704	0.839	1.420	1.192
15	0.589	0.767	1.698	1.303
20	0.490	0.700	2.040	1.428
25	0.406	0.637	2.464	1.570
30	0.333	0.577	3.000	1.732
35	0.271	0.521	3.690	1.921
40	0.217	0.466	4.599	2.145
45	0.172	0.414	5.828	2.414
50	0.132	0.364	7.549	2.747

21-16. Culmann's Method

a) Active Earth Pressure. Culmann's method permits one to determine

TABLE 21-2
ANGLES OF WALL FRICTION ϕ_1

	Rough backface surface		Smooth backface surface (bituminous coating or plastic sealing course)
Backfill material	Normal Case	For surcharge loads when $p_o \leqq 10t/m$, or upon intensive vibration of backfill	
1	2	3	4
Noncohesive soils			
dense	$\phi_1 \leqq (3/4)(\phi)$	$\phi_1 \leqq (1/2)(\phi)$	$\phi_1 = 0$
medium dense	$\phi_1 \leqq (2/3)(\phi)$	$\phi_1 \leqq (1/2)(\phi)$	$\phi_1 = 0$
loose	$\phi_1 \leqq (2/3)(\phi)$	$\phi_1 \leqq (1/2)(\phi)$	$\phi_1 = 0$
Cohesive soils			
soft	$\phi_1 = 0$	$\phi = 0$	$\phi_1 = 0$
stiff to hard	$\phi_1 \leqq (1/3)(\phi)$	$\phi = 0$	$\phi_1 = 0$

graphically the magnitude of the earth pressure and to locate Coulomb's most dangerous rupture surface.[8] By rotating the shown force triangle in a clockwise direction through an angle of $90° - \phi$, Fig. 21-18, vector, W, becomes

$$W = \frac{1}{2} \gamma (\overline{AB})(x),$$

parallel to the line, AD, of the natural slope, reaction, R, is parallel to the rupture line, AC, and vector, E_a, is parallel to the position line. The position line makes an incline with the inner or back face of the wall at the angle of $(\phi + \phi_1)$.

Hence, if the weights, W_n, of the various arbitrarily assumed rupture surfaces of the sliding soil wedges are set off to a certain force scale on the line of the natural slope, AD, from point A, and if from the end points of the weights the E_n-lines are drawn at the angle ψ, which means drawn parallel to the position line, then the end points of the E_n-lines will lie on the rupture surfaces (AB_n). Connection of the end points of the E_n-lines results in a curve, the so-called E_a-curve, which is termed Culmann's curve. A tangent, t-t, drawn to the curve parallel to the line of natural slope scales off to the same force scale to which the weights were drawn a maximum value of E, i.e., E_{max}, which represents then the magnitude of the active earth pressure, E_a.

A line $AF'C$ drawn through the heel-point, A, of the wall and the end point of $E_{max} = E_a$ determines the position of the most dangerous rupture surface, $AF'C$.

In case the ground surface is plane, i.e., points B, B_n, C, and D are on a line, then points ABB_1, ABB_2, ABC, ABB_n form triangles. If there is no surcharge on the ground surface, then there is no need to compute the weight of the various arbitrary soil wedges, but Culmann's construction can be carried out to a

geometric scale instead of to a force scale.
Because the weight of any soil wedge is

$$W = \tfrac{1}{2}\gamma(\overline{AB})(x),\qquad\qquad (21\text{-}45)$$

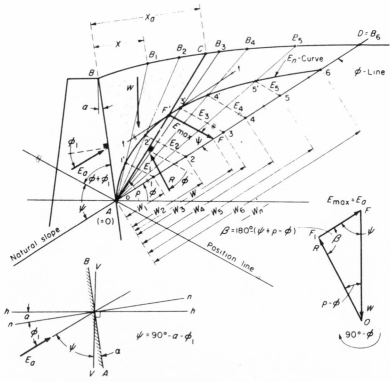

FIG. 21-18. Culmann's active earth pressure curve.

where $(\overline{AB})$ is the base of the wedge-shaped triangle, and x is the height of the triangle, the weight is proportional to x. Therefore, instead of plotting on AD the weights, W_n, of each of the soil wedges, the corresponding heights, x_n, or lengths proportional to x_n of the respective wedges can be plotted, the E_n-lines and the E_a-curve drawn, and the maximum E-ordinate, $F\text{-}F'$, for example, scaled off. The magnitude of the active earth pressure is then calculated from the following considerations:

$$E_a = W_a\frac{\overline{FF'}}{\overline{AF}} = \tfrac{1}{2}\gamma(\overline{AB})(x_a)\frac{\overline{FF'}}{\overline{AF}},\qquad\qquad (21\text{-}46)$$

where W_a = weight of the soil wedge at $E_{max} = E_a$;
γ = unit weight of soil;

x_a = height of triangle, ABC, at E_a;
$\overline{FF'}$ = ordinate to some scale (force scale) proportional to, and representing the maximum active earth pressure, E_a;
$\overline{AF}$ = a segment of line, which is proportional to and representing to some scale the weight of the active soil wedge.

Note that the expression $E_a = (W_a)(\overline{FF'})/(\overline{AF})$ is the same as that established from the force triangle, in Coulomb's theory, namely:

$$E_a = W\,\frac{\sin(\rho - \phi)}{\sin(\psi + \rho - \phi)}.$$

If there is a uniformly distributed surcharge on the ground surface, say p lb/ft², then

$$E_a = \tfrac{1}{2}\left[\left(\gamma + \frac{2p\cos\delta}{h}\right)(\overline{AB})\,\frac{x_a}{\overline{AF}}\right](\overline{FF'}), \tag{21-47}$$

where h = perpendicular distance from the heel point, A, of the wall to the ground surface line, BD, or its extension to the left of B.

Culmann's method is more general than the Poncelet method. It is particularly applicable with good results for the case when the ground surface is curvilinear, or irregular, or when the backfill material consists of a layered system of various densities. Also, the method is good when point D lies outside the drawing paper. It is likewise applicable to a system where the ground surface is superimposed with a surcharge of a uniformly distributed load of various intensities—p_1 and p_2, for example, Fig. 21-19. In the latter case Culmann's

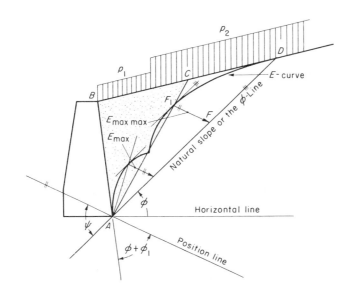

FIG. 21-19. Culmann's method for surcharge. Active earth pressure.

curve may have several maximum E-values. The maximum of the several maximum values, the so-called maximum maximorum, is then taken as the active earth pressure: $E_a = E_{max\ max}$. This $E_{max\ max}$ also determine the position of the most dangerous rupture surface, AC. The segment of line, AF, cut off by E_{maxmax} on the natural slope is the weight, W, of the sliding soil wedge, ABC.

Concentrated Surcharge. In the case where the ground surface is loaded with a concentrated linear surcharge load P per unit length of run of wall, one proceeds as follows. First, ignore the concentrated load, P, and plot the weights, W_n, of the arbitrarily assumed rupture wedges upon the ϕ-line in the manner given by the description of Coulomb's or Culmann's method (see also Fig. 21-20).

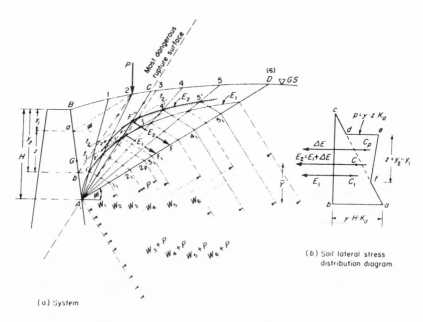

(a) System

(b) Soil lateral stress distribution diagram

FIG. 21-20. Culmann's method for concentrated surcharge. Active case.

Draw to the unsurcharged E-curve a tangent parallel to the ϕ-line and obtain the maximum active earth pressure, E_1. Then, add graphically to the head of the second weight-vector, W_2, the concentrated load P, and find point 2^P on the arbitrary rupture surface A-2. Then add to each of the weight vectors W_3, W_4, W_5 and W_6 the concentrated load, P, plot these vectors on the ϕ-line, and draw through the appropriate points a new Culmann's curve, E_2, $2^P F'' 4' 5'$. This new Culmann's curve, E_2, has larger E-ordinates than has the first Culmann's curve E_1. Draw a tangent t_2-t_2 to the second Culmann's curve and determine the maximum active earth pressure, $E_2 = F'' F$. Through that point, F'', where the E_2-vector intersects the tangent on the second E-curve, draw the most dangerous rupture surface $AF''C$ brought about by the concentrated load P. Note that on this rupture surface Culmann's E_1-curve experiences a discontinuity at F'. The composite Culmann's E-curve for weight and surcharge is now $A1'2'F'F''4'5'$.

The influence of the concentrated load, $\Delta E = E_2 - E_1$, upon the un-surcharged active earth pressure, E_1 is the difference between E_2 and E_1.

It can be assumed that the effect of ΔE becomes fully effective at such a depth where a rupture surface drawn through the point of application of P parallel to the most dangerous rupture surface A-F''-C intersects the back face of the wall (at point b). The upper limit of the influence of P is determined by spreading the load P under the angle of ϕ with the horizontal to hit the wall at point a.

The soil lateral stress distribution is shown in the stress distribution diagram, Fig. 21-20b. At point a on the back face of the wall, the influence of P is at its full (see diagram b, segment d-e), and then decreases over the depth z until it reaches

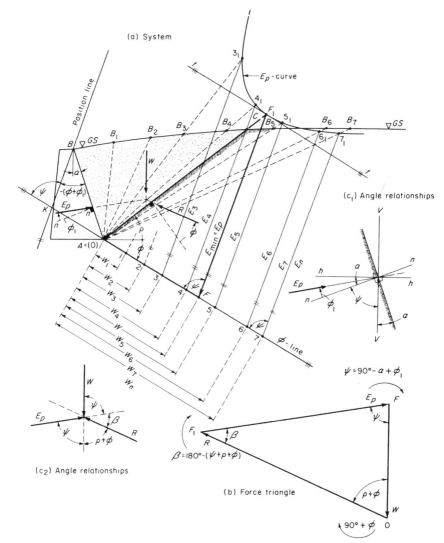

FIG. 21-21. Culmann's passive earth-pressure curve.

the value of zero at point b on the wall or point f in the stress distribution diagram.

The point of application, C, of the total lateral earth pressure, E_2, on the wall is determined by the position of the centroid, C, of the entire stress distribution diagram $abcdefa$.

b) Passive Earth Pressure. The determination of the passive earth pressure by Culmann's method is pursued in a similar manner as for the active earth pressure. The method is illustrated in Fig. 21-21.

Note that the natural slope (ϕ-line) is to be drawn through point A at an angle of $(-)\phi$, i.e., the ϕ-line must be drawn at an angle ϕ below the horizontal. On this ϕ-line, the weights, W_n, of the arbitrarily assumed rupture wedges, ABC_n, are plotted to a certain force scale. Through B, the position line, BK, is drawn at an angle of $(-)(\phi + \phi_1)$ (or to the left of the back face line, AB, of the wall). From the endpoints of the weights, W_n, draw the corresponding E_n magnitudes parallel to the position line. This means that the force triangles are rotated through an angle of $(90° + \phi)$ in the clockwise direction and placed on the ϕ-line. Connect the graphically obtained E_n-values to form Culmann's passive earth pressure curve, or the E_p-curve. The minimum ordinate, E_{min}, of the E_p-curve is determined from the ϕ-line by drawing a tangent, t-t, to the E_p-curve. This minimum E_n-ordinate represents, on the chosen scale, the magnitude of the passive earth pressure, E_p.

REFERENCES

1. K. Terzaghi, "Large Retaining-Wall Tests," *Engineering News-Record*, 1934, vol. 112, pp. 136-140, 259-262, 316-318, 403-406, 503-508.
2. H. Müller-Breslau, *Erddruck auf Stützmauern*, Stuttgart, Alfred Kröner Verlag, 1906, 1947.
3. C. A. Coulomb, "Essai sur une application des règles de maximis et minimis à quelques problèmes de statique relatifs à l'architecture." Mèmoires de la mathéma- tique et de physique, présentés à l'Académie Royale des Sciences, par divers savans, et lûs dans sés Assemblées, vol. 7, Année 1773, Paris, De L'Imprimerie Royale, 1776, pp. 343-382, plus two plates of drawings.
4. A. R. Jumikis, *Soil Mechanics*, Princeton, N.J., D. Van Nostrand Company, Inc., 1962, pp. 549-596.
5. A. R. Jumikis, *Mechanics of Soils* (Fundamentals for Advanced Study), Princeton, N.J., D. Van Nostrand Company, Inc., 1964, pp. 219-332.
6. J. Heyman, *Coulomb's Memoir on Statics.* Cambridge at the University Press, 1972.
7. A.R. Jumikis, *Active and Passive Earth Pressure Coefficient Tables,* New Brunswick, N.J., Rutgers—The State University, Bureau of Engineering Research, College of Engineering, Engineering Research Publication no. 43, 1962.
8. J.V. Poncelet, *Mèmoire sur la stabilitè des revètments et de leurs fondations.* Note additionelle sur les relations analytiques qui lient entre elles la poussée et la butée de la terre. *Memorial de l'officier du genie,* Paris, 1840, vol. 13.
9. C.A. Culmann, "Theorie der Stütz- und Futtermauern," Section 8 in *Die graphische Statik.* Zürich: Meyer und Zeller, 1866, pp. 545-633, (plus Plates 28-34).

SUGGESTIONS FOR FURTHER READING

1. K.Z. Andrawes, and M.A. Wl-Sohby, "Factors Affecting Coefficient for Earth Pressure," *Proc. ASCE,* Journal of the Soil Mechanics and Foundations Division, Paper 9863, Vol. 99, No. SM 7, 1973, pp. 527-539.
2. E.W. Brooker and H.O. Ireland, "Earth Pressure at Rest," *Canadian Geotechnical Journal,* Vol. 2, No. 1, February, 1965, pp. 1-15.
3. A. Caquot and J. Kérisel, *Traité de mécanique des sols,* Paris: Gauthier-Villars, 1956.
4. W.C. Huntington, *Earth Pressure and Retaining Walls,* New York, N.Y.: John Wiley and Sons, Inc., 1957.
5. A. Kézdi, *Erddrucktheorien,* Berlin: Springer-Verlag, 1962.
6. *Proc. ASCE,* of the Specialty Conference of Earth and Earth-Supported Structures, held at Purdue University, Indiana, June 11-14, 1972 (three volumes).
7. W.J.M. Rankine, "On the Stability of Loose Earth." *Phylosophical Transactions,* Royal Society, London, vol. 147, 1857.
8. K. Ross, W.J.H. Rennie and P.A. Cox, "The New Dry Dock at Belfast," Paper 7487, *Proceedings* of the Institution of Civil Engineers (London), Vol. 51, February, 1972, pp. 269-294.
9. M.G. Spangler and J.L. Mickle, "Lateral Pressures on Retaining Walls due to Backfill Surface Loads," Washington, D.C., Highway Research Record 144, 1956.
10. K. Terzaghi, *Erdbaumechanik auf bodenphysikalischer Grundlage,* Wien: Franz Deuticke, 1925, reissued in 1976.
11. K. Terzaghi, *Theoretical Soil Mechanics,* New York, N.Y.: John Wiley and Sons, Inc., 1948.
12. K. Terzaghi and R.B. Peck, *Soil Mechanics in Engineering Practice,* (2nd ed.), New York, N.Y.: John Wiley and Sons, Inc., 1967.
13. G.P. Tschebotarioff, *Foundations, Retaining and Earth Structures,* (2nd ed.), New York, N.Y.: McGraw-Hill Book Company, 1973.
14. Vereinigung Schweizerischer Strassenfachmänner (Swiss Union of Highway Specialists), *Stützmauern; Grundlagen zur Berechnung und Konstruktion; Bemessungstafeln.* (Murs de soutènement), Zürich, vol. 1, 1966, pp. 673-692.
15. C.S. Gillmor, Charles Augustin Coulomb: *Physics and Engineering in Eighteenth Century France,* Princeton, N.J.: Princeton University, Dissertation for degree of Ph.D., Princeton University, 1968.
16. C.S. Gillmor, *Coulomb and the Evolution of Physics and Engineering in Eighteenth-Century France,* Princeton, N.J.: Princeton University Press, 1971.

PROBLEMS

21-1. List as many possible forces as you know that may be acting singly or simultaneously on an earth-retaining structure.
21-2. Determine the active and passive earth pressures, without and with a surcharge of $p = 300$ lb/ft², exerted by a sandy, backfill soil. $H = 12$ ft, $\alpha = 0$, $\delta = 0$. The groundwater table is 4 ft below the ground surface (Fig. Prob. 21-2).
   Unit weight of dry soil: $\gamma = 100$ lb/ft³;
   Moisture content of soil above groundwater table: $m = 12\%$ by dry weight;
   $\phi = 30°$; $\phi_1 = 0°$; $G = 2.65$; $\gamma_w = 62.4$ lb/ft³;
   Porosity $n = 30\%$.
Draw to scale, complete the soil lateral stress distribution diagram, and calculate the magnitude of partial and total earth pressures. Also, calculate the points of applications of the partial and total earth pressures.

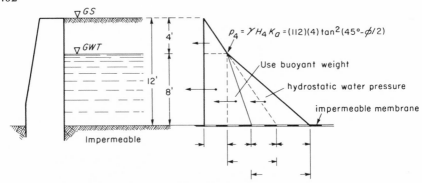

FIG. PROBLEM 21-2.

21-3. Given a two-layered system of soil as shown in Fig. Prob. 21-3.
    a) *No groundwater present.*
        Plot to scale the stress distribution diagrams
          i) for $c = 0$ for both layers,
          ii) for $c_1 = 0$ and $c_2 = 100$ lb/ft², and for both active and passive pressures.
        Note. Calculate active and passive earth pressures for all possible combinations.
    b) *Groundwater present.* Plot diagrams for c and c_1 as under a).
21-4. Determine analytically the position of the rupture surface in soil so that sliding of the retaining wall out of its position would just impend due to the lateral pressure of the soil wedge *ABC*, Fig. Prob. 21-4. The weight of the retaining wall is W pounds per linear foot of wall line. Unit weight of soil $= \gamma$; $\phi = 30°$; $\phi_1 = 0$ at the back-face; $\phi_1 = 32°$ at the base of footing.

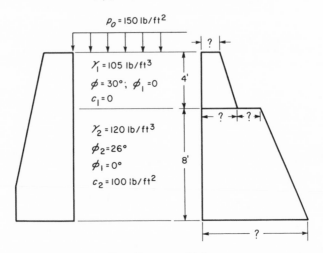

FIG. PROBLEM 21-3.

Required:
    a) Draw soil lateral stress distribution diagram.
    b) Show algebraically stability calculations against rotation of the system with and without earthquake considerations.

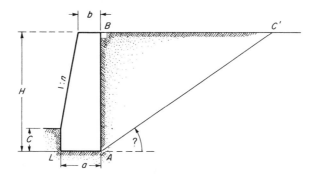

FIG. PROBLEM 21-4.

Note: Quantities not given should be assumed. Also, note that W is not given by a numerical value.

If the height of the wall is $H = 12$ ft, $\gamma = 100$ lb/ft³; $\phi = 30°$; $\phi_1 = 0$; $\phi_{c/s} = 0.60$, what should be the weight of the wall to attain an overall coefficient of stability of $\eta = 1.5$? Use Poncelet's method and compare the results with theoretical calculations.

21-5. Check the stability of the earth-retaining wall as shown in the Fig. Prob. 21-5.

The upper ground surface is subjected to a surcharge of 400 lb/ft². The backfill is a mixture of sand and gravel with some silt. The unit weight of this backfill material is 120 lb/ft³; $\phi = 30°$. The coefficient of friction between concrete and soil was found to be tan $\phi_1 = 0.50$. The allowable bearing capacity of the soil was found to be 4 ton/ft². Unit weight of concrete = 150 lb/ft³. The wall rests on compact soil.

    a) Determine total active earth pressure on the retaining wall
        i) analytically and
        ii) graphically (by Poncelet's method).

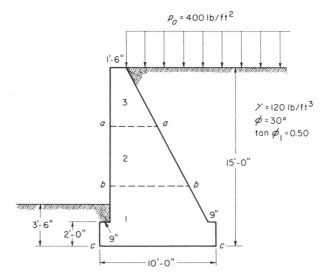

FIG. PROBLEM 21-5.

        iii) Find the position of the resultant pressure at the base *c-c* of the
           retaining wall.
    b) Determine active earth pressures on parts ①, ②, and ③ of the retaining
       wall; determine the position of the resultant pressure at the base *c-c* of
       the retaining wall.
    c) Compare the positions of the resultant pressure at *c-c* found by the three
       methods as above.
    d) Check compressive stresses in concrete in sections (*a-a*), (*b-b*), and contact
       pressure on soil at (*c-c*).
    e) Check the stability of wall against overturning.
    f) Check the stability of wall against sliding.
    g) Draw force and pressure diagrams.

21-6.   Given an earth pressure system as shown in Fig. Prob. 21-6. Determine the active
      earth pressure E_a by Poncelet-Culmann graphical methods and locate the position
      of the most dangerous rupture surface.

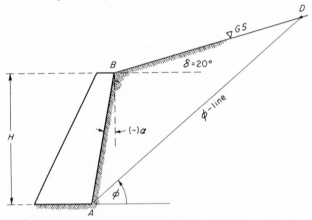

FIG. PROBLEM 21-6.

21-7.   For the soil-wall system shown, determine the total active earth pressure on the
      wall, as well as its point of application, and direction of action, on the wall.
      Also, establish the position of the most critical rupture surface $\overline{AC}$.
      Perform calculations in the SI units of measurement.

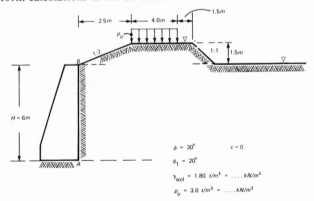

FIG. Problem 21-7.

21-8. Given a layered wall - earthpressure system as sketched in Fig. Problem 21-8.
Required: 1) Plot the system to a convenient geometric scale.
2) Plot active earth pressure distribution diagram to a stress scale
Show all pressure ordinates! Show all force positions and their
moment arms!
3) Determine magnitude of the total lateral active earth pressure on
the wall. i) Find point of application and its direction of E_a on the
backface of the wall.
4) Plot total lateral pressure distribution diagram taking into account
position of water levels on both sides of the wall. Find point of
application of total, resultant lateral forces on the wall; ii) and its
direction.
5) Explain how would you calculate factor of safety η_{sl} against sliding
of the wall on its base.
6) Explain calculation of factor of safety η_r against rotation of the wall.

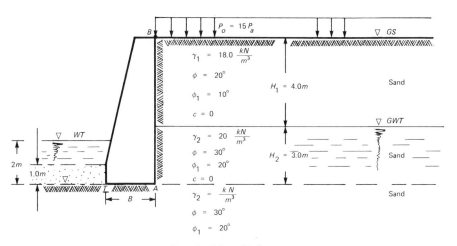

FIG. Problem 21-8.

21-9. Given a wall-earthpressure system as sketched.
Required: 1) Plot this system to a convenient geometric scale.
2) Plot active earth pressure distribution diagram to a stress scale.
Show all pressure ordinates! Show all force positions and their
moment arms.
3) Determine magnitude of the total lateral active earth pressure on
the wall. Show point of application of E_a on the wall-soil system and its
direction.
4) Calculate factor of safety η_{sl} against sliding on base of the wall.
5) Calculate factor of safety η_r against rotation.
6) Use SI system of units of measurement!

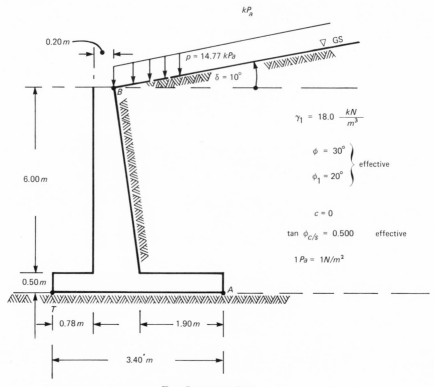

FIG. PROBLEM 21-9.

21-10. Which of the three earth pressure diagrams is correct or incorrect by their nature, and why?

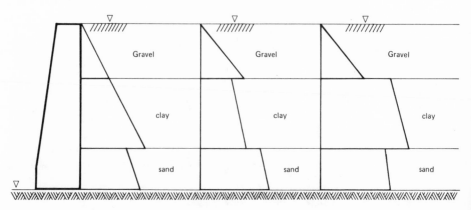

FIG. PROBLEM 21-10.

21-11. Refer to Fig. 21-19. If $H = 3.0$ m, $\alpha = +5°$; $\delta = +10°$; $\phi_1 = 0$; $\phi = 30°$; $\gamma = 18.83$ kN/m^3; $p_1 = 20$ kN/m^2 distributed over 2 m, and $p_2 = 30$ kN/m^2 distributed over 20 m, determine E_{amax} and $E_{amaxmax}$, and the position of the most dangerous rupture surface AC.

SHEETING AND BRACING OF TRENCHES

21-17. Application of Coulomb's Theory. Although sheeting and bracing of soil banks are temporary operations in foundation engineering, sheeting and bracing of vertical slopes and trenches and other open cuts against caving in can seldom be omitted. Even if of temporary nature (trenches, pits, etc.), the problem of safety in construction work requires careful investigation of the forces involved in the earth retaining systems. This is true the more so as the insurance companies require it, to prevent injuries to workmen and damage to, or loss of, material and construction equipment.

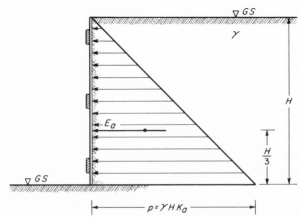

Fig. 21-22. Coulomb's triangular stress distribution diagram.

The lateral earth pressure on sheeting may be calculated, among other methods, by means of Coulomb's earth pressure theory. According to this theory the magnitude of the lateral earth pressure on timbering in a cut of a homogeneous soil increases like a hydrostatic pressure—linearly in simple proportion to depth, as in Fig. 21-22. For example, if $\gamma = 116$ lb/ft^3, $h = 7.0$ ft, $\phi = 30°$, then the lateral, total, active earth pressure E_a on the sheeting is

$$E_a = \tfrac{1}{2}\gamma h^2 K_a.$$

With $K_a = \tan^2(\pi/4 - \phi/2) = 0.334$, and $p = \gamma h K_a = (116)(7.0)(0.334) = 272$ (lb/ft^2), the total active earth pressure is

$$E_a = \tfrac{1}{2}(7.0)(272) = 950 \text{ (lb/ft)}.$$

The same calculation can be made by means of the SI units as follows.

For example, if $\gamma = 18.0$ kN/m^3, $H = 4.0$ m, $\phi = 30°$, then the total active earth pressure E_a on an inflexible wall is

$$E_a = \tfrac{1}{2} \cdot \gamma \cdot H^2 \cdot K_a$$

With $K_a = \tan^2(45° - \phi/2) = 0.333$, and $p = \gamma H K_a =$
$= (18.0)(4.0)(0.333) = (72)(0.333) \approx 24.0$ kN/m^2, the total active earth pressure is

$$E_a = (\tfrac{1}{2})(24.0)(4.0) = \underline{48 \ (kN/m)}.$$

21-18. Earth Pressure Distribution in Reality. The method of sheeting and bracing of vertical banks and the magnitude of the lateral earth pressure on the wall depend primarily upon the soil type encountered, and the flexibility of the wall.

Because the bracing system is usually somewhat elastic, the soil pressure distribution actually does not follow Coulomb's idealized straight-line rule mainly because of pressure redistribution and arching effect.

The problem as to how the lateral earth pressure distributes with depth over

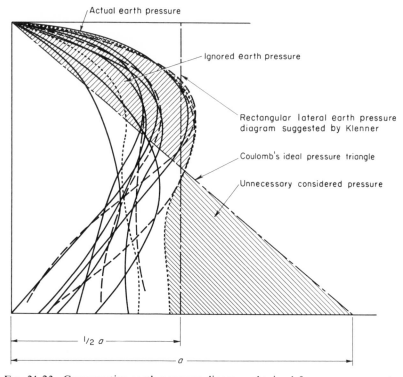

FIG. 21-23. Comparative earth pressure diagram obtained from measurements (curvilinear) and calculations (linear). After Klenner, Ref. 1.

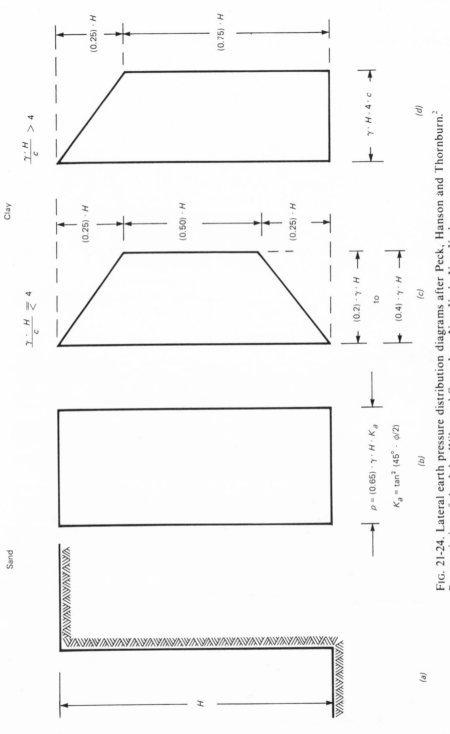

FIG. 21-24. Lateral earth pressure distribution diagrams after Peck, Hanson and Thornburn.[2] By permission of the John Wiley and Sons, Inc., New York, New York.

a shoring has been considerably discussed in the past. During the course of time several engineers have expressed the opinion that, based on observations, earth pressure does not follow the same laws everywhere, and that its point of application and distribution of its intensity depend to a great extent on the displacement of the shoring structure during construction periods and upon the type of soil.

Fig. 21-23 represents an earth-pressure diagram by Klenner.[1] The earth pressures were measured during the construction of the Berlin subway and with earthwork sheetings in Munich. The comparison of the measured earth pressure diagram with Coulomb's earth pressure triangle lead Klenner to suggest the use of a rectangular, lateral earth pressure diagram, the base of which is one half the base of the triangle. Although this rectangular diagram does not represent the true pressure distribution condition, it points out clearly that on flexible walls Coulomb's ideal linear pressure distribution is not valid. The upper part of the actually measured existing pressure is usually ignored using triangular pressure distribution, but the lower part of the pressure triangle is unnecessarily estimated and introduced in calculations.

For calculating active earth pressure on vertical, flexible, braced open excavation walls, Peck, Hanson and Thornburn[2] recommend to use their "apparent" lateral earth pressure distribution diagrams as shown in Figs. 21-24b, c and d (reproduced here by permission of the John Wiley and Sons, Inc. of New York, New York). Fig. 21-24a is a sketch of wall of a cut.

Fig. 21-24b is the diagram for cuts in dry or moist sand.

Fig. 21-24c is the diagram for clays if $\gamma \cdot H/c$ is less than 4.

Fig. 21-24d is the diagram for clays if $\gamma \cdot H/c > 4$ provided $\gamma \cdot H/c_b$ does not exceed about 4, where c is the average undrained shear strength of the soil beside the cut, and c_b is the undrained strength of the clay below excavation level.

The point of application of E_a so computed is determined by the position of the centroids of these lateral earth pressure distribution diagrams.

According to Peck et al.,[2] their lateral earth pressure distribution diagrams may also be used for calculating total active earth pressure on struts, soldier piles, as well as on back-tied sheet piling, and in pressure-grouted soil anchor problems.

REFERENCES

1. C. Klenner, "Versuche über die Verteilung des Erddruckes über die Wände ausgesteifter Baugruben," *Die Bautechnik,* July 4, 1941, no. 29, pp. 316-319.
2. R.B. Peck, W. E. Hanson, and T. H. Thornburn, *Foundation Engineering* (2nd ed.), New York, N.Y.: John Wiley and Sons, Inc., 1974, p. 461.

SUGGESTIONS FOR FURTHER READING

1. W. J. Armento, "Performance of Bracing Systems in Subway Excavations," *Proc. ASCE* of the Specialty Conference on Performance of Earth and Earth-Supported Structures, held June 11-14, 1972 at Purdue University, Lafayette, Indiana, vol. 1, part 2, pp. 1283-1302.
2. L. Bjerrum, C.J. Clausen and J.M. Duncan, "Earth Pressures on Flexible Structures

- a State-of-the-Art Report," *Proceedings of the 5th European Conference on Soil Mechanics* held in 1972 at Matrid, vol. 2, pp. 169-196.

3. R. Briske and E. Pirlet, "Messungen über die Beanspruchung des Baugruben-verbaues der Kölner U-Bahn," *Die Bautechnik,* No. 9, September, 1968, pp. 290-298.

4. R.G. Tait and H.T. Taylor, "Rigid and Flexible Bracing Systems on Adjacent Sites," Paper No. 11376, *Proc. ASCE,* Journal of the Construction Division, vol. 101, No. CO2, June, 1975, pp. 365-376.

QUESTIONS AND PROBLEMS

21-1. Why is sheeting of vertical banks practiced for the retaining of vertical banks in open excavations?

21-2. The vertical walls of a foundation trench 8 ft deep in a noncohesive soil are to be protected against caving in by rigid sheeting. The sheeting is supported by vertical planks. The planks are spaced 3 ft apart. They are to be braced with five horizontal braces, one at the bottom, one at the top, and three in between. Disregarding the top and the bottom braces, space the three braces so that each of them would be loaded with same pressure.

21-3. Compare lateral earth pressures E_a, calculated from Klenner's and Peck et al, pressure diagrams.

21-4. How do rapid draw-down, rainstorms, freezing, and thawing affect lateral earth pressures and the stability of laterally supported vertical earth banks in general, and in cases of saturated noncohesive and cohesive soils in particular?

Chapter 22

BEARING CAPACITY OF SOIL;
DEPTH OF FOUNDATION

22-1. Stability Requirements of a Foundation. The stability of a foundation depends upon the safety of a soil against 1) its failure in shear (associated with plastic flow of the soil material underneath the foundation, and lateral expulsion of soil from underneath the footing of the foundation) and 2) excessive vertical displacement, or settlement, caused by the process of consolidation of the soil under the foundation (elastic and plastic deformation). Therefore, in order not to endanger the structure, these are the two independent foundation stability requirements which must be met simultaneously: 1) there should be adequate safety against a shear failure within the soil mass, and 2) the probable differential and maximum settlements of the soil, viz., foundation, must be limited to safe, tolerable, acceptable magnitudes.

Naturally, the question arises: what is the maximum, allowable contact pressure that can be imposed on a certain type of soil by a certain type, size, and shape of a structure without causing distress to the structure by either of these modes of failure?

This question leads to the problem of rating soils as to their bearing capacity.

22-2. Rating of Soil. A soil for supporting structural foundations is rated by expressing its ability to support load without failures or deformations within the soil mass. The rating is given in terms of *bearing capacity*.

Definitions. The contact area between the soil and the base of the footing on which the load rests is called the *loaded*, or *bearing*, *area*.

Ultimate bearing capacity of a soil σ_u is understood to be the ultimate value of the average contact pressure, or stress, or load intensity transmitted by the base of the footing of the foundation to the soil, causing the soil mass to rupture, or fail in shear, or causing excessive settlement.

The ultimate bearing capacity of a soil-foundation system depends upon

    1) the type of soil and its properties
    2) the contact pressure applied to the soil
    3) the form and size of the footing in plan, and
    4) the depth of the footing below the ground surface.

Naturally, the engineer has to provide for adequate safety against bearing capacity failure (in shear and/or settlement).

Safe bearing capacity, or *allowable pressure*, on soil, σ_{adm}, is the ultimate bearing capacity divided by a factor of safety η:

$$\sigma_{adm} = \sigma_u / \eta.$$

Depending upon the importance and kind of structure, the factor of safety used is from $\eta = 2$ to about $\eta = 5$.

Sometimes, when settlement is the governing factor in stability considerations of a foundation, bearing capacity of a soil means the load intensity or contact pressure that may be applied to the soil without causing intolerable settlement of the structure.

A limit imposed on the total settlement of any one structural element of a foundation is understood to be the *tolerable settlement*. Depending upon the type of the structure, whether statically determinate or statically indeterminate, tolerable settlements are usually set from about $\frac{1}{4}''$ to about $1.0''$.

Accordingly, the safe bearing capacity of a soil is defined as the compressive stress on the soil that would bring about a predetermined amount of settlement, or tolerable settlement of the structure in question—a settlement which would not affect its function or structural integrity.

22-3. Sources of Obtaining Values of Soil-Bearing Capacity. The sources for obtaining soil-bearing capacity values for designing foundations are:

    1) building codes, official regulations, and civil engineers' handbooks;

    2) soil loading tests in place;

    3) laboratory testing of soils, and

    4) analytical methods of calculation.

22-4. Building Codes. Building codes, official bridge and building specifications, and engineers' handbooks usually contain tables of the safe values of bearing capacities (or "presumptive" bearing capacities as termed by the building laws of the City of New York) for various types of soils and rocks. Such values are compiled in these tables based on many years of observations in practice. Presumptive soil bearing capacity values are good as guides only in areas from which such values have been obtained.

Table 22-1 contains abridged excerpts from the Uniform Building Code[1] and the Building Code of the City of New York.[2] The values listed in this table are the maximum allowable bearing values.

Some books tabulating safe bearing values of soil include also a value for "quicksand." It should be remembered that there is no such soil type as "quicksand." Under proper hydraulic conditions any sand can be set into a "quick" condition.

Every application for increasing the soil-bearing value of a soil must usually be supported by pertinent facts based on test, or sometimes by theoretical considerations.

The presumptive soil and rock bearing capacity values and methods of procedures for determining them as prescribed by duly constituted building codes have a legal connotation, namely: in foundation design the bearing capacity values should not be exceeded except if the pertinent building code permits to do so under certain conditions. However, regardless of a rational and/or scientific method used for determining the soil and/or rock bearing capacity, one must refer to the pertinent building code under jurisdiction in order to guard against a legal technical violation.

Many engineers use soil-bearing capacity values, selected from building codes, in preliminary design of foundations and earthworks. However, it should be kept in mind that building codes do not protect one against failure, nor do they exempt one from responsibility if failure of the structure occurs due to excessive settlement or rupture of soil, or both. Therefore, it appears to be more appropriate to obtain the necessary soil-bearing capacity values from field and laboratory tests of soils. One should be aware that nature has made no safety contracts with engineers.

22-5. Soil-Loading Tests. A soil static loading test in the field is essentially a model test of a prototype foundation. The purpose of the soil-loading test is to determine the ultimate bearing capacity of a soil, from which the safe bearing capacity of soil can be established. The results of the soil-loading test are to be interpreted for a full-scale foundation, the interpretation being based on the corresponding theory.

The method for performing a soil static loading test is also regulated by the various building codes. The ASCE code, for example, says that the soil shall be tested in one or more places and at such levels as the conditions may warrant. The codes usually specify that for foundations a quadratic loading plate or concrete block, 1 to 2 ft^2 in size, should be used.

For the evaluation of the bearing capacity of soil for highway pavement support, loading plates 30 in. in diameter are employed.

A device for performing a direct soil static loading test is illustrated in Fig. 22-1. It consists of a stiff loading or bearing plate or a concrete slab or block upon which a hydraulic jack is supported. The jack exerts pressure against the dead weight on the platform inducing a reaction and transfers the pressure to the soil.

A direct soil static load test can also be performed without the jack. The pressure, transferred to the soil, is obtained by loading the bearing block directly with dead weight, the weight having been placed on a platform erected on top of the bearing block.

The settlements or vertical displacements of the base of the loading blocks are measured at three points by means of a leveling instrument, dial gauges, or are automatically recorded continuously. Measurements should be in reference to points which remain stable during the test.

To perform a direct soil static loading test, one must become familiar with the building code in question.

The data from the soil loading test, such as load, settlement, and time, are conveniently presented in a graphical form as shown in Fig. 22-2.

If it is desired to obtain the ultimate bearing capacity of a soil, then the direct

TABLE 22-1. SOIL-BEARING VALUES: PRESUMPTIVE CAPACITY

Soil and rock types	tons/ft²	kN/m²
Clay, soft, medium	1 to 1.5	0.0479 to 0.0718
Clay, stiff, medium	2.5	0.1197
Clay, compact	2	0.0958
Clay, hard	5	0.2394
Sand, fine, loose	2	0.0958
Sand-clay soils, compact	3	0.1436
Sand-clay soils, loose, saturated	1	0.0479
Sand, coarse, loose; compact fine; and		
gravel mixture, loose	3	0.1436
compact, with inorganic silt	2	0.0958
Gravel, loose; and compact coarse sand	4 to 6	0.1915 to 0.2873
inorganic silt soils	4 to 6	0.1915 to 0.2873
Sand-gravel mixture, compact	6	0.2873
very compact	10	0.4788
Hardpan and execptionally compacted		
or partially cemented gravels or sands	10 to 12	0.4788 to 0.5746
Rock, soft	8	0.3830
medium hard	40	1.9152
hard, sound	60	2.8728
Sedimentary rocks:		
shale	8 to 10	0.3820 to 0.4788
hard shales	8 to 10	0.3830 to 0.4788
limestones	10 to 20	0.4788 to 0.9576
sandstones	10 to 20	0.4788 to 0.9576
chalk and coral	8	0.3830
Foliated rocks:		
schist, and slate in sound condition	40	1.9152
Massive bedrock (igneous rocks):		
basalt, diorite, diabase, granite, lava		
trap rock in sound condition	20 to 40 to 100	0.9576 to 4.7880
Metamorphic rocks:		
gneiss	100	4.7880
marble	10 to 20	0.4788 to 0.9576
schist	20 to 40	0.9576 to 1.9152
slate	8	0.3830

static loading test of soil is performed till failure, i.e., till rupture of the soil occurs.

The safe soil bearing capacity for design purposes is assumed to be a fraction of the ultimate bearing capacity.

Discussion. The ASCE Code warns against choosing soil-bearing values directly from the results of loading tests without due regard for significant factors, such as soft underlying strata or the effect of loading different-sized areas. Load tests have been denounced by many authorities, mainly because too often the results of small-scale tests have been used indiscriminately, without adequate investigation or analysis.

The effect of surface loading of relatively small loading areas at the elevation of the foundation does not extend deep enough where soil layers may be encountered having less bearing capacity than at the surface (remember the concept of

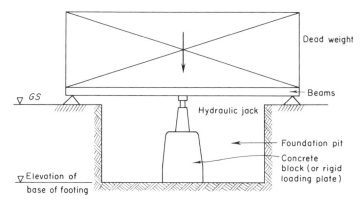

FIG. 22-1.   Principle of a device for soil static loading test.

"bulb of pressure"). Therefore, small loading plate tests have an unsatisfactory value for cohesive soils in respect to long-term consolidation, because consolidation of soil takes time, whereas the loading test allows only a fraction of the time needed for full consolidation. They may be satisfactory, however, in noncohesive soils.

The effects of deep foundations cannot be directly ascertained by surface loading.

The amount of settlement of loaded areas varies with the size of the area. Likewise, the bearing capacity of soil depends upon the size of the loading area as well as upon its shape and whether the block is or is not constrained around by a surcharge. From this point of view, the ultimate load causing rupture in soil by surface loading is not the same for the prototype foundation. Therefore, it is well to keep in mind the scale of the soil-loading test, particularly on cohesive soils, if the small-scale test results are to be applied to the prototype structure.

Besides the size of the foundation, the elastic properties of the loading plate and the foundation material, and the mode, type, and intensity of loading also affect the soil-loading test results.

A careful study of bearing capacity data obtained from bearing tests in the field on noncohesive soils may result in reasonably accurate values of the ultimate bearing capacity.

The bearing capacity data obtained from bearing tests in the field on cohesive soils are of the nature of the short-period loading test. Therefore, it is very difficult to evaluate from such tests the bearing capacity for a full-scale prototype foundation which will be in position over a long period of time.

The cost of field-loading tests on clay cannot nowadays be justified when soil

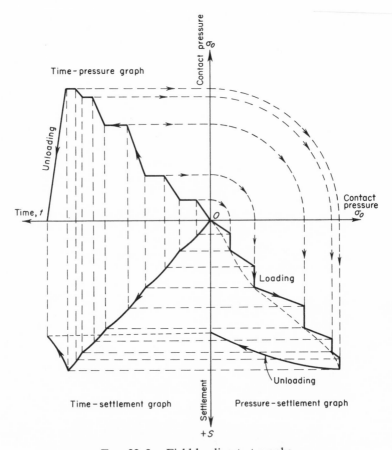

FIG. 22–2. Field loading test graphs.

borings, undisturbed soil samples, soil compression, and consolidation tests can conveniently and economically be made and/or obtained.

22-6. Laboratory Testing of Soils. The bearing capacity of a cohesive soil can also be evaluated from the unconfined compressive strength ($\sigma_3 = 0$) at failure. Theoretically, the bearing capacity of a cohesive soil is the value of the major principal stress σ_1 at failure in shear or by bulging. This stress at failure is the unconfined compressive stress, or the ultimate stress, q_u:

$$\sigma_1 = q_u = 2c \tan(45° + \phi/2), \tag{22-1}$$

or

$$\sigma_1 = q_u. \tag{22-2}$$

When $\phi = 0$, then the ultimate bearing capacity of the cohesive soil is

$$q_u = 2c \tag{22-3}$$

at the ground surface, where $h = 0$. The safe bearing capacity is then the ultimate bearing capacity divided by a factor of safety η, for which 3 is usually used as a normal figure:

$$\sigma_{\text{adm}} = q_u/\eta. \tag{22-4}$$

According to A. Casagrande and R. Fadum,[3] the allowable soil pressures commonly specified in building codes are conservative from the standpoint of safety against rupture of the clay; therefore, the indirect check of the ultimate bearing capacity of cohesive soil by means of the soil cylinder compression test is entirely satisfactory. Besides, compression tests on undisturbed cohesive soil cylinders are usually much less expensive than loading tests performed on sufficiently large bearing areas.

ANALYTICAL METHODS FOR CALCULATING SOIL-BEARING CAPACITY

22-7. Rankine's Formula.[4] Based on the theory of stress limit equilibrium conditions in an ideal soil at a point, the ratio of the major and minor principal stresses and a plane rupture surface, Rankine calculated the bearing capacity of soil as

$$\sigma_u = \gamma z \left(\frac{1 + \sin \phi}{1 - \sin \phi}\right)^2 = \gamma z \tan^4\left(\frac{\pi}{4} + \frac{\phi}{2}\right), \tag{22-5}$$

where $\sigma_u = \sigma_1$ = major principal stress = ultimate bearing capacity of soil,
γ = unit weight of soil,
z = critical depth for laying of foundation, and
ϕ = angle of internal friction of the ideal soil.

If the ultimate bearing capacity of the soil is known, then the critical depth z for laying of the foundation can be calculated.

This equation is good for a noncohesive soil, and for $z > 0$. It is, however, possible to extend Rankine's formula to cohesive soils.

22-8. Bell's Equation. Rankine's formula was modified by Bell[5,6] to be applicable for cohesive soils. In Bell's equation, both friction and cohesion are considered.

Bell considered the equilibrium of two adjacent elements of soil prisms, one just beneath the edge of a strip foundation and the other just outside, at a depth z below the ground surface, Fig. 22-3.

According to the classical earth pressure theory for cohesive soils, the contact pressure $\sigma_1 (= \sigma_u$ = the ultimate bearing capacity) induces on the elementary soil prism II a lateral active stress σ_{III}, tending to cause prism II to rupture in shear:

$$\sigma_{\text{III}} = \sigma_1 \tan^2(\pi/4 - \phi/2) - 2c \tan(\pi/4 - \phi/2). \tag{22-6}$$

This lateral stress σ_{III}, acting now laterally from prism II to prism I, should be resisted by the passive earth resistance stress σ_1:

$$\sigma_1 = \sigma_3 \tan^2(\pi/4 + \phi/2) + 2c \tan(\pi/4 + \phi/2), \tag{22-7}$$

where $\sigma_3 = \gamma z$. If this lateral stress σ_1 is barely large enough to rupture prism I, then the active stress σ_{III} is equal to the passive stress σ_1.

Setting $\sigma_{III} = \sigma_1$, obtain Bell's expression for the ultimate bearing capacity of a cohesive $(\phi - c)$ soil, $\sigma_1 = \sigma_u$:

$$\sigma_u = \gamma z \tan^4(\pi/4 + \phi/2) + 2c \tan(\pi/4 + \phi/2)[\tan^2(\pi/4 + \phi/2) + 1]. \quad (22\text{-}8)$$

When $c = 0$, then

$$\sigma_u = \gamma z \tan^4(\pi/4 + \phi/2), \quad (22\text{-}5)$$

which is the Rankine formula for the ultimate bearing capacity of a noncohesive soil.

When $\phi = 0$, then it follows from Eq. (22-8) that

$$\sigma_u = \gamma z + 4c. \quad (22\text{-}9)$$

When $\phi = 0$, and $z = 0$, then

$$\sigma_u = 4c, \quad (22\text{-}10)$$

which is Bell's ultimate bearing capacity of a pure cohesive soil.

Example. The magnitude of cohesion c of a soil, has been determined in the laboratory as being $c = 600$ lb/ft^2 = 28.73 kN/m^2. Calculate the ultimate bearing capacity σ_u.
Solution. By Eq. (22-10),
$\sigma_u = (4)c = (4)(600) = \underline{2400 \text{ (lb/ft}^2)} = \underline{1.2 \text{ (ton/ft}^2)} = \underline{(4)(28.73)} = \underline{114.92 \text{ (kN/m}^2)}.$

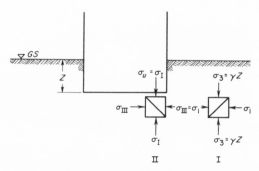

FIG. 22-3. Bell's system.

22-9. A. Casagrande-Fadum Illustration. Reasoning along the same lines as Bell did in his treatise on the supporting power of a clay soil, by utilizing the theory of stress condition in soil at a point, A. Casagrande and R. Fadum[7] presented a lucid illustration relative to major and minor principal stress conditions in cohesive soil induced by a structural load for the purposes of calculating the ultimate bearing capacity of soil. The system underlying these calculations is illustrated in Fig. 22-4.

The ground surface is loaded through a long strip foundation by a uniformly distributed load σ_u. The width of the strip foundation is $2b$.

In this system, the soil below the base line of the footing, as originally suggested by Terzaghi, is subdivided into three squares. The side of each of the squares is $2b$.

If the externally applied vertical surface pressure σ_u is applied to the saturated cohesive soil quickly, so that the clay soil has no time to consolidate, then the shear strength τ of the clay equals the cohesion c, i.e., $\tau = c$, as can easily be seen from the Mohr stress diagram. The shear strength envelope of the clay appears then to be a horizontal line the equation of which is $\tau = c$ (Fig. 22-4c). In this figure, Mohr's stress circle I represents the stress conditions in the soil at rupture of the elementary soil prism in the center of the block or zone I below the ground surface. From this stress diagram, it can be seen that the magnitude of the major principal stress when failure occurs is $\sigma_1 = \gamma b + 2c$, and the minor principal stress is $\sigma_3 = \gamma b$. Relative to the elementary soil prism in the center of the block or zone II (the middle block directly underneath the base of the footing), the horizontal stress, $\sigma_{III} = \sigma_1$, is the minor principal stress causing failure in shear of the clay mass. Blocks I and II act like a triaxial compression test failing in shear. Accordingly, $\sigma_1 = \gamma b + 4c$, which will bring about rupture.

Because γb is the pressure from the soil on the small elementary soil prism, it is deduced that to bring about failure the contact pressure σ_u exerted by the footing on the ground surface must be equal to $4c$, i.e.,

$$\sigma_u = 4c. \tag{22-10}$$

Hence, the ultimate bearing capacity of a saturated clay is

$$\sigma_u = 4c,$$

which is the same result as given by Bell.

If the magnitude of cohesion c of a clay is taken as approximately equal to one-half the unconfined compressive strength ($c = \sigma_c/2$), then the ultimate bearing capacity of clay for Bell's method of calculation is

$$\sigma_u = 4c = 4(\sigma_c/2) = 2\sigma_c. \tag{22-11}$$

Example. The unconfined compressive strength of a pure cohesive soil material has been tested to be $\sigma_c = 1000$ lb/ft^2 = 47.88 kN/m^2. Determine the ultimate bearing capacity of this material using the Bell-Casagrande method.
Solution.
Magnitude of cohesion:

$$c \approx \sigma_c/2 = 1000/2 = \underline{500 \text{ (lb/ft}^2)} = 47.88/2 = \underline{23.94 \text{ (kN/m}^2)}.$$

Ultimate bearing capacity:

$$\sigma_u = 4c = (4)(500) = \underline{2000 \text{ (lb/ft}^2)} = \underline{1 \text{ (ton/ft}^2)} = (4)(23.94) = \underline{95.76 \text{ (kN/m}^2)}$$

Applying on the ultimate bearing capacity a factor of safety $\eta = 3.0$, obtain the allowable soil bearing capacity

$$\sigma_{all} = \sigma_u/\eta \tag{22-4}$$

$$= 2000/3 = 667 \text{ (lb/ft}^2)$$

$$= 95.76/3 = \underline{31.92 \text{ (kN/m}^2)}.$$

On this soil, a fill whose unit weight is $\gamma_f = 120$ lb/ft^3 = 18.83 kN/m^3 can be

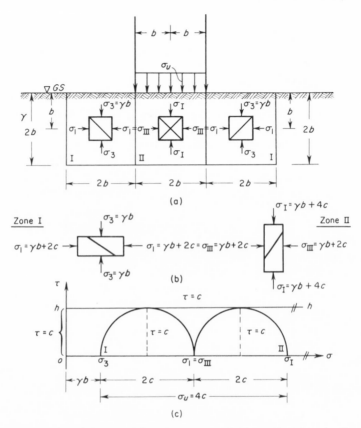

FIG. 22-4. Stress conditions at failure in a pure cohesive soil. After A. Casagrande
and R. E. Fadum, Ref. 7.

constructed z feet (m) high:

$$z = \sigma_{all}/\gamma_f = 667/120 = \underline{5.56 \text{ (ft)}}$$
$$= 31.92/18.83 = \underline{1.70 \text{ (m)}}.$$

SOIL-BEARING CAPACITY CALCULATIONS
BY MEANS OF THEORY OF PLASTIC EQUILIBRIUM

22-10. Prandtl's Theory. Prandtl[7,8] studied the process of penetration of hard
bodies, such as metal punchers, into another softer, homogeneous, isotropic
material from the viewpoint of plastic equilibrium. One of his systems of study
was a two-dimensional penetration problem in which a vertical puncher of width
$2b$ was applied to the horizontal surface of an infinitely extending body according
to Fig. 22-5. The puncher reminds one of a surface strip loading of very long
length perpendicular to the drawing plane. The contact surface between the
puncher and the other material is assumed to be smooth. In this figure,

AB = loaded region,
$FDCEG$ = boundary of plastic region against the elastic one,
$DF = GE$ = straight lines = tangents to curves $\overset{\frown}{CD}$ and $\overset{\frown}{CE}$,
$\overset{\frown}{CD} = \overset{\frown}{CE}$ = logarithmically spiraled curves,
$\alpha = \pi/4 - \phi/2$.

Interest in such studies led Prandtl to a solution for plastic equilibrium which explains lucidly the processes which take place in the softer body (material) upon vertical punching into its surface.

Upon application of a vertically guided puncher under high pressure to the softer horizontal material, a triangle, $\triangle ABC$, is pushed down inward into the material, and upon this downward penetration the triangles, $\triangle ADF$ and $\triangle BEG$, would be translocated obliquely and pushed out by the sectors ACD an dBCE. Through these pressures from $\triangle AOC$ and $\triangle BOC$ are transferred to $\triangle ADF$ and $\triangle BEG$, respectively. The right-hand part of Fig. 22-5 illustrates the stream lines of the plastic displacement. The left-hand part illustrates the stress trajectories.

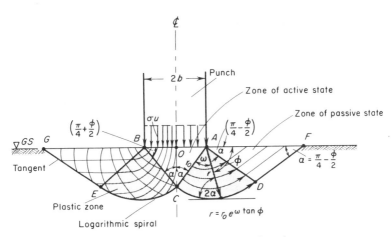

FIG. 22-5. Prandtl's system of study.

In $\triangle ABC$ there prevails a uniform stress condition: vertically the given large pressure (from the puncher), and horizontally a little lesser reactive pressure. The weight of the material in $\triangle ABC$ is disregarded. This triangular wedge, $\triangle ABC$, behaves like a rigid body and under pressure would move downward with no deformation. The triangular wedge $\triangle ABC$, directly underneath the base of the puncher, may be considered a zone of active state. The two triangular end-wedges may be considered as the zone of passive state.

Between $\triangle ADF$ and $\triangle BEG$, and the central triangle $\triangle ABC$, there are two sector-like elements, ACD and BCE. Curves CD and CE are sections of logarithmic spirals. The poles of these spirals are at points A and B. The radii in both sectors are sliding or rupture surfaces.

From Mohr's stress theory, and using Airy's stress function, Prandtl obtained a differential equation of the second order, the solution of which gives the analytical expression for the ultimate compressive stress σ_u (see Ref. 8):

$$\sigma_u = \frac{c}{\tan \phi} \left[\tan^2(\pi/4 + \phi/2) e^{\pi \tan \phi} - 1 \right]. \qquad (22\text{-}12)$$

This ultimate compressive stress σ_u on faces AC and BC is thus the ultimate bearing capacity at the surface AB of the punched material.

The true value of Prandtl's ultimate bearing capacity of a pure, plastic, cohesive soil is

$$\sigma_u = 5.14c. \qquad (22\text{-}13)$$

Prandtl's theory of plastic failure in a system where a vertical puncher is applied on a horizontal surface of a metal can be applied for calculating bearing capacity of soil. In such a case, Prandtl's theory is based on an analysis of the stress condition for the ultimate plastic failure of the soil.

The puncher can be considered to be the strip foundation, usually rigid masonry, loaded with a pressure σ_u over the width $2b$ of the footing.

The softer material into which the puncher penetrates would be the soil. The soil wedge immediately underneath the base of the footing is assumed to be weightless. Upon exhaustion of the shear strength of the soil, a two-sided expulsion of soil from underneath takes place according to the mode given in Prandtl's system, Fig. 22-5. This system, with some modifications as applied to soil, is illustrated in Fig. 22-6.

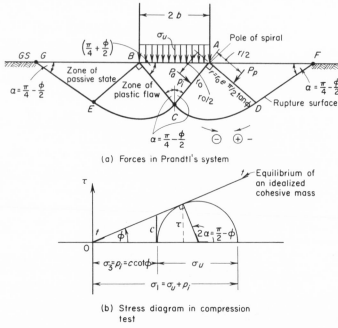

(a) Forces in Prandtl's system

(b) Stress diagram in compression test

FIG. 22-6.   Prandtl's system for a $(\phi - c)$ soil.

According to Prandtl's theory, the bearing pressure σ_u on the ground surface AB is transmitted through the soil wedge, $\triangle ABC$, on the face AC between the wedge and the plastic zone according to Pascal's law, undiminished and in all directions, Fig. 22-6a. Also, the initial stress p_i in the soil wedge, $\triangle ABC$, distributes hydrostatically according to Pascal's law. Hence, the pressure intensity σ_a from the active zone on face AC is

$$\sigma_a = \sigma_u + p_i, \qquad (22\text{-}14)$$

where

$$p_i = c \cot \phi,$$

(Fig. 22-6b) and where ϕ is the angle of internal friction of the (ϕ-c) soil.

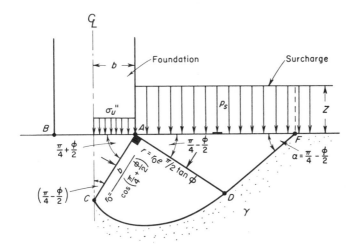

FIG. 22-7. Surcharge p_s added to Prandtl's system.

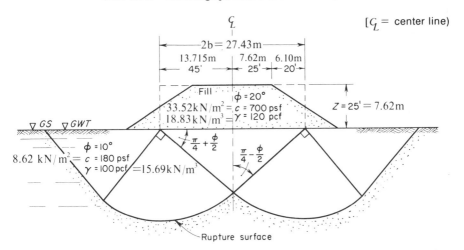

FIG. 22-8. Application of Prandtl's theory of plasticity for determining the bearing capacity of soil.

22-11. Terzaghi's Correction. To prevent Prandtl's ultimate bearing capacity σ_u from becoming equal to zero when $c = 0$, Terzaghi suggested an improvement to account for the weight (surcharge) of the soil: to the original quantity c in Prandtl's equation a factor c' was added, where

$$c' = \gamma t \tan \phi, \tag{22-15}$$

$$t = \frac{\text{area of wedges and sector}}{\text{length } GEC} = \tag{22-16}$$

$$= \text{an equivalent height of surcharge of soil material, and}$$

$$\gamma = \text{unit weight of soil.}$$

The area of wedges and a sector obviously means one half of the system. Then

$$\sigma_u = \frac{c + c'}{\tan \phi} \{[\tan^2(\pi/4 + \phi/2)]e^{\pi \tan \phi} - 1\}. \tag{22-17}$$

Now, when $c = 0$ and thus $\sigma_u \neq 0$, as for pure frictional soil, then σ_u is

$$\sigma_u = \gamma t \{[\tan^2(\pi/4 + \phi/2)]e^{\pi \tan \phi} - 1\}. \tag{22-18}$$

22-12. Taylor's Correction. In Taylor's work[9] there appears in Prandtl's equation for a half-width of footing a factor,

$$\gamma b \tan(\pi/4 + \phi/2) = \gamma b \sqrt{K_p}. \tag{22-19}$$

Then

$$\sigma_u = [c \cot \phi + \gamma b \tan(\pi/4 + \phi/2)]\{[\tan^2(\pi/4 + \phi/2)]e^{\pi \tan \phi} - 1\}, \tag{22-20}$$

where it is said that this factor, $\gamma b \tan(\pi/4 + \phi/2)$, which did not appear in the original Prandtl equation, was added later to account for strength by over-burden pressure. However nothing is said in that work as to how this factor was derived. The added surcharge p_s to the Prandtl system is shown in Fig. 22-7.

Example 1. The application of Prandtl's theory of plastic equilibrium to a soil mechanics problem is now illustrated by a concrete example.

Determine the bearing capacity (resistance to soil lateral expulsion from underneath a highway fill) of a fill-supporting soil which has a low cohesive strength. The system in question is illustrated in Fig. 22-8. The groundwater table coincides with the ground surface. The properties of the soil material in question are:

I. *Fill-supporting soil:*
   angle of internal friction: $\phi = 10°$
   cohesion: $c = 180$ lb/ft^2 = 8.62 kN/m^2
   unit weight of soil: $\gamma = 100$ lb/ft^3 = 15.69 kN/m^3
   effective (submerged) unit weight because of inundation:

$$\gamma_{sub} = \gamma - \gamma_w = 100 - 62.4 = 37.6 \text{ (lb/ft}^3)$$

$$= 15.69 - 9.80 \approx 5.90 \text{ (kN/m}^3)$$

II. *Fill-material:*
   angle of internal friction: $\phi = 20°$
   cohesion: $c = 700$ lb/ft^2 = 33.52 kN/m^2
   unit weight of soil: $\gamma_f = 120$ lb/ft^3 = 18.83 kN/m^3.

Solution. To perform the required analysis, first convert the trapezoidal, cross-sectional area of the fill into an equivalent rectangular cross section of the same height (25 ft = 7.62 m), as shown in Fig. 22-8. Then the width of the base of the fill is $2b = 90$ ft = 27.43 m.

Prandtl's equation, modified by Taylor, Eq. (22-20) will be used:

$$c_u = [c \cdot \cot\phi + \gamma \cdot b \cdot \tan(\pi/4 + \phi/2)] \left\{ [\tan^2(\pi/4 + \phi/2)] \cdot e^{\pi \cdot \tan\phi} - 1 \right\}.$$

Auxiliary calculations for fill-supporting soil:

$$c \cdot \cot\phi = (180)(\cot 10°) = (180)(5.671) \approx \underline{1021 \ (\text{lb}/\text{ft}^2)}$$

$$\tan(45° + \frac{10°}{2}) = \tan 50° = 1.192$$

$$\tan^2 50° = (1.192)^2 = 1.421$$

$$\gamma_{sub} \cdot b \cdot \tan(\pi/4 + \phi/2) = (37.6)(45.0) \cdot \tan(45° + \frac{10°}{2})$$

$$= (1692)(1.192) = \underline{2017 \ (\text{lb}/\text{ft}^2)}$$

$$e^{\pi \cdot \tan\phi} = e^{(3.14) \cdot \tan 10°} = e^{(3.14)(0.1763)} = e^{0.554} = 1.740$$

Ultimate bearing capacity of fill-suporting soil:

$$\sigma_u = (1021 + 2017)[(1.421)(1.740) - 1]$$

$$= (3038)(2.473 - 1) = \underline{4475 \ (\text{lb}/\text{ft}^2)} \approx 2.24 \ (\text{ton}/\text{ft}^2)$$

Pressure imparted by fill on fill-supporting soil:

$$\sigma = \gamma_f \cdot z = (120)(25) = \underline{3000 \ (\text{lb}/\text{ft}^2)} = 1.50 \ (\text{ton}/\text{ft}^2)$$

Factor of safety η against breaking of the 25 ft thick fill into the fill-supporting soil:

$$\eta = \sigma_u/\sigma = 2.24/1.50 = \underline{1.49}$$

Should the factor of safety be required to be $\eta = 3.0$, then

$$\eta = \sigma_u/\sigma = \frac{4475}{(120)(z)} = 3.0,$$

and the thickness, or height, z, of the fill should be only

$$z = \frac{\sigma_u}{\gamma_f \cdot \eta} = \frac{4475}{(120)(3.0)} = \underline{12.4 \ (\text{feet})}$$

Example 2. If in the previous example the fill-supporting soil is a pure clay whose cohesion is $c = 500 \ \text{lb}/\text{ft}^2$ and the unit weight is $\gamma = 105 \ \text{lb}/\text{ft}^3$, then the ultimate bearing capacity of the clay is calculated by Eq. (22-13) as

$$\sigma_u = (5.14) c = (5.14)(500) = \underline{2570 \ (\text{lb}/\text{ft}^2)} = 1.285 \ (\text{ton}/\text{ft}^2)$$

Neither the unit weight γ of the clay nor the width $2b$ of the fill enter into these calculations.

The same examples in SI units

Example 1.

Auxiliary calculations for fill-supporting soil

(modified Prandtl's equation 22-20):

$$c \cdot \cot\phi = (8.62) \cdot \cot 10° = (8.62)(5.671) = 48.88 \ (kN/m^2)$$

$$\gamma_{sub} \cdot b \cdot \tan(\pi/4 + \phi/2) = (5.90)(13.715) \cdot \tan(45° + \frac{10°}{2}) =$$

$$= (80.92)(1.192) = 96.46 \ (kN/m^2).$$

$$\tan^2 50° = (1.192)^2 = 1.421$$

$$e^{\pi \cdot \tan\phi} = e^{(3.14)\tan 10°} = e^{0.554} = 1.740.$$

Ultimate bearing capacity of fill-supporting soil.

$$\sigma_u = (48.88 + 96.46)[(1.421)(1.740) - 1]$$

$$= (145.34)(2.473 - 1) = \underline{214 \ (kN/m^2)}$$

Pressure caused by fill on fill-supporting soil.

$$\sigma = \gamma_f \cdot z = (18.83)(7.62) = \underline{143.5 \ (kN/m^2)}$$

Factor of safety η against breaking of the 7.62 m thick fill into the fill-supporting soil:

$$\eta = \sigma_u/\sigma = 214/143.5 = \underline{1.49}$$

Should the factor of safety be required to be $\eta = 3.0$, then

$$\eta = \frac{\sigma_u}{\sigma} = \frac{153}{(18.83)(z)} = 3.0,$$

and the thickness, or height, of the fill should be only

$$\eta = \frac{\sigma_u}{\gamma_f \cdot \eta} = \frac{153}{(18.83)(3.0)} \approx \underline{2.70 \ (m)}.$$

Example 2. If in the previous example the fill-supporting soil is a pure clay with cohesion $c = 23.94 \ kN/m^3$, then the ultimate bearing capacity of the clay (here surface loading) is calculated by Eq. (22-13) as

$$\sigma_u = (5.14) \cdot c = (5.14)(23.94) \approx \underline{123 \ (kN/m^2)}$$

Neither the unit weight of the clay nor the width of the fill enter into this calculation.

22-13. Terzaghi's Soil Bearing Capacity Formulas.

In the past, the problem of determining the soil bearing capacity for shallow foundation analytically has been dealt with by many researchers and engineers. However, many of the sofar proposed soil bearing capacity solutions still must stand the test of time before they can be accepted unquestionably. This problem relative to striving for theoretically exact solutions is still an acute one.

Among the many approximative solutions for the soil ultimate bearing capacity which are enjoying the greatest popularity today are those by Terzaghi[10] and Meyerhof.[13-17]

Based on Prandtl's theory of plastic failure (in soil), Terzaghi[10] presented a modified system of a *shallow strip foundation* as illustrated in Fig. 22-9. A strip or continuous foundation is one which is long as compared with its width. It thus

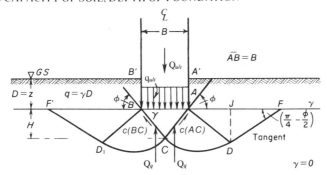

FIG. 22-9. Prandtl-Terzaghi's system.

presents a two-dimensional problem.

The shallow strip foundation or footing (D ≦ B) is loaded with an ultimate centrical vertical load $Q_{ult} = q_{ult} \cdot A$, and is laid at a depth D below the ground surface. Here q_{ult} is the ultimate soil bearing capacity and $A = (B)(1)$ is the contact surface area of the base of the footing for one unit of length of run of the footing; B is the width of the footing. The depth of the footing below the ground surface means that the horizontal surface at the base line elevation of the footing is loaded with a uniformly distributed surcharge load, $q = \gamma \cdot D$. The shallow footing may also be founded directly on the ground surface ($D = 0$).

In his ultimate bearing capacity analysis of the soil-strip foundation system, Terzaghi made the following assumptions:

1) the base of the foundation is rough, so that enough friction between the base and the soil can develop, meaning that no lateral displacement of the foundation can take place; only vertical displacement, viz., settlement can occur;

2) for cohesive soils, cohesion is accounted for;

3) the effect of the self-weight of the soil on the form of the rupture surface is disregarded in this analysis;

4) upon exhaustion of the shear strength of the soil, groundbreak is brought about over a clearly delineated form of a rupture surface;

5) the two-sided symmetrical rupture surface line $FDCD_1F_1$ delineating the rupture surface is a compound line consisting of two curved parts CD and CD_1, and two straight lines DF and D_1F_1. These lines are tangents to the curves CD and CD_1, at points D and D_1;

6) the curved parts, CD and CD_1 are assumed to be curved according to the mathematical curve of logarithmic spiral described by the polar equation

$$r = r_o \cdot e^{\omega \cdot \tan\phi} , \qquad (22\text{-}21)$$

where $r =$ any radius-vector of the spiral at an angle of amplitude ω measured from the initial radius-vector $r_o = \overline{AC}$

$e =$ base of the natural logarithm system, and

$\tan \phi =$ coefficient of internal friction of soil;

7) the line elements AC and BC are straight lines;

8) lines AC and BC form an angle ϕ (here ϕ is the angle of internal friction of

soil) with the horizontal drawn through point A and point B.

9) at point C, the course of the failure surface is tacitly assumed to be vertical, forming an angle $90° + \phi$ with the shear plane BC (Ref. 10, p. 122; Ref. 20, p. 28);

10) the ruptured, sliding wedge is volume-constant, and is being expelled laterally and up from the underneath the base of the shallow footing in the case of a dense soil, and the soil wedge slides as a solid disk;

11) the shearing resistance of the soil above the level of the base of the footing is disregarded.

The ultimate soil bearing capacity q_{ult} of the shallow system soil-strip-foundation is derived approximately from the equilibrium condition of the free-body $ACDJA$ acted upon by the various forces involved, accounting separately for the frictional effects as well as separately for the effects of cohesion. The results from these two effects are then added up.

At the instance of the groundbreak, the load Q_{ult} should be exactly equal to the shear strength or resistance in the rupture surface. Based on the property of the logarithmic spiral, all frictional forces pass through the pole of the spiral.

The total ultimate load Q_{ult} is obtained from the summation of all vertical forces which act on the surfaces AC and BC:

$$Q_{ult} = Q_c + Q_q + Q_\gamma \qquad (22\text{-}22)$$

where

$\qquad Q_c =$ effect of cohesive forces

$\qquad Q_q =$ effect of lateral surcharge q, and

$\qquad Q_\gamma =$ effect of weight of soil wedge $\triangle ABC$, viz., effect of width B of the foundation.

It should be noticed that such an analysis pertains only to one of the many possible positions of the groundbreak configurations. In order to find the position of the most critical rupture surface characterizing the worst stability condition of the soil-foundation system, for the same given ϕ, several more calculations should be made using other spirals by varying the position of the pole of the spiral. That position of the groundbreak configuration for which the Q_{ult}-value becomes a minimum is then to be considered as the most critical or most dangerous rupture figure of the groundbreak. Obviously, such a lengthy procedure for finding $Q_{ult\,min}$ involves a lot of computations. To facilitate an easy use of this method in practice, Terzaghi prepared the following ultimate bearing capacity equation:

$$\frac{Q_{ult}}{(B)(1)} = q_{ult} = c\,N_c + \gamma \cdot D\,N_q + (0.5)\gamma B\,N_\gamma, \qquad (22\text{-}23)$$

wherein $q_{ult} =$ general ultimate bearing capacity of soil for shallow strip or continuous footing ($D \leqq B$) with a rough base and for general shear in soil

$\qquad c =$ cohesion of soil

γ = unit weight of soil
D = depth of base of footing below ground surface
B = width of strip footing
$q = \gamma \cdot D$ = surcharge; also index for soil surcharge.

N_c, N_q and N_γ are the so-called Terzaghi's dimensionless critical bearing capacity factors. These N-factors are functions of the angle of internal friction ϕ of soil.

Thus, N_c = bearing capacity factor to account for cohesion
       N_q = bearing capacity factor to account for lateral surcharge, and
       N_γ = bearing capacity factor to account for the effect of the width B of the footing.

Notice again that the ultimate soil bearing capacity q_{ult} in Eq. 22-23 is equal to the sum contributed by cohesion c, soil lateral surcharge $\gamma \cdot D$, and the unit weight γ of the soil, viz., the effect of width B of the footing.

It was here mentioned earlier that this ultimate soil bearing pressure q_{ult}, which brings about a clearly defined rupture surface applies to the so-called general shear failure of the soil, viz., complete groundbreak. A general shear failure occurs in dense sands and stiff clays. In contradistinction, in loose sands and soft clays no sharply developed rupture surface figures develop. This kind of failure or rupture condition Terzaghi terms "local shear." The idea about the concepts of general and local shear is conveyed in Fig. 22-10. In this figure, curve G represents the condition of general shear in a dense or stiff soil. Just prior to rupture impending, the settlement of the soil material is relatively small, and the ultimate soil bearing capacity is well defined in such a pressure-settlement diagram. In Fig. 22-10, curve L represents the condition of local shear taking place in a loose or soft soil. Here the settlements are large, and local shear sets in mainly because of the large compressibility of the soil. The q_{ult}-point on such a pressure-settlement curve is decided upon arbitrarily where the curve, by observation, takes a relatively steep course. Large settlements may not be tolerated in practice.

In the case of a local shear, Terzaghi recommends that the cohesion and friction factors be taken as $2/3$ of the general shear factors. Thus $\tan\phi^1 = (2/3)\tan\phi$ and $c^1 = (2/3) \cdot c$. In such a case, for local shear Terzaghi's ultimate soil bearing capacity equation is:

$$q_{ult}^1 = (0.67) \cdot c \ N_c' + \gamma \cdot D \ N_q' + (0.5)\gamma \ B \ N_\gamma' \qquad (22-24)$$

where N_c', N_q' and N_γ' are bearing capacity factors for local shear.

For rapid calculations of the soil bearing capacity Terzaghi prepared ultimate bearing capacity factor graphs as shown in Fig. 22-11. The solid curves represent the N-factors for general shear, and the dotted ones represent the N'-factors for local shear.

An analysis of the N-factors reveal the following:
When $\phi = 0$, then $N_c = 5.7$, $N_q = 1$, and $N_\gamma = 0$ (see Fig. 22-11), and therefore when $D = 0$,

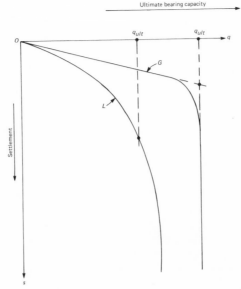

Fig. 22-10. Illustrating general (G) and local (L) shear failure curves.

$$q_{ult} = 5.7\,c \qquad\qquad (22\text{-}25)$$

In stability calculations of footings laid on saturated clay, immediately after completion of the structure, the undrained condition of such a soil is assumed ($\phi = 0$). When $\phi = 0$, the logarithmically spiraled rupture curve takes the form of a circular arc and Prandtl's equation when $D = 0$ transforms into

$$q_{ult} = 5.14\,c \qquad\qquad (22\text{-}26)$$

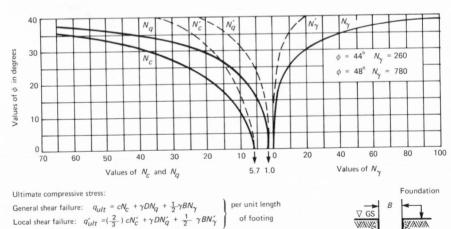

Fig. 22-11. Soil bearing capacity factors (after Terzaghi, Ref. 10).

Thus, because $N_\gamma = 0$, the ultimate bearing capacity on a cohesive soil is independent of the width of the footing.

The N_c-value in Prandtl's equation (22-26) is less than that in Terzaghi's equation (22-25) because Prandtl assumed a smooth base ($\phi = 0$), whereas Terzaghi assumed a rough base. Hence, the increase in the N_c bearing capacity factor in Terzaghi's equation over Prandtl's equation is because of the friction between the base of the footing and the soil in Terzaghi's analysis.

From this discussion, one notices that the third term in Terzaghi's ultimate bearing capacity formulas applies only to frictional soil, i.e., to ($\phi - c$)-soil as well as to ϕ − soils. In the latter case $c = 0$, and the first term in the ultimate bearing capacity equation vanishes. In a ($\phi - c$)-soil, where $\phi > 0$, the entire Terzaghi's equation is used.

Reduction in soil bearing capacity brought about by flooding of the construction site obtains in noncohesive soil materials only. In cohesive soils, a sudden and temporary inundation of the site affects the angle of shearing resistance practically very little. However, the effective pressure contributing to the shear strength of the soil may become very much reduced.

If the rupture surface of the groundbreak cuts the groundwater table, then the unit weight of the soil above the water table and the unit weight of the submerged part of the soil can be treated separately.

If the design load P from structure on soil is given, Terzaghi formulas can also be used for computing the necessary width B of the footing.

If the load on a saturated pure clay or on a varved clay is applied quickly as compared with the rate of expulsion of the excess pore water, pore water pressures in the soil are induced. In such a case, an unconsolidated undrained condition in the soil is brought about. Therefore bearing capacity of the soil-foundation system is evaluated based on test parameters as obtained from the *uu*- (or quick, Q) shear tests.

On the other hand, if the same types of soil as above were loaded slowly such that enough time is allowed to permit the excess pore water to drain out of the voids of the soil without inducing any excess pore water pressure, the bearing capacity of the soil-foundation system may be assessed based on those test parameters which are obtained from the consolidated drained (*c-d*) (or slow, S) shear tests.

To avoid failure in shear upon loading a saturated varved clay, such soils, in practice, are loaded appropriately slowly.

Terzaghi specialized the general ultimate soil bearing capacity formula, Eq. 22-23, for various other kinds of shallow footings ($D \leq B$).[10]

a) *Frictional-cohesive, or (ϕ-c)-soils* (Table 22-2):
   Rectangular footing:

$$q_{ult} = c \cdot N_c \; \gamma \; (1 + 0.3 \frac{B}{L}) + \gamma \cdot D \cdot N_q + (0.4) \cdot \gamma \cdot B \cdot N_\gamma, \quad (22\text{-}27)$$

where L = length of footing.

TABLE 22-2. SUMMARY OF TERZAGHI'S SOIL ULTIMATE
BEARING CAPACITY EQUATIONS FOR
SHALLOW FOUNDATIONS WITH A ROUGH BASE AND $(\phi-c) - SOILS$

Form of base of foundation	General Shear	Local Shear
	Equation	Equation
1	2	3
1. Strip (continuous)	$q_{ult} = c \cdot N_c + \gamma \cdot D \cdot N_q + (0.5) \cdot \gamma \cdot B \cdot N_\gamma$	$q'_{ult} = (2\ 3)c \cdot N'_c + \gamma \cdot D \cdot N'_q + (0.5)\gamma B N'_\gamma$
2. Square	$q_{ult} = (1.3)c \cdot N_c + \gamma \cdot D \cdot N_q + (0.4) \cdot \gamma \cdot B \cdot N_\gamma$	$q'_{ult} = (1.3) \cdot c \cdot N'_c + \gamma \cdot D \cdot N'_q + (0.4) \cdot \gamma \cdot R \cdot N'_\gamma$
3. Circular (R = radius)	$q_{ult} = (1.3)c \cdot N_c + \gamma \cdot D \cdot N_q + (0.6) \cdot \gamma \cdot R \cdot N_\gamma$	$q'_{ult} = (1.3) \cdot c \cdot N'_c + \gamma D \cdot N'_q + (0.6) \cdot \gamma \cdot R \cdot N'_\gamma$
4. Rectangle	$q_{ult} = c \cdot N_c (1 + 0.3 \frac{B}{L}) + \gamma \cdot D \cdot N_q + (0.4) \cdot \gamma \cdot B \cdot N_\gamma$	$q'_{ult} = (2\ 3) \cdot c \cdot N'_c \cdot (1 + 0.3 \cdot \frac{B}{L}) + \gamma D N'_q (0.4) \gamma B N'_\gamma$

Square footing:
$$q_{ult} = (1.3) \cdot c \cdot N_c + \gamma \cdot D \cdot N_q + (0.4) \cdot \gamma \cdot B \cdot N_\gamma, \qquad (22\text{-}28)$$

where $L = B$; $B \times B$;
Circular footing of radius R, on dense soil:

$$q_{ult} = (1.3) \cdot c \cdot N_c + \gamma \cdot D \cdot N_q + (0.6) \cdot \gamma \cdot R \cdot N_\gamma, \qquad (22\text{-}29)$$

b) *Noncohesive or ϕ-soils* ($\phi > 0$; c = 0)
Continuous footing:

$$q_{ult} = \gamma \cdot D \cdot N_q + (0.5) \cdot \gamma \cdot B \cdot N_\gamma \qquad (22\text{-}30)$$

Rectangular and square footings:

$$q_{ult} = \gamma \cdot D \cdot N_q + (0.4) \cdot \gamma \cdot B \cdot N_\gamma \qquad (22\text{-}31)$$

Circular footing:

$$q_{ult} = \gamma \cdot D \cdot N_q + (0.6) \cdot \gamma \cdot R \cdot N_\gamma \qquad (22\text{-}32)$$

c) *Pure cohesive or c-soils* ($\phi = 0$; c > 0)
Continuous footing:
Here
$$N_c = 5.71; \quad N_q = 1.0, \text{ and } N_\gamma = 0 \text{ (see Fig. 22-11)}:$$
$$q_{ult} = c \cdot N_c + \gamma \cdot D \qquad (22\text{-}33)$$

Rectangular and square footing:

$$q_{ult} = c \cdot N_c \cdot (1 + 0.3\frac{B}{L}) + \gamma \cdot D \qquad (22\text{-}34)$$

Circular footing:

$$q_{ult} = (1.3) \cdot c \cdot N_c + \gamma \cdot D \qquad (22\text{-}35)$$

If $\phi = 0$ and $c > 0$, part of the pure cohesive soil total bearing capacity from surcharge ($\gamma \cdot D$) is exactly compensated by the weight of soil removed by excavation. Therefore in footing design the *net bearing capacity q_{net}* is:

$$q_{net} = \sigma_o - \gamma D, \qquad (22\text{-}36)$$

where σ_o = contact pressure from structure on soil.
For rectangular footing on clay, Skempton[11] proposed the following net bearing capacity formula:

$$q_{net} = (5) \cdot (c) \cdot (1 + 0.2\frac{D}{B}) \cdot (1 + 0.2\frac{B}{L}) \qquad (22\text{-}37)$$

where D = depth of footing [$D \leq (2.5\ B)$]
B = width of footing
L = length of footing

For circular footings, set $D = B = L$:

$$q_{net} = (5) \cdot (c)(1.2)^2 \qquad (22\text{-}38)$$

The allowable soil bearing capacity σ_{all} is here obtained by dividing the net soil bearing capacity by a factor of safety η:

$$\sigma_{all} = \frac{q_{net}}{\eta} \qquad (22\text{-}39)$$

Example 1. Given a shallow strip footing $B = 3.0$ m wide. The footing is laid in a frictional-cohesive soil at a depth of $D = 2.00$ m below ground surface. The weight of the soil is $\gamma = 18.85$ kN/m^3; $\phi = 20°$, and $c = 30$ kN/m^2. Calculate the ultimate bearing capacity of the soil and determine its allowable bearing capacity using a factor of safety of $\eta = 3.0$.

Solution. $N_c = 18$; $N_q = 8$; $N_\gamma = 4$.

$$q_{ult} = (30)(18) + (18.85)(2.00)(8) + (0.5)(18.85)(3.0)(4) =$$
$$= 540.0 + 301.60 + 113.10 = \underline{954.70\ (\text{kN}/\text{m}^2)}$$
$$\sigma_{all} = q_{ult}/\eta = 954.70/3 = \underline{318.2\ (\text{kN}/\text{m}^2)}$$

Example 2. A shallow strip footing 2.0 m wide is laid in clay 2.0 m below the ground surface. The unit weight of this soil is 18.00 kN/m^3. The unconfined undrained shear strength of the clay specimen is $\tau_u = c = 20$ kN/m^2. Estimate the ultimate and safe bearing capacities of this clay.

Solution. $N_c = 5.71$; $N_q = 1.0$; $N_\gamma = 0$

$$q_u = c \cdot N_c + \gamma \cdot D \cdot N_q = (20)(5.71) + (18.00)(2.0)$$
$$= 114.20 + 36.00 = \underline{150.20\ (\text{kN}/\text{m}^2)}.$$
$$\sigma_{all} = q_u/\eta = 150.20/3 = \underline{50.07\ (\text{kN}/\text{m}^2)}$$

22-14. Form Factors. Aside from the form- or shape factors as they appear in Terzaghi's ultimate bearing capacity equations 22-23, 22-27, 22-28 and 22-29, for rectangular footings, Skempton[11] suggested a form factor

$$\zeta_c = 1 + (0.20)(B/L) \tag{22-40}$$

to be used in the cohesion term of Eq. (22-23), and a form factor

$$\zeta_\gamma = 1 - (0.20)(B/L), \tag{22-41}$$

to be used in term containing the width B of the footing in Eq. (22-23).

Based on experimental results with footings of different forms in plan, the following modified Terzaghi's soil ultimate bearing capacity equation for shallow foundations is gradually being accepted by the engineering profession in general use[12]:

$$q_{ult} = c \cdot N_c \cdot \zeta_c + q \cdot N_q \cdot \zeta_q + (0.5) \cdot \gamma \cdot B \cdot N_\gamma \cdot \zeta_\gamma \tag{22-42}$$

Herein, N_c, N_q and N_γ are the dimensionless bearing capacity factors for an infinitely long strip footing as before;

$q = \gamma \cdot D =$ geostatic pressure of soil; and

ζ_c, ζ_q and ζ_γ are dimensionless factors termed *shape-* or *form* factors of the footing in plan.

Like the N-factors, so the form factors (ζ) are functions of the angle of shearing resistance ϕ of the soil, and also the geometric configuration of the footing in plan.

The ζ-factors are also influenced by some other parameters (see Table 22-3). Table 22-3 is a compilation of various form factors for shallow foundations as recommended by De Beer in 1967 and modified by Vesić in 1970.[12] These recommended footing form factors are based on series of experiments performed at Ghent, Belgium, according to Vesić.

TABLE 22-3 FORM FACTORS FOR CENTRICALLY LOADED
SHALLOW FOOTINGS ACCORDING TO VESIĆ.[12]

Form of base of footing in plan	ζ_c	ζ_q	ζ_γ
1	2	3	4
1. Strip	1.00	1.00	1.00
2. Square	$1 + (\frac{N_q}{N_c})$	$1 + \tan\phi$	0.60
3. Circle	$1 + (\frac{N_q}{N_c})$	$1 + \tan\phi$	0.60
4. Rectangle	$1 + (\frac{N_q}{N_c})(\frac{B}{L})$	$1 + (\frac{B}{L}) \cdot \tan\phi$	$1 - (0.4)(\frac{B}{L})$

22-15. Meyerhof's Bearing Capacity Charts. Meyerhof extended the method of analysis for calculating soil ultimate bearing capacity of a centrically loaded strip footing for any depth, and published pertinent formulas and charts.[13-17] Meyerhof's results are presented in a similar manner like those as given by Terzaghi, namely by means of bearing capacity factors N, the basic difference between the two are in the magnitude of the N-values.

In his analysis, Meyerhof made use of the soil-foundation system as shown in Fig. 22-12. From this figure, it can be seen that in principle, Meyerhof's system, though similar to Terzaghi's one, differs from the latter in several ways. Here one notices that Meyerhof's assumed rupture surfaces extend above the base level of the footing up to the ground surface. Thus the shear strength of the soil from the base level up to the ground surface is considered.

In his ultimate bearing capacity analysis Meyerhof made the following assumptions:

1. Like Terzaghi, Meyerhof considered friction between the base of the footing and soil. This friction prevents the expulsion of the soil laterally from underneath the base of the footing. Hence, this friction increases the bearing capacity of the soil. This friction brings about a redistribution of the base contact pressures towards the middle of the footing thus relieving the edge points A and B of the footing. As known from Fröhlich's[18,19,20] critical pressure distribution theory at edges of the foundation, points A and B are the ones at which the plastic flow phenomenon in soil sets in first, and from which points the plastic flow propagates bringing about plastic zones in the soil.

   Friction within the soil mass beneath the footing increases proportionally to the width B of the footing.

2. For cohesive soils, cohesion is accounted for.

3. As said before, the assumed rupture surfaces, or shear zones in the soil extend not merely to the level of the base of the footing but also continues up to the ground surface. Thus, also for relatively shallow footings, the rupture surface extension in Meyerhof's bearing capacity analysis renders a larger bearing capacity than by means of Terzaghi's analysis.

4. The two-sided rupture surface curves CE (and CE') are assumed to be curved according to the mathematical curve of a logarithmic spiral.

5. Lines EF and $E'F'$ of the rupture surface are straight lines, i.e., tangents to the spiral curves at points E and E'.

6. Lines AC and BC of the elastic wedge $\triangle ABC$ are straight lines.

7. The soil wedge has a self-weight γ.

8. An equivalent, or substitute free ground surface AF is introduced forming an angle β with the horizontal. This angle β has a functional relationship with the width-to-depth ratio (B/D).

9. On the equivalent free surface, there acts an average substitute normal pressure σ_o, assumed to be uniformly distributed.

10. In order to obtain a minimum value of the N_γ-factor, Meyerhof varied the angle ψ between ϕ and $(45° + \phi/2)$.

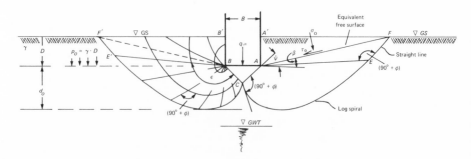

FIG. 22-12. Meyerhof's soil-foundation system.
Assumed conditions:
1) $D \leq B$
2) Soil is uniform to depth $d_o > B$
3) GWT is lower than d_o below base of footing
4) Soil properties: γ, ϕ, c.

11. The calculations for q_{ult} are repeated for several assumed rupture surfaces to obtain the position and size of the most dangerous rupture surface.

12. The position of the poles of the spirals is determined by stepwise approach by method of trial and adjustment.

Based on these assumptions, Meyerhof arrived at the ultimate bearing capacity equation:

$$q_{ult} = c \cdot N_c + \gamma D N_q + (0.5) \cdot B \cdot \gamma \cdot N_\gamma \qquad (22\text{-}43)$$

One notices that superficially, this equation by its construction is similar to that as given by Terzaghi (Eq. 22-23). However, Meyerhof's N-values depend not only upon the physical constants of the soil, but also upon the depth of the foundation, viz., angle β; the roughness of the base of the footing; the form of the rupture surface; the friction between the foundation and the soil, and the form of the footing in plan.

Considering the self-weight of the soil rupture wedge, Meyerhof's analytical q_{ult}-values show a favorable influence of the assumed curved rupture surface - the log spiral - on the ultimate bearing capacity. Also, Meyerhof found that when D exceeds B, the bearing capacity factors increase rapidly with increasing depth D. Meyerhof's analysis also brings out that a modest increase in cohesion and a simultaneous decrease in the angle of internal friction ϕ (viz., angle of shearing resistance), the soil bearing capacity decreases. Besides, the prolonged curved rupture surfaces in Meyerhof's analysis render for $\phi > 30°$ quite conspicuously large values of bearing capacity factors.

It is interesting to notice that based on his experiments, Meyerhof stated that for greater depths the actual ultimate loads do not agree with his theoretically obtained values. Therefore he proposed a reduction coefficient of about 0.85 for shearing strength to be used if the depth-to-width ratio, $D/B > 5$. Here 0.85 is an empirical soil compressibility factor.

Regardless of that in his assumptions and analysis Meyerhof tried to comprehend many possible factors and effects, his analysis is afflicted with some weaknesses. For example, as to the assumed uniformly distributed substitute stresses σ_o and τ_o on the equivalent free surface, in reality these stresses would be most likely distributed roughly triangularly. Further, for his D/B factor (pertains to load inclination and inclination of footing) which suppose to characterize the effect of friction between the foundation and the soil, Meyerhof gives only two limited values, $D/B = 0$ and $D/B = 1.0$ without any intermediate points. Also, the equivalent free surface cannot be located directly. Because of the dependence upon the angle β $[\beta = f(B/D)]$, and because it is necessary to determine the substitute pressure σ_o which can be done grapho-analytically, Meyerhof's analysis appears to be cumbersome to use for routine calculations of ultimate bearing capacity of the soil-foundation system.

Finally, the determination of the angle ϵ, i.e., of those points E and E' where the straight line parts of the rupture surface tangents the spirals, is very unsafe in this method of analysis, and is possible only by trial and adjustment.

In the past, Meyerhof's large bearing capacity values for pure noncohesive (granular) soils were viewed at with a great prejudice and caution. Nevertheless, it now appears, though, as if some latest soil bearing capacity experiments justify the large values quite well.[21]

To facilitate the use in practical calculations of ultimate bearing capacity, Meyerhof prepared his bearing capacity factor chart[22,23] as shown in Fig. 22-13. In this chart, the N-factors are dimensionless, prepared for a strip foundation with a rough base, and are functions of ϕ. Notice that Meyerhof's N-factors differ in magnitude from those as derived by Terzaghi, but the use of Meyerhof's N-factors are same as used in Terzaghi's calculations.

Meyerhof's equation 22-43 can be specialized for a pure ϕ-soil ($c = 0$), as well as for a pure c-soil ($\phi = 0$).

In his article on "The Bearing Capacity of Clays"[11] Skempton suggested that the ultimate bearing capacity of undrained saturated clays ($\phi_u = 0$) may be computed as

$$q_{ult} = c_u \cdot N_c + \gamma D, \qquad (22\text{-}44)$$

where c_u = cohesion under undrained condition
$\quad N_c$ = Skempton's bearing capacity factor,
$\quad \gamma$ = unit weight of soil, and
$\quad D$ = depth of footing below ground surface.

These N_c-factors depend upon the form of the footing in plan and upon the depth/width (D/B) ratio.

Fig. 22-14 shows Skempton's graphs for N_c as a function of D/B for circular or square footing ($B/L = 1.0$) and for strip footing ($B/L = 0$) for a soil whose $\phi_u = 0$. For a rectangular footing (BxL) where $B < L$, Skempton recommends to use the N_c-value for a square footing to be multiplied by

$$0.84 + (0.16)(B/L) \tag{22-45}$$

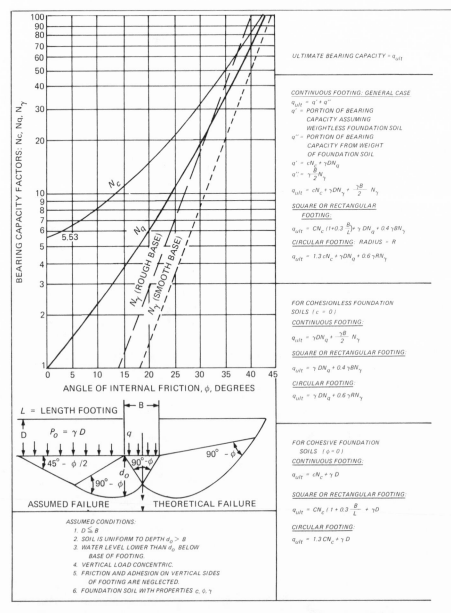

Fig. 22-13. Ultimate bearing capacity of shallow footings with concentric loads. After Meyerhof[22] and NAVFAC DM-7.[23]

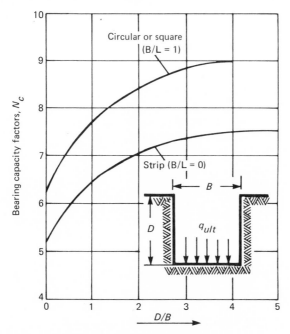

FIG. 22-14. Skempton's bearing capacity factors N_c as a function of D/B for $\phi_u = 0$.

22-16. Effects of External Factors on Ultimate Bearing Capacity. The external factors affecting soil bearing capacity are those which do not depend upon soil properties but rather depend either upon the mode of external loading or properties, viz., mode of orientation of base of the foundation footing.

1. Major examples of external loading are
   a) inclined loading on horizontal ground surface;
   b) eccentric loading with one way or two way eccentricity, on horizontal ground surface.
2. Examples of mode of orientation are
   a) inclined base of footing relative to the horizontal, and
   b) inclined ground surface relative to the horizontal

22-17. Effect of Externally Applied Inclined Loading. In practice, one frequently encounters an inclined resultant load acting on the base of the footing at an angle of inclination α with the vertical.

Among the many publications putting to the fore various proposals for calculating theoretically soil ultimate bearing capacity for obliquely loaded footings are that by Meyerhof.[15] His formulas and charts for determining q_{ult} of obliquely loaded shallow footings are practical and easy to use. Meyerhof derived a method for calculating q_{ult} for two cases, namely:

   i) the base of the footing is horizontal, and the direction of action of the load deviates from the vertical by an angle α (see Fig. 22-15).

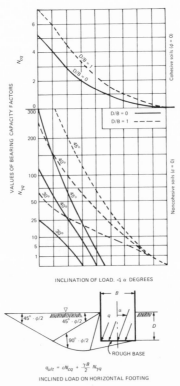

FIG. 22-15.   Bearing capacity factors after Meyerhof.[15]

    ii) the base of the footing forms an angle of inclination α wih the horizontal, and the base of the footing is perpendicular to the obliquely acting external load (see Fig. 22-16).

The ultimate bearing capacity for a horizontal footing, q_{vult}, is given by Meyerhof as the vertical component

$$q_{vult} = q \cdot cos\alpha$$
$$= c \cdot N_{cq} + (0.5) \cdot \gamma \cdot B \cdot N_{\gamma q} \qquad (22\text{-}46)$$

where N_{cq} and $N_{\gamma q}$ are the bearing capacity factors as functions of ϕ, D/B and α.

These bearing capacity factors include the effect of any skin friction. These factors are shown in Fig. 22-15 for shallow strip foundations in ϕ-soils and c-soils.

For an inclined footing with its base perpendicular to the load, the ultimate bearing capacity, according to Meyerhof[15] can be expressed in terms of the resultant bearing capacity

$$q = cN_{cq} + (0.5) \cdot \gamma \cdot N_{\gamma q} \qquad (22\text{-}47)$$

The values of the bearing capacity factors, exclusive of any skin friction, are given for shallow strip footings in Fig. 22-16 for ϕ-soils, as well as for c-soils.

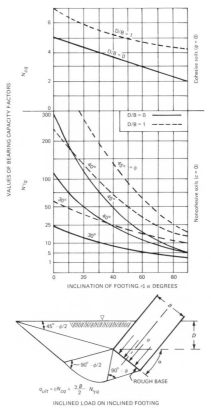

FIG. 22-16.   Bearing capacity factors after Meyerhof.[15]

22-18. Eccentric Loading. For eccentric vertical loading, Meyerhof[15] proposed a simple solution for calculating ultimate bearing capacity q_{ult} by assuming a reduced width B' of the footing the base of which is in contact with the soil (Fig. 22-17). The vertical load Q_{ult} on a shallow strip foundation with eccentricity e on the full base width B is assumed to act centrically over the reduced or effective contact area $= (B')(1.0)$.

The effective width B' calculates as

$$B' = (\frac{B}{2} - e)\, 2 = B - 2e, \qquad (22\text{-}48)$$

and the ultimate bearing capacity q_{ult} is calculated for a soil with self-weight γ, ϕ and c as for a centrally, vertically loaded foundation over its effective or reduced width $B' = B - 2e$ as

$$\begin{aligned} Q_{ult} &= q_{ult} \cdot B', \\ q_{ult} &= c \cdot N_{cq} + (0.5) \cdot \gamma \cdot B' \cdot N_{\gamma q} \end{aligned} \qquad (22\text{-}49)$$

These bearing capacity factors depend mainly upon ϕ and (D/B')-ratio.

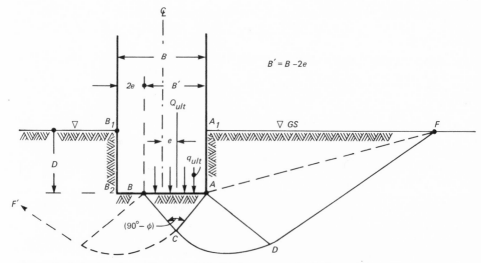

FIG. 22-17. Reduced or effective width B′ of an eccentrically loaded shallow foundation after Meyerhof.[15]

The q_{ult}-value so calculated by Eq. (22-49) is the base resistance to which, if needed, any skin resistance on the shaft or wall may be added to obtain the total ultimate bearing capacity.

Fig. 22-18 shows the reduction of base area of a rectangular footing at a two-way eccentricity. The ultimate load Q_{ult} is then computed as

$$Q_{ult} = q_{ult} \cdot A' \cdot \lambda = q_{ult} \cdot (B' \cdot L') \cdot \lambda, \qquad (22\text{-}50)$$

where λ = Meyerhof's form factor = $f(L'/B')$[14], and q_{ult} to be computed by Eq. (22-49).

In his contribution about "Bearing Capacity of Shallow Foundations" in the Handbook of Foundation Engineering, Vesić[12] presents the following modified bearing capacity equation to account for form of the footing, for inclination of load, for eccentricity, for tilt of footing, and for ground slope:

$$q_{ult} = \frac{Q_{ult}}{B' \cdot L'} = c \cdot N_c \cdot \xi_c \cdot \xi_{ci} + q \cdot N_q \cdot \xi_q \cdot \xi_{qi} + (0.5) \cdot \gamma \cdot B \cdot N_\gamma \cdot \xi_\gamma \cdot \xi_{\gamma i} \quad (22\text{-}51)$$

Herein,

$B' = B - 2 \cdot e_B$ = reduced or effective width of the footing
$L' = L - 2 \cdot e_L$ = reduced or effective length of the footing
e_B = eccentricity of the load in the direction of the width of the footing
e_L = eccentricity of the load in the longitudinal direction of the footing
ξ_c, ξ_q, ξ_γ = form factors
$\xi_{ci}, \xi_{qi}, \xi_{\gamma i}$ = convenient inclination factors easy to apply on the individual terms in Eq. 22-51.

For these factors the reader is referred to Reference 12.

Intensive research work goes on presently at various institutions and agencies to strive for plausible and accurate methods of determining the ultimate soil bearing capacity problem, especially that of inclined and eccentrically loaded foundations. Until better solutions than now will become available, engineers will continue to resort to presently known or available approximative solutions for evaluating the ultimate bearing capacity of various soil-foundation systems.

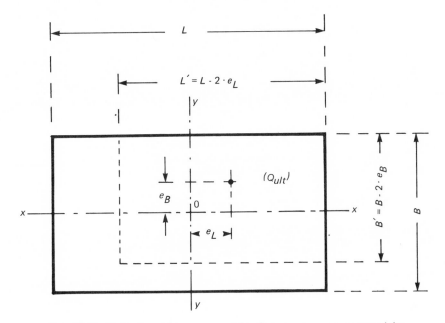

FIG. 22-18. Reduction of base area of footing at a two-way eccentricity.

22-19. Ultimate Bearing Capacity of Deep Foundations. A deep foundation is one that extends to a considerable depth below ground surface, and whose width or diameter is small as compared to depth of the foundation. In practice, a foundation is considered, arbitrarily, to be deep, if its depth D exceeds about twice the width B of the base of the footing, i.e., when $D>2B$, or when $D>4R$, where R is the radius of a deep foundation circular in cross-section.

Deep foundations are usually used where soil properties are inferior for shallow foundations. Deep foundations are used in some of the following applications.

1. For the transmission of structural loads through weak, nonuniform compressible soils and/or deep water to a firm stratum of soil, or gravel, or rock, if attainable.

2. When groundbreak or rupture of soil underneath a shallow foundation can be anticipated.

3. When the soil conditions are such that a washout and erosion of soil by scouring from underneath a shallow foundation may take place.

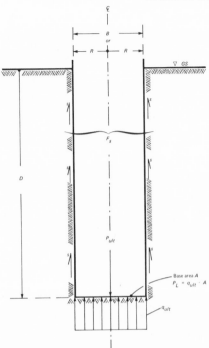

FIG. 22-19. Deep foundation.

$$P_{ult} = q_{ult} \cdot A + s \cdot U \cdot D$$

4. When a competent load-bearing soil lies at considerably great but practically attainable depth consistent with economy and present-day technology.

The ultimate load bearing capacity P_{ult} of a soil-deep-foundation system, such as a pier, for example (see Fig. 22-19), may be approximately calculated by the following formula:

$$P_{ult} = P_L + F_s = q_{ult} \cdot A + U \cdot s \cdot D, \tag{22-52}$$

wherein

$P_L = q_{ult} \cdot A$ is the total ultimate soil bearing capacity underneath the entire base area A of the pier,

q_{ult} = soil ultimate bearing capacity beneath the base of the pier,

$F_s = U \cdot s \cdot D$ = total mantle or skin resistance between pier material and soil,

U = perimeter of the pier,

s = average value of skin resistance between the mantle surface of the pier material and the soil at failure, and

D = embedment depth of the deep foundation in soil.

Notice that the ultimate load bearing capacity P_{ult} of the deep foundation is derived from two sources, namely: total ultimate load P_L on the soil, i.e., from ultimate soil bearing capacity at the base level of the pier, and the shaft resistance of the pier, popularly known as the "skin resistance" F_s (also the term mantle resistance is used).

Applying Terzaghi's ultimate bearing capacity to a square pier at its base on soil, the ultimate bearing capacity P_{ult} of the soil-pier system can be approximately calculated as

$$P_{ult} = q_{ult} \cdot A + UsD = B^2 (1.3 \, cN_c + \gamma DN_q + 0.4\gamma BN_\gamma) +$$
$$+ 4BDp_o \cdot \tan\phi_1 \cdot N_q \qquad (22\text{-}53)$$

where

$$s = p_o \cdot \tan\phi_1 \cdot N_q \qquad (22\text{-}54)$$

$$p_o = \tfrac{1}{2}\gamma \cdot D \cdot K_o \qquad (22\text{-}55)$$

K_o = earth pressure coefficient at rest; for a (ϕ-c)-soil, $K_o \approx 0.5$; for loose and dense sand, $K_o \approx 1.0$ and $K_o \approx 2.0$, respectively;

ϕ_1 = angle of wall friction (between soil and wall material), and all other symbols are the same as before.

For a circular pier on soil, P_{ult} calculates as

$$P_{ult} = \pi R^2 \cdot q_{ult} + UsD = \pi R^2 (1.3 \, c \cdot N_c + \gamma DN_q + 0.6 \cdot \gamma \cdot R \cdot N_\gamma) +$$
$$+ 2\pi RD \cdot \tan\phi_1 \cdot p_o. \qquad (22\text{-}56)$$

Example. Given a centrically loaded circular pier whose diameter is 4.0 m. The embedment depth of the pier is 5.0 m. Compute ultimate bearing capacity P_{ult} of the soil-pier system.

$\gamma = 18.0 \, \text{kN/m}^3$; $c = 5.0 \, \text{kN/m}^2$; $\phi = 18°$; $\phi_1 = 12°$; $\tan\phi_1 = 0.213$. $K_o = 0.50$; $R = 4.0/2 = 2.0$ (m). From Terzaghi's chart, Fig. 22-11, $N_c = 16$; $N_q = 6$; $N_\gamma = 3$; and $p_o = (\tfrac{1}{2})\gamma D \cdot K_o = (0.5)(18)(5.0)(0.5) = 22.5 \, [\text{kN/m}^2]$.

Solution.
By Eq. (22-56)

$$P_{ult} = (3.14)(2.0^2)[(1.3)(5.0)(16) + (18.0)(5.0)(6) + (0.6)(18.0)(2.0)(3)] +$$
$$+ (2)(3.14)(2.0)(5.0) \cdot (0.213)(22.5) =$$
$$= (12.56)(104.0 + 540.0 + 64.80) + 300.97 =$$
$$= (12.56)(708.8) + 300.97 = 8902.53 + 300.97 =$$
$$= 9203.50 \approx \underline{9204 \, [\text{kN}]} \approx 9.20 \, [\text{MN}]$$

System's ultimate bearing capacity:

$$p_{ult} = \frac{P_{ult}}{\pi R^2} = \frac{9204}{(3.14)(2.0^2)} = \frac{9204}{12.56} = 732.80 \, [\frac{\text{kN}}{\text{m}^2}] \quad .$$

$$\sigma_{all} = \frac{p_{ult}}{\eta} = \frac{732.80}{3} = 244.27 \approx 245 \, [\frac{\text{kN}}{\text{m}^2}] \quad .$$

22-20. Skin Resistance. For calculating bearing capacity of a soil-pier system, or for sinking operations of a caisson, as well as for other purposes, it is necessary to know the numerical values of the so-called "skin resistance" between various foundation mantle surface materials and the soil type encountered.

Average values of skin resistance are[24]

soft clay   150 -   600 lb/ft², or   7.18 - 28.73 kN/m²
stiff clay 1,000 - 4,000 lb/ft², or 47.88 - 191.52 kN/m²

The skin resistance may be related empirically to the average undrained (c_u) strength of the undisturbed clay between the ground surface and bottom of the pier.

The base resistance q_{ult} of a pier or that of a pile in clay is evaluated by means of the undrained shear strength c_u of the clay at the base level of the pier or pile, whichever the case is:

$$q_{ult} = c_u \cdot N_c \tag{22-57}$$

If the deep foundation is sunk, or a pile is driven entirely in the clay, the skin resistance is then based on the remolded shear strength value of the clay.

22-21. Negative Skin Friction. The negative skin friction is a downward dragging force acting on the embedded part of the shaft of a pier (or a pile),

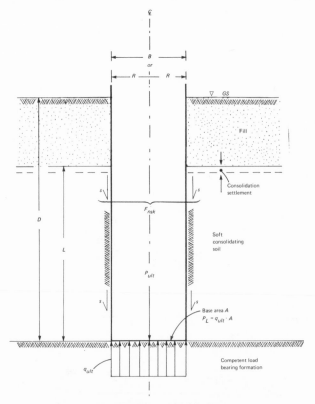

FIG. 22-20. Negative skin friction.
$$P_{ult} = q_{ult} \cdot A - F_{nsk}$$

known also as the shaft resistance of the pier. This force occurs because of the relative downward movement of a compressible, settling soil with respect to the pier shaft, whereas the pier laid on a competent stratum remains stationary. It is the downward movement of the consolidating soil that tends to drag the pier by shear along its mantle surface, thus imparting an additional load F_{nsk} on the base of the pier. Notice that the downward drag-force is equal to the shear resistance s of the soil times the area a_{ms} of the mantle surface of the embedded length L of the pier in the soil (Fig. 22-20). Thus, the ultimate bearing capacity P_{ult} of a pier subjected to negative skin friction F_{nsk} calculates as

$$P_{ult} = P_L - F_{nsk}, \qquad (22\text{-}58)$$

wherein

$P_L = q_{ult} \cdot A = $ total ultimate soil bearing capacity underneath the base area A of the pier;

$q_{ult} = $ soil ultimate bearing capacity beneath the base of the pier, to be determined by Eq. 22-23, or its specialized variations, whichever the case is. In these q_{ult}-equations, the test or strength parameters c and ϕ to use depend upon the problem in hand: they may be based on effective stresses, or total stresses. Likewise, the unit weight γ of the soil to use depends on whether the soil encountered is a dry one, or moist ($S<1.0$), or saturated ($S = 1.00$). In the latter case, the submerged (buoyant) unit weight should be used in calculations where appropriate.

$F_{nsk} = $ total negative skin friction between pier material and soil:

$$F_{nsk} = s \cdot U \cdot L; \qquad (22\text{-}59)$$

here

$s = $ shear strength, or unit shaft, or skin, resistance of pier material in contact with soil;

$U = $ perimeter of the pier, and

$L = $ thickness of soft consolidating soil (Fig. 22-20)

If it can be anticipated that the soft layer of soil will settle, the bearing capacity of the pier should be reduced to account for the negative skin friction brought about by the downward drag of the pier.

Thus, the phenomenon of the negative skin friction is undesirable for deep foundations as well as for friction piles in consolidating soils.

The negative skin friction phenomenon occurs often in consolidating soft clays, silts, mud, and organic soils such as peat, for example. Consolidation may be brought about naturally by self-weight of the soil; densifying a new fill over an existing loose soil; by vibrating equipment operating at the site; by construction operation at nearby sites; by traffic; by lowering of the position of the groundwater table, and from other possible causes.

22-22. Fröhlich's Critical Edge Pressure Theory. Fröhlich[18,19,20] expressed the opinion that the so-called allowable pressure on soil should be based not on the ultimate bearing capacity of the soil, but on the proportional limit. The equation,

$$p_{crit} = \frac{\pi(\gamma H + p_i)}{\cot \phi - (\pi/2 - \phi)}, \qquad (22\text{-}60)$$

is the critical edge pressure which characterizes the instant in the loading of the soil by a foundation (without wall friction) when the lateral expulsion of the soil begins and plastic settlements commence.

Here, γ = unit weight of soil,

H = depth of footing below ground surface,

$p_i = c \cot \phi$ = initial stress,

c = cohesion,

ϕ = angle of internal friction of soil.

For cohesive soils the general valid equation represents, therefore, nothing else but the proportional limit and should be considered a suitable basis for the evaluation of the allowable pressure on soil.

According to Fröhlich, the critical edge pressure (equal to the proportional limit $q_{t,R}$ in kilograms per square centimeter for noncohesive soil is

$$q_{t,R} = \frac{\pi(\gamma_s - \gamma_w)(1 - n)t}{\cot \phi_r - (\pi/2 - \phi_r)}, \qquad (22\text{-}61)$$

where γ_s = true specific weight of soil particles in kg/cm^3,

γ_w = unit weight of water in the voids of soil in kg/cm^3,

n = porosity,

$\gamma = (\gamma_s - \gamma_w)(1 - n)$ = effective unit weight of soil, in kg/cm^3,

t = depth of foundation, in cm,

ϕ_r = angle of internal friction of soil.

For a water-bearing sand and for dry sand the above typical values are, respectively:

$\gamma_s = 0.00265$ kg/cm^3	0.00265 kg/cm^3
$\gamma_w = 0.001$ kg/cm^3	0 kg/cm^3
$n = 0.394$	0.434 (assumed)
$\gamma = (\gamma_s - \gamma_w)(1 - n) = 0.001$	0.0015 kg/cm^3.

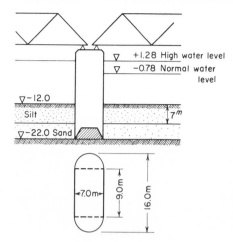

∇ +1.28 High water level
∇ -0.78 Normal water level

∇-12.0
Silt
∇-22.0 Sand

7^m

7.0 m 9.0 m 16.0 m

FIG. 22-21. Bridge pier.

The angle ϕ_r depends upon the density of the material, and its texture. When $t = 0$, then Eq. (22-61) transforms into zero. It is to be understood that in the case of a surface loading there occur flow phenomena of noncohesive soil even at the least pressure (the proportional limit is exceeded).

That the allowable soil pressure on noncohesive soils for $t = 0$ cannot be derived from the ultimate bearing capacity of soil is demonstrated by Fröhlich by the following example.

The ultimate bearing capacity on a noncohesive soil with $\gamma = 0.0015$ kg/cm^3 (dry sand) and $\phi_r = 35°$, loaded with a circular bearing area 30 m in diameter, is

$$\sigma_{ou} = 3000 \times 0.0015 \left(\frac{1 + 0.574}{1 - 0.574}\right)^2 = 61.4 \quad (\text{kg/cm}^2).$$

If the proportional limit is assumed to be $\frac{1}{4}$ of the ultimate, this method would still give allowable bearing capacity of about 15 kg/cm² which, for practical applications, is probably out of the question. Hence, according to Fröhlich, this example demonstrates that the concept of ultimate bearing capacity is unsuitable for the derivation of the allowable bearing capacity.

Example. Determine after Fröhlich the critical pressure for the bridge pier shown in Fig. 22-21.

1) For $\phi_r = 33°$. By Eq. (22-61),

$$q_{t,R} = 10.0 \times 0.576 = 5.76 \quad (\text{kg/cm}^2).$$

2) For $\phi_r = 35°$:

$$q_{t,R} = 10.0 \times 0.671 = 6.71 \quad (\text{kg/cm}^2).$$

The actual load of the pier in metric tons is calculated as follows:

Weight of pier	5500
Weight from bridge	500
Moving loads	700
	6700

Area of base of footing:

$$(16.0 - 7.0)(7.0) + (7.0)^2 \pi/4 = 101.5 \text{ m}^2.$$

Pressure on soil from vertical loads:

$$6700/101.5 = 66 \text{ t/m}^2 = 6.6 \text{ kg/cm}^2.$$

Wind and flow pressure on the downstream side, approximately 1.0 kg/cm².
Uplift at normal water level $(22.0 - 0.78)$ t/m² = 2.12 kg/cm².
Total pressure: $6.6 + 1.0 - 2.12 = 5.48$ kg/cm².

SOIL-BEARING CAPACITY DETERMINATIONS
FROM EXPERIMENTAL RESULTS

22-23. General Notes. Soil-bearing capacity problems can also be studied experimentally from the shape of the rupture surface developed in the soil at failure, brought about by the ultimate load of a structure upon exhausting the shear strength of the soil. Experimental results may be translated to natural, or full-scale, structures by means of the theory of similitude (by modeling).

In treating these problems of foundations supported on a level ground surface, the following methods of loading the foundation footing are usually encountered: a) vertically and concentrically, b) vertically and eccentrically, and c) obliquely.

It is known that one of the methods for the determination of the bearing capacity of soils and for stability calculations of the integral foundation system, "soil-footing-load," is based on failure considerations, by introducing a so-called "coefficient of safety" to avoid failure of the soil by shear.

For this purpose, it is necessary to know, besides the physical properties of the soil, how the shear failure or rupture surface in the foundation-supporting soil takes place and the shape of the rupture or sliding surface.

To learn this, researchers and engineers have suggested that assumed shapes of failure surfaces be used in such calculations. As seen in the previous discussion in this book, it is the practice to use various assumed shapes of rupture surfaces rather than determine them by experiment, or to base calculations on experimentally observed rupture surfaces. The reason for this is that it is difficult to determine the direction of the principal stresses in a fragmental medium such as a mass of soil. Because soil is an indeterminate and therefore a difficult material to study and work with, researchers usually perform their investigations relative to this subject on a small scale and with a cohesionless material, namely, dry sand. This permits excluding from their studies the effects of moisture and the apparent, or transitional, cohesion associated with it. A further factor to be considered is moisture and its migration with temperature changes.

22-24. Shapes of Rupture Surfaces. Every civil engineer encounters obliquely loaded foundations in his daily work, for example, wherever in addition to vertical loads, horizontal forces also act on a foundation. Such cases are foundations of vaults, arch-type bridges without ties, anchor blocks of suspension bridges, retaining walls, frameworks with horizontal reaction-components, dams, and hydraulic structures.

In order to perform calculations for the bearing capacity of a soil, for the depth of a foundation, or for the overall stability of a foundation acted upon by oblique loads, it is necessary to know the mode of failure in shear of the soil underneath the foundation. Once the equation of the experimental rupture curve has been established, the length of the curve, the differential sector-areas, and the areas of the segments of the ruptured earth mass can be calculated by means of the author's logarithmic spiral tables (Ref. 25), and stability analyses of the soil-foundation-load system performed.

The shape of the rupture surface in dry sand caused by vertical concentric and eccentric loads and by obliquely applied loads was studied by, among others,

A.R. Jumikis from 1933 to date.[19,20,26-31] Figures 22-22, 22-23 and 22-24 illustrate some examples of the author's experiments of two-sided and one-sided expulsion of a soil wedge from underneath the base of the footing of a foundation model.

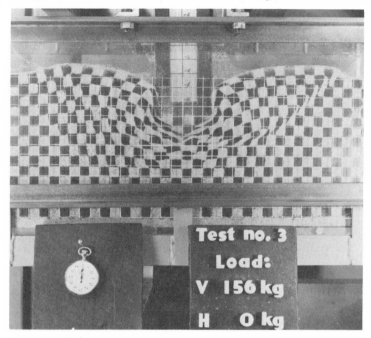

FIG. 22-22. Two-sided expulsion of sand from underneath the base of a centrically loaded foundation model. (Author)

The rupture surfaces were photographed, analyzed, mathematically and graphoanalytically treated; and polar equations for these rupture surfaces, viz., rupture curves, were determined.

The author's study revealed that the cylindrical rupture surface curve coincides remarkably well with the curve of a logarithmic spiral,[19,20,26,27,30] the general equation of which is

$$r = r_o e^{-\omega \tan \phi}, \tag{22-62}$$

where r = radius-vector,

r_o = reference vector, or a segment on the polar axis from the pole of the spiral cut off by the spiral at $\omega = 0$,

e = base of natural logarithms,

ω = amplitude, or angle between r_o and r, and

$\tan \phi = \tan(\pi/2 - \psi)$:

$\tan \phi$ = coefficient of internal friction of sand. For the sand used in this study $\tan \phi = 0.580$.

$(\pi/2 - \psi)$ = angle between a radius-vector and its corresponding normal of the spiral, see Fig. 22-25.

FIG. 22-23. Two-sided rupture surface from a vertical, centrically applied load. Raritan sand. (Author)

FIG. 22-24. One-sided rupture surface in Raritan sand under an obliquely loaded foundation model. (Author).

BEARING CAPACITY OF SOIL; DEPTH OF FOUNDATION
455

The minus sign at ω denotes that as the amplitude ω increases, the radius-vector decreases. This method was adapted for the convenience of analyses of experimental data.

Or else,

$$r = r_o e^{\omega \tan \phi},$$ (22-63)

in which case the radius-vector r increases as the amplitude ω increases.

A logarithmic spiral is a polar curve which intersects at a constant angle, $\psi = \pi/2 - \phi$, with all radius-vectors emanating from one point (the pole), Fig. 22-25.

The physical, or experimental, equation is obtained expressing r_o as a function of the applied resultant load, width of model, and other experimental parameters. The equilibrium condition of the soil-foundation-load system is expressed by comparing the driving and resisting moments, M_D and M_R, respectively.

There are no difficulties in drawing spirals, particularly when spiral tables or spiral templets are applied, or the rules for the construction of spirals are employed.

For plotting the logarithmically spiralled part of the rupture surfaces C-D (Fig. 22-9) or C-E (Fig. 22-12), or O'-O'' (Fig. 22-25), the author's physical logarithmic spiral tables can be conveniently used (Ref. 25).

The application of a logarithmically spiraled rupture surface to stability calculations possesses a great advantage over the other assumed surfaces, since it is not necessary to assume nor be concerned as to how the reactions in sand soil along the sliding surface are distributed or what their magnitudes are. This is because the logarithmic spiral possesses an important property: all radii-vectors pass through the pole of the spiral (moment arm for reactions is 0).

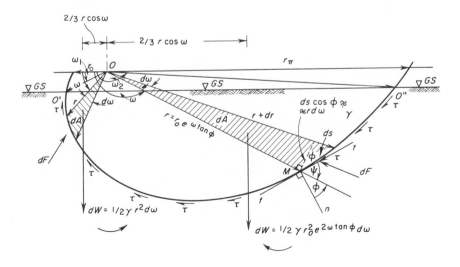

FIG. 22-25. Driving and resisting moments of weights of a spiraled soil wedge.

Hence all soil reaction moments are automatically excluded from our stability calculations by comparing active (driving) and reactive (resisting) moments.

The results of this experimental research are useful in studying the ultimate bearing capacity of sand soil at or below the ground surface and the nature of the rupture surface. The experimental research results are also of significance in checking published theoretical information and in analyzing the limits of its application.

For more discussion on author's experimental research pertaining to rupture surface curves in dry sand, see Refs. 19, 20, and 31.

Conclusions

1) Small-scale[26, 27, 30] and large-scale experiments[21] with vertically and obliquely loaded foundation models provide clear evidence of the nature and form of the rupture surface in sand.

2) Rupture in sand takes place in shear.

3) The study of obtained rupture surface curves in sand corroborates that they coincide very closely with the arc of the mathematical curve of a logarithmic spiral. By performing model experiments judiciously, the rupture surface curves are reproducible for identical conditions within the limits of experimental deviation.

4) By means of model law the logarithmically spiralled rupture surface curves can be modelled for prototype rupture curves.

5) By means of the logarithmically spiralled rupture surface curve, it is possible to establish a direct method of computing the factor of safety graphically and analytically as well.

6) There are no difficulties in drawing spirals, particularly when spiral tables[25] are used.

7) Although the logarithmically spiralled rupture curve has been criticized for one reason or another as being "impossible" or "wrong," small-scale as well as large-scale experiments have shown it to be possible. Fröhlich[32] showed that, insofar as the normal stress distribution along a rupture curve is concerned, the logarithmic spiral method is a statically determinate one. This is one of the important reasons why the logarithmic spiral method in equilibrium calculations of a soil-foundation system deserves attention. For stability, viz., factor of safety, calculations an "average center of rotation" was suggested by Fröhlich. For equilibrium the position of the point of rotation of the soil-foundation system is immaterial, hence it can be the pole of the spiral as well. In the latter case the application of a logarithmically spiralled rupture surface to equilibrium calculations possesses a great advantage over the other assumed rupture surfaces, namely, that it is not necessary to assume nor to be concerned as to how the reactions in sand soil along the rupture surface are distributed or what their magnitudes are. This is because the logarithmic spiral possesses an important property, namely: all radii-vectors (directions of soil reactions along the rupture curve) pass through the pole of the spiral (moment arm for reactions is zero).

Hence all soil reaction moments with respect to the pole of the spiral are automatically excluded from equilibrium calculations.

8) The use of models in soil mechanics is fully justified because their use has successfully stood the test of time. This is the case also in other fields of engineering endeavor, for example, in hydraulic structures engineering, in aeronautical engineering, in fluid mechanics, shipbuilding, heat transfer, and other branches of engineering. Model experiments are also of immense value as a visual aid. Besides, model experiments point out existing incomplete knowledge and even wrong hypotheses upon which certain solutions of engineering problems have hitherto rested.

9) Inasmuch as strength problems in various fields of engineering, among other methods studied, are also based on rupture conditions, the study of soil bearing capacity problems based on soil rupture conditions is justified by the same scientific-technical arguments upon which strength studies in the other disciplines of engineering rest.

Stability calculations based on true rupture surfaces of a correct soil-foundation-load system usually permit the design of a suitable structure and its basic dimensions, and hence the determination of a realistic cost of the structure.

10) To conclude, the results of this experimental research are useful in studying both the ultimate bearing capacity of sand soil at or below the ground surface and the nature of the rupture surface curves. The experimental results are also of significance in checking published information, and in analyzing the limits of its application.

11) It should be remembered that only from experiment is it possible to obtain for various kinds of soil and loading conditions numerical values of physico-mechanical properties and parameters entering into soil bearing capacity calculations and mathematical analysis as well. All physical laws have been derived from experiment.

The significance of the experiment in psammo-mechanics (sand mechanics) is much greater even than in the case of other divisions of mechanics, because phenomena and processes occurring in pouring bodies such as sand are more complex than in solid and/or liquid bodies, and are therefore less fully known.

12) Michelangelo said that the best investment of moneys in a structure is that which is spent for research: it is because from a research experiment one learns directly from nature, humbly, with no preconceived opinion.

REFERENCES

1. *Uniform Building Code*, Whittier, California: International Conference of Building Officials, 1976.
2. *Building Code of the City of New York*, Chapter 26, New York, N.Y.: Van Nostrand Reinhold Company, 1970, pp. 277.
3. A. Casagrande and R.E. Fadum, "Application of Soil Mechanics in Designing Building Foundations," Trans. ASCE, 1944, vol. 109.
4. W.J.M. Rankine, *A Manual of Applied Mechanics,* London, Charles Griffin and Co., 1885, pp. 219-220.
5. A.L. Bell, "The Lateral Pressure and Resistance of Clay, and the Supporting Power

458 STRENGTH PROPERTIES OF SOIL

of Clay Foundation," Minutes of *Proceedings, Institution of Civil Engineers,* London, 1915, Paper no. 4131.

6. A.W. Skempton, "Arthur Langtry Bell (1874-1956) and his Contribution to Soil Mechanics," *Géotechnique,* vol. 8, no. 4, 1958.

7. L. Prandtl, Über die Härte plastischer Körper, Nachrichten von der Königlichen Gesellschaft der Wissenschaften zu Göttingen (Mathematisch-physikalische Klasse aus dem Jahre 1920), 1920, Berlin, pp. 74-85.

8. L. Prandtl, "Über die Eindringungsfestigkeit (Härte) plastischer Baustoffe und die Festigkeit von Schneiden," *Zeitschrift für angewandte Mathematik und Mechanik,* vol. 1, no. 1, February 1921, pp. 15-20.

9. D.W. Taylor, *Fundamentals of Soil Mechanics,* New York, John Wiley and Sons, Inc., 1948, p. 573.

10. K. Terzaghi, *Theoretical Soil Mechanics,* New York, John Wiley and Sons, Inc., 1943, pp. 118-143.

11. A.W. Skempton, "The Bearing Capacity of Clays," *Proceedings of the British Building Research Congress (London),* 1951, vol. 1, pp. 180-189.

12. A.S. Vesić, "Bearing Capacity of Shallow Foundations," in *Foundation Engineering Handbook* (H.F. Winterkorn and H.Y. Fang, editors), New York, N.Y.: Van Nostrand Reinhold Company, 1975, pp. 121-147.

13. G.G. Meyerhof, "An Investigation of the Bearing Capacity of Shallow Footings on Dry Sand." *Proceedings of the 2nd International Conference on Soil Mechanics and Foundation Engineering,* held at Rotterdam, 1948, vol. 1, pp. 237-243.

14. G.G. Meyerhof, "The Ultimate Bearing Capacity of Foundations," *Géotechnique* (London), 1951, vol. 2, No. 4, pp. 301-332.

15. G.G. Meyerhof, "The Bearing Capacity of Foundations under Eccentric and Inclined Loads." *Proceedings of the Third International Conference on Soil Mechanics and Foundation Engineering,* held at Zürich, 1953, vol. 1, pp. 440-445.

16. G.G. Meyerhof, "Factors Influencing Bearing Capacity of Foundations," *Géotechnique* (London), 1955, vol. 5, pp. 227-242.

17. G.G. Meyerhof, "The Ultimate Bearing Capacity of Foundations on Slopes." *Proceedings of the 4th International Conference on Soil Mechanics and Foundation Engineering,* held in London, 1957, vol. 1, pp. 384-386.

18. O.K. Fröhlich, *Druckverteilung im Baugrunde,* Wien: Springer Verlag, 1934, p. 142.

19. A.R. Jumikis, *Mechanics of Soils: Fundamentals for Advanced Study,* Princeton, N.J.: D. Van Nostrand Company, Inc., 1964, pp. 128-140.

20. A.R. Jumikis, *Theoretical Soil Mechanics,* New York, N.Y.: Van Nostrand Reinhold Company, 1969, pp. 194-230.

21. H. Muhs, "Die experimentelle Untersuchung der Grenztragfähigkeit nichtbindiger Böden bei lotrecht-mittiger Belastrung." Berlin: *Mitteilungen der Deutschen Forschungsgesellschaft für Bodenmechanik [DEGEBO]* an der Technischen Universität Berlin, No. 27, 1971; No. 28, 1972.

22. G.G. Meyerhof, "Influence of Roughness of Base and Groundwater Conditions on the Ultimate Bearing Capacity of Foundations," *Géotechnique* (London) 1955, vol. 5, pp. 227-242.

23. Design Manual (*Soil Mechanics, Foundations, and Earth Structures.*) NAVFAC DM-7, Washington, D.C.: Department of the Navy, Naval Facilities Engineering Command, March, 1971, pp. 7-11-12, Figure 11-1.

24. K. Terzaghi and R.B. Peck, *Soil Mechanics in Engineering Practice* (2nd ed.), New York, N.Y.: John Wiley and Sons, Inc., 1967, p. 563.

25. A.R. Jumikis, *Stability Analyses of Soil-foundation Systems* (A Design Manual, based on logarithmically spiralled rupture surfaces), New Brunswick, N.J., Rutgers—The State University, Bureau of Engineering Research, College of Engineering, Engineering Research Publication no. 44, 1965. Contains 13 pages of log spiral tables.

26. A.R. Jumikis, *Experimental Research Concerning the Form of the rupture Surface in Dry Sand Caused by an Obliquely Loaded Foundation Model* (typewritten), Riga, 1944.
27. A.R. Jumikis, "Rupture Surfaces in Sand Under Oblique Loads," *Proceedings ASCE*, January 1956, vol. 82, no. SM. 1.
28. A.R. Jumikis, discussion on "Earth Pressures and Bearing Capacity Calculations by Generalized Procedures of Slices," by N. Janbu, *Proceedings*, Fourth International Conference on Soil Mechanics and Foundation Engineering, held August 1957, London, Butterworths Scientific Publications, 1958, vol. 3, pp. 235-238.
29. A.R. Jumikis, discussion on "An Investigation of Krey's Method for Bearing Capacity," by R.E. Hasson and E. Vey, *Proceedings*, First Pan American Congress on Soil Mechanics and Foundation Engineering, held September 7-12, 1959, at University City, Mexico, vol. I, pp. 131-137.
30. A.R. Jumikis, "The Shape of Rupture Surface in Dry Sand," *Proceedings*, 5th International Conference on Soil Mechanics and Foundation Engineering, held in Paris, France, July 17-22, 1961, Paper 3A, pp. 693-698.
31. A.R. Jumikis, "Rupture of Soil." Published in Proceedings of a Symposium on *Bearing Capacity and Settlement of Foundations*, held at Duke University April 5/6, 1965. Edited by A.S. Vesić. Durham, North Carolina: Department of Civil Engineering, School of Engineering, Duke University, 1967, pp. 103-107.
32. O.K. Fröhlich, "The Factor of Safety with Respect to Sliding of a Mass of Soil Along the Arc of a Logarithmic Spiral," *Proceedings of the Third International Conference on Soil Mechanics and Foundation Engineering*, Vol. 2, Zürich, 1953, pp. 230-233.

SUGGESTIONS FOR FURTHER READING

1. E.E. De Beer, "Experimental Determination of the Shape Factors and the Bearing Capacity Factors of Sand," *Géotechnique* (London), vol. 20, No. 4, 1970, pp. 387-411.
2. M. Bozozuk, "Foundation Failure of the Vanleek Hill Tower Silo," *Proceedings* of the ASCE Specialty Conference on Performance of Earth-Supported Structures held at Purdue University, June 11-14, 1972, vol. 1, Part 2, pp. 885-902.
3. O.K. Fröhlich, *Druckverteilung im Baugrunde,* Berlin, Springer, 1934.
4. Bent Hansen, *A Theory of Plasticity for Ideal Frictionless Materials.* Copenhagen: Teknisk Forlag, 1965.
5. Brinch J. Hansen, "The Philosophy of Foundation Design; Design Criteria, Safety Factors and Settlement Limits," published in *Bearing Capacity and Settlement of Foundations*, Proceedings of a Symposium held at Duke University, April 5-6, 1965.
6. Brinch J. Hansen, *A Revised and Extended Formula for Bearing Capacity*, Bulletin No. 28, Danish Geotechnical Institute, Copenhagen, 1970, pp. 5-11.
7. H. Muhs and K. Weiss, *Die Grenztragfähigkeit und Schiefstellung ausmittig-lotrecht belasteter Einzelfundamente im Sand nach Theorie und Versuch*, Berlin: Mitteilungen der deutchen Gesellschaft für Bodenmechanik (DEGEBO), No. 22, 1969.
8. H. Muhs and K. Weiss, "The Influence of the Load Inclination on the Bearing Capacity of Shallow Footings," *Proceedings of the 7th International Conference on Soil Mechanics and Foundation Engineering*, held at Mexico City, vol. 2, 1969, pp. 187-194.
9. R.L. Nordlund and D.U. Deere, "Collapse of Fargo Grain Elevator," *Proceedings ASCE*, Journal of the Soil Mechanics and Foundation Division, vol. 96, No. SM2, 1970, pp. 585-607.
10. R.B. Peck and F.G. Bryant, "The Bearing Capacity Failure of the Transcona Elevator," *Géotechnique* (London), vol. 3, 1953, pp. 201-208.
11. A.S. Vesić, "Bearing Capacity of Deep Foundations in Sand." *Highway Research*

Record No. 39, 1963.
12. A.S. Vesić, "Ultimate Loads and Settlements of Deep Foundations in Sand."
    Bearing Capacity and Settlement of Foundations. Durham, N.C.: Duke University,
    1967, pp. 53-68.
13. A.S. Vesić, "Analysis of Ultimate Loads of Shallow Foundations," *Proceedings
    ASCE*, Journal of the Soil Mechanics and Foundations Division, vol. 99, No. SM 1,
    1973, p. 45.
14. *Lecture Series on Deep Foundations*, March - April, 1975. Boston Society of Civil
    Engineers Section and American Society of Civil Engineers (a compilation of
    mimeographed lecture notes).

PROBLEMS

22- 1. Questions pertaining to bearing capacity of foundation soils.
   a) What are the stability requirements of a foundation?
   b) Define ultimate bearing capacity of soil.
   c) Define safe (or allowable) bearing capacity of soil.
   d) Describe methods of obtaining bearing capacity of soil.
   e) What are the deficiencies of bearing capacity values given by some
      building codes?

22- 2. If the vertical contact pressure on the soil exerted by the foundation is $\sigma_0 = 1.0$
   ton/ft²; if the allowable bearing capacity of a sand deposit is $\sigma_{adm} = 1.5$ ton/ft²
   at a factor of safety of $\eta = 2.0$; if the unit weight of the soil is $\gamma = 95$ lb/ft³,
   and the angle of internal friction of the sand is $\phi = 28°$, calculate and decide
   upon the depth of laying of foundation. Use Rankine's theory.

22- 3. Given: $\gamma = 110$ lb/ft³; $\phi = 20°$; $c = 600$ lb/ft². Calculate the minimum depth
   of foundation in this ϕ-c soil as well as for the ϕ-soil ($c = 0$) when $\phi = 20°$,
   for a factor of safety of $\eta = 1$ and $\eta = 3$ in both cases. Use Bell's method for the
   system shown in Fig. Problem 22-3.

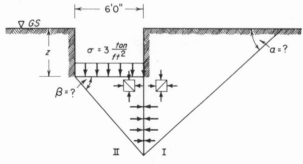

FIG. PROBLEM 22-3.

22- 4. A foundation footing the width of which is $B = 2b = 8$ ft rests on the ground
   surface of a clay. The unconfined compressive strength of this clay has been
   tested to be $\sigma_c = 2.0$ kg/cm². Calculate by the Bell-Casagrande method the
   ultimate bearing capacity of this clay.

22- 5. For the purpose of graphical comparison, plot $\sigma_u = f(\phi)$ of Prandtl's formula
   and all its modifications.

22- 6. Determine by Prandtl's method the magnitude of the pressure from a strip
   foundation at the ground surface and 3 ft below the ground surface which

would bring about failure in a cohesive soil material. Given: specific gravity of soil: $G = 2.67$, porosity: $n = 30\%$, angle of internal friction: $\phi = 30°$, cohesion, $c = 0.4$ kg/cm².

22- 7. In the illustrative example as given in the Prandtl's theory, assume that for maintaining the grade the height of the fill should be 25 ft. A counterweight is to be placed on the soil on both sides adjacent to the slopes of the fill (Fig. Problem 22-7). Calculate the height of this counterweight necessary to attain a factor of safety of $\eta = 3.0$ against breaking of the fill into the fill-supporting soil and thus preventing the lateral expulsion of soil out from underneath the fill.

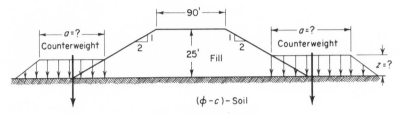

FIG. PROBLEM 22-7.

22- 8. Check factor of safety η for the example given in Prandtl's theory, using Prandtl's original equation and its modifications, and tabulate the results obtained.

22- 9. A pure clay has an unconfined compressive strength of $\sigma_c = 1$ kg/cm². If an 8 ft wide strip footing is founded 5 ft below the ground surface, what is the ultimate bearing capacity of the clay in kg/cm²? Apply Prandtl's theory. What is the ultimate bearing capacity of same clay if founded on the ground surface? ($c = \sigma_c/2$; $\sigma_u = (5.14)c = 2.57$ kg/cm².)

22-10. Using the results of the Prandtl-Terzaghi analysis, determine the size of a square footing founded 8 ft below ground surface and transmitting to the soil a load of 100 tons. Select a factor of safety η. Calculate dimensions 1) for the footing placed on a ϕ-c soil, when $\gamma = 105$ lb/ft³, $\phi = 28°$, and $c = 600$ lb/ft², and 2) for a footing placed on a pure cohesive soil (c-soil) if $\gamma = 112$ lb/ft³ and the shear strength of this material is $\tau = 800$ lb/ft².

22-11. Calculate by Prandtl-Terzaghi formulas the ultimate load per foot of length of a strip foundation, the width of which is $B = 2b = 8$ ft. The base of the footing is 8 ft below the ground surface. The soil physical properties are the same as those given in the previous problem.

22-12. Given a rectangular footing 3 m x 3 m, laid in a (ϕ-c)-soil 1.0 m deep. The unit weight of the soil is $\gamma = 18.00$ kN/m², its $\phi = 25°$ and $c = 15$ kN/m². Compute q_{ult} and σ_{all}, if $\eta = 3.0$

22-13. Given a circular footing whose radius is $R = 4.0$ m, and is laid 1.0 m below ground surface. The unit weight of the soil is $\gamma = 19.00$ kN/m³, its $\phi = 30°$ and $c = 0$. Calculate the ultimate bearing capacity for $D = 1.0$ m, and for a case if the footing is laid directly on the ground surface.

22-14. Given a clay soil whose ultimate unconfined compressive strength is $q = 100$ kN/m². Upon this clay formation, a fill is placed 3.0 m high. The compacted unit weight of the fill is 20 kN/m³.

    a) What is the factor of safety against groundbreak (rupture) of the clay brought about by the fill?

    b) Is it safe to construct the fill of the given height? Explain why yes or not.

    c) How high should the fill be in order that the clay-fill system attains a factor of safety of $\eta = 2.0$ at $\gamma = 20$ kN/m³ of unit weight of the fill?

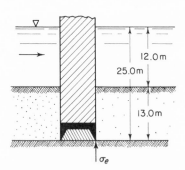

FIG. PROBLEM 22-15.

22-15. The edge pressure σ_e is reported to be for the structure as sketched in Fig. Problem 22-15 equal to 8.9 kg/cm². Check this value by calculating the allowable soil pressure after Fröhlich for $\phi_r = 33°$ and $\phi_r = 35°$.

$$(\phi_r = 33°: q_{t,R} = 13.0 \times 0.576 = 7.5 \text{ kg/cm}².$$
$$\phi_r = 35°: q_{t,R} = 13.0 \times 0.671 = 8.7 \text{ kg/cm}².)$$

22-16. Given for a water-bearing sand: $(\gamma_s - \gamma_w)(1 - n) = \gamma = 0.001$ kg/cm³ and for a dry sand: $(\gamma_s - \gamma_w)(1 - n) = \gamma_d = 0.0015$ kg/cm³.

   1) Assuming angles ϕ_r to vary from 28° to 40° in 2-degree intervals, prepare a table for Fröhlich's proportional limits $q_{t,R}$ in kg/cm² for these two types of soils for a $t = 1.0$ m depth of base of footing below the ground surface.
   2) Make your observations as to the effect of the groundwater on the proportional limit.
   3) For $\phi = 34°$ and $t = 3.00$ m, how large an effect has the groundwater upon the critical edge pressure as compared with dry sand? (From 2.796 kg/cm² to 1.863 kg/cm².)
   4) What is the effect of hydrostatic uplift of the two soils under discussion in (3)? (Reduction in pressure by 0.311 kg/cm².)
   5) What is the allowable bearing capacity of the two soils under discussion at $t = 3.0$ m? (2.796 kg/cm² for dry sand; 2.174 kg/cm² for water-bearing sand.)

Chapter 23

GROUNDBREAK

23-1. Stability Analysis against Groundbreak. General Notes. After calculating loads on an earth retaining wall; after analyzing stability of the wall against rotation and sliding; and after checking the contact pressures exerted by the wall on soil, one more stability analysis should be made, namely: stability of the soil-wall system against groundbreak, viz., terrain break.

By groundbreak or rupture of soil is understood the rupture of an earth mass because of exhaustion of shear strength of soil brought about by a foundation or retaining wall loading. Upon failure in shear of the soil, the ruptured soil mass together with the foundation or earth retaining structure (whichever the case may be) slides rotationally over a curved rupture surface.

Figures 22-22 through 22-25 show experimental groundbreaks brought about by shear failure of sand from a rigid foundation model.

Groundbreak endangers stability of the entire soil-foundation system. One of the causes of groundbreak is insufficient embedment depth of the foundation or earth retaining wall, combined, of course, with low shear strength of the soil. A narrow width B of the base of the wall, too, may be a reason for groundbreak. Increasing eccentricity and inclination of the resultant force R on the base, as well as rise of groundwater table (increase in uplift force) increase the danger of the soil-foundation system. Also, the danger of instability increases with cohesive soils at a high degree of saturation S. In the latter case, upon quick loading mobilization of the effective shear strength of the saturated cohesive soil cannot follow fast enough in accordance with increase in rate of compressive stresses because of the induced pore water pressure upon loading such a soil. In cohesive soils, the pore water pressure dissipates but relatively slowly.

In soil failure of the kind of groundbreak as described here, upon soil rupture the foundation and the ruptured mass of soil rotate as an integral disk and move out of their position. After the groundbreak has occurred, the stability of the soil-foundation system is destroyed, i.e., the soil material is finished.

Groundbreak of a wall-supported soil system may be considered to be a special case of failure by rupture of unsupported earth slopes.

Stability Analysis. In general, calculations for stability of foundations and earth retaining walls against groundbreak are similar to those for earth embankment slopes.[1,2,3] In principle, the analysis consists of determining factor of safety of a given or projected structure such as a wall-earth-pressure system for the worst loading condition that may ever occur during the service time of the structure.

Stability calculations against groundbreak may become necessary when
1) the foundation of an earth retaining wall is designed to be laid at an insufficient, shallow depth;
2) the width B of the base of the foundation is relatively small; or
3) when the shear strength of the soil is low.

The ultimate shear strength of the soil must be determined by appropriate tests. It is the shear strength of the soil that is used in determining the resultant moment M_R resisting rotational motion of the soil-foundation disk against a driving moment M_D tending to bring about rotation.

Because of the simplified assumptions in the analysis by using an arbitrarily assumed rupture surface curve, usually a circular one, and because of the unsure averaging relative to layered soil systems, as well as soil constants, the load bringing about failure in shear of soil can be ascertained but approximately. Also, because the nature of the distribution of the tangential resisting force F_R in the curved rupture surface has only a small influence upon the stability of the soil-wall system, in many cases Fröhlich's approximative method[4] of stability analysis of such systems against groundbreak may suffice (Figs. 23-1 and 23-2).

As said before, the circularly curved cylindrical rupture surface is used for approximative evaluation of stability of simple, uniform soil-foundation systems. For complex soil-foundation systems the use of the circularly curved rupture surface, however, is nevertheless indispensable and irreplaceable, because rigorous solutions which are available for ideal, uniform soil are extremely involved.

Figure 23-1 shows a simple soil-earth retaining wall system, and needs no detailed description. The soil is here given as uniform.

Select arbitrarily a center of rotation, point O, and calculate the weight G of the soil disk or wedge (segment) $DMASD$, rupture impending:

Area A of segment (include the area taken by part of the concrete wall in the segment):

$$A = (\pi \cdot r^2) \cdot \frac{(2\alpha)}{360°} - 2 \cdot \frac{1}{2} \cdot r \cdot \sin \alpha \cdot r \cdot \cos \alpha$$

$$= (r^2) \left[\frac{\pi \cdot \alpha}{180°} - (\sin \alpha) \cdot (\cos \alpha) \right] \qquad (23\text{-}1)$$

Weight G of segment:

$$G = (A)(1)(\gamma) = (\gamma) \cdot (r^2) \left[\frac{\pi \cdot \alpha}{180°} - (\sin \alpha) \cdot (\cos \alpha) \right] . \qquad (23\text{-}2)$$

Now resolve the inclined resultant force R at point P on the curve into normal and tangential components, N and T, respectively.

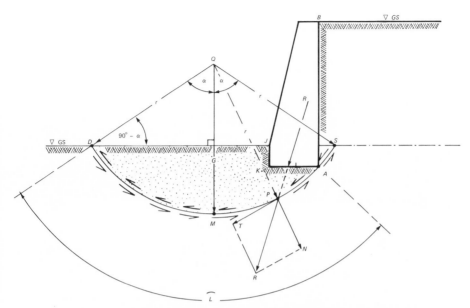

FIG. 23-1.   Soil-foundation-load system for groundbreak analysis.

Calculate driving moment M_D with respect to point O of rotation:

$$M_D = T \cdot r \qquad (23\text{-}3)$$

The resisting moment M_R with respect to point O is

$$M_R = [(N + G) \cdot \tan \phi + c \cdot L] \cdot r \qquad (23\text{-}4)$$

The factor of safety η against groundbreak is:

$$\eta = \frac{M_R}{M_D} = \frac{[(N + G) \cdot \tan \phi + c \cdot L] \cdot r}{T \cdot r} \qquad (23\text{-}5)$$

$$= \frac{(N + G) \cdot \tan \phi + c \cdot r \cdot (2\alpha)}{T} \qquad (23\text{-}6)$$

The least tolerable factor of safety η_{min} must be determined by trial and adjustment from several circles with different assumed position of their centers. Generally, it is required that

$$\eta_{min} \geqq \eta_{all} \quad . \qquad (23\text{-}7)$$

If $\eta_{min} < \eta_{all}$, the foundation could be laid at a greater depth, or the width B of the base of the foundation might be increased.

The calculated factor of safety depends very much upon the angle of internal friction ϕ of the soil. It must be determined very carefully because of variation in pore water pressures where this applies, of course. Also cohesion c is subject to careful determination because frequently c varies considerably even in one and

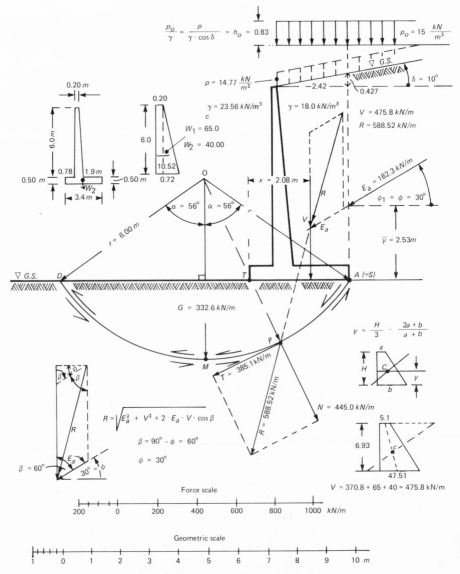

$$\frac{p_0}{\gamma} = \frac{p}{\gamma \cdot \cos \delta} = h_0 = 0.83 \qquad p_0 = 15 \frac{kN}{m^2}$$

$$p = 14.77 \frac{kN}{m^2} \qquad \nabla \, G.S. \qquad \delta = 10°$$

$$\gamma = 23.56 \, kN/m^3 \qquad \gamma = 18.0 \, kN/m^3$$
$$c$$

$$W_1 = 65.0 \qquad V = 475.8 \, kN/m$$
$$W_2 = 40.00 \qquad R = 588.52 \, kN/m$$

$$x = 2.08 \, m \qquad E_a = 182.3 \, kN/m$$
$$\phi_1 = \phi = 30°$$

$$\overline{y} = 2.53 m$$

$$\nabla \, G.S. \qquad D \qquad \qquad T \qquad \qquad A \,(=S)$$

$$G = 332.6 \, kN/m$$

$$y = \frac{H}{3} \cdot \frac{2a + b}{a + b}$$

$$T = 385.1 \, kN/m$$

$$N = 445.0 \, kN/m$$

$$R = \sqrt{E_a^2 + V^2 + 2 \cdot E_a \cdot V \cdot \cos \beta}$$

$$\beta = 90° - \phi = 60°$$

$$\phi = 30°$$

$$\beta = 60° \qquad 30° = \phi$$

$$V = 370.8 + 65 + 40 = 475.8 \, kN/m$$

Force scale

$$200 \quad 0 \quad 200 \quad 400 \quad 600 \quad 800 \quad 1000 \; kN/m$$

Geometric scale

$$1 \quad 0 \quad 1 \quad 2 \quad 3 \quad 4 \quad 5 \quad 6 \quad 7 \quad 8 \quad 9 \quad 10 \; m$$

FIG. 23-2.   Groundbreak analysis.

the same layer of soil. However, for reasons of safety, many engineers sometimes do not introduce c in stability calculations at all.

Example.

Stability Analysis Against Groundbreak. This analysis is performed for an assumed circular rupture surface according to Fröhlich.[4]

The problem involves a homogeneous soil. Select an arbitrary center of rotation, point O, and draw an arc of circle, arc AMD through the heel-point A. For soil rupture impending, calculate by geometry the weight G of the soil wedge (segment $DMAD$), see Fig. 23-2.

Area of segment:

$$A = (r^2) \cdot [\frac{\pi \cdot \alpha^\circ}{180^\circ} - (\sin\alpha)(\cos\alpha)]$$

$$= (6.0^2) \cdot [\frac{(3.14)(56^\circ)}{180^\circ} - (0.8290)(0.5591)] = 18.49 \ [m^2]$$

Weight of segment:

$$G = (\gamma)(A)(1.0) = (18.0)(18.49) = \underline{332.6 \ [kN/m]}.$$

Position of vertical resultant V (Fig. 23-2).

$$\overline{x} = \frac{(370.8)(2.31) + (65.0)(1.03) + (40.0)(1.70)}{475.8} = \underline{2.08 \ [m]}.$$

$$R = \sqrt{E_a^2 + V^2 + 2 \cdot E_a \cdot V \cdot \cos\beta} =$$

$$= \sqrt{(182.3)^2 + (475.8)^2 + (2)(182.3)(475.8)(0.500)} =$$

$$= \underline{588.52 \ [kN/m]}.$$

Driving moment M_D:

$$M_D = T \cdot r = (385.1)(6.0) = \underline{2310.6 \ [kN \cdot m/m]}$$

Resisting moment M_R:

$$M_R = [(N + G) \tan\phi + c \cdot L] r =$$

$$= [(777.6)(0.577) + 0 \cdot L] \cdot (6.0) = \underline{2692.1 \ [kN \cdot m/m]}.$$

Factor of safety η against groundbreak:

$$\eta = M_R/M_D = 2692.1/2310.6 = \underline{1.16 < \eta_{all}}$$

(Redesign and check η again! Try several rupture circles for the least factor of safety).

REFERENCES

1. A.R. Jumikis, *Soil Mechanics,* Princeton, N.J.: D. Van Nostrand Company, Inc., 1962, pp. 689-716.
2. A.R. Jumikis, *Introduction to Soil Mechanics,* New York, N.Y.: D. Van Nostrand Company, 1967, pp. 353-370.
3. A.R. Jumikis, *Stability Analyses of Soil-Foundation Systems:* New Brunswick, N.J.: College of Engineering, Bureau of Engineering Research, Rutgers - The State University of New Jersey. Engineering Research Publication No. 44, 1965.
4. O.K. Fröhlich, "Über den Sicherheitsgrad von Böschungen, Dämmen, und seitlichen gestützten Erdkörpern gegen Rutschung auf kreiszylindrischer Gleitfläche." *Österreichische Bauzeitschrift,* No. 4, 1949, p. 69.

Chapter 24

STABILITY ANALYSIS OF SLOPES

It is not the intent to include in this book all of the available methods of slope stability analyses and modifications thereof. They are too numerous in the technical literature, hence such a discussion is beyond the scope of this book. Rather, it is here pointed out that for the same problem many approaches to the solutions are possible, and that the factor-of-safety calculations vary from method to method, and from author to author.

24-1. Definitions. A slope is an inclined boundary surface between air and the body of an earthwork such as a dam, highway cut, or fill.

The concept "stability" is one of the most important one in civil engineering in general, and in geotechnical engineering in particular. Whatever the definition of the term "stability" is, this concept comprises some of the most important factors in engineering, namely: force, moment, and equilibrium. These factors and concepts form the basis of all civil engineering structural analyses and construction work.

Overstressing a soil material of an earth slope usually may bring about a sudden rupture with a rapid displacement or sliding of the ruptured soil mass, or gradual shear strain, causing distress to earth structures.

In soil mechanics, the topic "stability of slopes" is dealt with from two engineering viewpoints, namely:

1) the design of slopes of cuts and fills in advance of new earthwork construction in accordance with prescribed safety requirements, and
2) the study of stability of existing slopes of earthworks, slopes which are potentially unstable, or which have failed, or which have to be redesigned.

In the first instance above, the position of the toe-point of the slope is known, whereas in the second instance the position of the toe-point is not always known because of the destruction of the designed slope by its rupture and slumping down.

The concept of the "stability" of a slope is an indeterminate one because no slopes made in or of soil can be regarded as fully guaranteed for their stability during their performance over a period of many years. Climatic and hydrologic conditions, and man's activities in the immediate and/or adjacent area of the dam or other earthwork, may bring about, years later, changes affecting the stability of man-made and natural slopes. In particular, one should not overlook the possibility of the soil becoming saturated by water with time. Besides, cases are known of stable slopes whose factor of safety η with respect to failure in shear has been calculated to be less than unity, i.e., $\eta < 1.0$. For slopes of new earthworks it is advisable to maintain the factor of safety at $\eta = 1.5$ at least.

In earthworks, shear failures of soil materials are common phenomena, and result from inadequate stability analysis, or from incomplete assessment of the properties of the soil materials and possible variations in their properties with time, or both. They can also result from overloading the earthwork by various kinds of loads, such as externally applied loads, water in the voids of the soil, flow pressure, and other possible factors. In most cases it is the water in its various modes of occurrence which, in part directly and in part indirectly, is the cause of rupture of soil and hence failure of slopes.

24-2. Factors Contributing to Slope Failures. The stability of slopes depends upon the following factors:

1) the type of soil of which or in which the slope is made;
2) the geometry of the cross section of the slope (height, slope, for example);
3) weight and loads, and weight and load distribution (gravity is one of the principal causes of all slides);
4) increase in moisture content of the soil material. Water is the principal factor in promoting slides because it adds weight to the unit weight of soil; water decreases the magnitude of cohesion in soil, thus decreasing its shear strength. Water from atmospheric precipitation and the melt-waters of snow, upon entering into the soil, decrease the factor of safety η of the slopes in question. Water is the most aggressive factor contributing to many slides, particularly in unconsolidated soils;
5) decrease in shear strength of soil for reasons other than water;
6) vibrations and earthquakes.

Thus one possibility of reducing the degree of stability in slopes comes more to the fore: stability varies principally with the variation in the water regimen in the soil. Therefore, stability analysis of slopes of earthworks should be performed for the most dangerous conditions of the slope.

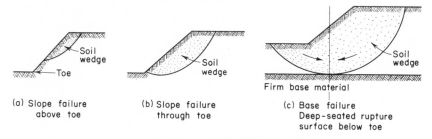

(a) Slope failure above toe   (b) Slope failure through toe   (c) Base failure Deep-seated rupture surface below toe

FIG. 24-1. Slope failures.

24-3. Mode of Rupture. As to the mode of rupture, the slope may fail basically in the following two ways:

a) the rupture surface sets in above the toe of the slope (Fig. 24-1), and the

rupture surface passes through the toe of the slope. Such failures are
known as slope failures;

b) the rupture surface is deep-seated and passes through the embankment-
supporting soil below the toe of the slope. This mode of slope failure is
known as the base failure.

The latter mode of failure takes place particularly when the soil beneath the
embankment is softer and more plastic than the slope-forming soil itself.

In practice, stability analysis of earth slopes is based on limit equilibrium
condition. In such a method of analysis, it is assumed that failure or rupture of a
slope takes place along an assumed or known rupture or sliding surface. Besides,
it is assumed that at limit equilibrium (rupture just impending) Coulomb's
rupture criterion is satisfied along the entire assumed form of rupture surface.
Also, the necessary shear strength of the soil for equilibrium is compared with the
actual shear strength of the soil along the rupture surface. The ratio of the
available, or actual shear strength (resisting shear strength) of the soil to the
necessary shear strength is regarded as the factor of safety against failure of the
soil mass of an earth slope in shear.

Because the earth slopes are usually long as compared with their height, the
stability analyses of earth slopes present a two dimensional problem, that of a
plane strain.

Thus, in principle, the possibility of rupture of an earth slope is assessed by
comparing resisting moments M_R to driving moments M_D, viz., forces F_R
resisting failure to those driving forces F_D causing failure. The factor of safety η
against failure in shear of a soil slope is expressed as a ratio

$$\eta = \frac{M_R}{M_D}$$

$$(24\text{-}1a)$$

$$\eta = \frac{F_R}{F_D}$$

24-4. Stability of Mass of Soil on an Inclined Plane. To start out with the
stability analysis of the triangular, homogeneous soil mass ABC, Fig. 24-2,
assume that it rests upon a firm, inclined surface AC, inclined at an angle ρ
with the horizontal. In this problem two kinds of stabilities must be checked,
namely,

1) the overall stability of the entire soil mass against sliding down the incline,
and

2) the stability of the slope AB proper against rupture in shear if the overall
stability of the earth mass against sliding down is satisfactory.

The principle underlying stability calculation of the triangular soil mass is the
failure in shear along the inclined plane AC when the driving forces exceed the
resisting forces. In such a calculation, it is assumed that the shear stress s
is distributed uniformly over the plane sliding surface AC. The calculations of
the stability of slopes here and throughout this book pertains to earthworks the
lengths (or shore line) of which are one unit of length perpendicular to the
drawing plane.

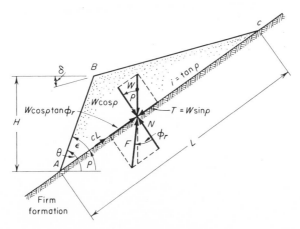

FIG. 24-2.   Soil mass on an incline.

In a stable system, the driving forces $\sum F_D$ should constitute only a fraction of the resisting forces $\sum F_R$. The factor of safety η of the system, characterizing the degree of stability of the soil mass on the incline, is expressed as

$$\eta = \frac{\sum F_R}{\sum F_D} = \frac{\tan \phi_r \sum N + cL}{\sum T}, \qquad (24\text{-}1)$$

where $\sum N = W \cos \rho =$ the sum of all effective normal forces to the sliding plane, and

$\sum T =$ the sum of all shear forces.

If $\eta > 1$, the soil mass on the incline may be considered as stable.

If $\eta = 1$, the system is at equilibrium.

If $\eta < 1$, the system should be regarded as instable as concerns pure static calculations. The factor of safety η is usually required to be $\eta \geq 1.5$.

If, in Eq. 24-2, $c = 0$, as for a noncohesive soil, then

$$\eta = \frac{\tan \phi_r \sum N}{\sum T} = \frac{\tan \phi_r W \cos \rho}{W \sin \rho} = \frac{\tan \phi_r}{\tan \rho}, \qquad (24\text{-}2)$$

where $\tan \rho = i =$ slope of the inclined, firm, plane sliding surface.

If a factor of safety η and the angle of internal friction ϕ_r are known, then the angle of incline should be

$$\rho = \arctan(\tan \phi_r / \eta). \qquad (24\text{-}3)$$

If ρ cannot be changed, then the coefficient of friction for a given η should be at least

$$\tan \phi_r = \eta \tan \rho. \qquad (24\text{-}4)$$

24-5. Stability of Slopes With a Plane Rupture Surface. In a homogeneous soil, failure in shear along a plane rupture surface may be assumed to take place in a surface such that the acting shear stresses are greater than the shear strength of the soil. The stability calculation is thus based on a shear plane AC

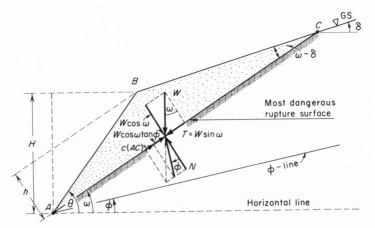

FIG. 24-3.   Slope system with plane rupture surface.

through the toe-line (A), and finding the so-called critical angle of the slope $\measuredangle \omega$ which corresponds to the most dangerous rupture surface (Fig. 24-3), at its maximum stressed surface.

The force equilibrium on plane AC is

$$c(AC) + N \tan \phi - T = 0. \tag{24-5}$$

Here $c(AC)$ is the so-called acting cohesive force, and $N \tan \phi$ is the acting frictional force, not to be confused with the soil resistance forces.

From Eq. (24-5) obtain by differential operations the critical angle ω of the slope, AC, of the native soil:

$$\omega = (\theta + \phi)/2. \tag{24-6}$$

This angle determines the position of the most dangerous rupture surface AC. For this angle the mathematical expression for the maximum value of developed cohesion c_{max} in the most dangerous rupture plane AC upon rupture is:

$$c_{max} = \tfrac{1}{2} \gamma H \frac{\sin^2 \dfrac{\theta - \phi}{2}}{\sin \theta \cos \phi}. \tag{24-7}$$

In other words, c_{max} is the necessary value a soil material with an angle of internal friction ϕ should possess in order that slope AB with a slope angle of θ still stays at a height H:

$$H = \frac{2c \sin \theta \cos \phi}{\gamma \;\; \sin^2 \dfrac{\theta - \phi}{2}}. \tag{24-8}$$

Note that c as well as H are independent of the slope δ of the ground surface.
When $\phi = 0$, then Eqs. (24-7) and (24-8) transform into

$$c_{max} = \tfrac{1}{4}\gamma H \tan(\theta/2),\tag{24-9}$$

and

$$H = 4(c/\gamma)\cot(\theta/2).\tag{24-10}$$

This equation shows that the greater the slope angle θ, the smaller the height of
the slope,

The overall factor of safety η for the critical plane is

$$\eta = \frac{\sum \text{Resisting forces}}{\sum \text{Driving forces}} = \frac{c(AC) + N\tan\phi}{T}.\tag{24-11}$$

If $c = 0$, then $T = N\tan\phi$, and $\tan\omega = \tan\phi$, or $\omega = \phi$.
For a factor of safety η,

$$\eta = \frac{\tan\phi}{\tan\omega},\tag{24-12}$$

or

$$\tan\phi = \eta\tan\omega.\tag{24-13}$$

It should be mentioned that stability analyses of slopes on plane rupture surfaces were studied by Coulomb,[1] Résal,[2] Français,[3] Collin,[4] and others.

Example 1. Given a finite slope whose upper ground surface is horizontal. The slope
angle is given as $\theta = 45°$, and the height of the slope is $H = 10$ m. The properties of the
soil are: Unit weight $= 16$ kN/m^3; $\phi = 15°$ (tan $15° = 0.2679$); $c = 29$ kN/m^2.

Calculate the factor of safety η against slope rupture over a plane rupture surface by
means of Culmann's method.

Solution.
  i) *Auxiliary quantities.*
a) *Position of the most dangerous (critical) rupture surface.*
  By Eq. 24-6,

$$\omega = \frac{\theta + \phi}{2} = \frac{45° + 15°}{2} = \underline{30°}$$

$\sin\omega = \sin 30° = 0.500$

$\cos\omega = \cos 30° = 0.866$

b) *Length $\overline{AC}$ of rupture plane.*

$$\overline{AC} = H/\sin\omega = 10/0.500 = \underline{20 \text{ [m]}}.$$

c) *Length $\overline{BC}$ between top point B of the slope and point C (intersecting point of upper
  ground surface line $\overline{BC}$ and rupture plane $\overline{AC}$).*

$$\overline{BC} = \overline{AC}\cdot\frac{\sin 15°}{\sin 135°} = (20)(0.2588)/0.7071 = \underline{7.32 \text{ [m]}}$$

d) *Area of soil mass above rupture plane $\overline{AC}$.*

$$A = \triangle ABC = (0.5)(\overline{BC})(H) = (0.5)(7.32)(10) = \underline{36.60 \text{ [m}^2]}$$

e) *Weight W of soil mass over rupture plane $\overline{AC}$ per 1 m run of cut (or fill).*

$$W = (\gamma)(A)(1.0) = (16)(36.6)(1.0) = \underline{585.6 \text{ [kN]}}$$

f) *Normal force N.*

$$N = W \cdot \cos\omega = (585.6)(0.866) = \underline{507.13 \text{ [kN]}}.$$

g) *Tangential shear force T.*

$$T = W \cdot \sin\omega = (585.6)(0.500) = \underline{292.8 \text{ [kN]}}.$$

h) *Total force of cohesion C.*

$$C = (c)(\overline{AC})(1.0) = (29)(20)(1.0) = 580 \text{ [kN]}.$$

i) *Factor of safety.*

$$\eta = \frac{F_R}{F_D} = \frac{N \cdot \tan \phi + (c) \cdot (\overline{AC})}{T}$$

$$= \frac{(507.13) \cdot (0.2679) + 580}{292.8} = \underline{2.44 \text{ (Answer)}}.$$

STABILITY OF SLOPES
CONSIDERING CURVED RUPTURE SURFACES

24-6. General Notes. There are several theories available for analyzing the stability of earthwork slopes, for example:

theory applying circular rupture surfaces;

theory applying circular rupture surfaces with the so-called friction, or ϕ-circle;

theory applying logarithmically spiraled rupture surfaces;

theory using cycloids, logoids and possibly other kinds of rupture surfaces.
The existence of so many theories merely points out just how complex the soil stabilty problems are. Besides, there is no satisfactory theory available for calculating the stability of slopes made in non-homogeneous soils.

24-7. Collin's Work on Landslides in Clays. The French engineer Alexandre Collin published in 1846,[4] a book on landslides in clays in which he describes his experiences with many ruptures of slopes made in clay, gained from building canals. Collin observed that ruptures of slopes occur at all seasons of the year, and in several instances even long after the earthworks were completed, mainly because of increased moisture content in these soils with time. The mode of rupture in clay masses were observed to be by deep-seated, rotational movements over a curved rupture surface. Collin suggested that the ruptured mass of soil slides down on a definite type of sliding surface, which is more or less of the type of a cycloid.

The reason for rupture of soil is given as the inadequate shear strength of the soil. Collin was also one of the early researchers who performed shear tests on clays, and showed that moisture affects greatly the shear strength of cohesive soils.

It is because of his clear understanding of the nature of the shear strength of cohesive soils that Collin's work should be regarded as a model on the subject of landslides in clays.

Stability analyses of slopes on cycloidal rupture surfaces were studied also by Frontard.[5]

24-8. Circular Sliding Surface. Nowadays one of the most commonly used types of curved rupture surfaces in stability analyses of slopes is the circular, cylindrical rupture surface. The circular, cylindrical rupture surface is, of course, merely a conventional one in order to simplify mathematical computations involved in the stability analysis. The use of the circular rupture surface may probably be justified for the three following reasons:

1) it approximately coincides with the real shape of the rupture surfaces observed in nature,
2) it is necessary to make a number of other assumptions for the mathematical analyses anyway, and
3) the circular rupture surface is easy to draw with a compass.

Because of the early extensive studies of ruptures of slopes of earthworks made by Swedish engineers, the circular rupture surface is often referred to as the Swedish circle method.

The stability analysis of slopes on circular rupture surfaces is actually a graphoanalytical method as suggested in 1916 by Petterson,[6,7] Hultin,[8] and Fellenius.[9,10]

24-9. Pure Cohesive Soils—Stability En Masse—Slope Failure. The principle of stability analysis of a slope en masse, as explained by Fellenius,[11,12] is now

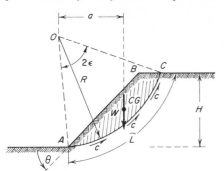

described as follows. In his works Fellenius expressly states that stability calculations of earth masses have for their object the determination of the properties of soil (cohesion and friction) *necessary for equilibrium* in different, assumed, circular sliding surfaces (Fig. 24-4). The method of analysis is based on the consideration that *that sliding surface which requires the greatest amount of cohesion c, and the greatest angle of internal friction ϕ, for equilibrium of the earth slope is the most dangerous one of all*, and that the degree

FIG. 24-4. W. Fellenius' system for pure cohesive soils.

of stability of the slope is expressed as the ratio of the shear strength s of the soil to needed strength of the soil.

In pure, homogeneous, cohesive soils the stability analysis of slopes is relatively simple.

The necessary amount of cohesion for equilibrium is

$$c = \frac{Wa}{\bar{L}R}. \tag{24-14}$$

Factor of safety, η:

$$\eta = s/c, \tag{24-15}$$

where $s =$ shear strength of soil,
  $Wa = M_D =$ driving moment, and
  $c\widehat{LR} = M_R =$ resisting moment.

If the circular arc $\widehat{AC}$ represents the most dangerous rupture surface, then the factor of safety η can also be formulated based on moment equilibrium as

$$\eta = \frac{M_R}{M_D} = \frac{s\widehat{LR}}{Wa} = \frac{s(2\epsilon)R^2}{Wa}. \tag{24-16}$$

When $\eta = 1$, rupture is just impending.
When $\eta > \eta_{\text{required}} \geqslant 1.5$, the slope is usually considered stable.
When $\eta < 1$, the slope is considered instable.

The position of the most dangerous rupture surface is found by the method of trial and error. This method consists of drawing several arcs through the toe of the slope by assuming different positions of the centers of the rupture circles. Each of the rupture circles thus assumed should be analyzed about each center chosen for the factor of safety. That circle which gives the least factor of safety among the circles analyzed is the *critical rupture surface*. The slope is considered to be stable if the least factor of safety η for the most dangerous rupture surface is $\eta \geqslant 1.5$.

TABLE 24-1. DIRECTIONAL ANGLES FOR LOCATING CENTER OF CRITICAL RUPTURE CIRCLE THROUGH THE TOE OF A SLOPE IN PURE c-SOIL*

Slope $\begin{array}{c}1\\ \diagup\hspace{-0.5em}\diagup \\ n\end{array}$ 1 : n	Slope angle $\theta°$	Directional angles		System of slope
		β_A	β_B	
1	2	3	4	5
$\sqrt{3}$: 1	60°	~29°	~40°	
1 : 1	45°	~28°	~38°	
1 : 1.5	33°41′	~26°	~35°	
1 : 2	25°34′	~25°	~35°	
1 : 3	18°26′	~25°	~35°	
1 : 5	11°19′	~25°	~37°	

* Compiled from Fellenius data, Reference (11).

Table 24-1 contains for various slope angles θ, auxiliary directional angles, β_A and β_B, for finding the position of the center of the most dangerous rupture surface through the toe of the slope made in a homogeneous, pure, cohesive soil. The method of finding the center O is illustrated in Fig. 24-5, by plotting angles β_A and β_B as shown. Should θ be different from those given in Table 24-1, then β_A and β_B may be interpolated for the angle θ under consideration from Table 24-1. To facilitate interpolation, β_A and β_B graphs based on values as shown in Table 24-1, can be plotted as functions of θ.

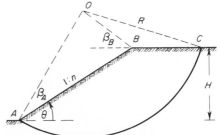

FIG. 24-5. Locating the center of the most dangerous rupture surface in pure cohesive soils for slope failure.

24-10. Tension Cracks. If there are tension cracks present in the cohesive soil, then below the depth, z, of the crack, rupture would occur along a curved rupture surface after the shear strength of the cohesive soil is exhausted. The finding of the most dangerous rupture surface is accomplished by the method of trial and error.

The most dangerous condition in the case of tension cracks would occur during rainy seasons when the tension cracks fill up with water and exert a hydrostatic pressure horizontally of the magnitude of

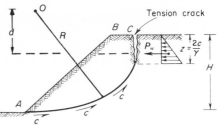

$$P_w = \tfrac{1}{2}\gamma z^2 = \frac{2c^2}{\gamma}. \qquad (24\text{-}17)$$

This pressure contributes to the total driving moment, see Fig. 24-6. In a $(\phi\text{-}c)$ soil,

FIG. 24-6. Tension crack.

$$z = \frac{2c}{\gamma}\tan(\pi/4 + \phi/2). \qquad (24\text{-}18)$$

For a pure cohesive soil, $z = 2c/\gamma$. $\qquad (24\text{-}18a)$
Frost, evaporation, and shrinkage affect the development of tension cracks and their depth.

A tension crack decreases the length of the arc of the circularly curved rupture surface.

Equations 24-18 and 24-18a for the depth z of the tension crack may render z-values which exceed any observed tension crack depth in the nature. Therefore, in practice some engineers use in tension crack calculations and hence in slope stability analyses in pure clays tension crack depths of about $z = 1.5$ m to about 3.0 m.

Tension cracks are usually the first indication of impending rupture of the soil mass of the slope.

If the tension crack is filled with water, the resulting hydrostatic pressure on the vertical wall of the crack in clay increases the driving moment by a value of $P_w \cdot d$ (Fig. 24-6). In such a case the factor of safety against a rotational rupture of the slope is reduced. The factor of safety calculates then as

$$\eta = \frac{M_R}{M_d} = \frac{c \cdot \overset{\frown}{L} \cdot R}{W \cdot a + P_w \cdot d} \quad , \tag{24-16a}$$

where d = moment arm of the hydrostatic force P_w with respect to point of rotation, viz., center of circle, O.

All other symbols are as before.

Example 2. Given a finite slope system in a pure clay as shown in Fig. 24-4a. The properties of the clay are: weight of rupture wedge per 1 m run of slope: $W = 1020 kN/m$. The undrained shear strength of the clay is $c_u = 40 \ kN/m^2$.

Calculate for the given position of the circularly curved rupture surface shown in Fig. 24-4a the necessary amount of cohesion needed for equilibrium, and determine the factor of safety for these conditions.

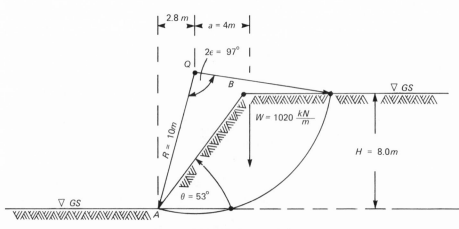

FIG. 24-4a. Example for stability analysis of a pure cohesive soil.

Solution.

a) *Length of arc* $\overset{\frown}{L} = \overset{\frown}{AC}$.

$$\overset{\frown}{L} = \frac{2 \pi R (2 \cdot \epsilon)}{360°} = \frac{(3.14)(10)(97°)}{180°} = \underline{16.9 \ [m]}.$$

b) *Necessary amount of cohesion, c.*

By Eq. 24-14,

$$c = \frac{W \cdot a}{\overset{\frown}{L} \cdot R} = \frac{(1020) \cdot (4.0)}{(16.9) \cdot (10)} = \underline{24.2 \ [kN/m^2]}.$$

c) *Factor of safety, η*.
   By Eq. 24-15,

$$\eta = s/c = c_u/c = 40/24.2 = \underline{1.65} \text{ (Answer)}.$$

24-11. Methods of Analyses. The routine of η-calculation as outlined above makes no distinction between the total and effective stresses. However, depending upon which kind of stress applies to the physical soil slope stability problem, the correspondingly appropriate test- or shear strength parameters must be employed. For example, if pore water pressure is relevant in a stability problem, stability calculations should be performed based on effective stress. In such a case one uses the shear strength parameters ϕ_{eff} and c_{eff} which parameters are based and determined on effective stresses.

As already mentioned in Chapter 19, under certain conditions the shear strength of the soil may be expressed based on total stress such as

$$\tau = \sigma_n \cdot \tan \phi + c, \tag{19-8}$$

where σ_n = normal stress,
or in terms of effective stress such as

$$\tau = (\sigma_n - u) \cdot \tan \phi_{eff} + c_{eff}, \tag{19-1}$$

where u = pore water pressure, known also as the neutral stress.

The effective horizontal normal stress $\overline{\sigma_3}$ is written as

$$\overline{\sigma_3} = \sigma_3 - u, \tag{14-33a}$$

and the effective vertical normal stress $\overline{\sigma_1}$ (intergranular stress) is written as

$$\overline{\sigma_1} = \sigma_1 - u, \tag{14-33b}$$

where σ_3 and σ_1 are minor and major principal stresses, respectively.

There are two main methods of earth slope stability analyses available, namely:

1) the so-called total stress method, and
2) the effective stress method.

1. Total Stress Method. In the total stress method, the undrained shear strength of soil is used as obtained from a) laboratory shear tests on soil, or b) vane shear tests.

The total stress analysis method is used

i) for analyzing stability of slopes of normally consolidated or slightly preconsolidated clays with little dissipation of excess pore water pressure, and

ii) when fill loads of soil are applied quickly upon a clay formation with no facilities to drain out the pore water.

For a completely saturated pure clay slope at undrained condition (condition immediately after forming the slope), the so-called total stress method, where $\phi_u = 0$, applies. In such a case, the undrained shear strength c_u is used:

$$\tau = s/\eta = c_u/\eta. \tag{24-19}$$

In such a case, Eq. 24-16 is written as

$$\eta = \frac{c_u \cdot (2 \cdot \epsilon) \cdot R^2}{W \cdot a} \tag{24-20}$$

In the case of a fully or partially submerged slope, the stability against rotational failure or rupture of the slope is calculated by using the submerged (buoyant) unit weight γ_{sub} of the soil mass for the submerged part of the slope.

The pore water pressure within the submerged clay slope is generally unknown, and is irrelevant in the total stress analysis.

2. Effective Stress Method. To account for pore water pressure u in earth masses such as earth slopes, for example, stability calculations against soil rupture are made in terms of the effective stress. In this method, the effective shear strength parameters ϕ_{eff} and c_{eff} are used. These parameters are to be obtained either from

    a) the effective stress test envelope, or

    b) ϕ and c are to be determined from cu tests.

The pore water pressures involved are to be established from seepage analyses or from consolidation tests, whichever the case is. Pore water pressures u act normal to rupture surfaces.

The effective stress method of analysis is used

    i) for analyzing long-term stability of, and drawdown in incompressible, permeable, coarse-particled soil materials. Here the parameter ϕ_{eff} is used. The c_{eff}-parameter is usually neglected. In this analysis, only pore water pressures resulting from gravitational water such as groundwater and / or seepage water are considered;

    ii) for analyzing dense, moderately compressible soil materials. Here the shear strength parameters ϕ_{eff} and c_{eff} are used. The pore water pressures involved are those brought about by steady seepage, or during a rapid drawdown, or consolidation. Pore water pressures are to be corroborated by means of observation data obtained by means of piezometers installed in the earthwork under study;

    iii) for analyzing stability of compressible soils where some drainage of water takes place while load is applied. Here the ϕ and c parameters, obtained from the cu compression tests are used. Pore water pressures are induced by groundwater and pore water from consolidation.

Usually, the noncohesive (granular) soils are completely drained. Therefore, stability calculations of slopes made in such soils, where $c_{eff} = 0$, are performed based on effective stress:

$$\tau = s/\eta = (\sigma_n - u) \cdot \frac{\tan\phi_{eff}}{\eta} \tag{24-21}$$

If the slope is subjected to seepage from impounded water by an earth dam made of noncohesive soil, the pore water (or neutral) pressure u is to be determined from the flow net.

24-12. Frictional-Cohesive Soils, (ϕ-c)-Soils—Stability En Masse—Slope Failure. If the slope forming soil is a (ϕ-c)-soil, one proceeds, in principle, similarly as described for pure c-soils (Fig. 24-7).

Principally, upon rupture, a frictional force $N \tan \phi$ and a cohesive force $c\widehat{L}$ are acting in the circular rupture surface. The driving force is $T = W \sin\alpha$, and the resisting force is $P = N \tan \phi + c\widehat{L}$. Again, the approximate degree of stability of a (ϕ-c)-slope can be judged from the factor of safety η, which is calculated based on the position of the most dangerous rupture surface:

$$\eta = \frac{M_R}{M_D} = \frac{PR}{TR} = \frac{(N \tan \phi + c\widehat{L})R}{TR} = \tag{24-22a}$$

$$= \frac{N \tan \phi + c\widehat{L}}{T} = \tag{24-22b}$$

$$= \frac{W \cos\alpha \tan \phi + c\widehat{L}}{W \sin\alpha} = \tag{24-22c}$$

$$= \cot\alpha \tan \phi + \frac{c\widehat{L}}{W \sin\alpha} = \tag{24-22d}$$

$$= \frac{\tan \phi}{\tan\alpha} + \frac{c\widehat{L}}{W \sin\alpha}, \tag{24-22e}$$

Or else,

$$\eta = \frac{M_R}{M_D} = \frac{\tau\widehat{L}R}{Wa}, \tag{24-22}$$

where $\tau = \sigma_e \tan \phi + c$ is the general equation for the shear strength of the soil, and

σ_e = effective normal stress on the rupture surface.

Simple as the foregoing Eq (24-22a) appears to be, in reality the stability calculations of slopes with circular rupture surfaces are very complex indeed. For this reason, and in order to obtain a clear insight into the partaking force system in the analysis, the calculations are best carried out graphically. The equilibrium equation of moments, $Wa \approx [(\tan \phi)N + c\widehat{L}]R$, when $\eta = 1$ in the case of ϕ and c being simultaneously present, holds only approximately, particularly for small angles of slopes θ, and hence may be used only for rough, preliminary calculations.

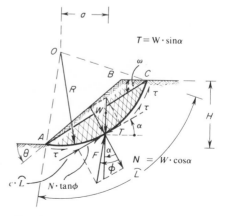

Fig. 24-7.   Stability system for a (ϕ-c) soil.

For simple finite slopes with $0° < \phi < 45°$, Fellenius[9-12] and Taylor[13] prepared convenient stability number charts which eliminate time consuming calculations by trial and error for fixing the position of the most dangerous or critical rupture surface and calculating η_{min}.

Example 3. Given an earth slope made in a moist (ϕ-c)-soil whose $\theta = 30°$; $H = 7.0$ m; length of rupture are $\overarc{L} = \overarc{AC} = 18.0$ m; radius of circle $R = 14.0$ m; central angle $2\epsilon = 78°$; $\gamma = 18$ kN/m^3; $\phi_{eff} = 20°$; $c_{eff} = 15$ kN/m^2. The normal force is given as $N = 210$ kN/m, and the driving force $T = 96$ kN/m.

Determine for this particular, single rupture surface the factor of safety of this slope. To find η_{min}, several other rupture surfaces must be tried and their η's determined.

Solution.
By Eq. 24-22b,

$$\eta = \frac{F_R}{F_D} = \frac{N \cdot \tan \phi_{eff} + c_{eff} \cdot \overarc{L}}{T}$$

$$= \frac{(210)(0.3640) + (15)(18.0)}{96.0} = 3.60 \text{ (Answer)}.$$

24-13. Friction-Circle Method. The friction-circle method of stability analysis of slopes is particularly applicable to (ϕ-c) soils.

The slope stability analysis by means of the ϕ-circle method is performed in terms of the total stress.

Suppose that the shear strength parameters are ϕ_u and c_u. Then the necessary shear strength τ_{nec} for equilibrium is

$$\tau_{nec} = s/\eta = (\sigma_n \cdot \tan \phi_u + c_u)/\eta = \sigma_n \cdot \tan \phi_{nec} + c_{nec}. \qquad (19\text{-}23)$$

Herein

$$\tan \phi_{nec} = \tan \phi_u/\eta_\phi \quad , \qquad (24\text{-}24)$$

and

$$c_{nec} = c_u/\eta_c \qquad (24\text{-}25)$$

Here c_u = undrained strength (when $\phi_u = 0$), and

$$\eta_\phi = \eta_c = \eta \quad . \qquad (24\text{-}26)$$

Now follows the routine of the general statics of the friction-circle system without regard of what kind of stress is to be used. It should be kept in mind, though, that the relevant shear strength parameters should be used in each particular case, of course.

The stability analysis by the ϕ-circle method can be performed in two ways, namely: 1) use a known cohesion of soil c and find the necessary angle of friction ϕ_{nec} for maintaining equilibrium, or, 2) use a known angle of friction of soil ϕ and determine the necessary amount of cohesion c_{nec} for keeping equilibrium.

The factor of safety η_ϕ relative to friction in the first case is then expressed as the ratio of the actual angle of friction ϕ to the necessary angle of friction ϕ_{nec}:

$$\eta_\phi = \phi/\phi_{nec}. \qquad (24\text{-}27)$$

In the second case the factor of safety η_c is expressed relative to cohesion as the ratio of the actually available cohesion of the soil to the amount of cohesion c_{nec} necessary for maintaining equilibrium:

$$\eta_c = c/c_{nec}. \tag{24-28}$$

The working of the ϕ-circle method, again, is by trial and error, whereby one tries to find for the same slope the most dangerous rupture surface. The principal

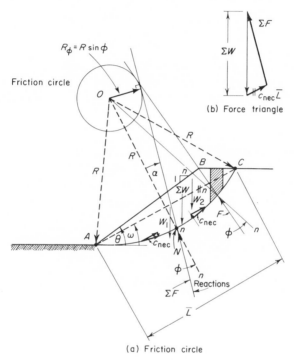

FIG. 24-8. Friction-circle system.

reasoning in this method is that for a definite ϕ-value (viz., c-value) that rupture surface is the most dangerous one which requires for equilibrium the greatest c-value (viz., ϕ-value).

With reference to Fig. 24-8, the forces of reaction F, at point N, for example, are directed against the direction of motion of the sliding soil wedge $ABCNA$. In such a case, it is assumed, based on statics principles, that at the instant of the impending rupture all reactive forces F along the circular rupture surface $\overset{\frown}{AC}$ form with the normal n-n (point N) to that rupture surface an angle ϕ, which is the angle of internal friction of the slope-forming soil. Therefore, in the case of a circular-cylindrical rupture surface, all reactions (from under each of the slices) would touch (tangent) a circle, the so-called friction or ϕ-circle, the radius of which is $R_\phi = R \sin \phi$. The ϕ-circle is concentric with the rupture circle of radius R. When $\phi = 0$, there is no ϕ-circle.

In the ϕ-circle system, with a known ϕ, for example, the following quantities are known:

1) magnitude of weight of sliding wedge and its direction of action;
2) direction of reaction F (at the known angle ϕ with the normal of the rupture surface), though the magnitude of F is not yet known;
3) the direction of the total cohesion $c\widehat{L}$ (along the rupture surface, viz., parallel to the chord, $\bar{L} = \overline{AC}$); its magnitude is not yet known.

To find the above-mentioned unknown quantities at equilibrium, the force triangle, viz., force polygon, is used, from which the magnitudes of reactions F and the necessary cohesion c_{nec} for equilibrium can be determined. In the case of equilibrium, the force triangle must close. From the magnitude of $c_{nec}\widehat{L}$, one determines the necessary cohesion for equilibrium and compares it with the available cohesive strength of the soil in question:

$$\eta_c = c_{avail}/c_{nec}. \qquad (24\text{-}29)$$

The direction and point of application of the total resultant, necessary cohesive force, $c_{nec}\widehat{L}$, acting along the circular sliding surface $\widehat{AC}$, is found as follows: assuming a uniform distribution of cohesion over the entire sliding surface, the sum of the components of c_{nec} of elementary cohesive forces parallel to $\overline{AC}$ (which equals $\bar{L}$) form a total moment M_c about point O (Fig. 24-9):

$$M_c = c_{nec}\bar{L}r_c, \qquad (24\text{-}30)$$

where r_c = arm of the cohesive moment (see Fig. 24-10).

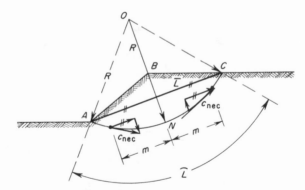

FIG. 24-9. Resolution of elementary force of cohesion.

The c_{nec}-components perpendicular to $\overline{AC} = \bar{L}$ are oppositely directed (Fig. 24-9), and do not contribute any moment (see Fig. 24-9).

This moment M_c, therefore, is also equal to the general expression of

$$M_c = c_{nec}\widehat{L}R \qquad (24\text{-}31)$$

or

$$c_{nec}\bar{L}r_c = c_{nec}\widehat{L}R, \qquad (24\text{-}32)$$

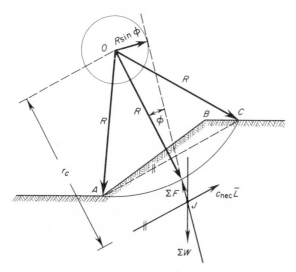

FIG. 24-10. Position of total cohesive force.

or the moment arm r_c of the cohesive force is

$$r_c = \frac{\widehat{L}}{\overline{L}} R. \qquad (24\text{-}33)$$

Because $\widehat{L} > \overline{L}$ by geometry, $r_c > R$. Hence, the direction of the total cohesive force $c_{nec}\widehat{L}$ to use in the force triangle (Fig. 24-8b) or polygon, whichever the case, is parallel to the direction of the chord AC.

The position of the total cohesive force $c_{nec}\overline{L}$ in the slope-friction angle system can now be determined by means of r_c and the direction of $c_{nec}\overline{L}$ from the force triangle (Fig. 24-8b). The point of application J of $c_{nec}\overline{L}$ is the point of intersection of $c_{nec}L$ with $\sum W$, through which point J, the third force $\sum F$, the reaction, passes so that $\sum F$ is tangent to the friction-circle. Now that the magnitude of $c_{nec}\overline{L}$ in the force triangle (Fig. 24-8b) is determined, the magnitude of the necessary cohesion c_{nec} can be computed.

24-14. Pure Cohesive Soils—Stability En Masse—Base Failure. If the slope-supporting soil below the toe line of the slope is the same material and has the same properties as the slope-forming material, then there may occur more dangerous rupture surfaces than that passing through the toe of the slope. The "more dangerous" rupture surfaces are deep-seated and are termed base failures (Fig. 24-11).

When AB is a slope of a straight line, then, according to Fellenius, the center O of the rupture surface $\widehat{AC}$ is situated on a vertical line drawn through the midpoint M of the slope AB, so that $a = a$, where $2a$ = horizontal projection of the slope.

When AB is a vertical wall, then the center O of the rupture surface is located on a vertical line drawn through the vertical wall. The stability analysis is performed by trial and error.

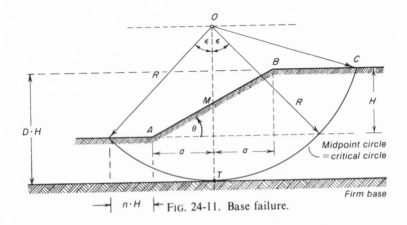

FIG. 24-11. Base failure.

Fellenius did find that for pure cohesive soils the position of the most dangerous rupture surface associated with deep-seated base failure is located very deep (theoretically infinitely deep), and has the value of the central angle of the circular rupture surface of $2\varepsilon = 133°34'$. However, the cohesion c_{nec} needed in the most dangerous rupture surface through a point a little under the toe of the slope is only slightly less than that needed in the infinitely deep-seated rupture surface:

$$c_{nec} = \tfrac{1}{4}\gamma H \sin 133°34' = (0.181)\gamma H. \qquad (24\text{-}34)$$

If the value of the cohesion c of a cohesive soil is known, then the critical height H_{crit} of the slope can be calculated by Eq. 24-34 as

$$H_{crit} = \frac{c}{(0.181)\gamma}. \qquad (24\text{-}35)$$

24-15. Stability Number. To facilitate calculations, Ehrenberg[14] uses for the cohesion a factor of safety η_c and calculates an auxiliary value of $c/(\eta_c \cdot \gamma \cdot H)$, and using Krey's $c/(\gamma \cdot H)$ graphs,[15] determines the height H of the slope, or the angle θ of the slope, whichever the case is.

To circumvent the cumbersome method of trial and error of the graphoanalytical procedure for evaluating the stability of homogeneous slopes in terms of total stress, Taylor,[13] based on the friction-circle method, worked out a simplified method of analysis similar to that as given by Ehrenberg, by combining the three parameters c, γ and H into a single parameter

$$N_T = \frac{c}{\gamma \cdot H}. \qquad (24\text{-}36)$$

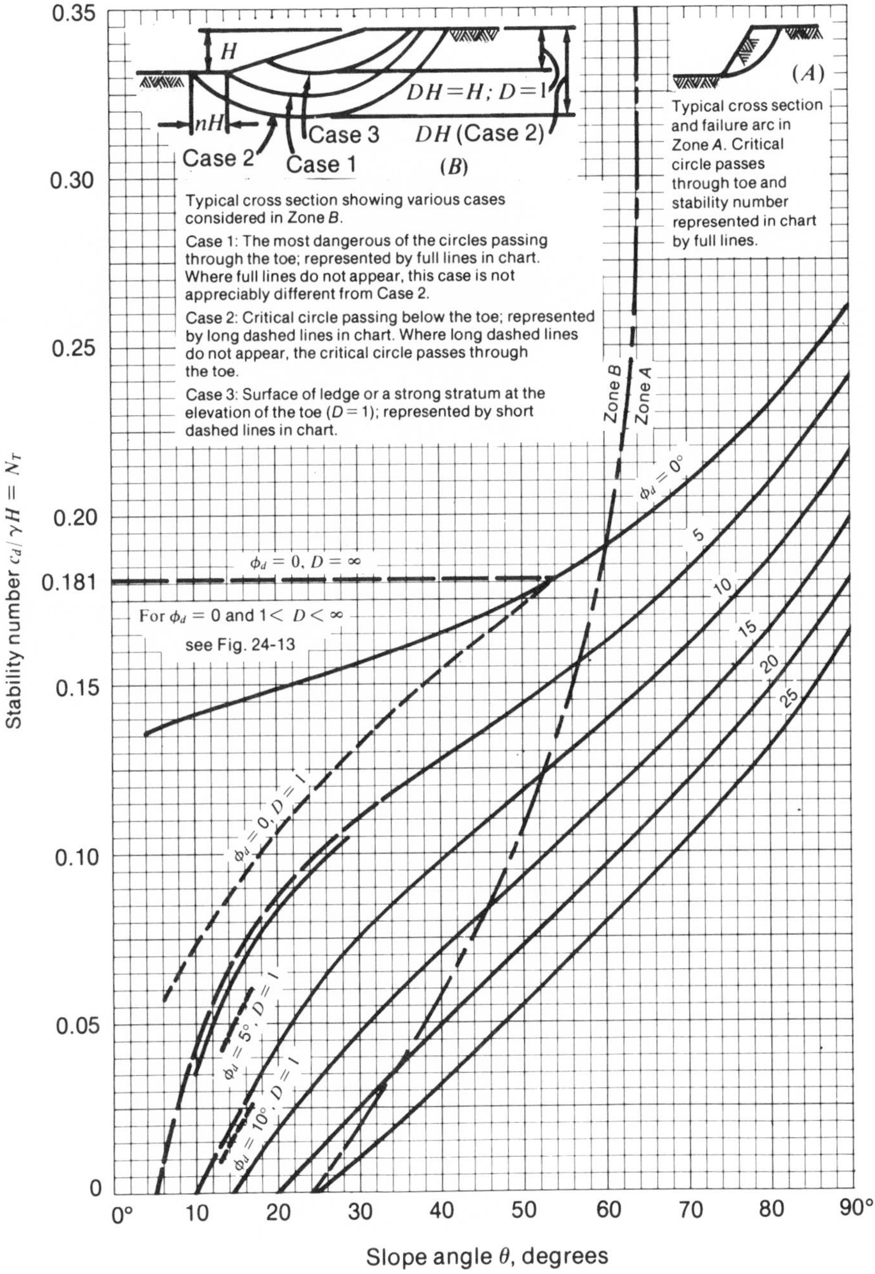
0.35
0.30
0.25
0.20
0.181
0.15
0.10
0.05
0
H
nH
Case 2
Case 1
Case 3
DH=H; D=1
DH (Case 2)
(B)
Typical cross section showing various cases considered in Zone B.
Case 1: The most dangerous of the circles passing through the toe; represented by full lines in chart. Where full lines do not appear, this case is not appreciably different from Case 2.
Case 2: Critical circle passing below the toe; represented by long dashed lines in chart. Where long dashed lines do not appear, the critical circle passes through the toe.
Case 3: Surface of ledge or a strong stratum at the elevation of the toe (D = 1); represented by short dashed lines in chart.
(A)
Typical cross section and failure arc in Zone A. Critical circle passes through toe and stability number represented in chart by full lines.
Zone B
Zone A
$\phi_d = 0°$
5
10
15
20
25
$\phi_d = 0,\ D = \infty$
For $\phi_d = 0$ and $1 < D < \infty$
see Fig. 24-13
$\phi_d = 0,\ D = 1$
$\phi_d = 5°,\ D = 1$
$\phi_d = 10°,\ D = 1$
Stability number $c_d/\gamma H = N_T$
0°
10
20
30
40
50
60
70
80
90°
Slope angle θ, degrees

FIG. 24-12. Taylor's chart of stability numbers. Ref. 13.

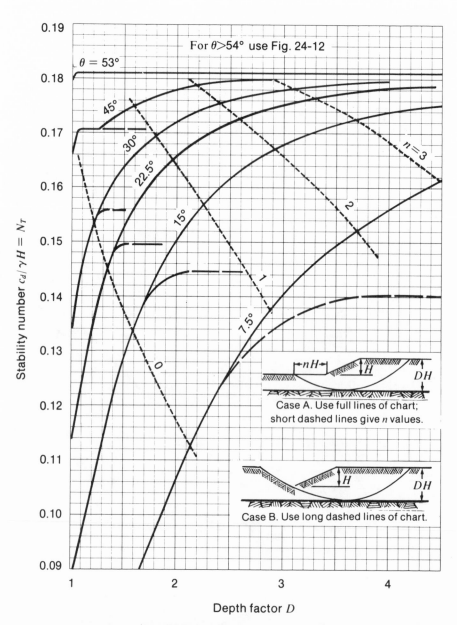

FIG. 24-13. Taylor's chart of stability numbers for the case of zero friction angle and limited depth. Ref. 13.

called by Taylor the *stability number*. It is dimensionless.

Taylor assumed that the cohesion c is constant with depth. Gibson and Morgenstern[16] published stability coefficients for slopes made in normally consolidated clays in which the undrained shear strength of the pure clay soil c_u (for $\phi_u = 0$) varies linearly with depth.

Taylor's stability numbers are presented in graphical forms as shown in Figs. 24-12 and 24-13. From these charts, it can be seen that the stability number N_T (given in terms of c, γ and H) is a function of slope angle θ; angle of friction of soil ϕ (Fig. 24-12), and depth factor D (Fig. 24-13). The depth factor D is a ratio of the depth DH below the upper ground surface to the firm base or stratum to the height of the slope H.

By means of the Taylor's charts, various problems of stability calculations of regular, finite slopes made in homogeneous soil materials for undrained condition can be made directly without actually locating the position of the most dangerous rupture surface at all.

Alas, in practice, earth slopes of reasonable heights are rarely made in, or of homogeneous soils. Even if the soil material is somewhat uniform texturally within the height of the slope, the unit weight as well as the strength of the soil varies considerably in their magnitude. Also, stability depends primarily on groundwater conditions: the changing water regimen within the soil mass changes the soil properties bringing about seepage, and thus pore water pressures in the soil. Therefore, under such conditions, it probably appears to be most appropriate, expedient and practical that the stability analysis for fixing the position of the center of the most dangerous circular rupture surface be performed by method of trial and adjustment rather than by the stability number method. It is because most soils encountered in earthworks are not homogeneous. The computing of the factor of safety in all of the methods of analyses, however, is still a common practice.

The routine of the application of Taylor's stability number to earth slope stability calculations will be illustrated by some numerically worked out examples.

Example 4. An earth slope with a slope angle of $\theta = 60°$ is to be made in a (ϕ-c)-soil whose properties are:

angle of internal friction: $\phi = 10°$

cohesion: $c = 12 \text{ kN/m}^2$

unit weight: $\gamma = 19 \text{ kN/m}^3$.

Determine the maximum actual height H of the slope to maintain a factor of safety of $\eta = 1.5$ relative to the height of the slope.

Solution.

Refer to Taylor's chart in Fig. 24-12. From this chart, for $\theta = 60°$ and $\phi = 10°$, the stability number $N_T = c_d/(\gamma \cdot H) = 0.14$. By Eq. 24-36, the critical height H_{crit} is:

$$0.14 = \frac{12}{(19) \cdot (H_{crit})} \quad ,$$

and

$$H_{crit} = 0.63157/0.14 = \underline{4.5 \text{ [m]}} ,$$

and

$$\eta_H = H_{crit}/H = 4.5/H = 1.5$$
$$H = 4.5/1.5 = \underline{2.9 \text{ [m]}} .$$

Example 5. An excavation 8 m deep is to be made in a soft clay. The properties of this clay are:

$$\phi = 0; \ c = 24 \text{ kN/m}^2; \ \gamma = 18 \text{ kN/m}^3.$$

The soft clay is underlain by a firm geological stratum at a depth of 14 m below the ground surface. Determine the magnitude of the slope angle θ at which slope rupture in clay is just impending.

Solution.
Refer to Taylor's chart in Fig. 24-13. Because here $\phi = 0$, the depth factor is:

$$D = \frac{[DH]}{H_{crit}} = 12/8 = 1.5$$

For rupture impending, $H_{crit} = 8$ m and Taylor's stability number calculates as

$$N_T = c_d/(\gamma \cdot H_{crit}) = 24/(18)(8) = 0.167.$$

From Fig. 24-13, for $D = 1.5$ and $N_T = 0.167$, the slope angle θ is scaled off as 32°, and $n \approx 0.6$.

The same results as in Examples 4 and 5 may be obtained by means of Terzaghi and Peck *stability factors* N_s, for which charts are given in Reference 17. These N_s factors are the inverse of Taylor's stability numbers N_T.

Example 6. Factor of safety with respect to height of slope. A 12 m high slope whose slope angle is $\theta = 45°$ was made in a saturated and very impervious soil. Consider that the slope material is completely submerged, and that after some time a complete, rapid drawdown will be brought about to a level somewhat below the toe-line of the slope. Determine the factor of safety η_H of the earth slope

  a) for the submerged condition before drawdown, and

  b) for the drawdown condition.

The laboratory undrained test results are:

$\phi_{eff} = 20°$

$c_{eff} = 28.73 \text{ kN/m}^2$

$\gamma = 20 \text{ kN/m}^3$ (total or bulk unit weight of the saturated soil).

Solution.
a) *Submerged condition.*
From Fig. 24-12, for $\theta = 45°$ and $\phi = 20°$, the stability number is $N_T = 0.062$.

$$N_T = 0.062 = \frac{c_{eff}}{\eta_H \cdot \gamma_{sub} \cdot H}$$

and

$$\eta_H = \frac{28.73}{(10.19)(12)(0.062)} = \underline{3.8 \text{ [m]}.}$$

b) *Sudden drawdown condition.*
Upon rapid or sudden drawdown (within a few days or a few weeks) of water table in a reservoir, the factor of safety of the earth slope against failure is temporarily reduced until equilibrium is again attained under a new hydraulic condition. Upon a sudden drawdown, the unit weight of the soil is increased, and the shear strength of the soil along the rupture surface is reduced because of the pore water pressure.
The weighted angle of friction ϕ_w:

$$\phi_w = \frac{\gamma - \gamma_w}{\gamma} \cdot \phi_d = \frac{(20 - 9.81)}{20} \cdot 20 = 10.2° \tag{24-37}$$

From Fig. 24-12, for $\theta = 45°$ and $\phi_w = 10.2°$, the stability number is $N_T = 0.106$, and

$$\eta_H = \frac{28.73}{(0.106)(20)(12)} = 1.13 \ .$$

Generally, a slope at a steady seepage condition is more stable than at a rapid drawdown condition.

Example 7. Factor of safety with respect to strength of soil.
Given a 12 m high slope whose $\theta = 45°$, $\phi_{eff} = 20°$, $c_{eff} = 28.73$ kN/m², and $\gamma = 20$ kN/m³. Analyse the slope for its stability.

a) *Submerged condition.*
Because the unknown factor of safety η_s with respect to strength appears is both $c_d = c_{eff}/\eta_s$ and $\tan\phi_d = \tan\phi_{eff}/\eta_s$, a method of solution by successive trial of approach should be used. For example, if required $\eta_s = 2.0$, the allowable height H_{all} of the slope can be determined as set forth.

$$\phi_d = \arctan\left(\frac{\tan\phi_{eff}}{\eta_s}\right) = \arctan\left(\frac{\tan 20°}{2.0}\right) = 10.3° \tag{24-38}$$

For $\theta = 45°$ and $\phi = 10.3°$, the stability number from Fig. 24-12 is $N_T = 0.106$.

$$N_T = 0.106 = \frac{c_{eff}}{\eta_s \cdot \gamma_{sub} \cdot H_{all}} = \frac{28.73}{(2)(10.19)(H_{all})} \tag{24-39}$$

$$H_{all} = \frac{28.73}{(2)(10.19)(0.106)} = \underline{13.3\,[m]} \ .$$

If $\eta_s = 2.1$, then

$$\arctan\left(\frac{\tan 20°}{2.1}\right) = 9.8°,$$

and from Taylor's chart, Fig. 24-12 obtain the stability number as $N_T = 0.109$.

$$H_{all} = \frac{28.73}{(2.1)(10.19)(0.109)} = 12.3\,[m].$$

For $\phi_d = 9.6°$, $H_{all} = 11.99$ m $\approx$ 12 m for $\eta_s = 1.06$

b) *Sudden drawdown condition.*
Again, a trial method of approach should be used. From the solution in Example 6, for the drawdown condition, the weighted angle of friction is $\phi_w = 10.2°$. Assume $\eta_s = 1.10$.

$$\phi = \arctan \left(\frac{\tan 10.2°}{1.10} \right) = 9.3°.$$

From Taylor's chart for $\theta = 45°$ and $\phi = 9.3°$ obtain the relevant stability number $N_T = 0.109$. Then

$$H = \frac{28.73}{(1.10)(20)(0.109)} = 11.98 \approx 12[\text{m}] \ ,$$

showing that the assumed trial value of $\eta_s = 1.10$ was correct. Hence the sought factor of safety is $\eta_s = 1.10$.

Bishop and Morgenstern[18] computed dimensionless stability coefficients for homogeneous slopes, in principle similar to Taylor's dimensionless stability numbers, but applicable to effective stress calculations. Their results are given in the form of charts.

24-16. Pure Cohesive Soils, (ϕ-c)-Soils—Stability Calculations by Method of Slices. If the cross section of a slope-forming body of soil is composed of pure cohesive soil layers, each layer of which has different shear strength properties; if a homogeneous slope is partially submerged; if through a homogeneous dam

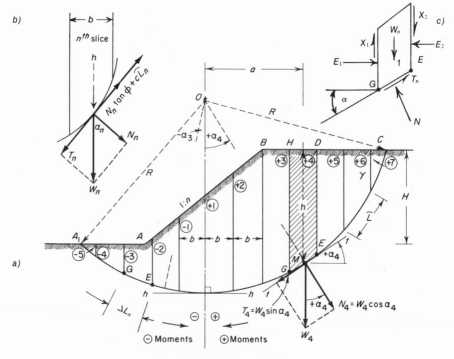

FIG. 24-14. Method of slices.

seepage takes place, or if the earthwork-forming slope is a broken one with steps and berms, then stability calculations of slopes over circular rupture surfaces can be more conveniently performed by the method of slices as originally shown by Petterson (see Refs. 5, 6).

The general routine for the method of slices is as follows. The cross section of the slope-forming mass of soil encompassed by the circular rupture surface is subdivided into a number of vertical, parallel elements or slices of equal width, such as shown in Fig. 24-14. The width of the slices is usually taken as $b \approx (0.1)R$. The weight of each slice W, for example, slice No. $+4$, is applied at the center of gravity of the slice and is projected on and allowed to act on the circular arc GE at point M, for example. The weight W is then resolved into normal and tangential components, N and T, respectively, where $N = W \cos \alpha$ and $T = W \sin \alpha$. Note that N passes through point M, as well as through O, the center of rotation. The weight of the slices is calculated by simplified geometric areas (rectangles, trapezoids, and triangles) as follows:

$$W_n = A_n(1)\gamma, \tag{24-40}$$

where $A(1) = V =$ volume of slice, and
$\gamma =$ unit weight of soil.
The algebraic sum of the tangential forces of all slices ΣT tends to shear the soil wedges along the impending circular rupture surface, and is resisted by the total resistance of the soil, $\tan \phi \, \Sigma N + c\widehat{L}$, whereby the normal force ΣN must be the effective normal force.

Generally, the free-body diagram of a slice is acted upon by the following forces (Fig. 24-14c):

$W_n = \gamma \cdot b \cdot h \cdot (1) =$ total weight of the n-th slice;
$N_n =$ total normal force of the slice;
     this force, generally, consists of two parts, namely: the effective normal force $N_{neff} = \sigma_{oneff} \cdot \widehat{L_n}$, ($\sigma_{oeff} =$ normal effective contact pressure of soil on the base of each slice), and the boundary neutral force $U_n = u \cdot \widehat{L_n}$, if present.
$u =$ neutral or pore water pressure;
$\widehat{L_n} =$ length of the curved base GE of the n-th slice. For purpose of simplifying calculations, $\widehat{L_n}$ may be replaced by a chord $\overline{GE}$, so that the base of the slice may be considered to be a straight line. In such a case $N_{eff} = \sigma_{oeff} \cdot (b/\cos\alpha) = \sigma_{oeff} \cdot (\Delta L_n)$, and $U_n = u \cdot (\overline{GE}) = (u)(b/\cos\alpha) = (u)(\Delta L_n)$;
$T_n = s_{nec} \cdot (\Delta L_n) =$ shear force on the base (Fig. 24-14c);
E_1 and $E_2 =$ total normal lateral interslice forces on the sides of a slice;
X_1 and $X_2 =$ tangential interslice forces on the sides of a slice;
$P, Q =$ any externally applied forces if present.

Generally, the interslice forces on the vertical boundaries or sides of the slice do not cancel out. Therefore they render the stability problem statically indeterminate. Hence, certain assumptions must be made about the interslice forces, and the stability analysis must be approached by method of trial and adjustment. One reason, therefore, that the factor of safety obtained for this force play is an inexact one.

Fellenius and Krey simplified the method of slices by assuming that the resultant of interslice forces on each slice is zero (Figs. 24-14a and 24-14b).

If the entire sliding ruptured mass of soil is considered when there is no water pressure in the tension cracks, then

$$(E_1 - E_2) = 0$$
$$(X_1 - X_2) = 0$$

Assuming that the above zero-relationships hold for each slice, the so committed error in the calculated factor of safety based on equilibrium of the entire soil mass should not be very large. Hence, for many practical problems, Fellenius' stability analysis by method of slices with no interface forces may be sufficiently accurate.

The advantage of the method of slices lies in the convenience of evaluation of the magnitude of the normal weight component N of each slice which permits summing them up as $\sum N$ to be used in stability calculations. Note that the weights of the slices to the right of the vertical through the center of rotation, point O, contribute to driving moments, whereas the slices to the left of the vertical contribute to resisting moments.

The degree of the stability of slope is evaluated by comparing driving moments with resisting moments about the center O of rotation:

$$\eta = \frac{M_R}{M_D} = \frac{(\tan \phi \sum N + \sum c\widehat{L})R}{R \sum T}. \tag{24-41}$$

The factor of safety η should satisfy in each case the prescribed requirements for η, a magnitude of which should be at least $\eta \geqslant 1.5$.

When $\phi = 0$, then

$$\eta = \frac{\sum (c\widehat{L})}{\sum T}. \tag{24-42}$$

Several circles must be analyzed, and for each circle the factor of safety η must be computed. The least factor of safety among them indicates the most dangerous rupture surface.

If in the earth slope material pore water pressure u is present because of seepage, for example, then this pore water pressure u on any base $\overline{GE}$ (Fig. 24-14) of any slice is determined from a corresponding flow net. The pore water pressure u acts normal to the base of the slice.

Considering the pore water pressure u, the factor of safety η of such an earth slope calculates in terms of effective stresses, viz., forces, as

$$\eta = \frac{C_{eff} + N_{eff} \cdot \tan\phi_{eff}}{T}, \tag{24-43}$$

or

$$\eta = \frac{\sum (c_{eff} \cdot L_n) + \left[\sum (W_n \cdot \cos\alpha_n - u \cdot \widehat{L_n})\right] \cdot \tan\phi_{eff}}{\sum (W_n \cdot \sin\alpha_n)} \tag{24-44}$$

If $\phi_{eff} = 0$, then

$$\eta = \frac{\sum (c_{eff} \cdot \widehat{L_n})}{\sum (W_n \cdot \sin\alpha_n)} \tag{24-45}$$

Here $C_{eff} = \sum (c_{eff} \cdot \widehat{L_n})$ = total effective resisting cohesive force acting in the total circular rupture surface;

$N_{eff} = \sum (W_n \cdot \cos\alpha_n - u \cdot \widehat{L_n})$ = resultant effective normal force;

$N_{eff} \cdot \tan\phi_{eff}$ = total effective resisting frictional force;

$u \cdot \widehat{L_n} = U$ = total neutral or pore water pressure on the base of any one slice, and

T = total driving (tangential) force.

For calculating slope stability by method of slices in terms of total stress, the shear strength parameters ϕ_u and c_u are used. In this case, $u = 0$ in Eq. 24-44. When $\phi_u = 0$, the exact value of the factor of safety sought is

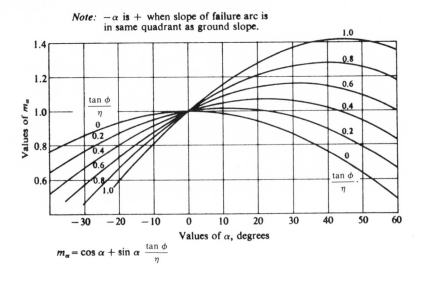

Note: $-\alpha$ is $+$ when slope of failure arc is in same quadrant as ground slope.

$$m_\alpha = \cos\alpha + \sin\alpha \; \frac{\tan\phi}{\eta}$$

FIG. 24-15. *Values of m_a.* [After Janbu et al. (1956)].

$$\eta = \frac{c_u \cdot \widehat{L_n}}{(W_n \cdot \sin\alpha_n)} , \tag{24-46}$$

where $\widehat{L_n}$ = length of arc of the circular rupture surface.

For calculating factor of safety for slopes if the rupture surface is circular and interslice forces are neglected, Janbu et al.[19] published the following procedure. The shear stress s along the base for a trial circle under consideration calculates as

$$s = \frac{c + (W_n/b) \cdot \tan\phi}{1 + \dfrac{\tan\phi \cdot \tan\alpha}{\eta}} . \tag{24-47}$$

Setting

$$\left(1 + \frac{\tan\phi \cdot \tan\alpha}{\eta}\right) \cdot \cos\alpha = m_\alpha, \qquad (24\text{-}48)$$

the factor of safety calculates as

$$\eta = \frac{\Sigma(s \cdot b/\cos\alpha)}{\Sigma(W_n \cdot \sin\alpha)} = \frac{\Sigma \left\{\dfrac{[c + (W_n/b) \cdot \tan\phi]b}{m_\alpha}\right\}}{\Sigma(W_n \cdot \sin\alpha)} \qquad (24\text{-}49)$$

Notice that this η-equation involves the m_α-quantity which, too, is a function of η. Therefore, for η, one must solve the η-equation 24-49 by trial of successive approximations. The η-equation calculations are greatly facilitated by a chart devised by Janbu et al.[19] as given in Fig. 24-15. From this chart the m_α-values are conveniently picked out and used in Eq. 24-49. Several other circles must be tried to find $\eta_{min} \geq \eta_{all}$.

In his stability analysis of earth slopes by method of slices considering parallel interslice forces and in terms of effective stress, Bishop[20] arrived at the following factor of safety formula η:

$$\eta = \frac{R}{\Sigma(W \cdot x)} \cdot \Sigma \left\{ (W \cdot \cos\alpha - u \cdot \Delta L)\tan\phi_{eff} + c_{eff} \cdot \Delta L + \right.$$

$$\left. + \tan\phi_{eff} \left[(X_1 - X_2)\cos\alpha + (E_1 - E_2)\sin\alpha\right] \right\}. \qquad (24\text{-}50)$$

Herein, R = radius of circle, and x = moment arm for W. For $(X_1 - X_2) = 0$ and $(E_1 - E_2) = 0$, Eq. 24-50 reduces to Fellenius method.

The approximate coordinates of the center of rotation, O_c, of the most dangerous circular sliding surfaces through the toe of the slope for $(\phi\text{-}c)$-soils, for which the factor of safety is a minimum, may be found by trial and error, starting with Fellenius' directional angles β_A and β_B for pure cohesive soils, Fig. 24-16 for which $\phi = 0$. The center O_o of such a circular sliding surface $\overset{\frown}{AC}$, having its center at point O_o, is also shown in Fig. 24-16. In order to find the critical center O_c for a $(\phi\text{-}c)$-soil, one may proceed as follows. From Fellenius' graphs it can be noted that the line on which all of the centers O_0, O_1, O_2, O_3,...O_c...O_n line up passes through point O_o and a point K, Fig. 24-16. Point K has the approximate coordinates of $x = (4.5)H$ and $z = H$. Hence, in order to establish the position line O_o-K, find point O_o by means of directional angles, β_A and β_B. Then plot point K with the coordinates $x = (4.5)H$, and $z = H$ as indicated on Fig. 24-16. Then draw through points O_o and K the position line on which the centers O_1, O_2, O_3,... O_n...of the trial circles lie.

Fellenius' graphs show that as the value of ϕ increases, the center O_n of the circular rupture surface moves up from point $O_o(\phi = 0)$ along the position line O_o-K.

The stability computation may now be performed as follows. Select on the position line (above O_o) several, say equally spaced, centers, O_1, O_2, O_3,..., O_{n-1}, O_n, and draw n circles through the toe-point A. Calculate for each circle

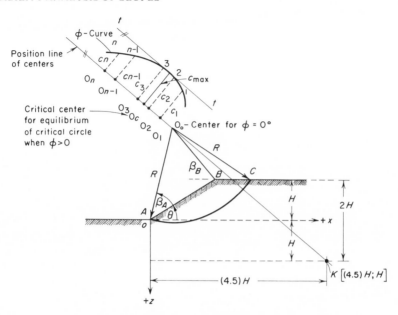

FIG. 24-16. Locating the center, O_c, for critical circle.

the amount of cohesion required to maintain equilibrium for the given value of ϕ of the soil:

$$\sum T = \tan \phi \sum N + c\widehat{L}, \qquad (24\text{-}51)$$

or

$$c = \frac{\sum T - \tan \phi \sum N}{\widehat{L}}. \qquad (24\text{-}52)$$

Then plot these calculated c-values as ordinates to a certain scale on the position line at points of centers for which these c-values were found. For example, plot c_1 at point O_1, c_2 at point O_2, . . ., and c_n at O_n. Connect the c-ordinates with a curvilinear line 1-2-3-$(n-1)$-n, the so-called ϕ-curve, and draw a tangent t-t to the curve and parallel to the position line O_o-K. The tangent to the ϕ-curve then scales off the maximum ordinate $= c_{max}$. This is the maximum value of the cohesion for maintaining equilibrium of the slope for a given ϕ. This maximum c-ordinate gives on the position line $(O_o$-$K)$ a point O_c which is the critical center of the critical rupture surface for ϕ and for which the factor of safety η is a minimum. With a radius of $R = (O_c - A)$ draw the critical rupture surface $\widehat{AC_c}$ along which the rupture would most probably take place, divide the slope-forming mass of soil on this circle into slices, determine $\sum T$, $\tan \phi \sum N$, and $c\widehat{L}$ (use ϕ and c obtained from tests of this particular soil), and calculate the factor of safety η:

$$\eta = \frac{\tan \phi \sum N + c\widehat{L}}{\sum T}. \qquad (24\text{-}53)$$

If this factor of safety is $\eta \geqslant 1.5$, the slope may be considered stable. If $\eta < 1.5$, the slope, or the height of the slope, must be redesigned.

The calculations can best be performed in a tabular form.

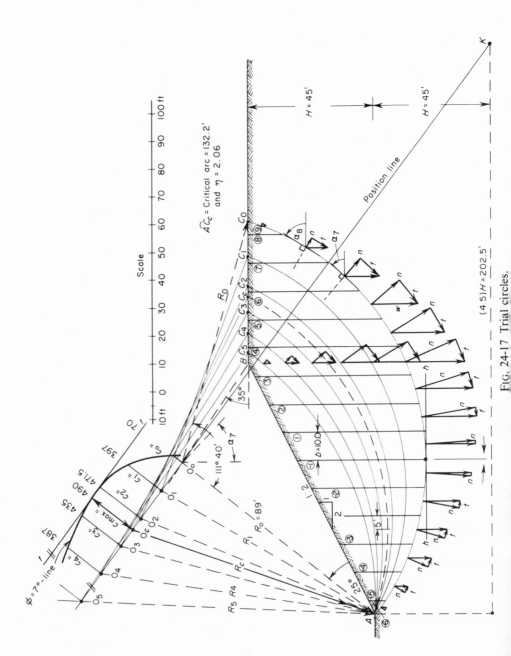

FIG. 24-17 Trial circles.

$$c = 1200\ \text{lb/ft}^2;\quad \phi = 7^\circ;\quad \gamma = 110\ \text{lb/ft}^3$$

Center of Curve	O_0		O_1		O_2		O_3		O_4		O_c	
Length of Arc	171.0'		153.5'		139.0'		126.0'		116.0'		132.0'	
Forces	2		3		4		5		6		7	
Slice Numbers (1)	n	t	n	t	n	t	n	t	n	t	n	t
−6	12.9	−10.5										
−5	107.2	−63.0	6.9	−4.0								
−4	206.0	−88.5	88.0	−39.1	7.0	−3.1					9.2	−3.2
−3	285.0	−84.6	168.0	−48.8	69.5	−20.6	7.8	−2.1			71.5	−16.2
−2	364.0	−63.4	256.0	−43.1	145.0	−24.6	59.6	−9.5	5.0	−1.0	140.0	−15.6
−1	423.0	−24.2	322.0	−18.1	224.0	−12.4	124.0	−6.6	54.8	−2.8	94.8	−2.6
1	468.0	+27.8	368.0	+20.7	276.0	+15.1	174.0	+9.2	114.9	+5.0	109.0	+3.0
2	510.0	88.7	404.0	68.9	307.0	50.8	224.0	35.6	149.0	22.5	242.0	27.0
3	522.0	155.0	423.0	123.0	324.0	91.8	244.0	65.7	175.0	45.0	271.0	61.5
4	508.5	218.5	396.4	176.0	324.0	134.4	248.0	97.5	183.0	68.3	287.0	97.9
5	447.0	263.0	394.0	228.0	309.0	173.1	250.0	120.6	184.8	92.1	284.0	134.8
6	334.1	273.0	298.0	234.0	268.0	202.0	223.0	150.5	169.5	110.0	259.0	165.5
7	236.4	256.0	195.0	210.0	177.0	178.0	169.0	157.0	127.0	113.8	212.0	179.6
8	111.5	186.0	86.3	50.3	71.5	103.0	75.0	94.6	92.5	102.0	187.0	151.2
9	8.5	23.2	4.1	13.8	8.3	16.5	3.8	5.6	5.9	8.2	107.7	49.6
$\sum n$ and $\sum t$	4544.1	1187.0	3409.9	971.6	2510.3	904.0	1802.2	718.1	1261.4	563.1	2274.2	832.5
η	1.63		2.15		2.11		2.22		3.46		2.06	
2ϵ	111°40'		99°00'		86°00'		76°00'		66°00'		$2\epsilon_c = 82°00'$	
c_{nec}	69.8		397.0		471.5		435.0		387.0		$c_{max} = 490.0$	

Example 8. A slope $1:2$, the height of which is $H = 45$ ft, is to be made in a (ϕ-c) soil the unit weight of which is $\gamma = 110$ lb/ft^3, the angle of internal friction, $\phi = 7°$, and the cohesive strength is found to be $c = 1200$ lb/ft^2. Compute the factor of safety, η, against rupture of slope. The minimum factor of safety should be $\eta = 2.00$. (Use slide rule).

Solution. (Refer to Fig. 24-17). The critical circle for a pure cohesive soil ($\phi = 0$) is drawn from the corresponding critical center, O_o, ($\eta = 1$). Center O_o is found by means of directional angles $\beta_A = 25°$ and $\beta_B = 35°$. Draw circle C_o, with point O_o as the center. Establish point K, and draw position line O_o-K, extending it beyond point O_o. The critical center, C_c, for the (ϕ-c) soil, when $\phi = 7°$, must be found by the method of trial and error. Assume, therefore, on the position line five points, O_1, O_2, O_3, O_4, and O_5, arbitrarily spaced at equal distances from each other. Draw curves C_1, C_2, C_3, C_4, and C_5. Slice up the soil mass above the curves with slices of equal width, $b = 10$ ft to scale, for example. For each curve, determine the weight, W, of each slice, and resolve it into normal and tangential components, n and t, respectively. Because weight is proportional to area, i.e., $w = a\gamma$, where $w = $ weight of slice, and $a = $ area of slice, calculate the area of each slice, and find

$$n = a \cos \alpha \qquad (24\text{-}54)$$

and

$$t = a \sin \alpha, \qquad (24\text{-}55)$$

or find the values of the a-components graphically. The sum of the normal and tangential components of the areas of all slices on one circle is then $\sum n$ and $\sum t$, Table 24-2. The normal and vertical forces, $\sum N$ and $\sum T$, respectively, resulting from the weight of the rupturing soil wedge, ABC, are:

$$N = \gamma \sum n, \qquad (24\text{-}56)$$

and

$$T = \gamma \sum t. \qquad (24\text{-}57)$$

For circles C_1, C_2, C_3, C_4, and C_5, calculate the maximum necessary cohesion c_1, c_2, c_3, c_4, and c_5, plot them at points O_1, O_2, O_3, O_4, and O_5 as ordinates and draw the $\phi = 7°$ line connecting these c_n-ordinates. For example, by Eq. (24-52), the necessary maximum cohesions for $\eta = 1.0$ were found to be

$$c_1 = 397 \text{ lb/ft}^2$$

$$c_2 = 471.5 \text{ lb/ft}^2$$

$$c_3 = 435.0 \text{ lb/ft}^2$$

$$c_4 = 387.0 \text{ lb/ft}^2, \text{ FIG. 24-17.}$$

Because from O_2 the cohesion drops from $c_2 = 471.5$ lb/ft^2 to $c_3 = 435$ lb/ft^2 at point O_3, the analysis of the fifth planned circle was omitted, since the maximum c_c-ordinate must be between points O_1 and O_3. The necessary maximum cohesion, c_{max}, for a soil with $\phi = 7°$ is found to be located at point, O_c, as shown in Fig. 24-17. The value of $c_{max} = 490$ lb/ft^2 was scaled off the drawing. Through point A is now drawn the critical circle, C_c, with point O_c as the center. This critical circle, with $c = 1200$ lb/ft^2 (given) is analyzed, and its factor of safety, as well as the factors of safety for the other circles is computed by Eq. (24-53). The critical rupture surface (for $\phi = 7°$ and $c = 1200$ lb/ft^2) is revealed to have the least factor of safety, namely, $\eta_c = 2.06 \approx 2.00$. All other factors are > 2.00. This indicates that the slope satisfies the prescribed value of factor of safety of 2.0. Therefore, with respect to $\eta = 2.0$, the slope for the given conditions may be considered safe.

The factor of safety for the pure cohesive soil, shown in Column 2, Table 24-2 is $\eta = 1.63$, but such a soil was not given for the analysis. The $\eta = 1.63$ is here shown only for comparison: note that, theoretically, friction adds to the factor of safety.

The slide-rule calculations in this problem are now given to elucidate some of the details involved in the foregoing analysis, and to illustrate the technique of the routine.

Necessary maximum cohesion for equilibrium when $\eta = 1.00$

Using the slope system as given in Fig. 24-4 or 24-8, Fellenius[11] calculated the necessary cohesion c_o for equilibrium as a function of the slope angle θ, the central half-angle ϵ, and the angle ω (see Fig. 24-8) of the chord subtending the most dangerous rupture surface $\overset{\frown}{AC}$ as

$$c_o = (1/4)(\gamma)(H) \cdot f(\theta, \epsilon, \omega), \tag{24-58}$$

where

$$f(\theta, \epsilon, \omega) = \left[(2)(\sin^2\epsilon)(\sin^2\omega)/\epsilon \right].$$
$$\cdot \left[(\cot\epsilon)(\cot\omega) - (\cot\epsilon)(\cot\theta) + (\cot\theta)(\cot\omega) - (2/3)\cot^2\theta + \right.$$
$$\left. + 1/3 \right] \tag{24-59}$$

By Eqs. (24-58) and (24-59), and with

$$\theta = 22°; \, \epsilon = 55°50'; \, \omega = 18°30'; \, \gamma = 110 \text{ lb/ft}^3; \, H = 45 \text{ ft},$$

$$f(\theta, \epsilon, \omega) = \frac{2 \sin^2 \epsilon \sin^2 \omega}{\epsilon} \cdot$$

$$\cdot \left[\cot \epsilon \cot \omega - \cot \epsilon \cot \theta + \cot \theta \cot \omega - \tfrac{2}{3} \cot^2 \theta + \tfrac{1}{3} \right] =$$

$$= \frac{(2)(0.827)^2(0.317)^2}{0.973} \cdot$$

$$\cdot \left[(0.679)(2.989) - (0.679)(2.475) + (2.475)(2.989) - \tfrac{2}{3}(2.475)^2 + \tfrac{1}{3} \right] =$$

$$= 0.564,$$

and

$$c_o = \tfrac{1}{4}(110)(45)(0.564) = 69.8 \approx 70 \text{ (lb/ft}^2).$$

The various angles may be calculated analytically from the geometry of the problem, or, if the drawing is made to a large scale, the angles may be scaled off by means of the protractor. Likewise, the radii, R, of the circles may be established. The lengths of the arcs, $\overset{\frown}{L}$, are obtained by calculation. By Eq. (24-52), and with $\tan\phi = \tan 7° = 0.1228$, and $\overset{\frown}{L}$ as given in Table 24-2 for the corresponding circles,

$$c = \frac{\sum T - \tan \phi \sum N}{\overset{\frown}{L}}, \tag{24-52}$$

$$c_1 = \frac{(971.6)(110) - (0.1228)(3409.9)(110)}{153.5} \approx 397.0 \text{ (lb/ft}^2)$$

$$c_2 = \frac{(904.0)(110) - (0.1228)(2510.3)(110)}{139.0} \approx 471.5 \ (\text{lb/ft}^2)$$

$$c_3 = \frac{(718.1)(110) - (0.1228)(1802.2)(110)}{126.0} \approx 435.0 \ (\text{lb/ft}^2)$$

$$c_4 = \frac{(563.1)(110) - (0.1228)(1261.4)(110)}{116.0} \approx 387.0 \ (\text{lb/ft}^2)$$

The maximum necessary cohesion, c_c, for the critical circle, C_c, is scaled off the drawing as $c_{max} = 490 \ (\text{lb/ft}^2)$.

The factors of safety, η, for circles C_1 through C_4, as well as for C_c, are calculated by Eq. (24-53) as

$$\eta = \frac{\tan \phi \sum N + c\widehat{L}}{\sum T} \tag{24-53}$$

$$\eta_1 = \frac{(0.1228)(3409.9)(110) + (1200)(153.5)}{(971.6)(110)} = 2.15$$

$$\eta_2 = \frac{(0.1288)(2510.3)(110) + (1200)(139.0)}{(904.0)(110)} = 2.11$$

$$\eta_3 = \frac{(0.1288)(1802.2)(110) + (1200)(126.0)}{(718.1)(110)} = 2.22$$

$$\eta_4 = \frac{(0.1288)(1261.4)(110) + (1200)(116.0)}{(563.1)(110)} = 3.46$$

$$\eta_c = \frac{(0.1288)(2274.2)(110) + (1200)(132.0)}{(832.5)(110)} = 2.06,$$

where $c = 1200 \ \text{lb/ft}^2$ is the actual, tested shear strength of the soil.

From the preceding discussions about the various methods of slope stability analyses, it becomes obvious that an important aspect in these analyses is the appropriate determination and use of the shear strength parameters ϕ and c. Laboratory tests must duplicate and analysis must be made for the worst conditions that an earth slope will ever encounter during its lifetime service. Much has been done and is still being done to perfect and interpret correctly laboratory test results of the ϕ and c parameters. It should be always kept in mind that a stability analysis is only good as the tests that determine these parameters. One should also be cognizant of that there is no substitute for a good, judiciously arranged and performed soil test, intelligent evaluation of test results and their correct application to the solution of various geotechnical problems.

24-17. Remedial Work Against Failures of Slopes. The scope of remedial work against the failures of earthwork slopes comprehends a variety of practices. Some such remedial means are:

   1) removing some weight of the slope-forming soil material which tends to cause failure, thus reducing the slope angle and weight of the slope-forming earthwork body as well (see Fig. 24-18). This will reduce the driving

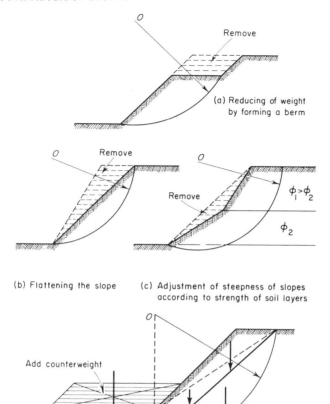

FIG. 24-18. Some means or remedy against rupture of slopes.

moment, thus increasing the calculated factor of safety;
2) providing some external support to hold back the toe of the slope by sheet piling, retaining wall, or counterweight at the toe (Fig. 24-18d), for example;
3) protection against undercutting of the slope;
4) providing a good and appropriate drainage system (Fig. 24-20), thus preventing the water from entering the earthworks. Deep drainage of slope (Fig. 24-19), under some conditions, may be very effective;
5) practicing good maintenance concerning slopes (Fig. 24-20), repair activities, water and snow;
6) consolidation;
7) increasing the shear strength of the soil within which the rupture surface may develop (drainage, electro-osmosis, soil stabilization by various mechanical and chemical means);
8) surfacing.

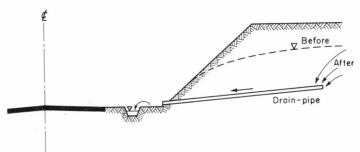

FIG. 24-19. Deep drainage of slope.

Since water seems to be the worst factor affecting the stability of slopes, drainage seems to be the most effective and practical method of controlling slides. Drainage facilities should be installed for the interception of the run-off waters and for diversion of water. Deep vertical and lateral drainage facilities for keeping the slopes dry can also be installed within the slope-forming body of earthworks.

24-18. Rupture of Slope Made of Frictional Soil. (Fig. 24-21) illustrates the shape of rupture surfaces of a slope made of frictional, dry soil. The top of the slope was loaded with a uniformly distributed ultimate contact pressure of $\sigma_o = 2.45$ kg/cm^2 (with no eccentricity, $e = 0$). One notes that a two-sided expulsion of soil from underneath the base of the footing takes place. The two-sided deformation is not symmetrical.

24-19. Summary of the Circular Rupture Surface Method

1) It is assumed that failure of a slope, upon the exhaustion of the shear strength of soil, takes place in shear suddenly along the whole curved rupture surface.

2) The shape of the curved rupture surface is an assumed one, namely that of the circular cylinder.

3) The circularly shaped rupture surface agrees approximately with the real one as observed in practice.

4) The approximate position, or coordinates, of the center of the circular rupture surface is an assumed one determined by the method of trial and error.

5) The average shear is assumed to be distributed uniformly along the predetermined rupture surface.

6) The rupture surface can conveniently be drawn by means of a compass.

7) The method of trial and error for finding the most dangerous rupture surface is somewhat cumbersome and time-consuming.

8) The calculated factor of safety against the rupture of slopes is not absolute.

9) The interaction of forces between neighboring slices may be neglected.

10) The method of slices is very useful for analyzing the stability of slopes of pure cohesive soils consisting of differing shear strengths. This applies particularly to slopes which are submerged, or if the slope-forming cross section is an irregular one.

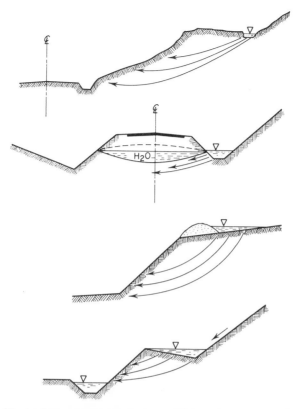

FIG. 24-20. Illustrating some maintenance problems of slopes relative to drainage.

FIG. 24-21. Deformation of slope made of dry sand and brought about by a surcharge load. (Author's study).

REFERENCES

1. C. A. Coulomb, *Essai sur une application des règles de maximis et minimis à quelques problèmes de statique relatifs à l'architecture.* Mèmoires de la mathématique et de physique, présentés à l'Académie Royale des Sciences, par divers savans, et lûs dans sés Assemblées, vol. 7, Année 1773. De L'Imprimerie Royale, Paris, 1766.
2. J. Résal, *Poussée des terres*, vol. 2, *Theorie des terres cohérentes.* Béranger, Paris, 1910.
3. J. F. Français, "Recherches sur la poussée des terres sur la forme et le dimensions des revêtements et sur les talus d'excavations," *Mèmoires de l'Officier de Génie*, Paris, vol. 4, pp. 157-193, 1820.
4. A. Collin, *Landslides in Clays*, translated by W. R. Schriever, University of Toronto Press, 1956.
5. M. Frontard, Cycloides de Glissement des Terres, Comptes Rendus Hebdomadaires, Academie des Sciences, Paris, pp. 526-529, 1922.
6. K.E. Petterson, "Kajraset i Göteborg den 5te mars 1916." *Teknisk Tidskrift,* Stockholm, 1916, nos. 30 and 31, p. 281-287 and 289-291, respectively.
7. K.E. Petterson, "The Early History of Circular Sliding Surfaces," *Géotechnique*, London, The Institution of Civil Engineers, 1955, vol. 5, pp. 275-296.
8. S. Hultin, "Grusfyllningar för kajbyggnader." *Teknisk Tidskrift,* Stockholm, 1916, no. 31, pp. 292-294.
9. W. Fellenius, "Kaj-och jordrasen i. Göteborg," Stockholm, 1918, no. 2, *Teknisk Tidskrift,* pp. 17-19.
10. W. Fellenius, "Calculation of Stability of Earth Dams." *Transactions*, 2d. Congress on Large Dams, held in Washington, D.C. 1936, U.S. Government Printing Office, Washington, D.C., 1938, vol. 4, pp. 445-462, p. 477
11. W. Fellenius, *Erdstatische Berechnungen mit Reibung und Kohäsion (Adhäsion) und unter Annahme kreiszylindrischer Gleitflächen,* Berlin, Wilhelm Ernst und Sohn, 1947, pp. 7-29.
12. Statens Järnvägars Geotekniska Kommision: Slutbetänkande. Stockholm, 1922, p. 57.
13. D.W. Taylor, "Stability of Earth Slopes," *Journal of the Boston Society of Civil Engineers*, Boston, Mass., July 7, 1937, vol. 24, no. 3.
14. J. Ehrenberg, "Standsicherheitsberechnungen von Staudämmen," *Transactions*, 2d Congress on Large Dams, held in Washington, D.C., U.S. Government Printing Office, Washington, D.C., 1938, vol. 4, pp. 331-389, pp. 356-357.
15. H.D. Krey, *Erddruck, Erdwiderstand und Tragfähigkeit des Baugrundes,* Berlin, Wilhelm Ernst und Sohn, 1936 (table between pp. 172 and 173).
16. R.E. Gibson and N.R. Morgenstern, "A Note on the Stability of Cuttings in Normally Consolidated Clays." *Géotechnique* (London), vol. 12, 1962, No. 3.
17. K. Terzaghi and R.B. Peck, *Soil Mechanics in Engineering Practice* (2nd ed.), New York, N.Y.: John Wiley and Sons, Inc., 1967, p. 237-242.
18. A.W. Bishop and N.R. Morgenstern, "Stability Coefficients for Earth Slopes," *Géotechnique* (London), vol. 10, 1960, No. 4, pp. 129-150.
19. N. Janbu, L. Bjerrum, and B. Kjaernsli, "Veiledning ved losning av fundamenterings oppgaver," ("Soil Mechanics Applied to Some Engineering Problems"), Norges Geotekniske Institut (Norwegian Geotechnical Institute), Publication No. 16, 1956, Oslo, Norway.
20. A.W. Bishop, "The Use of the Slip Circle in the Stability Analysis of Earth Slopes," *Géotechnique* (London), vol. 5, 1955, No. 1, pp 7-17.

SUGGESTIONS FOR FURTHER READING

1. E.B. Eckel, Editor, *Landslides and Engineering Practice*, Highway Research Board, Special Report 29, Washington, D.C.: National Academy of Sciences - National

Research Council Publication 544, 1958.

2. N. Janbu, *Stability Analysis of Slopes with Dimensionless Parameters*, Harvard Soil Mechanics Series No. 46, 1954.

3. N. Janbu, "Application of Composite Slip Surfaces for Stability Analysis," *Proceedings of the European Conference on Stability of Earth Slopes*, held in 1954 at Stockholm, Sweden. Vol. 3, 1954, pp. 43-49.

4. N. Janbu, "Earth Pressures and Bearing Capacity Calculations by Generalized Procedure of Slices." *Proceedings of the 4th International Conference on Soil Mechanics and Foundation Engineering*, held in 1957 in London, England, vol. 2, 1957, pp. 207-212.

5. J. Lowe III and L. Karafiath, "Stability of Earth Dams Upon Drawdown." *Proceedings of the 1st Panamerican Conference on Soil Mechanics and Foundation Engineering*, held in 1959 at Mexico City. Vol. 2A, 1959, pp. 537-552.

6. J. Lowe III, "Stability Analysis of Embankments," *Proc. ASCE*, Journal of the Soil Mechanics and Foundations Division, vol. 93, 1967, No. SM 4, pp. 1-33.

7. N. Morgenstern, "Stability Charts for Earth Slopes During Rapid Drawdown," *Géotechnique* (London), vol. 13., 1963, No. 2, pp. 121-131.

8. N.R. Morgenstern and V.E. Price, "The Analysis of the Stability of General Slip Surfaces," *Géotechnique* (London), vol. 15, 1965, No. 1, pp. 79-93.

9. E. Spencer, "A Method of Analysis of the Stability of Embankments Assuming Parallel Inter-Slice Forces," *Géotechnique* (London), vol. 17, 1967, No. 1, pp. 11-26.

10. E. Spencer, "Circular and Logarithmic Slip Surfaces," *Proc. ASCE*, Journal of the Soil Mechanics and Foundations Division, vol. 95, 1969, No. SM 1, pp. 227-234.

11. H. Borowicka, "Ein statisch einwandfreies Verfahren zur Ermittlung der Standsicherheit einer Böschung," Der Bauingenieur, September, 1970, No. 9, pp. 307-313.

PROBLEMS

24-1. The slope of a firm, inclined geologic formation is $i = 1 : 10$. Upon this inclined layer rests a mass of unconsolidated soil material, forming a slope angle with the horizontal of $\theta = 45°$. The ground surface AC of this soil mass is horizontal ($\delta = 0$). If the unit weight of the (ϕ-c) soil is $\gamma = 110 \, lb/ft^3 = 17.26 \, kN/m^3$, and the angle of internal friction is $\phi = 25°$, the cohesion is $c = 500 \, lb/ft^2 = 23.94 \, kN/m^2$, and the height of the slope is $H = 15.0 \, ft = 4.57 \, m$, calculate the factor of safety η of this slope.

24-2. If in the above problem the required factor of safety of the slope is $\eta = 1.5$, calculate the height H of the slope.

24-3. Given a pure cohesive soil, unit weight of soil γ, slope angle $\theta =$ constant by construction, and height of slope H. The upper ground surface above the slope is horizontal. Determine algebraically the maximum amount of cohesion in the plane rupture surface for a factor of safety of $\eta = 1.0$, and $\eta = 1.5$.

Also, find the angle ω of the most dangerous rupture surface. Express in terms of c, γ, and θ the maximum height H to which the slope will stand for $\eta = 1.0$ and for $\eta = 1.5$.

$$c = (½)\gamma H \tan (\theta/2); \qquad \omega = \theta/2; \qquad H = (4c/\gamma)\cot(\theta/2).$$

24-4. If in Fig. 24-3, $\theta = 40°$, $\delta = 40°$, $H = 15.0 \, ft = 4.57 \, m$, $\gamma = 110 \, lb/ft^3 = 17.26 \, kN/m^3$, $\phi = 20°$, and $c = 700 \, lb/ft^2 = 33.52 \, kN/m^2$, calculate for a ($\phi$-$c$)-soil the critical angle ω, the necessary cohesion to maintain the given slope at a 15.0-foot $= 4.57 \, m$ height, and the factor of safety of such a slope against rupture.

24-5. The shear strength of a slope (1 : 1.5) of a cut in a cohesive soil is $0.4 \, ton/ft^2 = 38.30 \, kN/m^2$. The weight of a circular sliding mass of soil with a slip circle through the toe of the cut is 50,000 lb per unit length $= 730 kN/m$ perpendicular to drawing plane.

The radius of the rupture surface is 32 ft = 9.75 m. The length of the arc of rupture is 55 ft = 16.74 m.

- a) Compute the factor of safety against sliding. The length of the rotational moment-arm a of the mass of sliding soil wedge with respect to the center of rotation is 11.0 ft = 3.35 m.
- b) If the factor of safety against sliding were $\eta < 1.5$, propose and sketch remedial measures so as to increase $\eta > 1.5$.
- c) Prepare an analytical expression for factor of safety η if on the bank of the slope there is a concentrated load P, distant d from the center of rotation, and located within the boundaries of the circular sliding surface.

(Assume all necessary reasonable engineering values not given in this problem).

24-6. Perform stability analysis of the downstream slope of the earth dam as shown in Fig. Problem 24-6. Expecially,

- a) Show all forces partaking in the system, as well as their magnitudes, points of application, and directions of action;

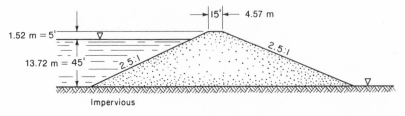

FIG. PROBLEM 24-6.

- b) Report and indicate on a drawing the most dangerous rupture surface, as well as the minimum factor of safety obtained in the analysis.
- c) Is the slope safe? If not, what remedial works would you recommend in order to increase the safety of the downstream slope?

Given: Unit weight of saturated soil mass, $\gamma_{sat} = 120$ lb/ft^3 = 18.82 kN/m^3; unit weight of water, $\gamma_w = 62.4$ lb/ft^3 = 9.81 kN/m^3; specific gravity of soil particles, $G = 2.66$; porosity of soil, $n = 40\%$; angle of internal friction of soil, $\phi = 15°$; cohesion, $c = 250$ lb/ft^2 = 11.97 kN/m^2.

24-7. In problem 24-6, determine the stability of the upstream slope after a rapid draw-down of water.

24-8. The total height of the slope is 50 ft = 15.24 m, and the submerged part of the slope is 30 ft = 9.14 m. The slope of the bank is 1 : 3. At the top of the bank a grain elevator is constructed at a center line 24 ft = 7.62 m from the edge and exerting a load of 30 tons per linear foot = 876 kN/m along the shore line of the bank. The soil is a homogeneous clay with a cohesive strength of 700 lb/ft^2 = 33.52 kN/m^2. It has a specific gravity of $G = 2.67$ and a void ratio of $e = 0.57$

- a) Check the stability and design a safe slope of the partially submerged embankment shown in Fig. Problem 24-8.
- b) Calculate factor of safety η if the depth of the water in the basin is 50 ft = 15.24 m.
- c) Compute factor of safety if the basin is empty.
- d) Calculate factor of safety if the slope is to be made in a noncohesive soil the angle of internal friction of which $\phi = 30°$. The specific gravity is $G = 2.65$ and the void ratio is $e = 0.25$.
- e) Calculate factor of safety if the slope is to be made in a cohesive soil the characteristics of which are $\phi = 6°$, $c = 700$ lb/ft^2 = 33.52 kN/m^2, and $G = 2.67$.
- f) Calculate factor of safety for the condition of a rapid draw-down of the water

level to the bottom of the basin (empty basin).
g) Evaluate stability when the entire slope is covered with an impervious layer (unsaturated embankment).

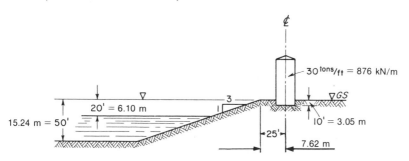

FIG. PROBLEM 24-8.   Stability problem.

24-9. Write algebraically a formula for the factor of safety, η, for the slope system as shown in Fig. Problem 24-9.

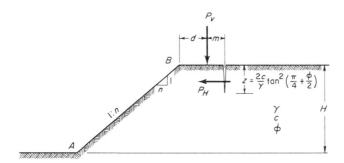

FIG. Problem 24-9. (Stability problem with a tension crack).

PART VI

Soil Exploration

Chapter 25

SOIL EXPLORATION

25-1. Introduction. Soil exploration at a proposed building site is to be considered similar in purpose to the material survey, because soils are construction materials in which, on which, or by means of which civil engineers build structures. This would seem to be so apparent that there would be no extra need to emphasize the importance of soil exploration. However, practice demonstrates that adequate soil exploration is frequently disregarded and even omitted. Lack of time, insufficient funds, or both, are often given as excuses. Cases are known in which, due to false economy or in an attempt to save funds or time, the final cost of the structure exceeded every reasonable limit. The result may even be the failure of the structure itself, thus causing great trouble to both builder and owner. This emphasizes the fact that it is the task of every civil engineer designing any construction always to give first preference to the factor of "safety." The "economy" factor should follow. In the light of safety, economic considerations should be regarded as secondary. This rule, however, does not exclude the postulate of economical and safe structures.

Besides, timely and intelligently made soil explorations are relatively cheap compared with the total cost of the structure, or even compared with the expenditure required merely for the revision of the project and redesigning of the structure to fit the real soil conditions in order to avoid serious trouble.

Efficient, safe, economical design and construction can be achieved only through thorough evaluation of soil conditions under and adjacent to a proposed structure. This, in turn, requires that adequate soil exploration at a proposed site should be made before any design of the foundation of a structure is started or the purchase of the lot made. It is best to pay attention to the bearing capacity and other geotechnical properties of soil prior to the purchase of the lot.

The site exploration should furnish information on groundwater-carrying layers, their numbers, depth; position of the groundwater table and its fluctuation; groundwater flow (direction and velocity), and aggressiveness with regard to soil and foundation materials.

Fluctuation of the groundwater table may cause structures to settle. Also, such fluctuations are very dangerous to foundations constructed on timber piles, especially to their upper sections, and timber rafts. They decay due to variations in the groundwater level. Such a condition is illustrated in Fig. 25-1, showing the foundation of the Boston Public Library. The situation was remedied by methods unaffected by the fluctuation of the groundwater table.

The owner, engineer, and builder should be further interested in the amount of compression of the soil, viz., the amount of settlement of the structure to be expected. The stability of loaded soil against shear failure is likewise important.

For evaluation of these problems, undisturbed soil samples in their natural state should be taken for laboratory treatment.

25-2. Soil Exploration Methods. Soil exploration can be grouped into two parts, namely, 1) preliminary explorations and 2) detailed exploration. Further distinction is made between a) shallow soil exploration and b) deep soil exploration.

Shallow soil exploration includes probings, auger borings, test trenches and test pits, shafts, and wells. Deep soil exploration includes test tunnels and deep borings.

25-3. Soil Borings. Soil exploration below the groundwater table is usually very difficult to perform by means of test trenches, pits, and auger-holes. These methods, therefore, are replaced by borings.

Boring is considered a method of deep soil exploration, in fact it is the most accepted and reliable method for this purpose. The boring is put down into the soil mainly to obtain suitable soil samples for performing tests for foundation engineering purposes.

FIG. 25-1.   Decayed tops of timber piles caused by fluctuating groundwater table. Courtesy of the Trustees of the Boston Public Library.

A boring in soil exploration is understood to be a cylindrical hole of relatively small diameter, usually from 2 to 8 in.

There are two principal types of equipment for making borings: the cable-tool drilling rig and the rotary drill. A cable-tool boring rig is shown schematically in Fig. 25-2. The bore-hole in soil is lined with a pipe to prevent the walls of the hole from caving in. The pipe or casing is driven in with a drop weight. The hole is advanced by a chopping bit. The boring is done by power machine or manually. The bit is screwed to a hollow drill rod supported on a tripod by a rope or steel cable over a pulley. The drill rod and the bit are hollow, and a stream of water under pressure is forced through the tools downward into the hole. Upon entering the bore-hole at its lower end, the stream of pressure water, or wash water, forces up to the surface loosened soil and/or rock particles and other debris in suspension and jets them out of the boring, thus cleaning the bore-hole.

25-4. Wash Borings. The soil suspension from the bore-hole is discharged in a tub, Fig. 25-2. If the tub is shallow or small in volume, the soil-water mixture

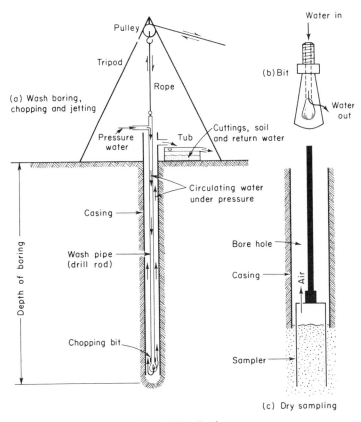

FIG. 25-2.   Boring.

with the fine particles in suspension goes over the overflow and the fine particles are washed away. The coarser soil particles settle down in the tub. The soil in the tube can be examined, but such an examination, if recorded and logged, gives a wrong impression about the composite soil and its texture because the fine particles such as clays and silts, which contribute to settlement and other negative properties of the soil, are washed away. The type of boring by which the soil samples are recovered from the wash water is generally called a "wash boring." The soil samples obtained from wash borings are disturbed. The soil material recovered from the tub is an inevitable mixture of the coarse soil particles from every layer the bit or drill passed through, and from this mixture it is almost impossible to interpret intelligently the geotechnical characteristics of a soil obtained by means of so-called "wash boring." Therefore, wash boring and soil samples from such borings should not be used for foundation engineering. Soil samples procured from wash water by the method of "wash borings" are unreliable for design purposes.

Warning should be given that soil exploration borings should never be made in the excavation of the foundation at points where the footings would rest and where artesian groundwater is present, because of the danger of overflooding the pit. Many construction sites have had to be abandoned for this reason.

25-5. Dry-Sample Boring. The advancement of a dry-sample boring is the same as described under wash borings. When, upon drilling the hole, a change in soil layers is felt, the drill rod is lifted off the bottom of the bore-hole, and washing of the hole continued until the wash water in the casing becomes clean. The chopping bit, or the drill, whichever the case is, is then removed and a cylindrical soil sampling spoon or a seamless, stainless steel sampling cylinder is attached to the drill rod. The sampling spoon or tube is forced into the virgin soil, a 90° twist is made to shear the soil sample off the soil mass, the rod with the soil sample in the sampler is raised out of the hole up to the ground surface, and a "dry soil sample" is obtained. The advancement of the bore-hole is then continued in the usual way until a new "dry soil sample" is taken. Soil samples are taken where a change in soil formations occurs, or, if the soil deposit is thick, soil samples are taken at predetermined intervals. Sometimes continued sampling is practiced.

As the boring operations continue, the soil samples are subjected to visual examination, identified, classified roughly, sealed to prevent moisture loss, and shipped to the soil mechanics laboratory.

In this method, as well as when soil samples are taken by means of a sampling spoon below the groundwater table, the soil samples are not truly dry in the real sense of the word. One remembers that the voids of the soil usually are filled to a certain degree with water. In practice the term "dry soil sample" in this kind of boring is merely a trade designation. However, the soil samples obtained by the "dry" method are not churned up, nor are the soil particles dispersed in a suspension.

Although forcing the soil sampler into the soil causes some disturbance in the soil about the periphery of the sampler, the soil sample thus recovered contains all of its textural contents because practically nothing has been washed away. This is the principal advantage of a dry-sample boring. Dry undisturbed soil samples from deep borings can be obtained with relative ease from cohesive soils. Sands are almost impossible to sample from deep borings in their undisturbed state. The soil exploration method by means of dry-sample borings is one of the most satisfactory methods used today for engineering purposes.

In the course of boring and sampling operations, the number of blows of a 140 lb rammer falling 30″ on a 2″ diameter sampler or spoon to penetrate the sampler 12 in. through a soil is recorded. This test is called the standard penetration test, and gives one a clue as to the strength or bearing capacity of the soil thus tested.

25-6. Mechanical Rotary Soil Drilling Unit. A mobile, mechanical drilling unit, modified after the drilling rigs used in oil drilling operations, has a hydraulic drilling rig mounted on a power truck. It consists essentially of a boom; a drilling mechanism to rotate the soil bit; a bit, or diamond core drill; a hydraulic jack to force the sampling tubes into the soil; water supply and pump; a settling tub to contain the recirculating "drilling mud" for coating the inside walls of the boring with an impervious skin of clay, thus preventing water from seeping in and out of the bore-hole and caving it in; a winch to hoist the sampling tubes, and a rammer for performing standard penetration tests into soil with the tube or sampling spoon.

If a compression test is to be performed on a soil sample, the soil sampling devices are forced down into the soil hydraulically in order to obtain an undisturbed soil sample. Small rotary rigs obtain samples by driving.

25-7. Soil Samplers. A soil sampler known as the *Shelby tube*, Fig. 25-3, is a thin-walled tube with a sharp cutting edge. This tube is attached to a ball check head. The ball check prevents washing out of the soil sample while being hoisted from the hole. The sampler is used for sampling undisturbed cohesive silts and soft clay. This sampler is forced into the soil by pressing or jacking under a steady pressure. After sampling, the sampling tube containing the sampler is detached, its ends sealed and capped, and the unit shipped to the soil mechanics laboratory for further treatment.

The *split-tube sampler* is a tube split longitudinally and held together by a ball check head and a hardened shoe, Fig. 25-4. When the sample is lifted up and the ball check head and shoe are unscrewed, the sampler opens like a book. Some types of split-tube sampler have a liner in them. Such a sampler is good for plastic soils.

The *stationary-type sampler* resembles a suction pump. When the inner plunger rod is pulled up, the soil sample is drawn into the sampling tube by holding the piston rod firmly in place and pressing the tube past the piston into the soil. The piston-created vacuum aids in the sampling of "hard-to-hold" fine silts. The piston-type soil sampler is illustrated in Fig. 25-5.

The *solid tube sampler*, Fig. 25-6, is intended for hard driving. It has a ball check and hardened, interchangeable shoes for various soil conditions.

Rather elaborate sampling devices have been devised for obtaining soil samples containing great amounts of water, or having very plastic properties. Such soil samples are "hard to hold" and slide out of the ordinary sampling tube back into the bore-hole.

25-8. Disturbed Soil Samples. In soil exploration two kinds of soil samples are taken, 1) disturbed samples and 2) undisturbed samples. A disturbed soil sample is one whose natural conditions, such as structure, texture, density, natural moisture content, and stress conditions, are disturbed.

Disturbed soil samples are sampled by means of a shovel, or obtained from auger borings and deep borings. In disturbed soil sampling, where the sampler penetrates the various soil layers, the different types of soil may become mixed or may lose a comparatively great percent of their moisture content. Also, the soil texture may be altered by the washing away of the fine-particle fractions. This can happen when sandy soils are sampled and brought up to the ground surface through the medium of groundwater. When improperly preserved and kept for a long period of time, the soil sample may lose its original color.

Preservation and storing of soil samples in cardboard boxes, match boxes, loosely covered cans, cigarette boxes, open wood boxes and the like, are not considered to be good practice; exposed, the soil samples dry out, change their natural color and, in the case of cohesive soils often crack. Hence, such soils do not represent the natural prototype soil correctly.

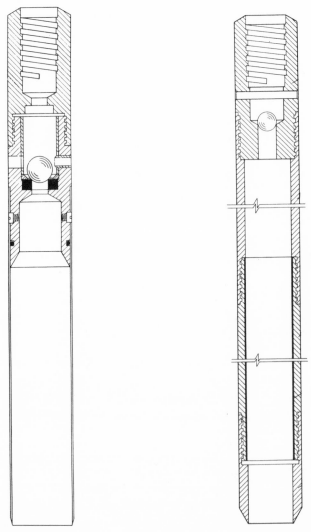

FIG. 25-3. Thin-walled Shelby tube   FIG. 25-4. Split tube sampler with
sampler.   Courtesy of Sprague and   liner. Courtesy of Sprague and Hen-
           Henwood, Inc.   wood, Inc.

The soil samples should be placed for further study or storage in sealed sampling tubes, paraffined and sealed in wooden boxes, in wide-necked jars, or other containers provided with air-tight lids to protect the sample from evaporation and hardening. In highway engineering practice, for certain soil tests the soils are sampled in bags.

25-9. Undisturbed Soil Samples. An undisturbed soil sample is understood to be one which is removed from the soil in its natural condition without disturbing its structure and the packing of the soil particles. Such a soil sample should

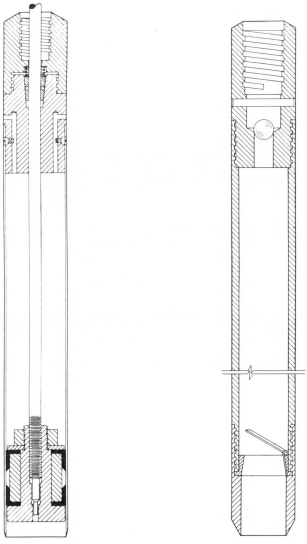

FIG. 25-5. Stationary piston type sampler. Courtesy of Sprague and Henwood, Inc.

FIG. 25-6. Solid tube sampler. Courtesy of Sprague and Henwood, Inc.

retain upon and after sampling all of its original natural physical and mechanical properties such as its structure, density, porosity, moisture content, and the stress condition of the soil. Unfortunately, the term "undisturbed" is only a relative one. This is because physically it is impossible to obtain a soil sample, to transport it, to handle and prepare it for tests in the course of laboratory investigation without disturbing it to some degree. The removal of any sample from its original environment is certain to disturb the sample to some extent. Undisturbed soil samples, therefore, should be sampled and handled with great care. The guiding principle in soil sampling work is to obtain samples which would reflect the soil prototype as nearly as possible.

Undisturbed soil samples, as already mentioned under Dry-Sample Borings, are obtained by forcing a thin-walled, seamless, stainless steel sampling cylinder into the soil at the bottom of the bore-hole, or at the bottom of a test pit, and/or shaft, or in their walls, or in the walls of a soil exploration tunnel. The forcing is accomplished by jacking, or a continuous push.

Undisturbed soil samples are used for testing the shear or compressive strength of the soil, for performing settlement analysis, and for determining the coefficient of permeability of a soil. Undisturbed as well as disturbed soil samples are used for determining the particle size analysis, the consistency limits of the soil, its compaction, and other properties.

After securing the soil samples in the cylinders, the joints of the caps are sealed with a waterproof adhesive tape. In case of lack of caps, the ends of the cylinder containing the soil sample may be double-coated with paraffin. The second coat is applied by dipping the ends of the cylinder into liquid paraffin. Then the soil samples are properly labeled and shipped to the soil mechanics laboratory for analyses. Between preserving and labeling the samples and shipping, the samples should not be left exposed to direct sun, rain, or freezing weather.

Undisturbed cube samples are first coated with paraffin, then wrapped in gauze, paraffinized, and put in wooden boxes in moist sawdust. The boxes are sealed (they should not be nailed because of vibrations; screws are preferable), labeled, and shipped to the laboratory.

The labels of the soil samples, as well as the sampling log, should contain the following information:

1) Date of sampling.
2) Locality.
3) Number of test pit or bore-hole.
4) Number of sample.
5) Sampling depth.
6) Ground elevation.
7) Thickness of soil layer.
8) Designation of soil.
9) Indication which end of the sample is "up".
10) Method of sampling (disturbed or undisturbed).
11) Sampling tool used.
12) Position of groundwater table.
13) Atmospheric conditions during sampling time.
14) Sampling performed by . . . .

25-10. Boring Log. The results of a soil boring should be documented in a boring log, Fig. 25-7. A boring log contains, for example, the following information:

1) Depth below ground surface.
2) Elevation of soil layers and groundwater table.
3) Thickness of layers.
4) Graphical symbol of the soil type.
5) Description of soil.
6) Position where soil sample is taken; whether disturbed or undisturbed.
7) Sample number.
8) Natural moisture content, in percent of dry weight of soil.
9) Number of blows of a 140-lb or 300-lb hammer falling 30 in. required to penetrate a 2-in.-diameter sampling device or a casing one foot into soil.
10) Notes indicating position of groundwater table, presence of tree roots, or other pertinent facts.

The boring log should also indicate the title of the project, job and/or contract number, location of the project, the boring number, surface elevation of the boring, date, and the name of the foreman in charge of drilling.

25-11. Boring Report. A boring report should contain
1) Situation plan of construction site drawn to scale and oriented with respect to north.
2) Location plan of borings indicating their coordinates from a reference axis, as well as the elevation of the ground surface at each boring with reference to a permanent surveyor's benchmark.
3) Description of the terrain.
4) Surface drainage conditions.
5) Probable source of free water.
6) Groundwater conditions.
7) The boring log, drawn to a stated scale, and containing information of soil types and thicknesses encountered.
8) Information on eventual difficulties and obstructions encountered in boring operations (sand in "quick" condition or boulders, for example).
9) Soil identification and results of classification test.

25-12. Common Soil Tests. Table 25-1 lists the commonly used soil tests aiding in the study of soil properties. The table indicates also the contents of the test results and gives some of the practical applications of the various test results. The objective of a soil test is the accurate prediction of the performance of a soil under various conditions of load, water concentration, and temperature.

25-13. Cost of Soil Exploration and Testing. Nothing impresses a civil engineer in charge more deeply than the stubborn conviction of the owner of the structure that soil testings are unnecessary, or that more borings are unnecessary, or that they increase the cost of the structure, or that they delay the construction work.

If the soil investigation plan is set up correctly, borings and laboratory soil tests decrease, and never increase, the cost of the project. Too often one learns the lesson of a bad soil condition only after failure has occurred. Experience indicates conclusively that in most cases the cost of soil exploration, compared

Method of boring: washing
Method of sampling: shelby piston and spoon
Total depth of hole: 59 ft
Size of casing: 4" BX
I.D. of shelby tubes: 2.8 in.
Size of spoon: 2 in.
Surface elevation: + 205 ft.

Hammer: on casing: 300 lb; 30" drop
on spoon: 300 lb; 18" drop
Time of boring operations: from January 10
to January 14, 19...
Date of Log: April 20, 19...
Prepared by A. R. J.

1	2	3	4	5	6	7	8	9	10	11	12	13	14
Scale of depth below ground surface in feet	Depth to layer in feet	Depth to bottom of sampling tube in feet	Sample tube and Sample Nos.	Recovery in.	Recovery. Jar sample	Soil tests	Nos. of blows per foot	Symbol	Number of blows per foot on casing.	Description	Wet and dry unit weights in lb/ft3	Moisture content by dry weight in %	Moisture distribution diagram
0.0 ▽ Ground Surface										▽ Ground-water Table			
1										Top Soil			
2	2'		1	17		U.C. U.C.			3 3	Light gray silty clay mottled with dark-yellow (rusty looking) oxidation stains.	132.0 98.6	33.8 38.1	40.8
3		3' 9"							10	Channelled with vertical roots of vegetal matter. Stiff-plastic. Very wet. Foul odor			24.7
4			2	Lost					27			29.7	
5	5' 6"								30				
6	6'		3	23		U.C. U.C.			30		151.1 101.1	50.0 46.2	27.1
7									34	Triaxial test	134.0	34.0	
8	8'		4	21		U.C. U.C.			30	Some little fragm. of slate. Dark gray clayey silt. Very wet.	91.7 129.2 102.2	24.3 26.5	20.4
9									48	Foul odor. Very wet. Consolidation test.			
10	10'		5	20		U.C.			45	The strong odor suggests gas from decomposed organic matter. Contains tiny mica particles and fragments of dark gray slate.	129.3 103.8	22.3 22.6 17.3	25.6 20.6
11									48			25.1	
12	12'					U.C.			79		129.3 101.8	25.1	

Moisture distribution diagram scale: 0 10 20 30 40 50%
P.l.

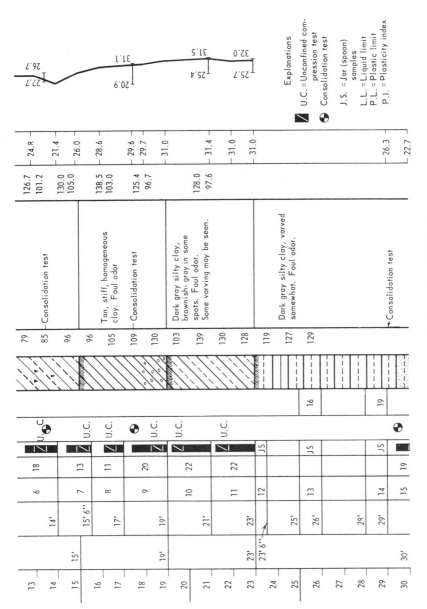

FIG. 25-7. Boring log (D-9).

TABLE 25-1. COMMONLY USED SOIL TESTS AND THEIR APPLICATIONS

No.	Soil Properties or Tests	Symbol or Description	Test Results	Practical Applications of Test Results
1	2	3	4	5
1	Unit weight	γ (lb/ft^3, g$_f$/cm^3, kg$_f$/m^3) kN/m^3	Weight per unit volume of soil	a) Density of a soil deposit b) Bearing capacity of soil c) Stability calculations of foundations, natural and artificial slopes d) Lateral earth pressures on walls and sheet piling e) Settlement analysis f) Freezing tests g) Classification of soils by density
2	Specific gravity	G (Dimensionless)	Ratio of density of soil solids to the density of water at $+4°C$	a) Volumetric and gravimetric relationships b) Density calculations c) Buoyant weight of soil d) Compaction of soil e) Hydrometer analysis f) Soil freezing tests
3	Porosity	n (volume of voids in percent based on total volume of soil)	Volume of voids of solid particles, water, and air	a) Evaluation of densification of sand b) Calculations involving physical properties c) Settlement calculations d) Permeability e) Volumetric and gravimetric relationships f) Soil freezing tests
4	Void ratio	e (in decimal fractions relative to volume of solids)	Ratio of volume of voids to volume of solid particles of soil	a) Volumetric and gravimetric relationships b) Calculations involving physical properties c) Settlement analysis d) Permeability e) Soil freezing tests

TABLE 25-1. COMMONLY USED SOIL TESTS (*Continued*)

No.	Soil Properties or Tests	Symbol or Description	Test Results	Practical Applications of Test Results
1	2	3	4	5
5	Soil moisture content	w (%)	Moisture content in percent by dry weight of solid particles of soil	a) Volumetric and gravimetric relationships b) Porosity: void ratio c) Relative density d) Classification of soil e) Comparison of soils of similar nature f) Soil compaction g) Soil freezing tests
6	Granulometry: mechanical analysis of soil (sieving)	Percentage of various soil fractions	Particle size accumulation curve for particles ≥ 0.074 mm (+No. 200 material)	a) Soil texture b) Identification and classification of soil c) Effective particle size, d_{10} d) Uniformity coefficient, $U = d_{60}/d_{10}$ e) Frost susceptibility of soil f) Permeability g) Evaluation of filters h) Soil mixtures for highway purposes i) Compaction of soils
7	Hydrometer analysis	Percentage of fractions	Particle size, < 0.1 mm	Same as No. 6.
8	Relative density	D (Dimensionless)	Porosity, viz., density attained in various degrees of compaction; wet and dry.	a) Density control of fills made of non-cohesive soils, and degree of compaction of fills, or state of density of natural granular deposits. For noncohesive soils only.
9	Compaction	W_d (lb/ft^3 or kg$_f$/m^3) kN/m^3	Maximum dry density at optimum moisture content	Compaction of subgrade and fills

TABLE 25-1. COMMONLY USED SOIL TESTS (*Continued*)

No.	Soil Properties or Tests	Symbol or Description	Test Results	Practical Applications of Test Results
1	2	3	4	5
10	Specific surface	A (cm²)	Surface area of soil particles in a unit weight (1 g) of soil or in a unit volume (1 cm³) of soil	a) Amount of moisture film in soil b) Soil moisture migration c) Electrokinetic phenomena in soil d) Frost susceptibility of soil
11	Combustion (ignition) test	b (g_f or lb) N	Weight of burned matter	a) Content of organic matter b) Settlement of structures on organic soils
12	Consistency (Atterberg) limits of cohesive soils	L.L. (%)	Liquid limit; moisture content in percent at 25 blows exerted by a test cup.	a) Soil classification b) Clue to shear strength of soil c) Stability of soil mass
		P.L. (%)	Plastic limit; moisture content in percent upon cracking of soil threads $\frac{1}{8}$ in. in diameter	a) Soil classification b) Soil plastic properties
		P.I. (P.I. = L.L. − − P.L.) (%)	Plasticity index; moisture in per cent	a) Soil classification b) Thickness of subbase courses c) Impermeable core material for earth dams d) Soil property index
		S.L. (%)	Shrinkage limit; percent of moisture at attained constant volume	a) Soil classification b) Usefulness of soil for earthworks c) Possibility of saturation

TABLE 25-1. COMMONLY USED SOIL TESTS (*Continued*)

No.	Soil Properties or Tests	Symbol or Description	Test Results	Practical Applications of Test Results
1	2	3	4	5
13	Permeability	k (ft/day or cm/s)	Coefficient of permeability at constant head or at falling head	a) Groundwater flow b) Seepage through earth dams c) Soil consolidation d) Lowering of groundwater table e) Grouting and injections f) Soil freezing tests
14	Capillarity	H (cm)	Capillary height in sand and silt	a) Soil moisture transfer b) Water loss from reservoirs by capillarity c) Frost penetration depth in soils for roads and airfields d) Soil susceptibility to frost
15	Consolidation	s (cm)	Settlement analysis	a) Preconsolidation load b) Compression c) Expansion d) Permeability e) Settlement analysis of soils and structures f) Soil swelling pressures on floors, earth-retaining structures, and tunnels.
16	Unconfined compression test (*Continued*)	α ϕ c (lb/in.^{2}or kg$_f$/cm^2) kN/m^2	Angle of rupture Test parameters: angle of internal friction cohesion	a) Unconfined compressive strength b) Unconfined shear strength c) Bearing capacity of cohesive soils d) Modulus of elasticity E

TABLE 25-1. COMMONLY USED SOIL TESTS (*Continued*)

No.	Soil Properties or Tests	Symbol or Description	Test Results	Practical Applications of Test Results
1	2	3	4	5
16	(*Continued*) Unconfined compression test	τ (lb/in.^{2} or kg$_f$/cm^2) kN/m^2	Shear strength parameters	e) Stability analyses of earth slopes f) Earth pressure calculations g) Depth of laying of foundations
17	Direct shear test	τ (lb/in.^{2} or kg$_f$/cm^2) kN/m^2	Same as No. 16	Same as No. 16
18	Triaxial compression test	τ (lb/in.^{2} or kg$_f$/cm^2) ϕ_{eff}; ϕ_u; c_{eff}; c_u; u	Same as No. 16	Same as No. 16 Pore water pressure u
19	Bearing capacity of soils	σ (lb/in.^{2}, tons/ft^2, kg$_f$/cm^2, or t/m^2) kN/m^2	Load-carrying capacity. Time-settlement curves	Evaluation of soil for supporting structures
20	Physicochemical properties	σ_0 ζ, E_s D D	Surface tension; electro-osmosis; thermo-osmosis; electrokinetic potentials; dielectric constants; base exchange; vapor diffusion; wetting; swelling	a) Chemical stabilization of soils b) Soil moisture migration c) Frost action in soils
21	Soil freezing tests	Δh Q ξ		a) Frost susceptibility of soils b) Frost heaves c) Amount of water absorbed by soil upon freezing d) Frost penetration depth in soil e) Soil performance under freezing and thawing conditions

TABLE 25-1. COMMONLY USED SOIL TESTS (*Continued*)

No.	Soil Properties or Tests	Symbol or Description	Test Results	Practical Applications of Test Results
1	2	3	4	5
21	(*Continued*) Soil freezing tests			f) Artificial freezing and thawing of soils for foundation engineering purposes
22	Model experiments		Similarity of model and prototype	Small-scale laboratory tests on various subjects pertaining to soil and foundation engineering
23	Large-scale tests			Large-scale tests in the laboratory and/or the field
24	Soil color tests		Color coordinates	Identification of soils

with the total cost of engineering projects, is very small. The relatively small cost involved in soil investigation in a great many instances varies from 1% to 2%, sometimes 3%, of the total construction cost. In many instances the cost of exploration of big jobs, depending upon geological and soil conditions, drops even below 1%. For example, Legget[1] writes that the cost of preliminary work, including geological and geophysical surveys and test drilling of the Bridge River Tunnel, B.C., Canada, was 0.3% of the cost of the tunnel, and that the cost of trial holes and boreholes made for the Battersea Power Station in London was 0.2% of the total cost and 1.5% of the cost of the main building foundations alone.

Soil investigation is of great value in that it furnishes a clear picture of the soil, its behavior under loads and under the influence of water, and the mutual interaction of soil and structure. Money and effort spent for soil investigation are never wasted. It is the cheapest insurance against expensive failures.

25-14. Engineering Soil Survey. The purpose of an engineering soil survey is to provide the engineer with a soil materials inventory showing the extent and distribution of the various soil types in relation to other prominent physical and cultural features of the earth's surface. The survey is documented in the form of engineering soil maps, and the technical information is embodied in the form of descriptive bulletins, following the principle that one has first to know what types of soil are available in an area.

Such an engineering soil survey was completed for the state of New Jersey in 1955. The area of New Jersey is of particular engineering significance, because through it, all of the major interstate highways radiate out of and into New York, carrying the world's largest traffic volume. In this respect, New Jersey may be considered a heavily traveled corridor state. It was the first state in the Union to have a complete state-wide engineering soil survey.

The objective of a soil survey is to identify, classify systematically, correlate, and describe the soil. The results describe the location, distribution, quantity and quality, as well as some geotechnical properties of soils related to locating

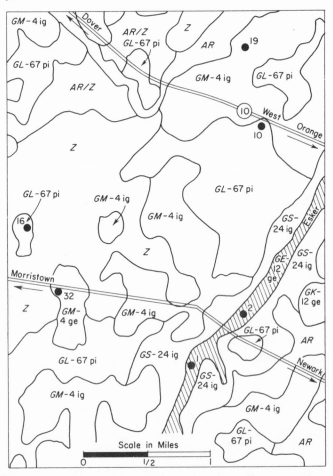

FIG. 25-8.   Part of an engineering soil map. Glacial soils. By permission of Rutgers University Press.

and relocating road alignments and finding suitable road construction material. The ultimate purpose of the survey is to help the engineer dealing with soils and highways to make important decisions in his work in order to facilitate design and construction of good roads.

It is very difficult to give definite instructions for performing an engineering soil survey. The techniques are learned best through contact or serving an apprenticeship with an experienced research group. However, the basic principles underlying an engineering soil survey are sketched in the following paragraphs.

25-15. Soil Maps. In field reconnaissance work it is very difficult to trace the extent of and changes in soil types from a position on the ground surface. Soil mapping, therefore, is based to a considerable extent on an engineering interpretation of aerial photographs. The evaluation of soil patterns and the

FIG. 25-9. Uncontrolled mosaic of Round Valley, N.J. By permission of Aero Service Corp.

interpretation of various factors discerned on the aerial photograph is an exercise in deductive reasoning. Where variations in the geology and soil patterns in the aerial photograph are revealed to be complex, field work is carried out to clarify the situation, and soil samples are taken for testing in the laboratory. Such was the procedure used in the performance of the comprehensive Engineering Soil Survey of New Jersey.

The results of this survey were described in appropriate soil bulletins. The bulletins described the geologic area and drainage conditions, and discussed from an engineering point of view the performance of the soil in highway work (pumping of joints, possible slides, damage to roads by frost action, suitability of the material for fill, ease or difficulty of alignment problems, the size of cuts and fills), and listed the engineering test values of the delineated soil types. Emphasis was put on information pertinent to highway construction. This engineering soil survey may be considered as something unique, useful, and new in the field of soil exploration and highway technology.[2,3,4,5,6]

A part of an engineering soil map showing an esker (*GE*), a kame (*GK*), glacial lake beds (*GL*), stratified drift (*GS*), ground moraine (*GM*), swamps (*Z*) and some highways is shown in Fig. 25-8. Black dots on this map indicate points from which soil samples were taken.

25-16. Aerial Photographs. The aerial photographs, mentioned previously in connection with soil exploration and the engineering soil survey, can be combined in a mosaic or photo map (note that the aerial photograph by itself is not a map), such as illustrated in Fig. 25-9 and used successfully as an effective aid in solving

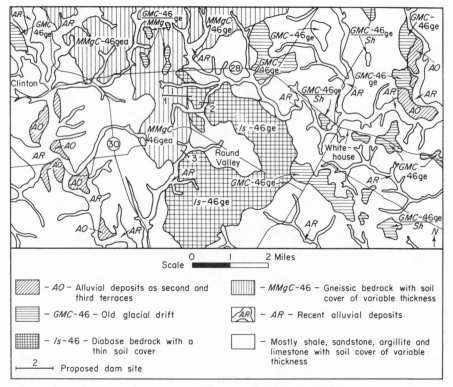

FIG. 25-10.   Part of an engineering soil map of the Round Valley area. By permission of Rutgers University Press.

certain engineering problems. This figure represents the Round Valley, encompassed by Cushetunk Mountain, in Hunterdon County, N.J., a proposed site of a reservoir. The horseshoe-like geologic feature is a diabase ridge. The dark areas are the shadows the ridges cast. The diabase was intruded into the Piedmont shale, sandstone, and conglomerate where it cooled and solidified beneath the surface. To keep the reservoir closed, three dams, 1, 2, and 3, Figs. 25-9 and 25-10, had to be built.

A part of the engineering soil map of the Round Valley area, prepared from aerial photographs, geologic, agronomic and highway base maps, field reconnaissance, soil sampling, and testing, is shown in Fig. 25-10. Note the horseshoe-like Cushetunk Mountain, the three proposed dam sites, the network of roads (solid lines), and the delineated soil and nonsoil areas. The reservoir is now completed.

REFERENCES

1. R.F. Legget (2nd ed.), *Geology and Engineering*, New York, McGraw-Hill Book Co., 1973.
2. A.R. Jumikis, *Engineering Aspects of Glacial Soils of the Newark Metropolitan Area of New Jersey.* Engineering Research Bulletin No. 42, Bureau of Engineering Research, Rutgers—The State University, New Brunswick, N.J., 1959.
3. W.W. Holman, R.K. McCormack, J.P. Minard, and A.R. Jumikis, *Practical Applications of Engineering Soil Maps* (Engineering Soil Survey of New Jersey), Report No. 22, Rutgers University Press, New Brunswick, N.J., 1957.
4. A.R. Jumikis, W.W. Holman, and J.R. Schuyler, *The Engineering Soil Survey and its Relation to Engineering Problems,* Highway Research Board Bulletin, no. 213, Washington, D.C., 1958.
5. A.R. Jumikis, "Geology and Soils of the Newark (N.J.) Metropolitan Area," *Journal of the Soil Mechanics and Foundation Division, Proc. ASCE,* Paper no. 1646, May 1958, New York.
6. A.R. Jumikis, "Engineering Soil Maps." *Proceedings of the 3rd International Congress I.A.E.G. - on Engineering Geology*, held September 4-8, 1978 in Madrid, Spain. Sect. 1, vol. 2, pp. 228-234.

OTHER USEFUL REFERENCES

1. American Society of Photogrammetry, *Manual of Color Aerial Photography,* Menasha, Wis., George Banta Publishing Company, 1968.
2. *1976 Annual Book of ASTM Standards, Part 19,* Designation: D 420-69 (Reapproved 1975): Standard Recommended Practice for Investigating and Sampling Soils and Rock for Engineering Purposes. ASTM, Philadelphia, Pa., 1976, pp. 62-66.
3. *1976 Annual Book of ASTM Standards, Part 19,* Designation: D 1452 (Reapproved 1972): Standard Method for Soil Investigation and Sampling by Auger Borings. ASTM, Philadelphia, Pa., 1976, pp. 205-206.
4. Bureau of Reclamation, *Earth Manual* (2nd ed.), Washington, D.C., U.S. Department of the Interior, Chapter II, 1974, pp. 65-164.
5. G.A. Fletcher, "Standard Penetration Test: Its Uses and Abuses," Paper No. 4395, *Proc. ASCE,* Journal of the Soil Mechanics and Foundations Division, vol. 91, No. SM 4, July, 1965, pp. 67-75.
6. H.Q. Golder and L.G. Soderman, "Merits and Mistakes of Geophysics in Civil

Engineering," *Proceedings of the 2nd Panamerican Conference on Soil Mechanics and Foundation Engineering*, held at Sao Paulo, Brazil, vol. 1, 1963, pp. 513-531.

7. M.J. Hvorslev, papers and reports prepared for the Committee on Sampling and Testing, American Society of Civil Engineers: a) March 1940, b) July 1940, c) January 1942, and d) 1943.

8. M.J. Hvorslev, *Subsurface Exploration and Sampling of Soils for Civil Engineering Purposes*, Waterways Experiment Station, Vicksburg, Miss., November 1949.

9. D.S. Jenkins, et al, *The Origin, Distribution, and Airphoto Identification of U.S. Soils*, Washington, D.C., Civil Aeronautics Administration publication, 1946.

10. A.R. Jumikis, "Standard Penetration Test," in *Foundation Engineering* (1st ed.). Scranton, Pa., Intext Educational Publishers, 1971, pp. 61-67.

11. R.F. Legget, *Cities and Geology*. New York, N.Y.: McGraw-Hill Book Company, 1973.

12. D.R. Lueder, *Aerial Photographic Interpretation*, New York, N.Y.: McGraw-Hill Book Company, 1959.

13. H.A. Mohr, Exploration of Soil Conditions and Sampling Operations, *Soil Mechanics Series*, 21, November 1943, Graduate School of Engineering, no. 376, Harvard University, Cambridge, Mass.

14. Rutgers University - The State University of New Jersey. College of Engineering. *Engineering Soil Survey of New Jersey*. A Joint Highway Research Project. New Brunswick, New Jersey. Engineering Research Bulletins Nos. 15 to 34 (Reports Nos. 1 to 21), 1950-1957.

    Report No. 1 is the first of a series of twenty-two reports and deals with soil environment and methods of research. Each of the subsequent reports is confined to a single county of New Jersey containing engineering soil maps.

15. T.E. Avery, *Interpretation of Aerial Photographs* (3rd ed.), Minneapolis, Minnesota: Burges Publishing Company, 1977.

16. G. Sanglerat, *The Penetrometer and Soil Exploration*, Amsterdam/Oxford/New York, N.Y.: Elsevier Scientific Publishing Company, 1972.

17. A.R. Jumikis, "Geotechnical Properties of Triassic Shale." *Proceedings of the 3rd International Congress I.A.E.G.* - on Engineering Geology, held September 4-8, 1978 in Madrid, Spain, Sect. II, vol. 1, pp. 211-217.

Appendices

Appendix I

GREEK ALPHABET

A α	Alpha		N ν	Nu
B β	Beta		Ξ ξ	Xi
Γ γ	Gamma		O o	Omicron
Δ δ	Delta		Π π	Pi
E ε	Epsilon		P ρ	Rho
Z ζ	Zeta		Σ σ ς	Sigma
H η	Eta		T τ	Tau
Θ θ	Theta		Υ υ	Upsilon
I ι	Iota		Φ φ	Phi
K κ	Kappa		X χ	Chi
Λ λ	Lambda		Ψ ψ	Psi
M μ	Mu		Ω ω	Omega

KEY TO SIGNS AND NOTATIONS

Symbol	*Description*
A	Area; shear area; stressed area; specific surface. Also, a coefficient in an equation. Fraction of soil by dry weight
Å	Ångström; $1 \text{ Å} = 1 \times 10^{-4} \mu = 1 \times 10^{-7}$ mm
A_e; A_{eff}	Effective areas
A_{av}; A_m; A_o; A_t	Areas
ASCE	American Society of Civil Engineers
ASTM	American Society for Testing and Materials
AASHTO	American Association of State Highway and Transportation Officials
a	Coefficient; length; acceleration; fraction weight of soil, in percent, retained on a sieve; cross-sectional area; are
a_{ms}	Mantle surface
a_v	Coefficient of compressibility
a_1	Same as a but passing sieve
a^2	Capillary constant
B, B^1	Coefficient; constant; fraction of soil; British thermal unit; buoyant force. Width of foundation
BPR	Bureau of Public Roads

537

b	A coefficient; length; fraction weight of soil, in percent, retained on a sieve; weight of burned matter
b_1	Same as b but passing that sieve
C	A constant; a constant of integration; a temperature range on the Centigrade scale; a fraction of soil. Total amount of cohesion
C_c	Compression index
C_e	Expansion index
$°C$	Degree centigrade
$\mathcal{C}_L$	Center Line
CAA	Civil Aeronautics Administration
CBR	California Bearing Ratio
C_D	Drag coefficient
cd	Consolidated drained test
c	A coefficient; a constant; cohesion of soil; specific heat. Test parameter
c_{eff}	Effective cohesion
c_u	Cohesion from undrained test
cu	Consolidated undrained test
c_1	Fraction weight of soil, in percent, retained on sieve. Same passing that sieve. Heat capacity
c_{nec}, c_o	Necessary cohesion
cm	Centimeter
const	Constant
c_v	Coefficient of consolidation
D	Diameter; relative density of sand; dielectric constant; seepage pressure; fraction of soil; drag force. Depth of foundation
D_s	Total seepage pressure
DIN	Deutsche Industrie Normen (German Industrial Norms)
d	Differential; a coefficient, diameter; thickness; an index-symbol for "developed"
d_1	Fraction weight of soil, in percent, retained on a sieve; same passing through that sieve
$d_{10}; d_e$	Effective size of soil particle, or 10% diameter
d_{60}	60% diameter of soil particle
E	Modulus of elasticity; soil fraction; earth pressure
E_a	Active earth pressure
E_o	Earth pressure at rest
E_p	Passive earth pressure (earth resistance)
E_s	Streaming potential. Modulus of elasticity. Stiffness modulus of soil.
E.L.	Elastic limit

E.M.F.	Electromotive force
e	Base of natural logarithmic system (2.7182...). Also, void ratio, fraction weight of soil, in percent, retained on a sieve
e_B; e_L	Eccentricities
e_1	Fraction of soil, in percent by dry weight, passing a sieve; void ratio
e_{ave}	Average void ratio
e_f	Final void ratio
e_i	Initial void ratio
e_{max}	Maximum void ratio
e_{min}	Minimum void ratio
e_o	Void ratio at time $t = 0$
e_x, e_y	Eccentricities
F	A function of. Also, force; shear force; a focal point; also, a temperature range (or number of degrees) on the Fahrenheit temperature scale
F_{nsk}	Negative skin resistance (friction)
F_s	Total mantle or skin resistance
°F	Degrees Fahrenheit
f	A function of. Also, coefficient of friction; also, length
ft	Feet
$f(x)$	Function of x
G	Specific gravity of soil particles; also, a symbol for gravelly soil. Weight of capillary column of water. Weight of soil. Weight of structure
GC	Clayey gravel
GE	Glacial esker
GK	Glacial kame
GL	Glacial lake bed; also, gelation limit of soil
GM	Ground moraine
GMM	Glacial marginal (terminal) moraine
GO	Glacial outwash
GP	Poorly graded gravel
GS	Glacial stratified drift
G.S.	Ground surface
G_s	Specific gravity of soil particles
GW	Well graded gravel
G.W.T.	Groundwater table
G_w	Specific gravity of water
g	Acceleration of gravity $= 981$ cm/s$^2 = 32.2$ ft/s^2; also, mass gram; also, dry weight of a soil fraction
g_f	Force gram

H	Height; depth; thickness; capillary height; also, a horizontal force; also, a fraction of soil
HRB	Highway Research Board
h	Height; depth; thickness; capillary height; height of outcrop of the uppermost seepage line. Also, fraction weight of dry soil, in percent, retained on a sieve. Also, pressure head
h_1	Fraction of a soil, in percent, passing a sieve
h_c	Capillary height. Critical hydraulic head
h_f	Height of artesian fountain
h_o	A particular height
h_{max}	Maximum height
h_{min}	Minimum height
h_n	Hydrostatic head
h, h_1, h_2	Height of triangles. Also, thickness of layers of soil
ha	Hectare
h	Hour
I	Moment of inertia. Also, electric current
i	Hydraulic gradient
in.	Inches
i_u	Hydraulic pressure gradient
J	Fraction of soil
j	Fraction weight of soil, in percent, retained on a sieve
j_1	Same as above, but passing a sieve
K	Coefficient. A temperature range on the Kelvin scale, Coefficient of heat transmission. Coefficient of Boussinesq's stress distribution in a homogeneous medium
$^{\circ}K$	Degree Kelvin
K_a	Trigonometric earth pressure coefficient for the active case
K_o	Earth pressure coefficient at rest
K_p	Trigonometric earth pressure coefficient for the passive case
K_η	Viscosity correction factor for water
K, K_1	Thermal conductivity of frozen soil
k	Coefficient. Coefficient of permeability of soil
k_{ave}	Average coefficient of permeability. Also, geometric mean permeability
k_{aw}	Permeability when voids are filled with air and water
k_1, k_2, k_3	Coefficients of permeability
$k_1 \perp$	Coefficient of perpendicular permeability
$k_1 \parallel$	Coefficient of parallel permeability
k_h	Coefficient of horizontal permeability
k_v	Coefficient of vertical permeability
kg	Mass kilogram

kg_f	Force kilogram
km	Kilometer
kN	Kilo-newton
L	Length or linear dimension. Also, latent heat of fusion Filtration length
L'	Length of footing
L_o	Length
L.L.	Liquid limit
L_1, L_2	Filtration length
l	Liter $= 1000 \text{ cm}^3$
log	Common (Brigg's) logarithm to the base 10
ln	Natural logarithm of, or logarithm to the base of e $= 2.7182...$
M	Mass. Also, moment; bending moment. Number of flow channels.
M_D	Driving moment
M_R	Resisting moment
M_v	Compression modulus
MIT	Massachusetts Institute of Technology
MN	Meganewton
m	Meter. Also, mass. Poisson's number $m = 1/\mu$
max	Maximum
maxmax	Maximum maximorum
min	Minimum
mm	Millimeter
m_v	Amount of linear compression
m_α	Factor
N	An integer. Normal force. Also, number of squares between two adjacent equipotential lines. Also, a variable. Number of equipotential drops
N	Newton
N_R	Reynolds number
N_T	Taylor's stability number
N_c, N_q, N_γ	Bearing capacity factors
N.L.	Non-liquid
N.P.	Non-plastic
n	Any number. Number of blows. Number of cubes. Porosity of soil. Geometric mean: $n = \sqrt{ab}$. Also, number of equal drops in pressure head.
n_a	Relative volume of air voids
n_f	Number of blows
n_{max}	Maximum porosity
n_{min}	Minimum porosity
n_s	Relative volume of solid particles

n_w Relative volume of water in soil

O Origin of coordinates; a geometric point. Center. Also, zero
OH   Inorganic, plastic silt
OL   Inorganic silt
↖   Index of various quantities
↙   Degree (of temperature or angle).

P Force; load
$P.I.$ Plasticity index of soil
$P.L.$ Plastic limit of soil. Also, plastic limit of steel; proportional
                  limit
PRA   Public Roads Administration
Pt   Peat
P_L Ultimate bearing capacity of soil
P_{ult} Ultimate capacity of a pier
p Half-parameter of parabola. Total stress. Uniformly distributed
                  load. Surcharge
p_a Active earth pressure ordinate
$\overline{p}$ Effective pressure
p_c Capillary pressure
p_{crit} Critical pressure
p_e Effective stress
p_i Initial stress
p_o Initial stress. Also, surcharge. Lateral earth pressure ordinate
                  at rest
$\overline{p}_o$ Initial effective pressure
p_p Stress at proportional limit; passive earth pressure ordinate
p_{pr} Preconsolidation load, stress
p_y Stress at yield point
p_1, p_2, p', p'' Pressure
$\overline{p}_1$ Final effective pressure
p_u Ultimate strength

Q Quick shear test
Q_L Latent heat of fusion
Q_c Consolidated quick test
Q, Q_1, Q_2 Discharge; yield
Q.E.D.   quod erat demonstrandum (which was to be proved, or shown)
Q_{ult} Ultimate load
q Discharge
$q_{t,R}$ Critical edge pressure
q_u, q_{ult} Ultimate bearing capacity of soil

R Radius of influence. Resultant force

r	Radius
r_o	Radius of well. Initial radius. Radius of circle
r_1	Radius of curvature. Also, inside radius
r_2	Outside radius
S	Degree of saturation. Surface tension. Sandy soil. Drained or consolidated slow shear test
SI	Système International d'Unités
SL	Sand-clay mixtures
$S.L.$	Shrinkage limit of soil
S.M.	Sand-silt mixtures
SP	Poorly graded sand
SW	Well graded sand
s	Sensitivity of clay. Settlement of soil. Settlement of structure. Skin friction
s_1, s_t	Settlement
s, s_{max}	Draw-down; maximum draw-down
T	Temperature. Variable. Shearing force (tangential force)
T_g	Groundwater temperature
T_f	Freezing temperature $= 0°\,C = 32°\,F$
T_s	Surface temperature
T_1, T_2	Temperatures
t	Metric force ton $= 1000$ kg$_f$
$t, t_1, t_2, t_t, t_o, t_\infty$	Time; time intervals
$\tan\alpha$	$= i = dy/dx =$ Hydraulic gradient; slope
$\tan\phi$	Coefficient of internal friction of soil; test parameter
U	Coefficient of uniformity of soil; also, perimeter
U.S.	Ultimate strength
U.S.C.	Unified soil classification
USDA	United States Department of Agriculture
u, u_t	Neutral stress
ud	Unconsolidated drained test
uu	Unconsolidated undrained test
u_i	Initial pore water (neutral) pressure
u_o	Pore water (neutral) pressure at time $t = 0$
V	Volume; total volume of soil. Volts. Vertical load.
V_a	Volume of air
V_f	Final volume of soil sample after drying
V_i	Initial volume of soil sample before drying
V_L	Volume of liquid
V_n	Volume of voids
V_s	Volume of solid particles
V_v	Volume of voids

V_w	Volume of water
V_1	Volume of cylinder
V_2	Volume of cylinder
V_3	Vibrated volume of sand
v	Flow velocity. Velocity
v_v	Specific loss of pore water
W	Weight of soil; weight of soil particle. Total hydrostatic pressure
W_d	Dry weight. Dry density in soil compaction
W_r	Weight of hammer
W_s	Weight of solids
W_v	Weight of water occupying all voids (saturation)
W_w	Weight of water
w	Moisture content, in percent
w_i	Initial moisture content
$w_{L.L.}$	Moisture content at liquid limit
$w_{P.I.}$	Plasticity index
$w_{P.L.}$	Moisture content at plastic limit
w_{sat}	Moisture content at saturation of soil
$w_{S.L.}$	Moisture content at shrinkage limit
w_1, w_2	Moisture contents
x	An unknown quantity. Abscissa. A coordinate. Variable radius
x_1	A coordinate
Y.P.	Yield point
y	A coordinate
Z	Swamp
z	A coordinate. A variable. Depth. Length of gallery
∇	Symbol to indicate a particular surface, for example ground-water table, or road surface, or ground surface, or any elevation on soil profiles
α (alpha)	A constant. Angle of rupture. Angle of wetting. Slope angle of a line. Angle of discharge face of a dam. Angle of batter. Coefficient of thermal diffusivity $= K/c\rho = K/C = \alpha$
β (beta)	A constant. Angle. Angle of slope of a line
β_s	Angle of slope of a chord
γ (gamma)	Unit weight

γ_d	Dry unit weight of soil
γ_{eff}	Effective unit weight of soil
γ_f	Unit weight of fill
γ_s	Unit weight of soil
γ_{sat}	Unit weight of saturated soil
γ_{sub}	Submerged unit weight of soil
γ_w	Unit weight of water $= 62.4 \text{ lb}/\text{ft}^3 = 1 \text{ g}_f/\text{cm}^3 = 1000 \text{ kg}_f/\text{m}^3 = 9.81 \text{ kN}/\text{m}^3$

Δ (delta)	Difference. Increment. Decrement
ΔH	Absolute deformation
Δe	Amount of compression. Change in void ratio
Δh	Compression. Change in thickness. Frost heave
Δh_1	Deformation
ΔL	Length increment, decrement
Δp	Pressure increment
Δt	Time increment
Δv	Velocity increment. Loss of moisture upon drying. Decrease of moisture
Δw	Decrease in moisture content. Change in w
$\Delta x, \Delta y, \Delta z$	Coordinate increments (decrements)
δ (delta)	Angle of slope of ground surface

ϵ (epsilon)	Strain. Central half-angle; relative deformation; relative settlement
ϵ_v	Volumetric strain
ζ (zeta)	Electrokinetic (zeta) potential. Form factor

η (eta)	Dynamic viscosity of water. Also, factor of safety; efficiency; frost danger
η_{all}	allowable factor of safety
η_T	Coefficient of dynamic viscosity of water at T° C
η_{20}	Coefficient of dynamic viscosity of water at +20° C

θ (theta)	Angle of slope with horizontal; angle

λ (lambda)	A coefficient. Ratio. Specific conductivity of water. Electrical conductivity of a conductor. Form factor

μ (mu)	A coefficient. Micron: $1 \text{ micron} = 1\mu = 1 \times 10^{-4} \text{ cm} = 1 \times 10^{-3} \text{ mm}$. Also, degree of consolidation Coefficient of internal friction of soil: $\mu = \tan \phi$. Poisson's ratio
$\mu\mu$	Millimicron: $1\mu\mu = 1 \times 10^{-7} \text{ cm} = 1 \times 10^{-6} \text{ mm}$

ν (nu)	Kinematic viscosity (cm²/s). Fröhlich's stress concentration factor.

ξ (xi)	Frost penetration depth
π (pi)	Geometric ratio of circumference of a circle to its diameter = = 3.14159 ...
ρ (rho)	Radius. Radius of curvature. Angle of rupture. Density
ρ_L	Density of water
ρ_v	Density of vapor
ρ_1	Unit weight of water
Σ (sigma)	Summation of
$\overset{n}{\underset{1}{\Sigma}}$	Summation of . . . from 1 to n
σ (sigma)	Stress. Normal stress. Also, surface tension, in dynes/cm
σ_{adm}, σ_{all}	Allowable (safe) bearing capacity of soil
σ_{ave}	Average stress
σ_e, σ_{eff}, $\overline{\sigma}$	Effective stress
σ_{max}	Maximum stress
σ_{min}	Minimum stress
σ_n, σ_{neff}	Normal stress; normal effective stress
$\sigma_{n_{eff}}$	Normal effective stress
$\sigma_\circ$	Surface tension. Contact pressure on soil
σ_R	Radial stress in space (Boussinesq's theory)
σ_r	Horizontal radial stress. Also resultant stress
σ_T	Surface tension at T°C
σ_t	Tangential stress in Boussinesq's theory
σ_u	Ultimate stress; ultimate bearing capacity of soil
σ_v	Vertical stress
σ_x, σ_y, σ_z	Stress components
σ_z	Vertical stress in Boussinesq's theory
σ_1	Major principal stress
σ_2	Intermediate principal stress
σ_3	Minor principal stress
σ^*	Surface tension, in g_f/cm or in dynes/cm
τ (tau)	Shear stress. Shear strength. Time factor
τ_1, τ_2	Slope angles of tangents
τ_{max}	Maximum shear stress
τ_r	Remolded shear stress of clay
τ_u	Ultimate shear strength of clay
τ_{xy}, τ_{yz}, τ_{zx}	Shear stresses
Φ (phi)	Function of. Designation of an equipotential line. Airy's stress function
ϕ (phi)	Function of. Angle of internal friction of soil. Angle of friction

	between backfill material and wall
ϕ_{eff}, $\overline{\phi}$	Effective friction angle; test parameter
ϕ_r	Angle of internal friction of soil
ϕ_u	Test parameter from undrained test
ϕ_1	Wall friction angle
ψ (psi)	Angle. Designation of a flow line
Ω (Omega)	Angle
ω (omega)	Angle. Amplitude; angle of chord. A polar coordinate
$\triangle \triangledown$	A symbol for a geometric triangle.

Appendices II and III

DYNAMIC VISCOSITY TABLES FOR WATER
DYNAMIC VISCOSITY CORRECTION FACTOR TABLES FOR WATER

Prepared by A. R. Jumikis

In analyzing soil freezing experiment and permeability data, there is a need for dynamic viscosity values of water in the freezing range of temperatures, as well as for values of viscosity for whole degrees and for every decimal of degree.

The viscosity values found in various publications are not usually given for such close temperatures. Therefore, it was expedient to prepare such viscosity tables, which would be useful for work in connection with studies on freezing soil systems and on soil moisture migration. The viscosity and the viscosity correction tables were calculated and prepared based on N. E. Dorsey's data found in his book entitled *Properties of Ordinary Water-Substance* (New York, Reinhold Publishing Corporation, 1940), the viscosity values for most part of which are based on *International Critical Tables for Numerical Data, Physics, Chemistry and Technology*, published for the U.S. National Research Council by the McGraw-Hill Book Co., Inc., New York, 1929, vol. 5, p. 10.

The published viscosity values were plotted to a large scale on millimeter paper, the viscosity ordinates were connected by a curve, and the viscosity values for each decimal of a degree of temperature were scaled on such a curve and tabulated. The work on freezing soil systems was sponsored by the National Science Foundation, Washington, D.C., and performed in the Soil Mechanics and Foundation Engineering Laboratory of the Department of Civil Engineering at Rutgers—The State University, New Brunswick, New Jersey.

Appendix II
Dynamic Viscosity of Water, $\eta[g/(cm\ sec)]$ Table

T°C	0	0.1	0.2	0.3	0.4	0.5	0.6	0.7	0.8	0.9
−10	0.0260	—	—	—	—	—	—	—	—	—
−9	250	0.0251	0.0252	0.0253	0.0254	0.0255	0.0256	0.0257	0.0258	0.0259
−8	240	241	242	243	244	245	246	247	248	249
−7	230	231	232	233	234	235	236	237	238	239
−6	220	221	222	223	224	225	226	227	228	229
−5	0.02140	0.02142	0.02146	0.02151	0.02156	0.02162	0.02168	0.02175	0.02183	0.02191
−4	2050	2060	2067	2075	2083	2092	2100	2110	2120	2130
−3	1979	1980	1987	2000	2007	2015	2022	2030	2036	2044
−2	1910	1915	1922	1930	1935	1943	1950	1956	1965	1972
−1	1840	1847	1853	1860	1866	1873	1880	1887	1895	1902
0	0.01790	0.01795	0.01799	0.01803	0.01808	0.01813	0.01818	0.01824	0.01830	0.01835
0	0.01790	0.01785	0.01778	0.01773	0.01766	0.01760	0.01754	0.01748	0.01742	0.01736
1	0.01730	0.01724	0.01718	0.01712	0.01706	0.01700	0.01694	0.01687	0.01682	0.01675
2	1670	1663	1657	1651	1647	1640	1635	1629	1623	1617
3	1610	1605	1600	1594	1588	1583	1578	1573	1568	1564
4	1560	1555	1551	1546	1543	1539	1535	1531	1528	1524
5	1520	1515	1510	1505	1501	1493	1487	1484	1478	1475

DYNAMIC VISCOSITY OF WATER, η[g/(cm sec)] TABLE (continued)

T°C	0	0.1	0.2	0.3	0.4	0.5	0.6	0.7	0.8	0.9
6	0.01470	0.01466	0.01463	0.01458	0.01454	0.01450	0.01446	0.01442	0.01438	0.01434
7	1430	1426	1422	1418	1414	1410	1406	1402	1398	1394
8	1390	1387	1382	1377	1373	1370	1365	1361	1357	1353
9	1350	1345	1342	1338	1334	1330	1326	1322	1318	1313
10	1308	1305	1301	1298	1293	1290	1285	1282	1278	1275
11	0.01271	0.01268	0.01264	0.01261	0.01258	0.01254	0.01350	0.01246	0.01243	0.01240
12	1236	1233	1229	1226	1222	1218	1215	1212	1208	1205
13	1202	1199	1196	1193	1190	1186	1183	1180	1176	1173
14	1171	1166	1164	1161	1157	1154	1151	1148	1145	1143
15	1140	1136	1133	1131	1128	1125	1122	1119	1116	1113
16	0.01111	0.01107	0.01104	0.01101	0.01098	0.01095	0.01093	0.01090	0.01087	0.01084
17	1082	1078	1076	1073	1070	1068	1065	1062	1059	1056
18	1055	1051	1048	1046	1043	1040	1038	1035	1033	1030
19	1029	1025	1022	1020	1016	1014	1012	1009	1007	1006
20	1005	1003	1000	0998	0995	0993	0991	0988	0986	0983

DYNAMIC VISCOSITY OF WATER, $\eta[\mathrm{g}/(\mathrm{cm\ sec})]$ TABLE (continued)

T°C	0	0.1	0.2	0.3	0.4	0.5	0.6	0.7	0.8	0.9
21	0.00981	0.00979	0.00976	0.00974	0.00972	0.00969	0.00967	0.00965	0.00962	0.00960
22	958	956	953	951	949	947	945	942	940	938
23	936	933	931	929	927	925	922	920	918	916
24	914	912	910	908	906	904	902	900	898	896
25	894	892	890	888	886	884	882	880	788	786
26	0.00874	0.00872	0.00870	0.00868	0.00866	0.00864	0.00862	0.00860	0.00858	0.00856
27	854	852	850	848	846	845	843	841	839	837
28	836	834	832	830	828	826	824	823	821	819
29	818	816	814	812	811	809	807	806	804	802
30	801	799	798	796	794	792	791	788	787	785
31	0.00784	0.00782	0.00781	0.00779	0.00777	0.00776	0.00774	0.00772	0.00771	0.00769
32	768	766	764	763	761	760	758	757	755	754
33	752	751	749	748	746	745	743	742	740	739
34	737	736	734	733	731	730	728	726	725	724
35	722	720	719	718	716	715	714	712	711	709
36	0.00708	0.00707	0.00705	0.00704	0.00703	0.00701	0.00700	0.00699	0.00697	0.00696
37	695	693	692	691	689	688	687	685	684	683
38	681	680	679	677	676	675	673	672	670	669
39	668	667	666	665	663	662	661	660	658	657
40	656	—	—	—	—	—	—	—	—	—

APPENDIX III

DYNAMIC VISCOSITY CORRECTION FACTORS, η_T/η_{20} FOR WATER

Calculated and prepared by A. R Jumikis

$T°C$	0.0	0.1	0.2	0.3	0.4	0.5	0.6	0.7	0.8	0.9
−10	2.58706	—	—	—	—	—	—	—	—	—
−9	2.48756	2.49751	2.50746	2.51741	2.52736	2.53731	2.54726	2.55721	2.56716	2.57711
−8	2.38805	2.40796	2.40796	2.41791	2.42786	2.43781	2.44776	2.45771	2.46766	2.47761
−7	2.28855	2.30845	2.30845	2.31840	2.32835	2.33830	2.34825	2.35820	2.36815	2.37810
−6	2.18905	2.19900	2.20895	2.21890	2.22885	2.23880	2.24875	2.25870	2.26865	2.27860
−5	2.12935	2.13134	2.13532	2.14029	2.14527	2.15124	2.15721	2.16417	2.17213	2.18009
−4	2.03980	2.04975	2.05671	2.06467	2.07263	2.08159	2.08955	2.09950	2.10945	2.11940
−3	1.96915	1.97014	1.97711	1.99004	1.99701	2.00497	2.01194	2.01990	2.02587	2.03383
−2	1.90049	1.90547	1.91243	1.92039	1.92537	1.93333	1.94029	1.94626	1.95522	1.96218
−1	1.83084	1.83781	1.84378	1.85074	1.85671	1.86368	1.87064	1.87761	1.88557	1.89253
0	1.78109	1.78606	1.79004	1.79402	1.79900	1.80398	1.80895	1.81492	1.82089	1.82587
0	1.78109	1.77611	1.76915	1.76417	1.75721	1.75124	1.74527	1.73930	1.73333	1.72736

DYNAMIC VISCOSITY CORRECTION FACTORS, η_T/η_{20} FOR WATER (*continued*)

$T°C$	0.0	0.1	0.2	0.3	0.4	0.5	0.6	0.7	0.8	0.9
1	1.72139	1.71542	1.70945	1.70348	1.69751	1.69154	1.68557	1.67860	1.67363	1.66666
2	1.66169	1.65472	1.64875	1.64278	1.63880	1.63184	1.62686	1.62089	1.61492	1.60895
3	1.60199	1.59701	1.59203	1.58606	1.58009	1.57512	1.57014	1.56517	1.56019	1.55621
4	1.55223	1.54328	1.54328	1.53830	1.53532	1.53134	1.52736	1.52338	1.52039	1.51641
5	1.51243	1.50746	1.50248	1.49751	1.49353	1.48557	1.47960	1.47661	1.47064	1.46766
6	1.46268	1.45870	1.45572	1.45074	1.44676	1.44278	1.43880	1.43482	1.42084	1.42686
7	1.42288	1.41890	1.41492	1.41094	1.40696	1.40298	1.39900	1.39502	1.39104	1.38706
8	1.38308	1.38009	1.37512	1.37014	1.36616	1.36318	1.35820	1.35422	1.35024	1.34626
9	1.34328	1.33830	1.33532	1.33134	1.32736	1.32338	1.31940	1.31542	1.31094	1.30646
10	1.30149	1.29850	1.29452	1.29104	1.28656	1.28358	1.27860	1.27562	1.27164	1.26865
11	1.26467	1.26169	1.25771	1.25472	1.25174	1.24776	1.24378	1.23980	1.23681	1.23383
12	1.22985	1.22686	1.22288	1.21990	1.21592	1.21194	1.20895	1.20597	1.20199	1.19900
13	1.19601	1.19303	1.19004	1.18706	1.18407	1.18009	1.17711	1.17412	1.17014	1.16716
14	1.16507	1.16019	1.15820	1.15522	1.15124	1.14825	1.14527	1.14228	1.13930	1.13731
15	1.13432	1.13034	1.12736	1.12537	1.12238	1.11940	1.11641	1.11343	1.11044	1.10746

DYNAMIC VISCOSITY CORRECTION FACTORS, η_T/η_{20} FOR WATER (continued)

T°C	0.0	0.1	0.2	0.3	0.4	0.5	0.6	0.7	0.8	0.9
16	1.10547	1.10149	1.09850	1.09552	1.09253	1.08955	1.08756	1.08457	1.08159	1.07860
17	1.07661	1.07263	1.07064	1.06766	1.06467	1.06268	1.05970	1.05671	1.05373	1.05074
18	1.04975	1.04577	1.04278	1.04079	1.03781	1.03482	1.03283	1.02985	1.02787	1.02487
19	1.02388	1.01990	1.01691	1.01492	1.01094	1.00895	1.00696	1.00399	1.00199	1.00099
20	1.00000	0.99761	0.99502	0.99303	0.99034	0.98805	0.98587	0.98328	0.98109	0.97810
21	0.97611	0.97363	0.97114	0.96915	0.96716	0.96437	0.96218	0.96019	0.95721	0.95522
22	0.95323	0.95124	0.95124	0.94626	0.94427	0.94228	0.94029	0.93731	0.93532	0.93333
23	0.93134	0.92835	0.92636	0.92437	0.92238	0.92039	0.91741	0.91542	0.91343	0.91144
24	0.90945	0.90746	0.90547	0.90348	0.90149	0.89950	0.89751	0.89552	0.89353	0.89154
25	0.88955	0.88756	0.88756	0.88358	0.88159	0.87960	0.87761	0.87562	0.87363	0.87164
26	0.86965	0.86766	0.86567	0.86368	0.86169	0.85970	0.85771	0.85572	0.85373	0.85174
27	0.84975	0.84776	0.84577	0.84378	0.84179	0.84079	0.83880	0.83681	0.83482	0.83283
28	0.83184	0.82985	0.82786	0.82587	0.82388	0.82189	0.81990	0.81890	0.81691	0.81492
29	0.81393	0.81194	0.80995	0.80796	0.80696	0.80497	0.80298	0.80199	0.80000	0.79800
30	0.79701	0.79502	0.79402	0.79203	0.79004	0.78805	0.78706	0.78407	0.78308	0.78208

DYNAMIC VISCOSITY CORRECTION FACTORS, η_T/η_{20} FOR WATER *(continued)*

$T°C$	0.0	0.1	0.2	0.3	0.4	0.5	0.6	0.7	0.8	0.9
31	0.78009	0.77810	0.77711	0.77512	0.77313	0.77213	0.77014	0.76815	0.76716	0.76517
32	0.76517	0.76218	0.76019	0.75920	0.75721	0.75621	0.75422	0.75323	0.75124	0.75024
33	0.74825	0.74526	0.74527	0.74427	0.74228	0.74129	0.73930	0.73830	0.73631	0.73532
34	0.73333	0.73233	0.73034	0.72935	0.72736	0.72636	0.72437	0.72238	0.72139	0.72039
35	0.71840	0.71641	0.71542	0.71442	0.71243	0.71144	0.71044	0.70845	0.70746	0.70547
36	0.70447	0.70348	0.70149	0.70049	0.69950	0.69751	0.69651	0.69552	0.69353	0.69253
37	0.69154	0.68955	0.68855	0.68756	0.68557	0.68457	0.68358	0.68159	0.68059	0.67960
38	0.67761	0.67661	0.67562	0.67363	0.67263	0.67164	0.66965	0.66865	0.66666	0.66567
39	0.66467	0.66368	0.66268	0.66169	0.65970	0.65870	0.65771	0.65671	0.65472	0.65373
40	0.65273	—	—	—	—	—	—	—	—	—

Appendix IV

THE INTERNATIONAL SYSTEM OF UNITS (SI)
(Système International d'Unités)

Units

The international system of units (SI for short) in all languages is a modernized or revised version of the metric system. The SI system was established by international agreement to provide a common framework for measurements in all fields.

The SI units are built upon the following six base units:

Quantity	Unit	Symbol
length	meter	m
mass	kilogram	kg
time	second	s
electric current	ampere	A
thermodynamic temperature	kelvin	K
luminous intensity	candela	cd

kg = kilogram (a mass unit)
kg_f = force kilogram (a force unit)

Internationally, instead of force kilogram, the term "newton" (N) is used:

$$1 \text{ N} = (1/9.80665) \text{ kg}_f$$
$$1 \text{ kg}_f = 9.80665 \text{ N} = 9.80665 \text{ kg} \cdot \text{m/s}^2$$

The unit of force, the newton, is defined as the force which causes a 1-kilogram mass to accelerate at a rate of 1 meter/s². The newton is equivalent to exactly 10^5 dynes. Conversion factors for force apply only under standard acceleration of 9.80665 m/s² due to gravity. For conversion factors between the customary and SI units refer to Appendix V.

Use of SI Units in Soil Mechanics And Foundation Engineering

In soil mechanics and foundation engineering the SI units of measurement apply as follows:

acceleration	in m/s^2
acceleration of gravity	g in m/s^2
area	in cm^2; m^2
earth pressures and resistances	E_a, E_o, E_p, in N/m or N
forces of all kinds	in N, kN, MN
length; depth displacement; settlement; deflection	in m; cm in cm
moment of inertia I, J	in cm^4
power	HP, in w, J/s, or Nm/s

pressure, stress:
    allowable pressure on soil and rock
    contact pressure on soil
    stress in soil; stresses in foundation
        materials
    shear stresses; cohesion
    mantle (skin) friction
    modulus of elasticity
	
	σ_{all}, in N/m^2, or kN/m^2
	σ_o, in N/m^2, or kN/m^2
	
	σ, in N/m^2, or kN/m^2
	τ_1, s, in N/m^2, or kN/m^2
	τ, c, s, in N/m^2
	E, in N/m^2, kN/m^2, MN/m^2

static moment; torque; work; energy	M, in $N\cdot m$ or $kN\cdot m$, or $MN\cdot m$ or in J, or ws
subgrade reaction of soil; unit weight of soil	p, in N/m^3; kN/m^3 γ, in N/m^3; kN/m^3
Velocity; coefficient of permeability	(v); k, in m/s
volume	in mm^3; cm^3; m^3

TABLES OF UNITED STATES CUSTOMARY
MEASURES AND WEIGHTS

Linear Measure

1 inch (in.) = 0.083 333 ft
1 foot (ft) = 12 in. = 0.333 333 yd
1 yard (yd) = 36 in. = 3 ft
1 mile (mi) = 63,360 in. = 5280 ft = 1760 yd

Area Measure

1 square inch (in.^{2}) = 0.006 944 ft^2 = 0.000 771 605 yd^2
1 square foot (ft^2) = 144 in.^{2} = 0.111 111 1 yd^2
1 square yard (yd^2) = 1296 in.^{2} = 9 ft^2
1 acre   = 43,560 ft^2 = 4840 yd^2
1 square mile (mi^2) = 640 acres

Cubic and Liquid Measure

1 cubic inch (in.^{3})   = 0.000 578 704 ft^3
1 cubic foot (ft^3)   = 1728 in.^{3} = 0.037 037 yd^3
1 cubic yard (yd^3)   = 27 ft^3
1 pint (pt)   = 28.875 in.^{3}
1 quart (qt)   = 2 pt = 57.75 in.^{3}
1 U.S. gallon (gal)   = 4 qt = 8 pt
                          = 231.00 in.^{3} = 0.133 680 ft.^{3}
                          = 0.833 British imperial gal
1 British imperial gal = 1.201 U.S. gal
1 ft^3 = 7.481 U.S. gal
1 British ton of water = 270.91 U.S. gal
                          = 224 British imperial gal

Avoirdupois Weight

1 ounce (oz) = 0.0625 lb
1 pound (lb) = 16 oz
1 kip   = 1000 lb
1 short ton = 2000 lb = 0.893 long tons
1 long ton   = 2240 lb = 1.12 short tons

1 lb of water fills 27.68 in.^{3} = 0.01602 ft^3 = 0.1198 gal
1 ft^3 of water at 60°F (15.54°C) weighs 62.4 lb
1 U.S. gal of water at 62°F (16.65°C) weighs 8.3364 lb

TABLES OF METRIC MEASURES AND WEIGHTS

Linear Measure

1 micron (μ)   = 0.001 millimeter
1 millimeter (mm) = 0.1 cm
1 centimeter (cm) = 10 mm = 0.01 m
1 meter (m)   = 100 cm = 1000 mm = 0.001 km
1 kilometer (km)   = 1000 m

Area Measure

1 square centimeter (cm^2) = 100 square millimeters (mm^2)
1 square meter (m^2)   = 10,000 cm^2 = 1 × 10^6 mm^2
1 hectare (ha)   = 10,000 m^2
1 square kilometer (km^2) = 100 ha = 1 × 10^6 m^2

Cubic and Liquid Measure

1 cubic centimeter (cm^3) = 1000 cubic millimeters (mm^3)
1 cubic meter (m^3)   = 1 × 10^6 cm^3 = 1 × 10^9 mm^3
                          = 999.973 liters
1 liter = 1000 milliliters (ml) = 1000 cubic centimeters (cm^3)
1 liter of distilled water at 4°C weighs 1 kg$_f$
1 cm^3 of distilled water at 4°C weighs 1 g$_f$

Weight

1 gram (g$_f$)   = 1000 milligrams (mg$_f$) = 0.001 kilogram (kg$_f$)
1 kilogram (kg$_f$) = 1000 g$_f$
1 metric ton (t)   = 1000 kg$_f$

TABLES OF METRIC AND NONMETRIC EQUIVALENTS

Length

1 mm = 0.03937 in.	1 in. = 25.4 mm = 2.54 cm
1 cm = 0.3937 in. = 0.0328 ft	1 ft = 30.48 cm = 0.305 m
1 m = 39.370 in. = 3.281 ft = 1. 094 yd	1 yd = 91.4 cm = 0.914 m
1 km = 3280.8 ft = 0.621 mi	1 mi = 1609.35 m = 1.609 km

Area

1 mm^2 = 0.002 in.^{2}	1 in.^{2} = 6.452 cm^2
1 cm^2 = 0.155 in.^{2}	1 ft^2 = 929.034 cm^2
= 0.001076387 ft^2	= 0.0929 m^2

$$1 \text{ m}^2 = 10.764 \text{ ft}^2 \qquad 1 \text{ yd}^2 = 0.836 \text{ m}^2$$
$$= 1.196 \text{ yd}^2 \qquad 1 \text{ mi}^2 = 259 \text{ ha}$$
$$1 \text{ ha} = 2.471 \text{ acres} \qquad 1 \text{ acre} = 0.405 \text{ ha} = 4046.849 \text{ m}^2$$
$$1 \text{ km}^2 = 247.104 \text{ acres}$$
$$= 0.386 \text{ mi}^2$$

Cubic and Liquid Measure

$$1 \text{ cm}^3 = 0.061 \text{ in.}^3 \qquad 1 \text{ in.}^3 = 16.387 \text{ cm}^3$$
$$1 \text{ m}^3 = 61024.044 \text{ in.}^3 \qquad 1 \text{ ft}^3 = 28,316 \text{ cm}^3$$
$$= 35.3148 \text{ ft}^3 \qquad = 0.028316 \text{ m}^3$$
$$= 1.308 \text{ yd}^3 \qquad 1 \text{ yd}^3 = 0.765 \text{ m}^3$$
$$= 264.173 \text{ U.S. gal}$$

$$1 \text{ liter} = 0.035315 \text{ ft}^3 \qquad 1 \text{ U.S. gal} = 3.785 \text{ liters}$$
$$= 0.26420 \text{ U.S. gal} \qquad 1 \text{ British gal} = 4.545 \text{ liters}$$
$$= 0.22007 \text{ British gal} \qquad 1 \text{ ft}^3 = 28.316 \text{ liters}$$
$$= 61.025 \text{ in.}^3$$

Weight. Force

$$1 \text{ g}_f = 0.002205 \text{ force pounds (lb}_f) = (9.80665)(10^{-3}) \text{ N}$$
$$1 \text{ kg}_f = 2.205 \text{ force pounds (lb}_f) = 9.80665 \text{ N}$$
$$1 \text{ t}_f = 2204.622 \text{ force pounds (lb}_f) = (9.80665)(10^3) \text{ N}$$
$$= 1.102 \text{ short tons} = (9.80665)(10^3) \text{ N}$$
$$1 \text{ lb}_f = 0.4536 \text{ kg}_f = 4.44822 \text{ N}$$
$$1 \text{ short ton} = 0.907 \text{ t (force ton, t)} = (8.89644)(10^3) \text{ N}$$

$$1 \text{ N} = (1.00000)(10^5) \text{ dynes}$$
$$= (1.01971)(10^2) \text{ g}_f$$
$$= (1.01971)(10^{-1}) \text{kg}_f$$
$$= (1.01971)(10^{-4}) \text{ t}$$
$$= (2.24809)(10^{-1}) \text{ lb}_f$$
$$= (2.24809)(10^{-4}) \text{ kips (k)}$$
$$= (1.12405)(10^{-4}) \text{ ton}$$

$$1 \text{ atmosphere} = 760 \text{ mm mercury at } 0°\text{C}$$
$$= 29.92 \text{ in. mercury at } 0°\text{C}$$
$$= 33.90 \text{ ft of water}$$
$$= 10.33 \text{ m of water}$$
$$= 10.333 \text{ tons/m}^2 = 1.0333 \text{ kg/cm}^2$$
$$= 14.70 \text{ lb/in.}^2 = 2117 \text{ lb/ft}^2 = 1.058 \text{ ton/ft}^2$$

Velocity

1 ft/s   = 30.481 cm/s
1 ft/min = 0.5080 cm/s
1 mi/h   = 44.7041 cm/s
1 mi/min = 2682.2 cm/s
1 mi/h   = 1.609 km/h
1 km/h   = 27.7778 cm/s = 0.6214 mi/h
1 m/min   = 1.6667 cm/s = 3.281 ft/min = 0.05468 ft/s

Rates

1 m^3/s   = 1000 liters/s = 35.31 ft^3/s = 264.2 U.S. gal/s
1 ft^3/s = 7.48052 gal/s = 28.32 liters/s = 0.02832 m^3/s
1 gal/s   = 0.1337 ft^3/s = 3.785 liters/s = 0.003785 m^3/s
1 liter/s = 1000 cm^3/s = 0.03531 ft^3/s = 0.2642 gal/s

Conversion Factors
Compound Units

1 g_f/cm^2 = 0.001 kg_f/cm^2 = 0.01 t/m^2 = (9.80665)(10) N/m^2
              = 2.05 lb/ft^2 = 0.0142 lb/in^2 = 0.001025 ton/ft^2

1 kg_f/cm^2 = 10 t/m^2 = (9.80665)(10^4) N/m^2
              = 2039.2 lb/ft^2 ≈ 1 ton/ft^2 = 14.223293 lb/in^2.

1 t/m^2 = 0.1 kg_f/cm^2 = (9.80665)(10^3) N/m^2 = 1000 kg_f/m^2 =
              = (1.024)(10^{-1}) ton/ft^2 = 204.81 lb/ft^2 = (1.42233) lb/in^2

1 lb/in^2.   = 144 lb/ft^2 = 0.072 ton/ft^2
              = 0.070307 kg_f/cm^2 = 703.07 kg_f/m^2 = (6.89475)(10^3) N/m^2

1 lb/ft^2 = (6.944)(10^{-3}) lb/in^2. = 0.005 ton/ft^2
              = 0.48825 g_f/cm^2 = 4.882 (10^{-4}) kg_f/cm^2 = (4.78802)(10) N/m^2

1 ton/ft^2 = 2000 lb/ft^2 = 13.89 lb/in^2.
              = 976.5 g_f/cm^2 = 0.9765 kg_f/cm^2 = 9765 kg_f/m^2
              = 9.765 t/m^2 ≈ 1 kg_f/cm^2 = (9.57605)(10^4) N/m^2

1 N/m^2 = 1 Pa (Pascal)
              = (1.01972)(10^{-2}) g_f/cm^2
              = (1.01972)(10^{-5}) kg_f/cm^2
              = (1.01972)(10^{-1}) kg_f/m^2
              = (1.01972)(10^{-4}) t/m^2
              = (1.45038)(10^{-4}) lb/in^2.
              = (2.08854)(10^{-2}) lb/ft^2
              = (1.04427)(10^{-5}) ton/ft^2

1 at   = 1 kg_f/cm^2 = 736 torr = 1 technical atmosphere
1 atm   = 1.0335 kg_f/cm^2 = 760 torr = 1 physical atmosphere

Unit Weight γ
Force per unit volume: F/V.

1 N/m^3
$= (1.01972)(10^{-4})$ g_f/cm^3
$= (1.01972)(10^{-7})$ kg_f/cm^3
$= (1.01972)(10^{-1})$ kg_f/m^3
$= (1.01972)(10^{-4})$ t/m^3
$= (3.68394)(10^{-6})$ $\text{lb/in}^3.$
$= (6.36586)(10^{-3})$ lb/ft^3
$= (3.18293)(10^{-6})$ ton/ft^3

$1 \text{ g}_f/\text{cm}^3$
$= (9.80665)(10^3)$ N/m^3
$= (1.00000)(10^{-3})$ kg_f/cm^3
$= (1.00000)(10^3)$ kg_f/m^3
$= 1.00000$ t/m^3
$= (3.61272)(10^{-2})$ lb/in^3
$= (6.24279)(10)$ lb/ft^3
$= (3.12140)(10^{-2})$ ton/ft^3

$1 \text{ kg}_f/\text{cm}^3$
$= (9.80665)(10^6)$ N/m^3
$= (1.00000)(10^3)$ g_f/cm^3
$= (1.00000)(10^6)$ kg_f/m^3
$= (1.00000)(10^3)$ t/m^3
$= (3.61272)(10)$ $\text{lb/in}^3.$
$= (6.24279)(10^4)$ lb/ft^3
$= (3.12140)(10)$ ton/ft^3

$1 \text{ kg}_f/\text{m}^3$
$= 9.80665$ N/m^3
$= (1.00000)(10^{-3})$ g_f/cm^3
$= (1.00000)(10^{-6})$ kg_f/cm^3
$= (1.00000)(10^{-3})$ t/m^3
$= (3.61272)(10^{-5})$ lb/in.^3
$= (6.24279)(10^{-2})$ lb/ft^3
$= (3.12140)(10^{-5})$ ton/ft^3

1 t/m^3
$= (9.80665)(10^3)$ N/m^3
$= 1.00000$ g_f/cm^3
$= (1.00000)(10^{-3})$ kg_f/cm^3
$= (1.00000)(10^3)$ kg_f/m^3
$= (3.61272)(10^{-2})$ $\text{lb/in}^3.$
$= (6.24276)(10)$ lb/ft^3
$= (3.12138)(10^{-2})$ ton/ft^3

1 lb/ft^3
$= (1.57092)(10^2)$ N/m^3
$= (1.60185))(10^{-2})$ g_f/cm^3
$= (1.60185)(10^{-5})$ kg_f/cm^3
$= (1.60185)(10)$ kg_f/m^3
$= (1.60185)(10^{-2})$ t/m^3

$$= (5.78124(10^{-4}) \quad \text{lb/in.}^3$$
$$= (5.00000)(10^{-4}) \quad \text{ton/ft}^3$$

$$\text{1 ton/ft}^3 \quad = (3.14184)(10^5) \quad \text{N/m}^3$$
$$= (3.20379)(10) \quad \text{g}_f/\text{cm}^3$$
$$= (3.20379)(10^{-2}) \quad \text{kg}_f/\text{cm}^3$$
$$= (3.20379)(10^4) \quad \text{kg}_f/\text{m}^3$$
$$= (3.20379)(10) \quad \text{t/m}^3$$
$$= 1.15741 \quad \text{lb/in.}^3$$
$$= (2.00000)(10^3) \quad \text{lb/ft}^3$$

NAME INDEX

SUBJECT INDEX